Models for Production
and Operations Management

Models for Production and Operations Management

Elwood S. Buffa, Ph.D., Professor of Production and Operations
Management, University of California, Los Angeles

 John Wiley & Sons, Inc., New York · London

to E.E.B. C.M.B. J.C.B. L.C.B.

Preface

The objective of *Models for Production and Operations Management* is to present an introduction to the analytical methods that have been developed by people in operations research, management science, and industrial engineering. To accomplish this, the book has been written in relatively nonmathematical style, attempting to present concepts and ideas without indulging in naive oversimplification.

The book is designed for the individual, or for a course, where the objective is to develop a comprehension of these new methods so that in operations situations one can make intelligent decisions based on the results of analysis by staff specialists. This certainly requires a keen understanding of how the basic model in question is constructed and how it functions. It does not, however, require any deep understanding of underlying mathematical derivations and manipulations. Although symbolism is a necessary part of the presentation, the book is meant to be written in English, not the language of mathematics. For those who wish to develop themselves as staff specialists in production and operations analysis, this book should serve as an introduction which may be followed by deeper penetration into many of the individual topics in subsequent courses.

This book should serve well the growing number of instructors who feel that the concepts and methods of production and operations analysis can best be covered by organizing the material around the analytical methods, rather than on the basis of the problem areas as has been traditional. Although emphasis has been placed on some of the more recent developments, such as linear programming, waiting line models, and simulation, some of the older methods and models are also covered in the three chapters of Part II, "Models of Flow and Man-Machine Systems."

I assume that the student has had a basic course in statistics, and, therefore, that he understands something about distributions, measures of central value, and variability. Nevertheless, Chapter 6 presents a review of these basic ideas on which to build further discussions on statistical control, sampling, and waiting line models. In general, only the basic mathematical skills are required, not going beyond rudimentary operations without direct explanation of the techniques involved in the book itself. Derivation is held to an absolute minimum. In one place in Chapter 14, which deals with a general model of investment, I felt it necessary to resort to the integral calculus. Also, in Chapter 14, in discussing basic inventory models, I felt it necessary to include in appendices a derivation for lot size models that use the differential calculus. The text explanation, however, makes it possible to skip over the mathematical derivation if it seems to be relatively unimportant to the concepts developed.

There is the inevitable question, "What is the place of this book with respect to my first book, *Modern Production Management?*"

My first book was intended to be a departure from the traditional descriptive course in production management. To accomplish this, it focuses on the economics of the broad problems of production management, constructed on a somewhat broader analytical base than has been the case in previous books. The subsequent rather broad acceptance of these ideas led me to develop the present book, which carries this departure from tradition a step further. Both books are basic, and the choice between them is a matter of an instructor's individual orientation and preference. However, it may well be true that many instructors will see the present book as a second-semester course following the first book. If this were done, there is only a small overlap of materials between the two books, occurring mainly in Part II.

Pacific Palisades, California
March, 1963

ELWOOD S. BUFFA

Acknowledgments

Particular thanks are due to the many graduate students in my seminar who made specific contributions, through discussions and class papers, to various sections of the book. Outstanding in this regard were Professors Jack Alcalay, Andrew Grindley, and Arnold Reisman and Mr. George McFadden, who took part in the seminar during the fall of 1961.

Where specific ideas, illustrations, or quotations are used, direct acknowledgment is given by footnotes or references. This list of people is too long to be included here. Nevertheless, the book could not have been written without the use of and reference to these materials. I acknowledge with pride the fact that the general subject matter of this book is based on the works of many individual researchers who have made the subject a field of study worthy of careful attention.

Finally, I wish to thank Professor Gordon C. Armour of Indiana University, who read the entire manuscript as an anonymous reviewer. His comments and constructive criticisms were of great importance in developing and refining the manuscript to the present form, and I was delighted when I finally learned with whom I had been working.

E. S. B.

Contents

part I

INTRODUCTION

1

Science in Management

The growth of science in management since the end of World War II is one of the most exciting developments ever to come on the business and industrial scene. It has produced managerial obsolescence in many functions of business, and at a minimum has created a feeling of uneasiness in the hearts of men who see the developing power of analytical techniques applied to management problems. It has hastened the development of professionalism in management.

The seeds that would grow into the branching treelike applied science were planted originally by Frederick W. Taylor (6),* at the turn of the century. Taylor, who was trained as an engineer, applied his fertile mind to the reduction of the worker's art and trade knowledge to a set of empirically derived work rules which improved productivity in such skills or trades as metals machining, pig iron handling, shoveling, and others. In developing these improved working procedures, tools, and systems, Taylor resorted to careful experimentation as a basis for the development of his improved systems. More important than the improvement of specific management work systems was the general philosophy of "scientific management" which Taylor expounded. Taylor believed that management could be reduced to an applied science in many of its aspects and became the zealous proponent of scientific management, devoting much of his later life to the preaching of this philosophy. Taylor did not envision or predict the course of events by which the applied science and methodology would develop, or the character of science in management at its current stage of development.

Following the great impetus given by war operations research

* Numbers in parentheses refer to references at the end of chapters.

3

during World War II, there was a rapid development of the application of mathematical and statistical models to business and industrial problems. Although the greatest proportion of these applications have occurred in the production or operations functions of business, marketing, financial, and general management functions have also benefited. During the same war and postwar period, technology produced concepts of automatic control and data processing undreamed of by the pioneers of scientific management. The pace of automation of operations and computation quickened, and many people spoke of the effects on our economy and society as being comparable to a second industrial revolution. One of the outstanding developments of this trend for management science has been computer simulation. Problems of incredible complexity which could not be approached by mathematical methods could be approached through simulation. Simulation provided a laboratory for management to test the ultimate effects of policies without actually disrupting operations. Also, the computer provided the basis for rapid integrated management controls. The end results of this technological trend may well become the most important from a social and economic point of view.

Meanwhile, other branches of management science which focus on the human being as an individual and as a member of work groups have also developed rapidly. These disciplines have their roots in experimental psychology and physiology, sociology, and the behavioral sciences in general. One main stem of this activity has to do with the organization of work (job design), the measurement of work, and human engineering. Other main stems have dealt with communications and organization, motivation, leadership, and many other questions of great significance to large and small organizations.

Management and Management Science

Management has always been practiced mainly as an art. As an art, management teaches through experience. To be sure, the art has progressed tremendously, but usually these experiences represent special cases, and very little of what was learned is transmitted. Forrester (4) states:

> The advancement of an "art" eventually reaches a plateau. The human lifetime limits the knowledge that can be gained from personal experience. In an art, experiences are poorly transferred from one location to another or from the past to the present. Historical experiences lack a framework for relating them to current problems. One company's experiences cannot be directly and meaningfully used by another.

If management art has indeed reached a plateau, further development may be paced by the rate at which managerial experience can be generalized into a common frame of reference that is applicable to different companies in different industries, managed by different men. This might be stated as a general objective of management science; that is, to develop a body of knowledge which is transferable.

Without doubt, the general area of usefulness that we must allot to the art in management far exceeds the area for management science today. Perhaps a more unfortunate observation is that practicing art, and management science, have a very small area in which there is an overlap—that is, much too small a proportion of the knowledge of the embryonic science of management has trickled into active use. It would be easy to shrug off this unhappy result by assigning the cause to the inertia of thought of practicing managers. Although inertia undoubtedly accounts for some of the lag, the more important reasons are probably that management scientists have preferred to talk to each other about management problems they have concocted rather than the real problems the manager faces. Too often, the management scientist feels that his task has been completed when a paper (often exhibiting mathematical elegance) has been published in an academically oriented journal (which the practicing manager does not, and cannot read, because it is written in a language that is foreign to him). Usually the same ideas and results can be translated into the English language with the help of charts and graphs, but there is an apparent hesitancy to do this because such a paper may be misjudged by academic colleagues as work of "low power." We face a breakdown of communications.

The criticism that management scientists too often work on problems that they themselves construct, rather than the real problems, has less long-run significance than the failure of communications, in this author's view. We must all agree that management science is embryonic. Early models in any science are usually highly idealized. They may assume linear relationships where known nonlinearity exists. They may ignore factors which enter the problem but which are not the major factors. They may ignore some interactions between factors. Nevertheless, models which ignore some known factors often have good enough predictive value, and their relative simplicity makes solutions possible. On the other hand, the more realistic and complex models may not be soluble. At a minimum, these early models have value as stepping stones to more realistic models, ones that may ultimately have enough predictive accuracy to be of value as practical working models.

Management and Decision Making

Management's primary function is to make the decisions that determine the future course of action for the organization over the short and the long term. These decisions have to do with every conceivable physical and organizational problem; they may deal with markets and marketing channels, financial planning, personnel procurement policies, alternate plans for expanding production facilities, policies for material procurement, labor control, and so on. More often than not the decisions involved cut across functional lines.

Decision theory is directed toward determining how rational decisions ought to be made. It attempts to establish a logical framework for decisions that correlates science and the world of models with the real world for various alternative lines of action. These decisions are concerned with everything that goes on in the organization. For day-to-day operating or repetitive decisions, a set of decision rules makes possible continuity and smooth operation, for example the decision rules which determine the amount of materials to be ordered at one time. Larger-scale decisions, such as the determination of an overall plan for expansion, or the decision to float a new bond issue, employ the same general concepts of decision theory, but occur only occasionally.

As new managerial problems occur, they are usually faced by management with the only tools available—managerial experience, judgment, and intuition. Decisions are made on this basis because they must be made; however, these decisions may become formalized into policies and procedures to guide future decisions. These decisions may be classified as almost semiautomatic and are normally the domain of middle management. In some instances a problem may lend itself to the refinement of formal decision models, thus providing automatic decision rules. This flow is diagrammed in Figure 1, and the relative areas seem to represent the importance of each of these areas in management decisions today. We should not assume that management science is working only at the automatic decision rule level. It is certainly true that the objectives of management scientists are to move as many problem areas as possible to the most automatic level possible; however, management science is working at all of the levels. Where highly realistic working models can be developed, decisions may be reduced to automatic decision rules, thus expanding the scope of that small triangle. In addition, management science may help to formalize policies and questions which previously had

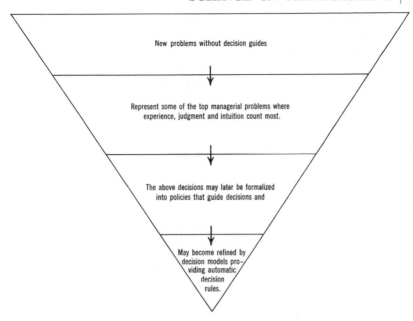

New problems without decision guides

↓

Represent some of the top managerial problems where experience, judgment and intuition count most.

↓

The above decisions may later be formalized into policies that guide decisions and

↓

May become refined by decision models pro-viding automatic decision rules.

Figure 1. The refinement of new problems into policies and automatic decision rules. The relative areas may represent the approximate position of judgment, policy, and automatic decision making today.

been decided only on the basis of experience, judgment, and intuition. Where the real world problems are too complex for present-day models to handle effectively, management science may be able to formalize part of the problem so that intuitive decisions can be made more effectively. Finally, management science may be able to help define more effectively some of the new problems. We wish to expand progressively the relative size and scope of each of the areas representing the application of management science at the expense of any of the areas representing a lesser application of scientific methodology.

In decision making, management selects from a set of alternatives what is considered to be the best course of action. To judge which of the alternatives is best, however, we must have criteria and values that measure the relative worth of the alternatives, and a system for forecasting the performance of the alternative courses of action. These elements, taken together, form the basis for a decision criterion which balances off the desirable and undesirable characteristics of the alternatives. The difficulties come in establishing the comparability of the various criteria that may conflict and in determining the future performance of the alternatives. Much of what we will discuss has to do with these forecasting systems, for they are models of the operating mechanisms with which we are dealing. Figure 2 shows the structure of this decision-making process.

In Figure 2 we have indicated that we wish to select the alternative that maximizes desirability. Since we are dealing with future values, what is the meaning of this term? What is the probability of attaining the results forecasted, or conversely, what is the risk of not attaining these results? Actually, the final net desirability is weighted by the probability of attainment so that for decision purposes we are dealing with *expected values.*

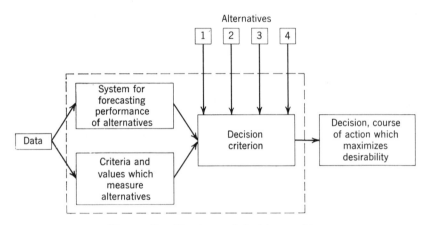

Figure 2. Structure of decision making.

Let us illustrate this point briefly. If we were placing bets at the track, a "long shot" might pay $150 on a $2 ticket whereas a "favorite" might pay only $3. If the long shot had only a 1.5 per cent chance of winning, and the favorite had an 80 per cent chance, we should choose the favorite, because the probability weighted value is $2.40 versus $2.25 for the long shot. To be sure, if the favorite wins, our actual profit is much more, but the probability of winning is so small that a rational decision maker would choose the favorite. In a more typical business situation, we may want to select the best method for performing a given task. Perhaps one alternative involves a manual system which has been proven practical so that we are quite sure of attaining the forecasted result. The second alternative involves the design and perfection of a machine to perform the operation. In this latter situation we are breaking new ground, and this involves some risks. These risks are, for example, that a practical machine may cost somewhat more than expected initially and that the maintenance and operating costs of the system may be somewhat greater than anticipated. The risks mean that the probability of attaining the forecasted benefits of the machine system are something less than 100 per cent, perhaps 75 per cent. For decision purposes, then, the potential measured benefits of the machine system over the manual system need to be scaled down by the factor 0.75.

Although we are always dealing with expected values in decision-making problems, we will note that in the majority of instances no apparent account has been taken of attainment probabilities in the models with which we deal. This does not mean that the probabilities have been ignored. Rather, it means that the probabilities of attainment of the various alternatives are all equal, or that we have no basis for saying that they are not equal.

Models

In the decision-making structure of Figure 2, models are the bases of the prediction systems, and are vital to the formal decision-making process. Indeed, they are vital to an intellectual attack on any problem. Models come to us from scientific methods. The scientist attempts to duplicate in some kind of model the behavior of the system or subsystem with which he is working. Once he has achieved this parallelism between the real world situation and his model, it is usually easier to manipulate the model to study the characteristics in which he is interested than it is to try to work with the real world system.

Models are invariably abstractions to some degree of the actual systems for which we wish to predict performance. A prominent example is the aerodynamicists' model used in conjunction with wind tunnels. Since he is primarily interested in aerodynamic performance, shape is the main characteristic of concern, and other factors in flight, such as weight, strength of individual parts, etc., are ignored. Therefore the characteristic of shape is carefully duplicated in the model and the other factors are ignored. By abstracting only the characteristic of shape, such a study is much more economical, and infinitely more economical than attempting to study aerodynamic performance on actual aircraft. Using the model, the aerodynamicist can make measurements more easily and manipulate variables at will, and all at fairly low cost. By abstracting from the real world system he can focus his attention on a much simpler system without great loss because some details have been ignored.

A model is useful in a practical sense when it accurately duplicates the behavior of the real world system. If a model does not accomplish this, it is useful only insofar as it provides information and insight into the development of a new model. Models must be validated, sometimes repeatedly. Certainly the first planetariums did not predict the movement of planets and stars perfectly, but by correlating the predictions of the model with actual observed data, corrections could be introduced into the model which improved predictions. Also, as technology and science advance, new situations develop that require the revision and up dating of models (such as the discovery of new stars in the case of the planetarium, or the development of supersonic flight in the case of wind tunnel models). Figure 3 shows the structure of successive steps in the development of an acceptable model with intermediate validations of models with data from the real world.

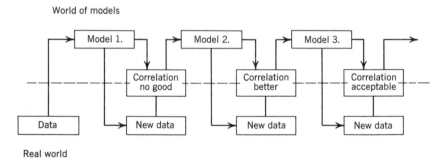

Figure 3. Steps toward the development of an acceptable model.

Kinds of models. Models may be classified as iconic, analogue, and symbolic. *Iconic* models retain some of the physical relationships of the things they represent, that is, they look like the real thing, but they are usually scaled up or down. Good examples are the aerodynamicists' models, planetariums, engineering blueprints, globes of the world, photographs, and of course, the three-dimensional models of physical facilities often used in architecture and factory planning. Iconic models preserve physical relationships, although not necessarily all physical relationships. As with other kinds of models, only those characteristics of interest to the study are retained, which results in both economy and relative simplicity. Iconic models are useful to study conditions that prevail at a given time, much as a photograph freezes action. They are not particularly useful for the study of dynamic situations, nor helpful in discovering relationships between variables in a system.

Analogue models establish a relationship between a variable in the system and an analogous variable in the model. Thus a graph of sales by months uses the length of lines as analogous to the magnitude of sales and time. An electrician's schematic diagram uses lines to show electrical connections. Various kinds of flow charts use lines as analogous to material flow. One of the most useful analogues used in technological work has been the electrical analogue. Analogue computers establish a relationship between variables in a real world problem and an electrical system. Analogue models are often useful for the study of dynamic situations. Usually, changes in an analogue model can be made more easily than in an iconic model, so they can fit more different situations, and thus have greater generality.

Symbolic models substitute symbols for components or variables in the real world system, and the symbols are generally related mathematically. The symbolic system then is a model of some aspect of the real situation. For example, Newton's second law of motion, $F = ma$, states a relationship between three variables; force, mass, and acceleration. The great advantage of symbolic models is that interrelationships between variables can be uncovered through manipulation of the model, and these interrelationships might not be made obvious by less powerful means. The symbolic model is the most difficult and expensive to construct, yet it is usually more general in application and yields the most information. Symbolic models have been used most commonly in the sciences. Today, however, the business world is becoming aware of the power of symbolic models in many business problems.

Advantages and disadvantages of models. Models provide the most effective means yet developed for predicting performance. Indeed, it is hard to conceive of a prediction system which is not finally a model. To construct a model of a real process or system, careful consideration of just which elements of the system need to be abstracted is required. This in itself is usually a profitable activity, for it develops insights into the problem. When building a model, we are immediately struck with the magnitude of our ignorance. What do we really know? Where are the gaps in available data? It is often impractical, or impossible, to manipulate the real world system to determine the effect of certain variables. Business systems are typical, for to use the business system itself as a laboratory could be disastrous, and at a minimum, very costly.

The dangers in using predictive models lie in the possibility of oversimplifying problems to keep models in workable form. The decision maker may place too much faith in a seemingly rigorous and complete analysis. Even though the quantitative analysis makes no pretense at accounting for some factors, and does not include intangible and human values, it is often true that an executive is drawn to the decision indicated by a limited model without a careful weighing of the total problem, including the factors not reduced in the model. Presumably, the formal decision-making process has as its ultimate objective the reduction of as many decisions as possible to the automatic region of Figure 1, where the model is so complete that its performance as a predictor is nearly perfect.

Summary

Science in management is growing rapidly, yet poor communication between the management scientist and the operating manager tends to introduce a lag in the actual use of known methods. One strong branch of management science views management in its decision-making function, attempting to reduce as many decisions as possible to a set of automatic decision rules. This development is directed toward the determination of how decisions ought to be made. Another branch of management science which is based in the behavioral sciences emphasizes human values, and is directed toward the study of how decisions are actually made in the living organization.

Models and model building are an integral part of formal decision theory, and they are the focus of this book. Models are the mechanism by which predictions of performance of a process or system are made, and they may be the basis of valuable control mechanisms. When criteria and values tend to be objective and when models are good predictors, decisions based on them seem scientific, almost automatic. On the other hand, when criteria and values are vague and where quantitative aspects of models can account for only a portion of the problem, decisions rest heavily on judgment and experience.

REFERENCES

1. Boulden, J. B., and E. S. Buffa, "The Strategy of Interdependent Decisions," *California Management Review,* Vol. I, No. 4, 1959, pp. 94–100.

2. Bross, I. D. F., *Design for Decision,* The Macmillan Company, New York, 1959.
3. Dalton, M., *Men Who Manage,* John Wiley and Sons, New York, 1959.
4. Forrester, J., *Industrial Dynamics,* John Wiley and Sons, New York, 1961.
5. Koontz, H., and C. J. O'Donnell, *Principles of Management,* McGraw-Hill Book Company, New York, 2nd ed., 1959.
6. Taylor, F. W., *Scientific Management,* Harper and Brothers, New York, 1947.

2

Models and the Production Function

Although management science is in general applicable to the entire organization, the majority of the work done to date has been done in the setting of the production or operations function. The result is that the area of overlap between managerial art and management science is somewhat greater for operations than for general management and the management of other functions. This book deals with the methodologies of many different kinds of models as applied to production and operations systems. The models discussed are some that have proved to be of value in the analysis of certain phases of operational systems. We shall now define what we mean by production, attempt to place it in an overall setting, develop generalized descriptive models of production systems, and finally describe the general nature of problems encountered. We will use the terms "production" and "operations", or the terms "production systems" and "operations systems" as being synonymous.

What is Production?

Production is the process by which goods and services are created. Production systems combine materials, labor, and capital resources in an organized way with the objective of producing some good or service. Production systems may occur in factories, banks, offices, retail stores, hospitals, etc. In all instances, some input to the system is being processed within the system to produce a good or service as an output. We are, in fact, dealing with the operations phase of any enterprise.

Boundaries of the Production System

Let us first attempt to subdivide the entire organization into functional subsystems. One subsystem will describe a single function or a component of a function, which may be executed by many persons or machines in different geographic locations. In attempting to apply the definition of production given earlier, we shall assign the *single* function of "creation" of goods and services to production. To perform this function, the production system requires inputs from other subsystems of the organization, such as service inputs (for example, maintenance, supervision, plant layout design, etc.) and control inputs (for example, measurement, data processing, planning, control, order and sales information processing, forecasting, etc.). Although the other subsystems and their functions in an organization could be subdivided in other ways, it is convenient for our purposes to define the following subsystems in addition to the production subsystem just described:

1. *Policy-formulating system.* The function of this system is to adapt basic organization policies to information reflecting present and forecasted future conditions. Conceivably, we could have incorporated this function in the general control function described in 2. In both subsystems, the basic function is the gathering and data processing of information with the purpose of planning and of control. The only reason for the separate definition of our policy-formulating system is that it has a line authority characteristic which is not a necessary part of the control system.

2. *Control system.* The basic function of the control system is the transformation of information. As we shall see, this function may be subdivided into component functions. It is entirely conceivable that the transformation of information can ultimately be handled completely by machines and computers.

3. *Intermediate organization systems.* For convenience, we shall define intermediate organization systems with functions to provide the necessary *service* to other subsystems of the organization or to some subsystems of the environment which directly affect the organization subsystems. We are including here such services as supervision, delegation of authority, the transmitting of decisions, as well as the other kinds of service which we have already mentioned.

Figure 1 places the production system in context with the other subsystems, showing the broad scheme of information flow and physical flow between the various subsystems and between the enterprise

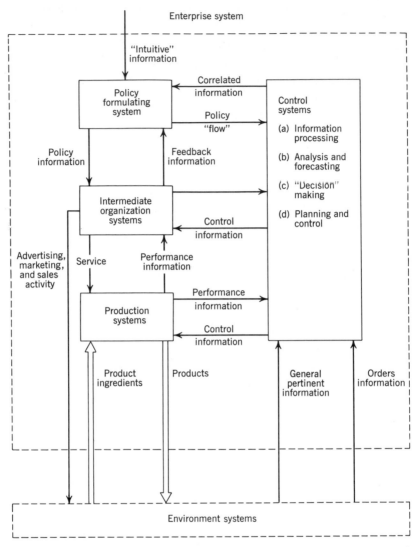

Figure 1. Interaction between production subsystem, other organizational subsystems and environment systems. From J. A. Alcalay and E. S. Buffa, "Conceptual Framework for a General Model of a Production System," Mimeographed Discussion Paper.

system as a whole and the environment. Here, the environment represents the broad economic, social, and physical factors which have an effect on the enterprise system. Figure 2 shows the production system in relation to control subsystems. Here we see that measurements taken from within the production system (for example, time requirements for operations, costs, raw material, and in-process inventory levels, etc.) together with information from other organization subsystems are fed into the data-processing system. The data-processing system in turn feeds transformed information on operations to the two subsystems for day-to-day control of operations and for forecasting and planning. Higher-level, longer-term control represents an integration and transformation of information from the other subsystems as shown.

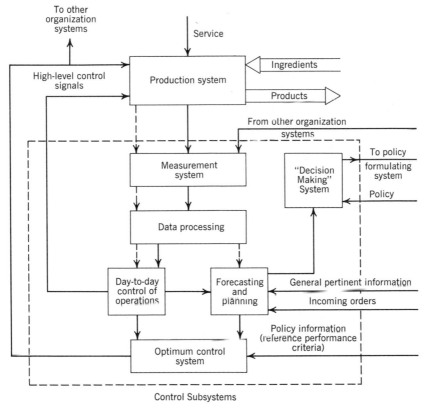

Figure 2. Production system in relation to control subsystems. *Ibid.*

Ideally, we would like to construct a single mathematical model of the production system, within the framework indicated by Figures 1 and 2, which would forecast the operation of any production system, given the characteristics of the production system and the various related subsystems. This is much too ambitious at the present stage of development of models of production and operations systems. Currently, we must be satisfied with models that tend to account only for small parts of the problems we shall define later in this chapter. Nevertheless, it is important to maintain the "system's" point of view just described and summarized by Figures 1 and 2. The basic reason for this is that there are inevitably interactions between the various subsystems of the enterprise and local solution of local problems often results in "suboptimization," that is, the best solution viewed from within the subsystem, but not the best solution when viewed within the system as a whole. In general, our present capability does not permit the strict adherence to this systems point of view. In attempting to approach it, however, we shall attempt to apply this principle: Models of operations should be as broad as practicable, taking account insofar as is feasible, with the power of existing technique, of interactions between various subsystems; whenever a reasonably validated model indicates incremental gains which exceed incremental costs, we assume that the systems view has been approached.

A Generalized Descriptive Model of Production

Let us now attempt to describe the generalized nature of production or operations activity. According to our definition, the factory, the office, the supermarket, the hospital, etc., all represent special cases with special characteristics. Our production system has inputs that represent the material, parts, paper work forms, and the customers or patients, as the case may be. The input will be processed in some way by a series of operations, whose sequence and number are specified for each input. The operations may vary from one only, to any number, and may take on any desired characteristics; they may be mechanical, chemical, assembly, inspection and control, dispatching to the next operation, receiving, shipping, personal contact (such as an interview), and paper work operations. The outputs of our system are completed parts, products, chemicals, service to customers or patients, or completed paper work. There is provision for storage in our system after the receipt of the input and between each operation in the system. The time and storage may vary from zero to any finite value. Inputs are transported among all operations in the system. Any means of transportation may be supplied, including self-transportation in the case of clients and customers. Our model also has an information system and a decision maker. The information system interconnects all the physical activities and provides a basis for management decision. The information system may provide continuous feedback of information regarding the progress of work, its quality, and other factors for control purposes, or it may provide data for special studies to revise and improve operations. These functions provide the equivalent of a "nervous system" for the model. Figure 3 represents our production system.

Production systems may occur in series; for example, when completed products are shipped from the factory to a warehouse, they are leaving the factory system only to arrive at a second production system, called a warehouse. In this way the two systems may be considered as parts of one large system. Systems may also occur in parallel, such as when a number of factories produce similar products and supply several market areas. For solving some problems these factories may be considered one large production system. The nature of the problem under study will usually determine the boundaries of the production system. Now let us consider what would happen to an input to the system. After being received, the input goes into storage to take its turn in the processing. By some set of priority rules, it is drawn from storage to begin processing. These rules might be: first in–first out, time or date required for completion or delivery, urgency, or some other system of priority rules. The input is then processed according to a predetermined sequence. Let us assume the sequence b, d, c. From initial storage the input goes to operation b and is placed in temporary storage to await processing there. We assume that operation b has already some assigned work or load and, therefore, our input takes its place in line (in storage) and will be processed at b according to the priority decision rules established. After being processed at b it is transported to d, placed in storage, drawn out according to priority rules, processed, and so on through the entire sequence of operations. One of the operations may be an inspection. The operation just preceding shipment may be a packaging operation, preparing the item for shipment.

If we are speaking of a high-volume, standardized, fabricated part, the operations may be placed in sequence and may be interconnected by conveying equipment. The storages would take place on the conveyors themselves, and the decision rules are first in–first out. If we are speaking of a hospital, the storages may take place in waiting rooms or in hospital beds. The priority rules may be first in–first out, with urgency exceptions. Many of the tasks are mobile as in the instance of the hospital, for example, when nurses give shots or medication. In a supermarket, products are received

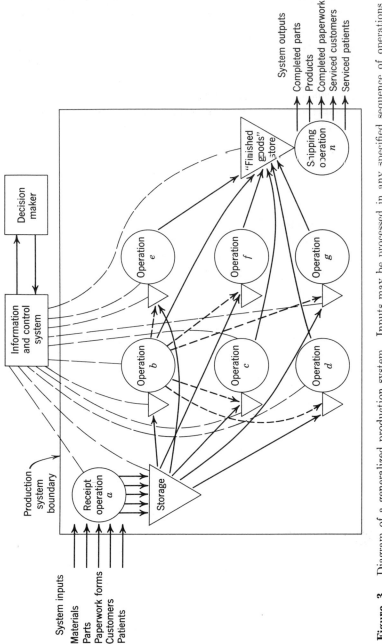

Figure 3. Diagram of a generalized production system. Inputs may be processed in any specified sequence of operations and are transported between operations. The number of operations may vary from one to any finite number. Storage occurs between all operations, and the time in storage may vary from essentially zero to any finite amount. *Note:* There are interconnections between all combinations of operations-b through f although only those originating at b are shown. The information system interconnects all activities and provides the basis for management decision.

and stored on display shelves. Customer receiving is practically nonexistent as an operation. A customer picks the desired items from the shelves, transports them, and takes his place in line for the single operation of checkout. In soap manufacturing by the continuous process, materials are received and stored. They are then taken from storage in a large quantity, dissolved, and pumped through a series of chemical operations, so that transportation and storage between operations occur in the pipes. The material is chemically processed while it moves, and emerges as soap. It is then packaged and shipped. The operations of a bank may be considered in a parallel way. Consider the handling of a check presented for payment at a cashier's window. Customers take their place in line and are normally served on a first come–first served basis. The sequence of operations which follows may take the form of an inspection of cash balances for a certain account, a comparison of signatures, a stamping of the check as paid, counting of money, etc. Later, the check goes through a sequence of operations which adjusts the appropriate account balances, prepares daily and monthly reports, and so on.

The job shop manufacturing situation, where custom products are fabricated and assembled, is undoubtedly the most complex type of production system. Take a space satellite and its propulsion system, for example. Thousands of individual parts must be fabricated and assembled into subassemblies, and thence, into final assemblies. This activity must be dovetailed to fit a complex schedule, so that operation time is available when it is needed to provide parts for subassemblies and final assemblies. The pattern or flow of the multitude of parts from operation to operation is so complex that it can only be visualized by some abstract means of representation Many of the parts require operation time on the same machines, but the operations occur at different times in the overall manufacturing cycle. The problem of loading the operations in such a way that they can be utilized effectively is obviously a difficult one. Table I summarizes inputs, processes, and outputs for different kinds of production systems.

Continuous versus Intermittent Models

Continuous flow production systems are those where the facilities are standardized as to routings and flow, since inputs are standardized. Therefore, a standard set of processes and sequence of processes can be adopted. Continuous models are represented in practice by production and assembly lines, large-scale office operations processing

TABLE I. Inputs, Processes, and Outputs for Different Kinds of Systems Which Create a Good or Service

Facility	Input	Conversion Process	Output
Bank:			
teller window	Customers	Cash checks, make deposits	Serviced customers
accounting office	Canceled checks, deposit slips, etc.	Adjust balances of accounts	Status of accounts, reports
Supermarket:			
store and display shelves	Merchandise	Receive, unpack and store on shelves	Merchandise ready for sale
check-out counters	Customer with purchases	Checkout, add up bill, receive payment and make change; package	Customer with purchases, less cash
Factory	Raw material, parts and supplies	Change shape or form by fabrication and assembly; package	Completed parts and products
Hospital:			
patients' rooms, operating rooms, laboratories, etc.	Patients	Examinations, shots, tests, operations, etc.	Serviced patients

forms by a standard procedure, continuous flow of chemical operations, and many others. Intermittent production situations are those where the facilities must be flexible enough to handle a wide variety of products and sizes, or where the basic nature of the activity imposes change of important characteristics of the input (change in product design). In instances such as these, no single sequence pattern of the operations is appropriate, so the relative location of the operations must be a compromise that is best for all inputs considered together. Transportation facilities between operations must be flexible to accommodate the wide variety of input characteristics as well as the wide variety of routes that the inputs may require. These conditions commonly define an intermittent production system—intermittent because the flow is intermittent. Considerable storage between opera-

tions is required so the individual operations can be carried on somewhat independently, resulting in ease of scheduling and in fuller
utilization of men and machines. In practice, intermittent production
is represented by custom- or job-order machine shops, hospitals,
general offices, batch chemical operations, and many others. As we
have shown, our generalized descriptive model in Figure 3 can be
made to fit both the intermittent and continuous flow situations by
the specification of some of the detailed characteristics. We have
assumed intermittent flow in our model and defined it in general
enough terms that the specification of a fixed operation sequence, the
specification of continuous flow transportation facilities, the assumption of low-storage times between operations, and a first in–first out
set of priority decision rules would all determine continuous flow
conditions. The continuous flow situation is common enough today,

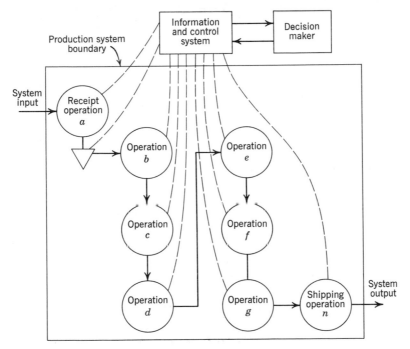

Figure 4. Diagram of a continuous flow production system. Input-output
characteristics are standardized, allowing standardization of operations and their
sequence. Minor storage of inputs occurs after receipt. Once on the transportation system, any storage between operations is combined with transportation.
In the ideal situation the operations are also combined with transportation so
that the inputs are processed while they are being moved.

however, that we tend to think in terms of the dichotomy of continuous and intermittent flow models. Therefore, we have constructed the special case of continuous flow as a separate model in Figure 4.

Basic layout types fit into this intermittent-continuous classification of production systems. When a system is designed for the intermittent conditions, equipment of the same type is grouped together according to the functions performed, such as in Figure 5. Here we

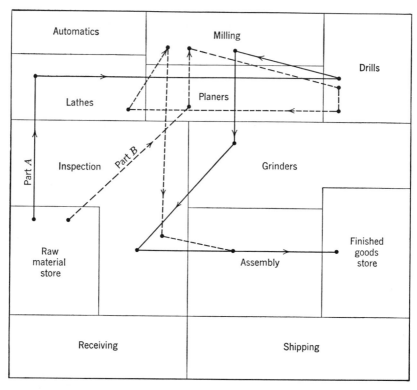

Figure 5. Process or functional layout. Machines are arranged in functional groups. Parts take various routings as dictated by their design requirements. Illustrative routes for two parts *A* and *B* are shown. Parts are moved from operation to operation in batches or lots and stored temporarily at each work station to await their turn.

see a layout for a machine shop that is process oriented, and this type of layout is commonly called process layout, or sometimes, functional layout. The continuous flow model that we have discussed results in

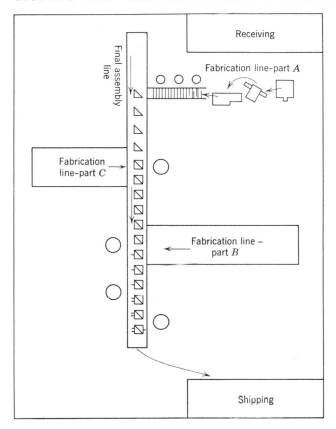

Figure 6. Product or line layout. Machines and equipment are arranged according to the sequence of operations required to fabricate and assemble. Machines and workers are specialized in the performance of specific operations, and parts approach continuous movement.

a layout illustrated by Figure 6, where the location of equipment is determined by the sequence of operations to be performed on the product. This type of design is commonly called product layout because the layout is oriented around the product produced. An equally common name for this type of design is line layout. If similar equipment is required for both parts A and B in Figure 6, it would normally be duplicated in the two lines, even though the equipment was not fully utilized for either part. Actually, most layouts are a combination of process and product in manufacturing activity, with fabrication operations generally following process layout and assembly operations generally following product layout.

Process layout is commonly employed when the same facilities must be used to process a wide variety of items for which the processing sequence varies and perhaps is changing. Quite often the volume of individual items is quite low, even though the total volume may be high for the entire system. The prime requirement of layout is for flexibility of operation sequence, flexibility of part or product design, and flexibility of the volume of individual items being processed.

When the conditions for a product or line layout are met, the result is a low-cost system of production. We might summarize these conditions as follows:

1. An adequate volume that makes possible reasonable equipment utilization.
2. Reasonably stable demands for the product or service.
3. Product standardization.
4. Parts interchangeability.
5. Continuous supply of material.

Each of these requirements needs qualification. There is no one volume that we can point to as being "adequate." Instead, economic analysis determines the break-even volume between process and product layout for a given situation. Stable demand is required to justify the special layout and tools necessary so that at least a minimum run can be foreseen. This is also related to product standardization, since changes in product design have the same general effect on the system as on stable demand. In manufacturing, parts interchangeability is required so that no special reworking or fitting is needed on the line, since this condition disrupts the flow of work because of imbalance.

The Problems of Production and Operations Management

Using our generalized model as a background, let us outline the nature of problems generated in a production system. These problems require two major types of decisions, one that relates to the design of the system and one that relates to the operation and control of the system (that is, both long-run and short-run decisions). The relative balance of the emphasis on such factors as cost, service, reliability of both functional and time performance, depends on the basic purposes of the total enterprise or institution and on the general nature of the goods or service being produced. In general, economic enterprises will probably emphasize cost, consistent with quality and delivery commitments. Hospitals may emphasize reliability and service, consistent with cost objectives, etc. A classification of problems follows.

A. Long-run decisions related to the design of production and operations systems.

   1. *Selection of equipment and processes.* Usually, alternate equipment and processes are available for a given need. Operations management must make decisions that commit capital of the enterprise and its basic approach to production.

   2. *Production design of items processed.* Production costs interact strongly with the design of parts, products, paperwork forms, etc. Design decisions often set the limiting characteristics of the cost and processing for the system.

   3. *Job design.* Job design is an integral part of the total system design, involving the basic organization of work, as well as the integration of human engineering data to produce optimally designed jobs.

   4. *Location of the system.* Location decisions can, in some cases, be important where the balance of cost factors determined by nearness to markets and to material supply are critical.

   5. *Facility layout.* Decisions related to design capacity, basic modes of production, number of shifts, use of overtime and subcontracting, must be made. In addition, operations and equipment must be located in relation to each other in a pattern that minimizes overall material handling cost. The latter requirement is most difficult for the complex intermittent model where routes vary.

B. Decisions related to the design of operation and control systems.

   1. *Inventory and production control.* Decisions must be made concerning how to allocate productive capacity, consistent with demand and inventory policy. Feasible schedules must be worked out, depending on the loads on men and machines, and the flow of production must be controlled.

   2. *Maintenance and reliability of the system.* Decisions must be made regarding maintenance effort, recognition of the random nature of equipment breakdowns, and recognition that machine down-time may itself be associated with important costs or loss of sales.

   3. *Quality control.* Decisions must be made to set the permissible levels of risk that bad parts are produced and shipped, or that errors are made, as well as the risk that good parts are scrapped. Control costs must be balanced

against the probable losses due to passing defective material or services.

4. *Labor control.* Labor is still the major cost element in most products and services. Planning operations require an appraisal of the labor component.

5. *Cost control and improvement.* Day-to-day decisions must be made which involve the balance of labor, material, and certain overhead costs.

The relative importance of these problems in operations management varies considerably, depending on the nature of individual production systems. Nevertheless, every system has these problems in some degree. For example, replacement policy may occupy a dominant position in production systems where the capital investment per worker is very large, as in the steel industry. On the other hand, replacement policy may occupy a minor role in a production system that is represented by a large labor component or a large material cost component. Part of the art of operations management involves the sensing of the relative importance of these various components in a given situation.

The various analytical methods we will discuss find application in many of the problem areas outlined. For example, any of the physical and schematic models discussed are of great importance in job design, layout, production control, labor control, and cost improvement. Flow charts and assembly charts have been used with good effect in analyzing overall product flow so that the components of a production system could be related properly. Physical models of systems aid in visualizing the overall interacting effects of each component of the system and in allocating space to activities in the most effective way. Other kinds of flow charts aid in the design of specific activities involving labor, or the design of a man-machine system. Symbolic models find rather different fields of application. For example, statistical methods have been found to be of great value in product quality control, work measurement, a determination of the optimal combination of control factors (such as in the chemical industries), and in the design of experiments to determine the effects of variables in the operation of production systems. Of course, inventory and production control models have direct application in those areas. Waiting line models have been found to be valuable as aids to job design, the determination of capacities of facilities like unloading docks, check-out counters, storage facilities, and tool cribs, as well as the analysis of inventory systems, labor requirements for multiple machine operation, and for maintenance systems. Programming models have been found to be of value in the analysis of distribution systems, plant location, production programming, waste control, and so on. Replacement models have been found to be of value in the selection of equipment and processes, and in general where comparisons of alternate systems or subsystems of production are to be made. Competitive models have future significance in the analysis of bidding procedures and for the development of basic strategies that an organization should follow to maximize its position with respect to competitors. Simulation models have already found application in a wide variety of problems that deal with both the design of production systems and with the operation and control of systems. Simulation models may be used in practically all situations where mathematical models have application; however, their field of advantage is where the complexity required by the problem makes mathematical analysis difficult or impossible. In these situations, simulation can be used where mathematical methods fail.

The Need for a System Point of View

Many of the problems of production interact with each other. For example, job design may interact with the material handling system used, the design of the thing being processed, the equipment or process being used, and the overall facility layout. An optimal inventory policy to follow is partially dependent on the means by which production levels are controlled. The best process (in instances where alternatives exist) may depend on whether idle labor or equipment is available. Thus if we were to study inventory problems in isolation, ignoring the effects of changes in production level, we would develop a suboptimal solution to the problem, because the solution that minimizes inventory costs might result in very high costs associated with production fluctuations. The policy we wish to determine is one that would minimize all costs affected. Therefore, the broader the point of view taken in attempting to solve the problem, the less likely it is that factors will be ignored which bear significantly on the final result. This, then, is the guide to the determination of the limits of the production system under study.

Achieving this systems concept in practical application is difficult for two important reasons: first, as we mentioned earlier, present-day models fall short of this ideal, and second, it requires crossing established functional lines of authority within organizations. This latter factor is of great practical significance because of the human relations problems involved in gaining support for proposals that may tear down personal empires or threaten individuals within organization structures.

REVIEW QUESTIONS

1. Define the term *production*.

2. What is meant by the term *operations?* How does it differ from the term production?

3. Describe the nature of interactions between the production subsystem and other organizational subsystems within the total enterprise system.

4. Discuss the nature of interactions between the enterprise system and the environment systems.

5. How do we define intermediate organization systems? What are the comparable functions performed by organizational units in a factory system?

6. What control subsystems are common in a manufacturing organization?

7. Using the diagram of Figure 2 as a background, outline a system for labor cost control, quality control, and inventory control.

8. Using the generalized descriptive model of production as a background, select an activity which you know and show that the general model is applicable to it.

9. Differentiate between intermittent and continuous models of production. What kinds of facility layout are applicable to each?

10. Name and discuss the short- and long-run problems of operations management.

part II

MODELS OF FLOW AND MAN–MACHINE SYSTEMS

3

Graphic, Schematic, and Physical Models of Flow

Graphic, schematic, and physical models have proved of value in the analysis of many kinds of production problems, particularly those of flow, layout, and the relationships of men and machines. The principal function of these kinds of models is in helping to visualize some of the complex interrelationships that occur. For example, the flow charts we will discuss may show the relationship of operations to be performed on the various parts of an assembled product. Thus, insight into possible approaches to the design or improvement of a production system for the product is facilitated. Similarly, a chart showing the time relationships between a man and his machine may provide insight into the possible reorganization of activities to improve the utilization of the man, the machine, or both. Table 1 shows a

TABLE I. Classification, Information Displayed and Use of Graphic, Schematic, and Physical Models

Model	Information Displayed	Use
Assembly charts	Relationship of assembled parts	Flow analysis
Operation process chart	Relationship of productive operations and parts	Flow analysis
Product flow process charts	Relationship of operations, transports, storage and inspections	Flow analysis
Flow diagrams	Relation of flow to physical layout	Flow and layout analysis
Procedure flow charts	Relationship of paper work operations	Analysis of paper work flow

TABLE I (Continued)

Model	Information Displayed	Use
Sequence analysis	Relationship of departmental areas in a process layout	Layout analysis, process layout
Two- and three-dimensional templates	Relationship of machinery and equipment	Layout analysis
Gantt charts	Time relationships of orders, inventories, machine-time allocations	Schedule and load analysis
Schedule diagrams	Time relationships of processing parts	Schedule analysis
Operator charts	Relationship of the activity of the hands	Man analysis
Micro-motion or "Simo" charts	Time relationship of the activity of the hands	Man analysis
Multiple activity charts	Time relationship of activities of men and/or machines	Man-machine analysis
Balance charts	Grouping of activities for a production line	Labor balance

classification of these kinds of models together with the use and information displayed by each.

Models of Product Flow

Assembly charts. An assembly chart shows the relationship of parts for an assembled product. It shows the make-up of subassemblies, their relationship to the product as a whole, and to the assembly operations required. Figure 1 shows a capacitor assembled and partially assembled. Although the capacitor is a fairly simple assembled product with only eleven different parts plus the impregnating material, inerteen, the assembly chart in Figure 2 yields a great deal of information about the way the product is assembled. We see that there are two subassemblies and note the sequence of assembly and inspections or tests. For example, the first subassembly, SA-1, is made up of two parts, part number 4, aluminum foil, and part number 6, flat leads. Analysis of the chart could deal with alternate sequences of assembly or the advisability of more or fewer subassemblies.

The actual usefulness of an assembly chart is a function of the complexity of the product. For a product as simple as the capacitor, its value is limited because the same level of analysis could probably be carried on without the chart. For a complex product such as an airplane, missile, or a piece of electronic equipment, however, an as-

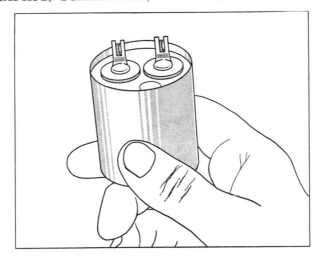

Figure 1. A capacitor, showing its several parts.

sembly chart would be of great assistance in planning the gross features of a production system for the product.

Operation process charts. The operation process chart is
developed from the structure of the assembly chart, but simply adds
more information concerning the actual fabrication of the parts which
make up the assembled product. Assuming that the product is already

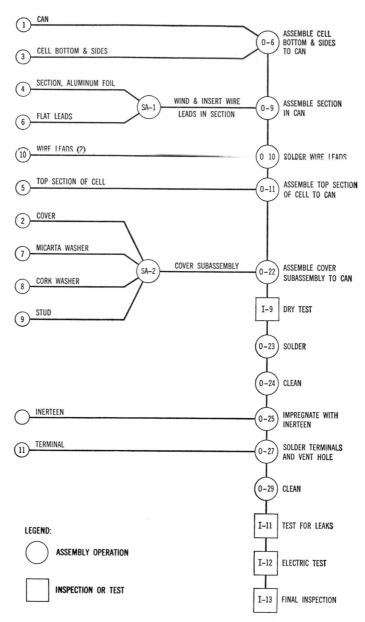

Figure 2. Assembly chart for capacitor of Figure 1.

engineered, we have available complete drawings and specifications of the parts, their dimensions, tolerances, and materials to be used. From the data on "what to make" (drawings and specifications) and "how many to make" (contracts or sales forecasts), we must develop a plan for "how to make." This means that decisions will have to be made concerning which parts to manufacture and which to purchase. The engineering drawings and specifications will indicate the materials to be used, the location and sizes of holes to be drilled, surfaces to be finished, etc. With this information, a knowledge of the quantities required, and a knowledge of the appropriate production processes, the most economical processes and sequences of processes can be specified.

The result of all of this effort to specify "how to make" can be summarized in the form of the operation process chart, an example of which is shown in Figure 3 for the capacitor. Note that a great deal of information in addition to operation sequences is summarized on the chart. Parts raw material is specified, and purchased parts are labeled B.O., indicated as horizontal lines flowing into assembly operations (parts 3, 5, 11, and inerteen). The numbers to the left of symbols for operations and inspections are estimates of the per piece time standards for performance of the activities, or where B.W. is indicated the work is performed on a "day work" basis with no time standard available.

Notice how the operation process chart appears as a schematic diagram for the flow and manufacture of the product. It indicates the basic flow from machine to machine as well as the structure of how parts are related in the subassembly and assembly processes. In the development of the design of a production system to produce the product, basic questions can be raised regarding the necessity of certain operations, as well as possibilities for combining and rearranging operation and inspection sequences to improve physical flow.

Product flow process charts. The flow process chart is similar in concept to the operation process chart except that it adds more detail and has a slightly different field of application. The flow process chart adds transportation and storage activity to the information already recorded in an operation process chart. Thus, whereas the latter focuses only on the productive activity, the flow process chart focuses on nonproductive activities as well.

The nonproductive activities of moving the material from place to place and storing it (while it waits for men and equipment to be-

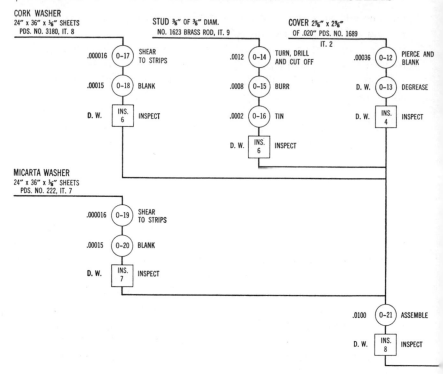

Figure 3. Operation process chart for a capacitor showing productive operations and inspections and their sequence relationships. Courtesy Westinghouse Electric Corporation.

come available) actually represent by far the major amount of the total time spent in the overall cycle for many of the production systems which occur in business and industry today. These nonproductive activities require labor and equipment for transportation, loading, and unloading; capital investment for the plant storage space; and carrying charges on the inventory. Naturally, management is strongly motivated to focus attention on these activities so that their expenditures can be minimized within the framework of minimum overall production cost. It is obvious that decreasing in-process inventories by reducing lot sizes to an extremely low level might result in much higher material handling costs and idle direct labor at machines.

In general, the operation process chart would be used at the broadest level dealing with entire complex products, and the flow process chart would be used with a smaller segment of the product. There is overlap, however, in the areas of their actual use. As an example let

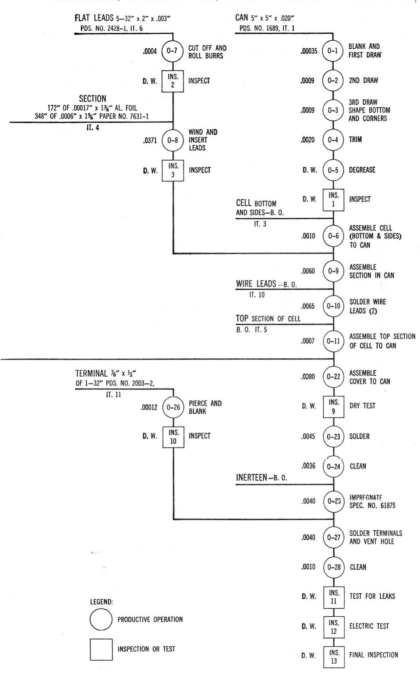

us take the manufacturer of the potentiometer shaft shown in Figure 4. The product flow process chart for the potentiometer shaft is shown in Figure 5. Note that additional symbols have been adopted to code the activities of transport and storage. Note how clearly the chart shows the occurrence of the various operations, transports, storages, and inspections.

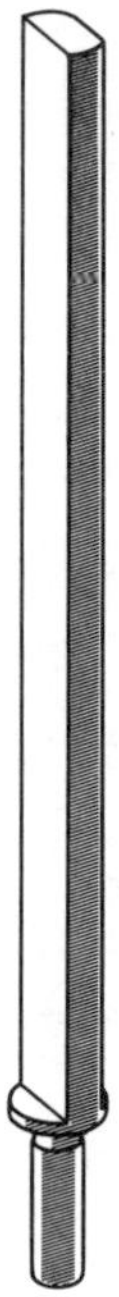

In the use of such a chart, every detail of the process is questioned, first with the objective of completely eliminating steps that cannot be justified, and second with the objective of combining operations. Let us see what sort of questions might be raised about the manufacture of the potentiometer shafts. First, we see that the shafts travel a total of 715 feet before they are ready to be assembled into the final product. This in itself seems excessive for such a simple part. Analysis of this flow shows that the raw material starts on the first floor, moves to the second floor, moves back to the first floor for inspection, then to the basement for storage, and finally to the seventh floor assembly area when the shafts are actually needed. Reference to the flow diagram of Figure 6 which relates the movement to the physical layout of a plant emphasizes this excessive movement. The improvement of this flow pattern depends on the possibility of relocating one or more of the departmental areas, and this depends on the flow patterns of other products as well. Another question to be raised

Figure 4. A potentiometer shaft. Flow-process chart shown in Figure 5.

is, "Is it necessary for these parts to go to the manufactured parts storeroom, since they are always used in the assembly area?" The parts are small, and a large quantity of them could be stored at the point of use in the assembly area. Another question to be raised relates to the preoccupation with counting the number of parts at various stages in the process. Part counts are made and recorded at four different points. It is unlikely that all these checks for quantity are necessary.

Procedure flow charts. Although charting the flow of paperwork systems is basically similar to that of charting the flow of a manu-

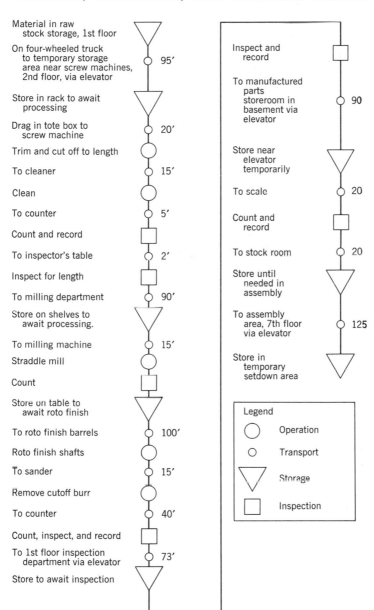

Figure 5. Product flow-process chart for the manufacture of potentiometer shafts.

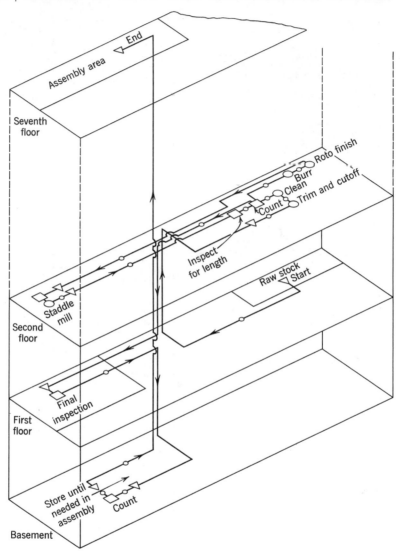

Figure 6. Flow diagram for manufacture of potentiometer shafts.

factured product, the characteristics of paperwork flow problems demand some modifications from the product flow charts which were discussed previously. Some of the differences required are indicated by the modified set of symbols which are commonly used:

⊚ 1. *Origin.* This signifies the origin of a document or a record and is similar in concept to the operation symbol used in product flow charts. It indicates the beginning of the flow of the record resulting from the *first* information of any kind placed on a form, a single record, or a multiple-part record, whether it is handwritten, typed, punched, or stamped.

◕ 2. *Adding to the record.* This symbol is used any time subsequent writing or other additional information is placed on the form.

◯ 3. *Handling.* This symbol is used for operations such as sorting, folding, stapling, separating copies, matching, etc.

○ 4. *Move.* The small circle indicates movement or transportation as with the product flow chart. The word, "to" is often inserted inside the circle.

☐ 5. *Inspection.* As with the product flow chart, a square is used when the record itself is checked for accuracy and when errors found are corrected. Often, paperwork accompanies product flow, and if the inspection is of the product itself, rather than of the paperwork, the paperwork itself is usually indicated to be in a state of delay.

▽ 6. *Delay.* The triangle symbol is used as with the product flow process chart. It is used when a record is filed, held at a desk, is awaiting pickup, is destroyed, etc.

△ 7. *Relationship* This symbol is used when one form causes something to happen to another form. The form being charted then is said to have an effect, or a "relationship" to the other document.

Because of the common necessity for multiple copies to accomplish the needed control, procedure flow charts are often complex and long. Figure 7 is an example of a procedure flow chart for a stores requisition of material. Such a chart can be subjected to the same kind of questioning applied to a product flow chart to determine the necessity of various copies as well as the necessity of some of the operations in the sequence. The existence of multiple copies often results in duplication of checks and balances as well as in duplication of permanent files. A schematic model of the entire system makes it possible to study the needs of the system as a whole.

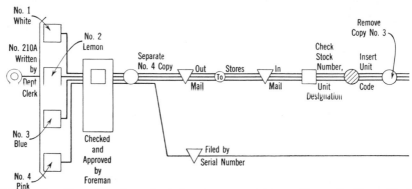

Figure 7. Procedure flow chart for stores requisition. From G. Close, *Work Improvement,* John Wiley and Sons, New York, 1960, Fig. 6.11, pp. 144–145.

Models of Facility Layout

Layout is the integrating phase of the design of a production system. The basic objective of layout is to develop a production system which meets requirements of capacity and quality in the most economical way. Here the specifications of what to make, how it is to be made, and how many to make, become the basis for developing an integrated system of production. This integrated system must provide for machines, work places, and storage in the capacities required so that feasible schedules can be determined for the various parts and products; a transportation system which moves the parts and products through the system; and auxiliary services for the production, such as tool cribs and maintenance shops, and for personnel, such as medical facilities and cafeterias. The graphical model of sequence analysis used in developing process layouts and the physical models to be discussed have value in representing certain phases of layout problems.

Operation sequence analysis. The major problem of a strictly "layout" nature in process layout is the determination of the most economical relative location of the various process areas. The best arrangement is not immediately obvious, except for trivial cases. This fact is emphasized by the realization that for only six process areas arranged in a simple grid, as in Figure 8, there are 6! (six factorial) or $6 \cdot 5 \cdot 4 \cdot 3 \cdot 2 \cdot 1 = 720$ arrangements possible. Fortunately, only 45

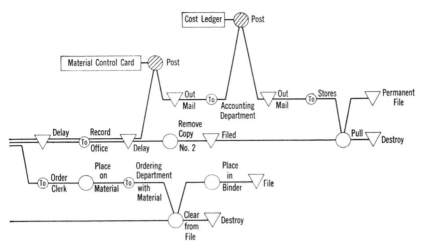

Figure 7 (continued).

of them are really different in terms of their effects on idealized measures of material-handling cost. The number of combinations goes up very rapidly as we increase the number of process areas. Let us consider the nature of an objective function in this situation. The major criterion for selecting an arrangement is material-handling cost. Thus, we want an arrangement that places the process areas in locations relative to each other, such that material-handling cost for all parts is minimized. Therefore, if we examined the required material-handling activity between departments A and C of Figure 8 and found that it

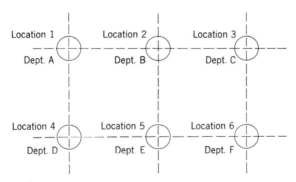

Figure 8. There are $6! = 720$ arrangements of the six process areas in the six locations of the grid.

was heavy compared to AB, we would want to consider switching the locations of departments B and C. But before concluding that this switch would be advantageous, we want to see if this advantage would be wiped out by an increase in the relative material-handling activity between DB and DC. We might take as our measure of material-handling cost the product of the distance times the number of loads that must be moved in some period of time. For each combination of arrangements, then, we could simply add up the load–distance products between all combinations of departments. The combination with the smallest total is the basic arrangement that we are looking for. To formalize this statement of our objective, our measure of effectiveness, E is;

$$E = \sum_{ij} A_{ij} X_{ij} = \text{minimum}$$

where A_{ij} = number of loads per week, month, or period required, to be transported between departments i and j, and X_{ij} = distance between departments i and j.

This measure of effectiveness closely approximates material-handling costs. Each material-handling operation requires certain fixed times associated with picking up the load, positioning it to set down, etc. These costs, mainly labor costs, would be about the same for large or small loads, and need not be considered unless alternate handling systems are considered as a part of the analysis. The variable costs associated with a material-handling operation (mainly labor plus power) are related to distance.

The data we need are the number of loads that must be transported between all combinations of work centers. This type of data can be summarized from routing sheets which indicate operation sequences, and from engineering drawings. The route sheets indicate sequences; from the drawings of the parts themselves and the production rates, we can determine the number of parts transported at one time, and, therefore, the number of loads. Table II shows a summary of the number of loads per month for all combinations of work centers for a typical small production situation. We idealize our problem by assuming a structure similar to Figure 8, with circles representing the functional groupings of equipment. We regard departments as being adjacent if they are either next to each other, as are A and B, or diagonally across from each other, as are A and E, in Figure 8. Nonadjacent locations are those that are more than one grid unit away from each other, horizontally, vertically, or diagonally, represented by AC, AF, DC, and DF in Figure 8. We can see now that for our idealized

TABLE II. Load Summary

(Number of loads per month between all combinations of work centers.)

From						To					
Departments	Rec. 1	Stores 2	Saw 3	Eng. Lathe 4	Turret Lathe 5	Drill 6	Mill 7	Grinder 8	Ass'y 9	F.G. 10	Ship 11
Receiving 1		600									
Stores 2			400	100			100				
Saw 3				350	50						
Engine Lathe 4						100	450				
Turret Lathe 5							50				
Drill 6				100					150	100	
Mill 7						50		450	100		
Grinder 8						200			250		
Assembly 9										500	
Finished Goods 10											600
Shipping 11											

layout the measure of effectiveness reduces to minimizing the sum of the nonadjacent loads (unit distance) × (loads). For problems of reasonable size, the minimum nonadjacent (distance) × (load) solution is fairly readily seen by graphical methods. We have an initial solution which may be improved by inspecting the effect of changes in location. When an advantageous change is found, the diagram is altered.

This graphical approach to the solution is accomplished by placing the information contained in the load summary, Table II, in an equivalent schematic diagram in which circles represent work centers (functional groups of machines), and labeled connecting lines indicate the number of loads transported between work centers, as in Figure 9. Figure 9 is a first solution obtained merely by placing the work centers on the grid, following the logic from the pattern indicated by Table II. When all lines are on the diagram and labeled we have an initial solution which may be improved by inspecting the effect of changes in location. When an advantageous change is found, the diagram is altered. For example, in Figure 9 we see immediately that work center 4 has a total of 300 loads that are transported to or from work centers that are not adjacent, that is, 2 and 6. If 4 is moved to the location between 2 and 6, all loads to and from 4 become adjacent. Further inspection shows that 200 nonadjacent loads must be transported between work centers 6 and 8. Is an advantageous shift possible? Yes, by moving 9 down and placing 8 in the position vacated by 9, the

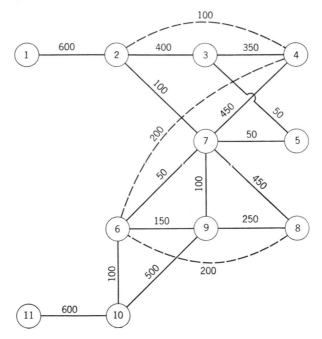

Figure 9. Initial graphic solution developed from load summary of Table II. It can be seen by inspection that 4 can be moved to the position between 2 and 6 to eliminate 300 nonadjacent loads. Also, the positions of 8 and 9 are improved by replacing 9 by 8 and moving 9 to the position just below 8.

number of nonadjacent loads is reduced from 200 to 100. Figure 10 shows the diagram with the changes incorporated.

Further inspection reveals no further advantageous shifts of location, so we adopt Figure 10 as our ideal schematic layout, which has a $2 \times 100 = 200$ load-distance rating. For larger problems, the grid distance becomes an important part of the measure of effectiveness, because work centers might be separated by two, three, or four grid units. Figure 10 is not a provable optimum solution, because we have no test of optimumality. The ideal schematic diagram is now the basis for developing a physical layout in which the work centers or department locations are specified.

The block diagram. Now that we know how the work centers should be located in relation to each other in our idealized layout, we can use the idealized schematic diagram as a basis for developing a block diagram in which the physical areas required by the work centers

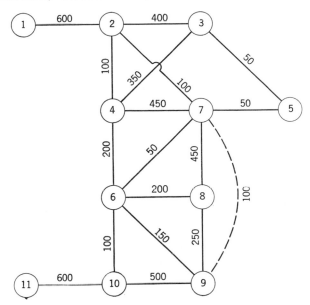

Figure 10. Ideal schematic diagram incorporating changes suggested by Figure 9. No further location changes yield improvement.

take the same relative locations. Estimates of the areas required by each work center can be developed from the number of machines required in each center, and the floor area required by each machine. Commonly, the machine areas are multiplied by a factor of 3 or 4 to obtain an estimate, or first approximation, of the total area required, including working space for the operator, material storage, and pro rata aisle space.

The block diagram is developed by substituting estimated areas for the small circles in the idealized schematic layout. Initially this can be done with block templates, in order to find an arrangement compatible with both the flow pattern of the ideal schematic diagram and the various size requirements for work centers. Figure 11 shows such an initial block diagram for our example. We can see that the essential character of the ideal schematic diagram is retained. Figure 11 obviously does not represent a practical solution as yet, however. Slight variation of the shapes of work areas will make it possible to fit the system into a rectangular configuration and meet the possible shape and dimension restrictions that may be imposed by the site, or by an existing building if we are dealing with relayout. Figure 12 shows such a block diagram.

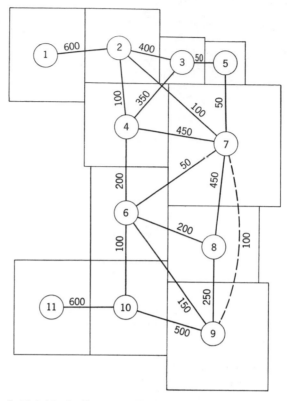

Figure 11. Initial block diagram. Estimated work center areas substituted for circles in the ideal schematic diagram of Figure 10, using block templates for estimated area requirements.

The block diagram represented by Figure 12 presents a frame of reference for the development of the details of layout. Now we can proceed with aisle layout, machine arrangement within work centers, work place layout, the design of plant and personnel areas, the selection of specific material-handling equipment, etc., knowing that the work centers are located relative to each other in an economical way.

When the block diagram is complete, combinations of work centers can be made for practical departmentalization. These combinations can be based on work center sizes, the number of workers involved, similarity of work, and other criteria important to the particular application.

The detailed layout phase will undoubtedly require minor shifts in space allocation and shape. Here, the templates and physical models

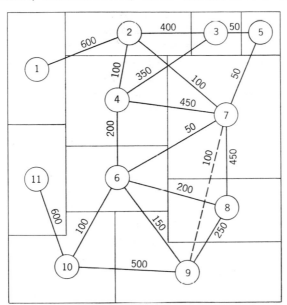

Figure 12. Block diagram which takes account of rectangular building shape and other possible restrictions of shape and dimension imposed by site, but still retains approximate work center area requirements and optimal flow pattern.

discussed in the following section become valuable aids in visualizing the developing details. Standards for minimum machine spacing, aisle widths for different uses, and column spacings for different building designs all exist in handbook form (7, 9, 12, 16). The graphical model which we have discussed is appropriate for relatively simple problems; however, as the number of work centers increases the complexity of the problem increases rapidly, and a more powerful technique, such as system simulation, is required. For example, although there are 45 different relative location patterns possible when there are 6 departments, as noted before, there are 119,750,500 different patterns for 12 departments. A simulation model for this basic problem has been developed and is discussed in Chapter 18 on simulation.

Physical models of facility layout. Layouts and models using two- and three-dimensional templates have a wide area of application in the development and planning of new facilities, as well as in the re-layout of existing facilities. These graphic aids are important in visualizing the development of the design of a complex production system. The resulting layout expresses the designer's specification of the location of all equipment, storage areas, aisle space, utilities, etc., and the relationships between machines and departments. It is important, however, not to mistake the activity of preparing and locating templates on a layout board for the broader activity of facility layout. The templates themselves are tools. Other kinds of analysis must supplement the layout; that is, economic analysis helps to determine the location, the design capacity, whether the plant represented by the layout is to operate on one, two, or three shifts, which parts to buy and which to manufacture, and what equipment to select. Analyses of work methods and relationships of parts and the products help to determine work areas required and relative locations of activities. Studies of "balance" will determine what the basic design of an assembly line should be. These are typical of supporting analyses and indicate that the two- and three-dimensional layouts cannot stand alone.

Two-dimensional templates are by far the most commonly used. They can successfully represent the plan view of a layout and can show floor utilization fairly well. Figure 13 shows two types of tem-

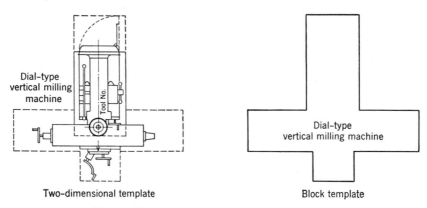

Two-dimensional template   Block template

Figure 13. Two types of machine templates.

plates. The "block" template shows the outline of the maximum projected area of a machine; that is, if tables or other parts move, the outline shows the maximum movement in the horizontal plane. The two-dimensional template gives additional detail, showing the outline of the machine itself, the dotted lines indicating maximum table movements.

The important characteristics of these templates are dimensional accuracy and flexibility in use. Flexibility in use means that the template can be fixed firmly enough in place so that it will not be moved by jarring or by air movement, but not fixed permanently because it may be necessary to make changes. There are various alternatives that meet these requirements in varying degrees. Some of the most satisfactory materials are the plastic templates, which already have an adhesive backing, used in conjunction with a cross-sectioned plastic sheet as a backing material. The cross-sectioning provides the measurement scale. Consequently, very little actual measurement is required, and the resulting layout can be run through blueprint or ozalid machines for duplication. This type of template is available commercially for virtually all standard machines, as well as for many kinds of auxiliary equipment. Colored adhesive tapes are used to represent walls, aisle lines, etc. Figure 14 is an example of a layout using this

Figure 14. A layout using plastic templates and backing with colored tapes for wall sections. Courtesy General Electric Company (5).

media. Figure 15 shows the ease with which templates are cut out and applied.

Three-dimensional templates or scale models add an element of realism, which can sometimes be justified where the visualization of height is of considerable importance, and also where people not ac-

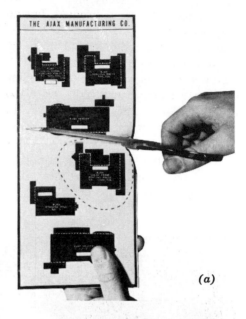

Figure 15. (*a*) Plastic templates may be cut from strip without following closely the outline of the template. (*b*) After stripping off backing, template adheres to plastic grid and may be moved at will. Courtesy General Electric Company.

quainted with layout practice must pass judgment on the result. It is often felt that anything that can be done to help these people visualize the proposals is worth the extra expense. Die-cast models are available commercially for virtually all standard equipment, and they are made

Figure 16. Portion of a three-dimensional model layout. From G. Close, *Work Improvement,* John Wiley and Sons, New York, 1960, Fig. 6.3, p. 133.

in considerable detail. Figure 16 shows a portion of the layout using this media. Practically all the items shown are available, that is, columns, waste barrels, skids, pallets, machines, etc. The heavy cross-sectioned plastic sheet used for the base provides the scale to minimize measuring.

Graphic Models of Line Balance

Balance is the central problem in designing a production or assembly line. This is not to minimize the other problems of physical positioning of equipment, material-handling devices, the design of special tools, and work place layout, for in many instances solutions to these problems will contribute to the balance of the line. Balance refers to the equality of output of each of the successive operations in the sequence of a line. If they are all equal, we say that we have perfect balance and we expect smooth flow. If they are unequal, we know that the maximum possible output for the line as a whole will be dictated by the slowest operation in the sequence. This slow operation, often called the bottleneck operation, restricts the flow of parts in the line in much the same way that a half-closed valve restricts the flow of water, even though the pipes in the system might be capable of carrying twice as much water. Thus where imbalance exists in a line, we have wasted capacity in all operations, except the bottleneck operation.

To achieve balance to the best of our ability, we need to know the performance times for the smallest possible whole units of activity, such as tightening a bolt, making a solder joint, etc., and the knowledge of the flexibility that we have in the sequence of these elements or activities. There are, of course, certain limitations on the sequence of the elements. For example, a washer must go on before the nut, wires must be joined physically before they can be soldered, a hole must be drilled before it can be reamed and reamed before it can be tapped. On the other hand, the sequence may be irrelevant, as the order in which a series of nuts are put on. This sequence flexibility is important in helping us specify the groups of elements making up operations or stations for the line which achieves the best balance.

Let us see the nature of the problem through an example. Figure 17 shows the cylinder subassembly for a typical small air compressor

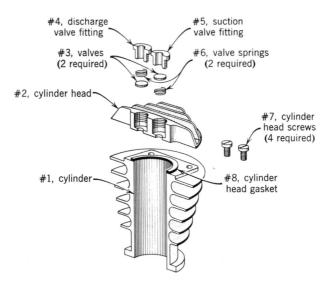

Figure 17. Cylinder subassembly for a typical air compressor.

with the parts named and numbered. By examining the assembly, we can readily see the sequence restrictions that we would have to observe. In assembling the cylinder head to the cylinder, the cylinder head gasket (part No. 8) would have to be positioned first. Also, in assembling the discharge valve unit, the valve itself (part No. 3) must go in first, followed by a valve spring (part No. 6), and finally by a discharge valve fitting (part No. 4). A similar procedure for the suction valve unit would be followed, but the sequence of the valve and spring would be reversed. These are the sequences that must be observed,

TABLE III. List of Assembly Elements Showing Sequence
Restrictions and Performance Times for the
Cylinder Subassembly of Figure 17

Element	Performance Time, Seconds	Element Description	Element Must Follow Element Listed Below
a	1.5	Position cylinder head gasket (No. 8) on cylinder (No. 1)	—
b	2.0	Position cylinder head (No. 2) on cylinder (No. 1)	a
c-1	3.2	Position a cylinder head screw (No. 7) in hole and engage threads	ab
c-2	3.2	Repeat	ab
c-3	3.2	Repeat	ab
c-4	3.2	Repeat	ab
d-1	1.5	Tighten a cylinder head screw	abc
d-2	1.5	Repeat	abc
d-3	1.5	Repeat	abc
d-4	1.5	Repeat	abc
e	3.7	Position valve (No. 3) in bottom of discharge hole	—
f	2.6	Position valve spring (No. 6) on top of valve in discharge hole	e
g	3.2	Position discharge valve fitting (No. 4) in hole and engage threads	ef
h	2.0	Tighten discharge valve fitting	efg
i	3.1	Position 2nd valve spring (No. 6) in bottom of suction hole	—
j	3.7	Position 2nd valve (No. 3) on top of spring in suction hole	i
k	3.2	Position suction valve fitting (No. 5) in hole and engage threads	ij
l	2.0	Tighten suction valve fitting	ijk

because the cylinder subassembly cannot be assembled correctly any other way. On the other hand, it makes no difference whether the valve units are assembled to the cylinder head before or after the cylinder head is assembled to a cylinder. Similarly, which valve unit is assembled first is irrelevant. The cylinder head is joined to the cylinder by four screws. All four of them need not be assembled at the same time, and there is no required sequence for their assembly.

These element sequence restrictions are summarized in Table III so that we can use the result to advantage. The assembly elements listed in Table III are, in general, broken down into the smallest whole activity. Note, for example, that the screws and the valve fittings are first positioned and the threads engaged so that tightening can take place separately, perhaps as a part of the next station or some subsequent station. In addition, for each element, we note in the far right-hand column, the element or elements which must precede it. Thus elements a, e, and i can take any sequence, because no elements need precede them. Element d, position cylinder head on cylinder, however, must be preceded by element a, position cylinder head gasket on cylinder. Element c-1 must be preceded by elements a and b. The repetition of a is not absolutely necessary, since we know that b must be preceded by a. With this information, together with the element times, also given in Table III, we can construct the diagram shown in Figure 18.

Figure 18 merely reflects in a graphical way the sequence requirements that we have determined. For convenience, the performance times are indicated beside the elements. Now we can proceed with the grouping of elements to obtain balance. But balance at what level? What is to be the capacity of our line? This is an important point and one which makes a balancing problem difficult. With no restriction on capacity, the problem would be simple; we could take the lowest common multiple approach. For example, if we had three operations that required 3.2, 2.0, and 4.0 minutes respectively, we could provide eight work places of the first, five of the second, and ten of the third, so that the capacity of the line would be 150 units per hour at each of the operations, all in balance. But capacity has been specified by balance, rather than by considerations of product demand and economics.

We must take the capacity of the line as given and develop good balance within that restriction. For illustrative purposes, let us assume that we must balance our line for a 10-second cycle. A completed unit would be produced by the line each 10 seconds, and to meet this capacity requirement no station could be assigned to more than 10 seconds worth of the elements shown on the diagram of Figure 18. Proceeding,

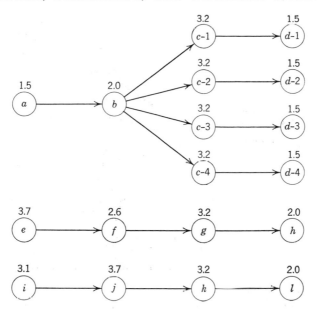

Figure 18. Diagrammatic representation of the sequence requirements shown in Table III. Numbers indicate performance times of elements.

then, we could group the elements into station assignments. The total of all element times is 45.8 seconds; therefore, with a 10-second cycle, five stations would be the minimum possible. Any solution that required more than five stations would increase direct labor costs. Figure 19 shows one solution that yields five stations. Although this is a simple example, it illustrates the conceptual problems of line balancing. Jackson[*] has developed a computational procedure for large-scale problems of the type we have illustrated.

Schedule and Load Analysis

Another dimension of the concept of flow in a production system is related to the schedule of operations and the load on productive equipment. There are two valuable types of graphic models which we shall discuss, the schedule diagram and the Gantt charts.

The *schedule diagram* is actually related to the assembly chart which we discussed earlier. It takes the basic structure of assembly,

---

[*] J. R. Jackson, "A Computing Procedure for a Line-Balancing Problem," *Management Science*, Vol. 2, No. 3, April 1956, pp. 261–271.

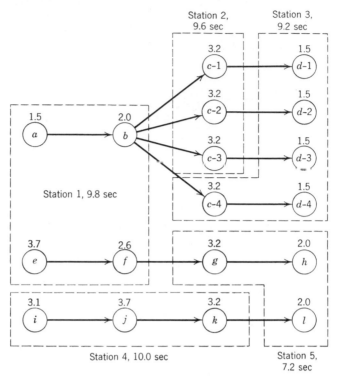

Figure 19. A solution to the line balancing problem which requires no more than 10 seconds per station and does not violate the element sequence requirements.

subassemblies, parts fabrication, material procurement, etc., and relates them to a time scale. Figure 20 is an example of a schedule diagram for an assembled product. Beginning with the receipt of the customer's order, the schedule diagram shows the time schedule that must be met at the various stages of planning and scheduling, material procurement, parts fabrication, subassembly, and assembly in order that the final product be shipped by the target date. For a complex product, such as an airplane, a missile, or a complicated electronic component, such charts are of considerable value. For a complex engineered product, time would also have to be allowed for a product engineering design to be completed.

For the example of Figure 20, notice how the beginning of final assembly establishes due dates for the subassemblies A, B, etc., which in

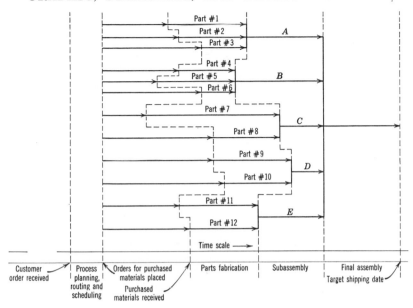

Figure 20. Schedule diagram for an assembled product.

turn establish target dates for completion of parts fabrication for each of the parts which make up a given subassembly. By working backward with these various time requirements, an overall schedule of the various phases of activity can be developed. This schedule, however, must take account of the availability of labor and equipment. The following discussion of Gantt charts provides this kind of data as well as other information.

Gantt charts and their modern counterpart help provide information about the production schedule, and measure progress against that schedule, the load on departments or individual machines, and the availability of equipment or manpower. The plans and progress against plans are plotted in relation to time.

Several kinds of Gantt charts are used. Figure 21 shows the example of the *Gantt project planning chart* which may be used to map out a detailed plan to accomplish target objectives. Figure 21 represents a plan to manufacture an assembled product so that the availability of parts for assembly dovetails with the fabrication and assembly time required as shown by the schedule diagram of Figure 20. Note that the final assembly is scheduled to begin during the week of April 25, before all the subassembly units have been completed.

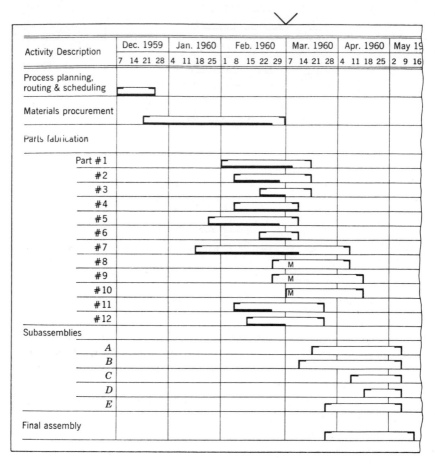

Figure 21. Gantt project planning chart based on schedule diagram of Figure 20. At the beginning of the week of March **7**, material procurement is one week behind schedule so that the fabrication of parts 8, 9, and 10 has been held up.

As subsequent subassemblies are completed, they will be taken to the final assembly area. The schedule could in this case undoubtedly be compressed further by applying the same overlapping scheduling to the subassemblies in relation to the parts fabrication.

The overall scheduling of this project depends in part on the availability of men, machines, and materials. Therefore, the same basic concepts of the Gantt chart may be applied. Figure **22** shows

Turret Lathe Dept.								
	Mach. No.	March	April	May	June	July	August
Gisholt #2	321						
Gisholt #4	422						
Warner and Swasey #2	729						
Warner and Swasey #2	730						
Warner and Swasey #5	810						
Bullard vert. turret #1	769						

Figure 22. Gantt load chart. Light lines show per cent of month that machines have scheduled work. Heavy lines show cumulative load.

a *Gantt load chart* for some of the machines which might be used in fabricating the various parts in our assembled product. It shows the overall projected load on these machines month by month, together with the accumulated backlog of work. Figure 23 shows greater detail; for each machine it shows the orders schedule with the total time reserved for each order. This is called a *Gantt layout chart* or a *Gantt reserved time planning chart.* It shows at a glance the status of a given order. Similar charts could be maintained on materials or men. The charts must be maintained to be of any value as tools for planning, scheduling, and control. If we use paper and pencil charts similar to those illustrated in Figures 21, 22, and 23, the task of maintenance can be considerable. If, for example, the Gantt layout chart had to be modified to accommodate the fabrication of a new rush order, the entire sequence might have to be rescheduled. This is one reason why mechanical boards have been developed. They allow changes to be made rather quickly by the shifting of pegs or cards.

Even with the mechanical boards, the problem of maintenance is considerable, especially in large complex installations, and this often results in discarding any attempt at the close control implied by the charts. The role of the electronic computer and modern programming methods is of great importance here. If we use the hand methods of developing the best schedule represented by the charts, the number of alternatives will often be very large, and selecting the

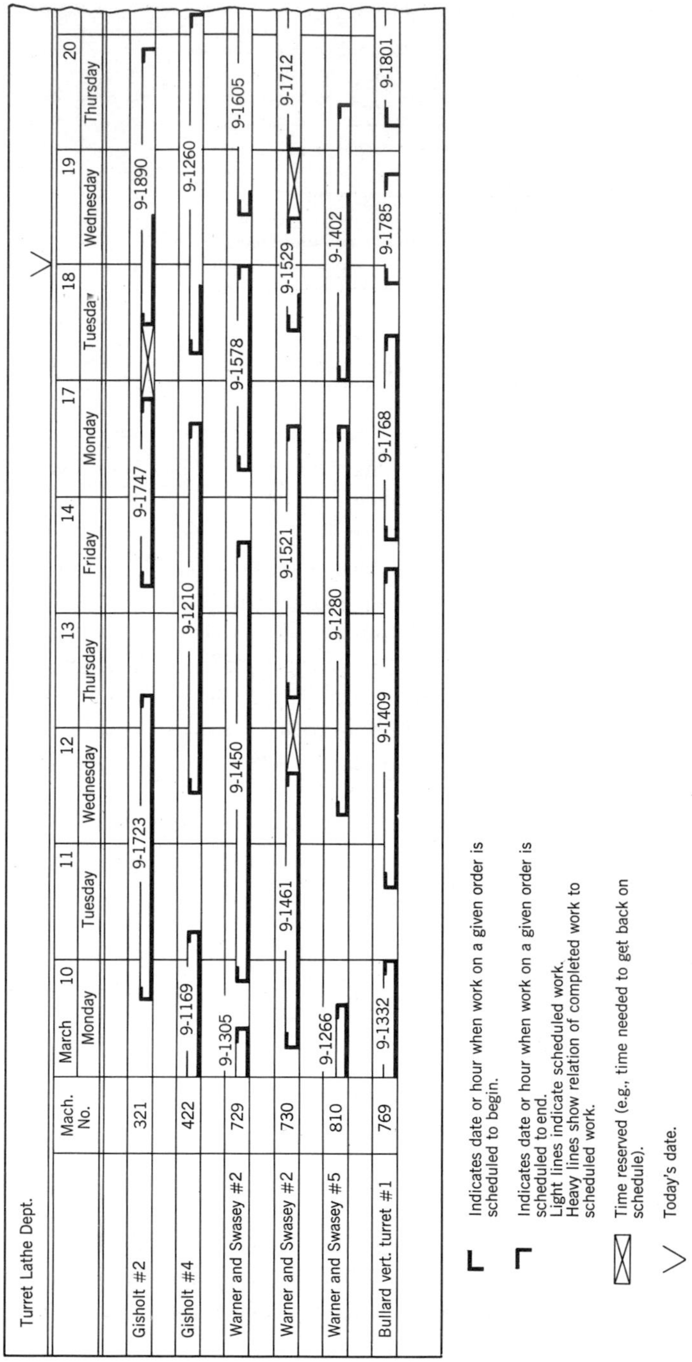

Figure 23. Gantt layout, or reserved time planning chart.

best schedule becomes a trial-and-error process. A high-speed computer can be set up to make the trials very quickly.

Summary

The models presented here represent much of the traditional analytical technique of production and operations management. They are of considerable importance for the kinds of problems for which they were designed and developed. They are, however, somewhat limited to relatively simple kinds of analysis. In most instances, the graphic models are oversimplified. For example, a flow-process chart does convey information about the productive and nonproductive activities required in the processing sequence; however, it ignores the probabilistic nature of the flow problem. A more realistic representation of the flow problem recognizes it as a network of waiting lines. Operation sequence analysis as a model representing the relative location of facilities breaks down rapidly as the scale of the problem approaches the size of real systems, and it does not account for differing material-handling systems within the same plant. A computer simulation model has been found to be more efficient and realistic. The graphic models of schedule and load provide important concepts for the planning and control of operations, but they do not consider the probability of attaining a given schedule, and they are too cumbersome for large-scale problems. The modern counterpart, PERT, with a computer program, determines a minimum cost schedule and can handle projects as complex as the Polaris missile nearly as easily as a simple project. Many of the newer analytical techniques have been forced in their development by the oversimplification and inadequacies of the traditional graphic techniques.

We must recognize, however, that the graphic models have not been entirely replaced by the newer methods. In some instances, the new methods attack a somewhat different kind of problem, often greater in scope, leaving the graphic model in its traditional role. Also, the graphic models continue to serve an important function in systematic data gathering and in helping us to visualize the scope and general relationships of the system under study. We must note, too, that the methods of analysis discussed here are not independent of the methods of economic analysis. The main criterion for the best layout, manufacturing process, work flow, or schedule, is established by comparative economic analysis. Thus, in developing a method of performing an operation, the most economical way known to us may appear to be a crude one, where the volume is low. As volume increases, greater use of tools, mechanization, and automation become justified.

REFERENCES

1. Armour, G. C., and E. S. Buffa, "A Heuristic Algorithm and Simulation Approach to Relative Location of Facilities," *Management Science*, Vol. 9, No. 2, January 1963.
2. Barnes, R. M., *Motion and Time Study*, John Wiley and Sons, New York, 5th ed., 1963.
3. Buffa, E. S., *Modern Production Management*, John Wiley and Sons, New York, 1961.
4. Buffa, E. S., "Sequence Analysis for Functional Layouts," *Journal of Industrial Engineering*, Vol. 6, No. 2, March–April 1955, p. 12.
5. Carter, H. B., *Techniques for Making Plant Layouts*, General Electric Company, Schenectady, N. Y., 1954.
6. Close, G., *Work Improvement*, John Wiley and Sons, New York, 1960.
7. Ireson, W. G., *Factory Planning and Plant Layout*, Prentice-Hall, Englewood Cliffs, N. J., 1952.
8. Krick, E. V., *Methods Engineering*, John Wiley and Sons, New York, 1962.
9. Mallick, R. W., and A. P. Gaudreau, *Plant Layout: Planning and Practice*, John Wiley and Sons, New York, 1951.
10. Maynard, H. B., *Industrial Engineering Handbook*, McGraw-Hill Book Company, New York, 1956.
11. Mundel, M. E., *Motion and Time Study*, Prentice-Hall, Englewood Cliffs, N. J., 2nd ed., 1955.
12. Muther, R., *Practical Plant Layout*, McGraw-Hill Book Company, New York, 1955.
13. Nadler, G., *Motion and Time Study*, McGraw-Hill Book Company, New York, 1955.
14. Nadler, G., *Work Design*, Richard D. Irwin, Homewood, Ill., 1963.
15. Niebel, D. W., *Motion and Time Study*, Richard D. Irwin, Homewood, Ill., 1955.
16. Reed, R., *Plant Layout*, Richard D. Irwin, Homewood, Ill., 1961.

REVIEW QUESTIONS

1. Contrast physical, graphic, and schematic models in production analysis. What kinds of problems yield to these kinds of analysis?

2. What is the difference between assembly charts, operation process charts, and flow process charts? What sorts of problems might call for the use of each?

3. Why does the charting of paper work flow as opposed to the flow of a manufactured part call for a modification of flow process charting procedures?

4. In what ways do flow charts oversimplify the representation of the flow problem?

5. What is the measure of effectiveness used in the operation sequence analysis model of relative location of facilities? How could this measure be modified to take account of the use of different kinds of material-handling systems within the same layout?

6. Under what conditions would three-dimensional templates be useful and justified in developing physical models of layout?

7. What measure of effectiveness might we use in a graphical model of line balance?

8. What information is shown on a schedule diagram? What sort of processing situation requires the consideration of this kind of information?

9. What are the various kinds of Gantt charts and what are their fields of application? In what ways do Gantt charts and schedule diagrams oversimplify the real situation which they represent?

PROBLEMS

1. Construct an assembly chart for the caster shown in Figure 24, assuming that parts 2, 3, 4, and 5 form a subassembly. The subassembly is later joined to the shaft and the end of the shaft is staked (flattened). The wheel and axle are then assembled to the housing and joined permanently by staking one end of the axle.

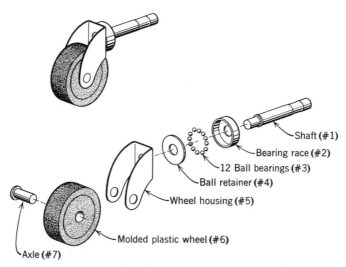

Figure 24. Drawing of a caster showing the assembly relationship of its parts.

Assume that the plastic wheel and the ball bearings are purchased outside and that the other parts are fabricated in-plant. Lead times required for the purchase of materials (overall time to prepare orders, transmit them to vendors and receive them in plant ready for use) are as follows:

Wheels	5 days
Bearings	10 days
Sheet metal for housing and retainer	3 days
Bar stock for bearing race shaft and axle	3 days

Fabrication and assembly times (overall flow times) for an order of 500 casters are estimated as follows:

Shaft	4 days
Bearing race	10 days
Wheel housing	3 days
Ball retainer	2 days
Axle	2 days
Subassembly	7 days
Assembly and pack	5 days

Construct a schedule diagram to indicate minimum total lead time required for an order of 500 casters.

2. Given the following additional information about the processes for the fabricated parts and assembly operations of the caster described in Problem 1, develop an operation process chart.

Part #1,	Operations	Machine	Production Rate, Parts per Hour
Shaft	1. Cut to length	Cutoff lathe	100
	2. Turn finished shape	Lathe	40
	3. Inspect	Bench	40
Part #2,			
Bearing race	1. Turn and drill	Lathe	50
	2. Deburr	Tumble barrel	250
	3. Inspect	Bench	50
	4. Heat treat (outside operation)		5 days required
	5. Inspect	Bench	50
Part #4,			
Retainer	1. Shear stock	Press	250
	2. Pierce hole	Press	250
	3. Blank and form	Press	100
	4. Deburr	Tumble barrel	500
Part #5,			
Wheel housing	1. Shear stock	Press	250
	2. Pierce 3 holes	Press	100
	3. Blank and form	Press	100
	4. Deburr	Tumble barrel	250

Part #7, Axle	Operations	Machine	Production Rate, Parts per Hour
	1. Cut to length	Cutoff lathe	100
	2. Form head	Swaging press	100
Subassembly, assembly and packing	1. Subassembly	Bench	20
	2. Assemble and pack	Bench	30

3. An organization does job machining and assembly and wishes to relay-out its production facilities so that the relative location of departments better reflects the average flow of parts through the plant. Below is shown an operation sequence summary for a sample of seven parts, with approximate area requirements for each of the thirteen machine or work centers. The numbers in the columns headed by each of the parts indicates to which work center number the part goes next. Just below the sequence summary is shown a summary of production per month and the number of pieces handled at one time through the shop for each part.

    a. Develop a load summary showing the number of loads per month going between all combinations of work centers.
    b. Develop an ideal schematic layout.
    c. Develop a block diagram that reflects the approximate area requirements given and results in an overall rectangular shape.

Machine or Work Center	Area, Square Feet	Work Center Number	Part						
			A	B	C	D	E	F	G
Saw	50	1		2	2				2
Centering	100	2		4	3				3
Milling machines	500	3	5	9	5	5		4	4
Lathes	600	4		5, 7	7		5	10	5
Drills	300	5	8	3	4	11	7		6
Arbor press	100	6					11		7
Grinders	200	7		12	12		6		8
Shapers	200	8	9			3			9
Heat treat	150	9	11	4					10
Paint	100	10						11	11
Assembly bench	100	11	12	13	13	13	13	13	12
Inspection	50	12	13	11	11				13
Pack	100	13							

Production Summary

			A	B	C	D	E	F	G
Pieces per month			500	500	1600	1200	400	800	400
Pieces per load			2	100	40	40	100	100	2
Loads per month			250	5	40	30	4	8	200

4. Following is a list of assembly elements showing the sequence restrictions and performance times. Develop a diagram showing the sequence requirements and determine an element grouping that minimizes the number of stations (groups of elements), does not violate sequence restrictions, and produces 10 units per hour.

Element	Performance Time, Minutes	Element Must Follow Element Listed Below
a	4	—
b	3	a
c	5	ab
d	2	—
e	4	abc
f	6	abcd
g	2	—
h	3	dg
j	5	dgh
k	2	—
l	3	k
m	4	kl

5. Select an activity familiar to you in which something is processed by a series of operations, for example, the registration procedure in a university, and construct a flow process chart. Measure the approximate time that the item being processed spends actually being processed, waiting, traveling, and being inspected for quality, quantity, or accuracy.

4

Models of Man-Machine Systems

In spite of the great advances in computer and automation technology, manual labor at various levels is predominant today. This situation will be in effect for a long time and, therefore, we should expect that the design of jobs and of the methods used will continue to be emphasized in operations management. Even in an automated system today, labor is very necessary in a surveillance capacity. In such situations, an operator of an automated system may be seated in front of a control board which continually flashes information about the progress of the process. It is important, then, that these display panels be designed to transmit the essential information to the operator with minimum error. Under such conditions of automation, the effect of errors may be more serious than before because the operator is dealing with very expensive equipment and with high-volume processing systems. Wrong decisions could result in tons of scrap.

Perhaps the majority of business and industrial manual jobs today consist of some combination of man and machine or at least of man and mechanical aids. Where there is a fixed machine cycle, such as exists in most machine tool processes, the design of the machine in relation to the operator is of great importance. The location and design of controls, working heights, information displays, the flow of work, safety features, and the relative utilization of both the man and the machine in the cycle are all important determinants of quality, productivity, and worker acceptance of the job situation. Many jobs are strictly manual, such as assembly, maintenance, and heavy labor. Here mechanical aids or tools are common, and we need to consider the design of those tools from the point of view of the user; in addition, we must consider layout of the workplace, the flow of work, and physical and mental fatigue produced by these job conditions. In all types of jobs there is an interaction between the worker and his physical environment. In some situations environmental factors of heat, humidity, light, noise, and hazards can produce serious effects on measures of fatigue, productivity, quality, health, and worker acceptance of the job.

Models of man–machine systems need to take account of all of these physical, physiological, and psychological factors.

Man

Man is the dominant element in job design. He has certain physiological, psychological, and sociological characteristics which define both his capabilities and his limitations in the work situation. These characteristics are not fixed quantities but vary from individual to individual. This does not mean, however, that we cannot make predictions about human behavior; rather, it means that predictive models of human behavior must reflect this variation. To take a physical factor as an example, the distribution of the arm strengths of men indicates the per cent of the male population that can exert a given force. This distribution also indicates the limitations in demand for arm strength. The average man can exert a right-hand pull of 120 pounds. If we designed a machine lever that required the operator to exert this force, approximately half the male population would be unable to operate the machine. On the other hand, the distribution also tells us that about 95 per cent of the male population can exert a right-hand pull of 52 pounds. A lever designed to take this fact into account will accommodate a large proportion of the male population.

In performing work, man's functions fall into three general classifications:

1. *Receiving information* through the various sense organs, that is, eyes, ears, touch, etc.

2. *Making decisions* based on information received and information stored in the memory of the individual.

3. *Taking action based on decisions.* In some instances the decision phase may be virtually automatic because of learned responses, as in a highly repetitive task. In others the decision may involve a high order of reasoning and the resulting action may also be complex.

The general structure of a closed-loop automated system is parallel to the foregoing concept. Wherein lies the difference? Are automatic machines like men? Yes they are in certain important respects. Both have sensors, stored information, comparators, decision makers, effectors, and feedback loops. The differences are in man's tremendous range of capabilities and in the limitations imposed on him by his psychological and sociological characteristics. Thus machines are much more specialized in the kinds and range of tasks that they can perform. On the other hand, machines perform tasks as faithful servants, reacting mainly to physical factors; for example, bearings may wear out because of a dusty environment. But man reacts to his psychological and sociological environment as well as to his physical environment. The latter fact requires that one of the measures of effectiveness of job design be worker acceptance, or job satisfaction.

Man's effectiveness as an element in the production process depends on a number of factors which include: matching job requirements to his physiological and psychological limitations, layout and work flow, overall organization of his part in relation to the broad plan of manufacture, the design of his tools and processes, and his motivation and job satisfaction.

Where man surpasses machines. Although there are few really objective guides to the allocation of tasks to men and machines on other than an economic basis, a subjective list of the kinds of tasks most appropriate for men and for machines is given by McCormick (15).

Human beings appear to surpass existing machines in their ability to do the following:

1. Detect small amounts of light and sound.
2. Receive and organize patterns of light and sound.
3. Improvise and use flexible procedures.
4. Store large amounts of information for long periods and recall relevant facts at the appropriate time.
5. Reason inductively.
6. Exercise judgment.
7. Develop concepts and create methods.

Existing machines appear to surpass humans in their ability to do the following:

1. Respond quickly to control signals.
2. Apply great force smoothly and precisely.
3. Perform repetitive and routine tasks.

4. Store information briefly and then erase it completely.
5. Perform rapid computations.
6. Perform many different functions simultaneously.

Such a list raises the question: Why do not business, industry, and government use men and machines according to these guides? Certainly we have all observed that man is used extensively for tasks given in the list for machines. The answer lies in the balance of costs for a given situation. Both labor and machines cost money; when the balance of costs favors machines, conversions are normally made. In many foreign countries, low-cost labor in relation to the cost of capital, dictates an economic decision to use manual labor in many tasks for which man is not well suited. Because of relatively high wages in the United States, machines are used much more extensively.

The Design of Jobs

When we speak of the *design of jobs,* we are thinking of two broad areas: job content and work methods. Given the job content, the work methods design is meant to develop the optimal combination of all variables of the job. We shall discuss in a moment the measures of effectiveness in these situations. If we accept a given job content and then try to arrive at some optimal combination of the remaining variables, however, we run the risk of suboptimization, because job content is also a major determinant of effectiveness.

Thus in a typical case we may have taken an entire complex assembly process and broken it down into a series of operations so that the product could be produced on an assembly line. The line was designed to meet certain capacity-demand requirements, such as an output of 480 units per 8-hour shift, or 1 per minute. Output, then, dictates the maximum content of each of the operations, which can take no longer than one minute each. What is more, there is a certain required sequence of assembly, so that operation 1 takes the elements that come first which require 1 minute or less, operation 2 the second 1-minute group, etc. Of course there is usually some flexibility as to sequence, so that by rearranging the sequences we end up with the job content in each operation that seems to make the most sense.

In other situations, the process, the machine, the physical layout, time requirements, and traditions are likely to play a dominant role in determining job content. Each resulting job or operation can be analyzed from the several points of view, which are presented in

Chapters 5 and 6, in order to produce an optimally designed job. *But how would this optimal design compare with other basic alternatives of job content?* We can see that if we were to consider as a part of the problem all possible alternatives of job content, there would be a baffling number. Unfortunately there is very little information available to guide us here, and the result in practice is that such considerations as the machines, layouts, production quotas, and machine and conveyor pacing, often dictate job content.*

Since Adam Smith, the main guide for determining job content has been *division of labor.* We have accepted this idea almost completely. Adam Smith specified no limit to division of labor, and the principle has been applied as a one-way mechanism to achieve the maximum benefits of job design. Jobs have been broken down to the point where the worker finds little satisfaction in performing his tasks. In recent years there has been a reaction against excessive job breakdown; a few investigators found that combinations of operations to create jobs of greater scope recaptured the worker's interest, and increases in productivity, quality level, etc., were reported. A new term, *job enlargement,* appeared, and practical applications of job enlargement described in the literature verified the findings of the investigators. Unfortunately, although exponents of job enlargement recognize that division of labor can be carried too far, they have not been able to specify any principles or guides on how far to go in the other direction. Job enlargement, too, is a one-way mechanism. It does, however, provide a balancing force through the inclusion of job satisfaction as a major criterion of successful job design. The ultimate answer lies in research attempts to isolate the factors that determine an optimal combination of tasks to make up jobs. This effort has been called *job design.*†

Management objectives in job and methods design. Lehrer stated succinctly the objectives of job design in profit-making organizations as: "To make money," and "to make money."‡ He says, "Although these appear to be identical objectives, they differ considerably. The first 'to make money' is a short-range objective. It

* See L. E. Davis, R. R. Canter, and J. Hoffman, "Current Job Design Criteria," *The Journal of Industrial Engineering,* Vol. VI, No. 2, March–April 1955, pp. 5–8, and G. Nadler, *Work Design,* Richard D. Irwin, Homewood, Ill., 1963, Chapter 3.

† See L. E. Davis, "Toward a Theory of Job Design," *The Journal of Industrial Engineering,* Vol. VIII, No. 5, September–October 1957, pp. 305–309.

‡ R. N. Lehrer, "Job Design," *The Journal of Industrial Engineering,* Vol. IX, No. 5, September–October 1958, pp. 439–446.

implies immediate survival and the short-range prosperity of the organization. The second 'to make money' deals with the long-run objectives of the organization. It is concerned with survival over a prolonged period, and the proper relationship of the organization with society and the economy as a whole."

This quotation summarizes fairly well the past and present point of view of American business and industry. It emphasizes the economic criterion as the controlling factor of the organization, and considers other criteria as effective mainly insofar as they meet economic requirements. Thus a quality criterion often reduces to an economic criterion when the job design that improves quality levels also improves productivity. For example, removing fatiguing elements of a job commonly improves productivity; eliminating hazards may reduce insurance premium rates, as well as improve overall productivity; designing tasks that increase employee satisfaction often also improves productivity. There certainly are instances where the various subcriteria do not correlate with the economic criterion, however. To obtain higher-quality levels often demands increased costs, and the value of the reduced scrap may not counterbalance the higher labor costs. To reduce the risk of hazards to extremely low levels might be very costly.

In Taylor's time the noneconomic criteria would have been shrugged off. Today, however, jobs and methods are frequently designed or altered to meet noneconomic needs. It is true that the economic criterion is dominant, and job and methods designs are seldom set or altered without reference to the effects on costs. Most often, costs are regarded as the "quantitative" measure, with noneconomic criteria being considered in the list of "intangible" advantages or disadvantages.

What is involved in the design of jobs? Conceptually the design of jobs can be divided into the determination of job content and the determination of the actual methods of execution. As we have already noted, there is very little in the way of guides or principles to help us determine optimal job content. In general, job content is not consciously designed, but, rather, is the result of limitations of product designs, machine designs, layouts, production quotas, pacing effects, and of the desire to make skill requirements uniform within jobs. Within these limitations, the scope of jobs is determined, on the one hand, by a desire to gain the advantages inherent in division of labor, and, on the other hand, by a desire to design jobs that meet worker satisfaction needs. Whether an organization tends toward finely divided jobs or enlarged jobs depends on its managerial philosophy, traditions, and degree of investment committed in existing systems.

The design of job methods has received much attention since the time of Taylor. Over the years, considerable handbook data has been compiled which may be drawn on to develop methods designs which tend to optimize productivity and other measures of effectiveness for a given set of conditions. These data pertain to control of the work environment, physiological measures of body strength and sizing, psychological factors related to the various sensory inputs to the human operator, principles of the arrangement and flow of work, and fatigue and work schedules. These data are applied within a framework of physical and economic limitations. Figure 1 shows the relation of these factors in determining job content and job methods. Physical limitations may relate to existing products, machines, and layouts. Economic limitations refer both to the economic resources of the organization and to the justifiable expenditures on a given project; the latter depend to a great extent on the volume and market stability of the products. Thus the work methods design for a high-volume automotive part, such as a spark plug, will justify careful study from all points of view, and will also justify expenditures of funds for machines, jigs, fixtures, and other special tools. On the other hand, job designs to produce a novelty toy, which may cease to exist in six months, might be quite crude. Here again, we see the dominant position of the economic criterion. Thus, a given job design is likely to be a temporary thing which may change with gross changes in the volume and market stability of the part or product.

Who designs jobs and work methods? In industrial organizations the professional designer of jobs and work methods is the industrial engineer. In many less formalized organizations, however, foremen and managers at various levels design jobs. In most nonmanufacturing organizations, managers and supervisors are responsible for determining job content and methods design. The wide variety of organizations and of people holding responsibility for job design makes dissemination of the known data a difficult problem. Since, for most of these people, job design is only a part of their responsibility, they have tended to rely on existing standard workplace designs and on basic equipment (such as office desks, typewriters, benches, and standard machine tools) to fix many of the characteristics of the job, and actual details of method are often left to the workers themselves.

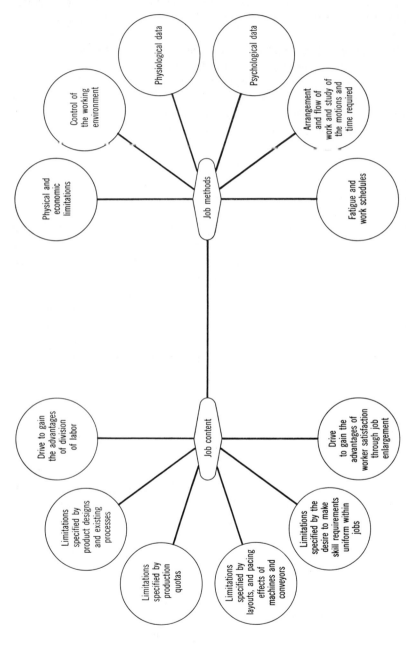

Figure 1. Relationship of factors determining job content and job methods.

PSYCHOPHYSIOLOGICAL DATA

In the post-World War II era there has been an increasing acceptance and recognition of the need to design workplaces and machines to fit the human operator better. This has reversed a previous trend of trying to select the few people from the working population who had certain special abilities or characteristics that made it possible for them to operate monster machines. During this earlier era there was an emphasis on finding people who could perform as if they had six fingers per hand or three hands, eyes in the backs of their heads, swivel hips, or legs that were double jointed at the knee. There was a need to find business and industrial freaks because the emphasis in machine design was on functional performance. The successful design engineer accomplished miracles of functional design. Indeed, he had solved the limiting part of the total engineering problem; that is, if the machine did not perform functionally, the human problem vanished.

During this era, industrial engineers worked feverishly to patch up functional designs by relocating controls, putting extensions on levers to multiply the effect of workers' muscles, etc., but they were limited by the original design of the machine. In this same period, industrial engineers began to develop some of the necessary psychophysiological data that helped them establish the limits of normal working areas, design foot pedals, scales, and displays, and establish principles of the effective use of the human hands and body. Psychologists and physiologists were busy with other activities and, in general, were not interested in the practical problems of business and industry. From the safe distance of the laboratory, a few psychologists and physiologists offered criticism of what was being done in industry, but they did not offer their special knowledge and skills in any great degree until the postwar period.

Since World War II the picture has been different. Experimental psychologists and physiologists, largely subsidized by government projects, have been working to compile a large store of data on the human operator and his relation to machines. Many of these data are applicable to business and industry, as well as to the military. But unfortunately most data take the form of scattered experimental results in learned journals, which are read by other psychologists and physiologists and which seldom reach the people who actually design jobs in any form that they can use. Much effort is needed to integrate these data into an overall framework.

The data reported here are in summary form and come from various original sources; they are all classified as psychophysiological, whether they were originated by industrial engineers, physiologists, or psychologists.

Anthropometric Data

One of the areas of physiology which provides basic data for job designers is anthropometry, the measurement of the physical size of the human body and of other characteristics, such as physical strength. Data of this nature make it possible to specify work area limits, the height of chairs and work tables, the design of levers and handwheels, so that the physical strength of the majority of the

TABLE I. Selected Body Measurements for Adults

(in inches)

Body Variable	Male			Female		
	Me-dian	SD	Range	Mean or Me-dian	SD	Range
Height	69.2	2.43	61.4–78.0	63.2	2.48	55.0–73.0
Sitting height: erect	36.4	1.20	32.7–40.6	34.1	1.02	30.7–34.4
Shoulder breadth	18.0	0.77	15.4–20.5	13.4	1.22	8.7–19.3
Chest depth	8.2	0.63	6.3–11.0			
Seat breadth: standing	14.0	0.75	11.8–18.5	15.0	1.03	11.8–18.9
Hip breadth: seated	15.3	1.11	12.0–21.3	14.6	1.04	12.1–20.6
Trunk height	23.8	0.93	19.7–27.2	24.6	3.02	Not given
Back height	28.6	1.26	23.6–33.1	26.7	1.11	21.1–30.1
Shoulder-elbow	14.7	0.68	10.6–16.9	13.3	1.93	Not given
Forearm	18.8	0.79	15.8–22.1			
Forward arm reach	35.2	1.56	29.5–40.6	31.8	1.29	28.3–35.4
Total arm span	71.5	2.75	62.2–80.7			
Elbow height	9.6	0.89	6.7–12.0	9.7	0.89	7.0–12.0
Buttock-knee	23.6	1.06	19.3–27.6	22.6	0.96	19.7–26.7
Seat length	18.9	0.96	15.4–23.1	18.2	1.04	15.2–22.2
Knee height	22.0	0.94	18.1–25.6	17.2	1.07	Not given
Seat height	19.0	0.89	15.6–22.0	18.1	0.89	15.4–20.6
Knee breadth	8.1	0.49	6.7–11.0			
Foot length	10.4	0.46	8.3–12.2	9.6	0.40	8.9–10.9
Foot breadth	4.0	0.17	3.4–4.8			
Hand breadth	3.5	0.19	3.0–4.0			

Adapted from E. J. McCormick, *Human Engineering*, McGraw-Hill Book Company, New York, 1957, Table I is based on various original sources.

working population is not overtaxed. Table I is a general summary of selected body measurements for adults.

Work area limits. Many tasks, such as assembly work, the operation of many types of machines, and much clerical work, are performed while the worker is seated or standing at a bench, table, or desk. Figure 2 shows the maximum and normal work areas that are based on the actual measurement of people. Movements beyond the maximum work area require that the trunk of the body be moved and, for repetitive operations, these trunk movements are fatiguing. Similar guides for locating materials, supplies, tools, and controls are available in three dimensions.

Chair and table heights. Since there is so much manual and clerical activity, the height of chairs and work tables is important. The two are closely related, and table height is commonly specified in relation to the elbow, so that adjustments in either chair or table height from the floor can be made to give greatest comfort to individual workers. A study by Ellis (9) corroborates earlier estimates by Barnes (1) that the work surface height should be about 3 inches below the elbow. Actual work table and chair heights then depend on whether the setup is designed for sitting-standing or sitting only.

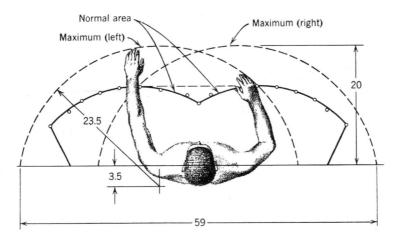

Figure 2. Dimensions in inches of maximum working areas in the horizontal plane as proposed by Barnes, with normal work area proposed by Squires. (From R. M. Barnes, *Motion and Time Study,* John Wiley and Sons, New York, 5th ed., 1963; P. C. Squires, *The Shape of the Normal Work Area,* Navy Department, Bureau of Medicine and Surgery, Medical Research Laboratory, New London, Conn., Report 275, July 23, 1956.)

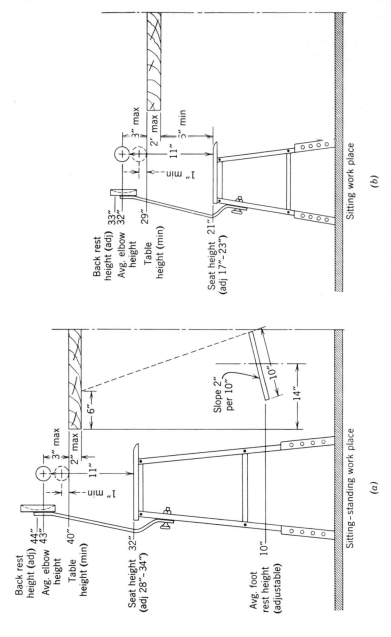

Figure 3. Industrial chair and table height standards for men.

Figure 3 summarizes the dimensions used as standard data for male employees by some industrial concerns. These dimensions accommodate the majority of employees, but compensations for the very short or very tall can be made by adjusting chair heights or by blocking up chairs or tables.

Strength and forces of body movements. A knowledge of the forces that can be exerted by most of the working population is important in order that we can design machines and tools which do not require operators with unusual physical strength. Rather exhaustive population measurements have been made for arm strength (in various directions and different starting positions), grip strength, turning strength (such as turning a door knob), elbow and shoulder strength, and back and leg strength.*

* A good summary of the results of these studies can be found in E. J. Mc-Cormick, *Human Engineering*, McGraw-Hill Book Company, New York, 1957, Chapter 12.

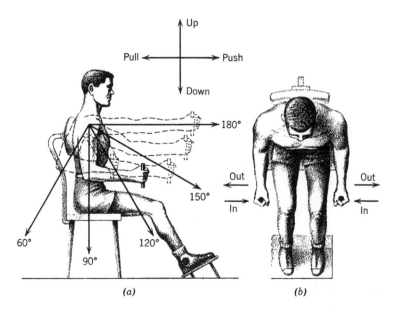

Figure 4. Subject positions for arm strength study. Data shown in Table II. (*a*) Side view of subject, showing various angular positions of upper arm. For each position, maximum strength was determined for pull, push, up, and down movements shown in *b*. (*b*) Top view of subject showing in and out movements made at each of the arm positions shown in *a*. Adapted from Hunsicker (11).

Typical of such data is that developed for the USAF at Wright Air Development Center for arm strength in a seated position. Subjects were measured for maximum push, pull, upward force, and downward force for various angular positions (see Figure 4). Table II summarizes the results for the maximum forces exerted by the 5th percentile of the measured group. These figures, then, represent forces that nearly all males can equal or exceed. Jobs designed so that required arm forces do not exceed these values can draw on almost anyone in the male population and expect their arm strength to be adequate. In general, from Table II we can see that left hand strength is consistently less than that for the right hand, and that pushes and pulls are weaker when the arm is down at the side. As to upward and downward movements, however, greater force

TABLE II.   Arm Strength, in Pounds, of Movements in Various Directions for Different Angular Positions of Upper Arm

Angle of Arm, degrees	5th Percentile			
	Left	Right	Left	Right
	Pull		*Push*	
180	50	52	42	50
150	42	56	30	42
120	34	42	26	36
90	32	37	22	36
60	26	24	22	34
	Up		*Down*	
180	9	14	13	17
150	15	18	18	20
120	17	24	21	26
90	17	20	21	26
60	15	20	18	20
	In		*Out*	
180	13	20	8	14
150	15	20	8	15
120	20	22	10	15
90	16	18	10	16
60	17	20	12	17

Adapted from P. A. Hunsicker, *Arm Strength at Selected Degrees of Elbow Flexion*, SAF, Wright Air Development Center, Technical Report 54–548, August 1955 (11).

can be exerted when the arm is down at the side. Pull is slightly better than push, down slightly better than up, and in better than out.

Speed and Accuracy of Motor Responses

A motor response is one that involves physical movement and/or control of body parts. It is a muscular activity. Since man's hands are his most important asset for the performance of muscular tasks, we find that most of the available data pertain to the hands. Thus in designing tasks that involve positioning elements, for example, a knowledge of where in the work area positioning can be accomplished most accurately may affect the workplace layout.

Positioning elements. Much experimental effort has gone on to determine how positioning elements of various types can best be accomplished. A number of interesting results have been shown, some expected and some unusual. For example, Barnes (1) showed that it takes somewhat longer (about 17 per cent) for positioning elements that require visual control than when some sort of mechanical guide or stop is used to establish the exact final desired position of the part or hand. The implications of this fact tend to corroborate the idea of a fixed and definite location for everything. The rapid typing speeds attained by the touch system are based partially on this fact, since key locations are fixed. Conceptually, it is the difference between finding something in a carefully indexed and maintained file or in a stack of papers.

Briggs (4) performed a set of positioning experiments where *speed and accuracy* were the criteria. The task required subjects to move back and forth between a buzzer and a target with a metal stylus. When the stylus was pressed against a 3-inch square or circle, the buzzer was actuated. The stylus was then moved 14 inches to a paper target through which it was punched. The measure used was the number of punch marks on the target in a 20-second trial. The target size was varied, and the angular position of the buzzer was varied, as in Figure 5. In a second experiment the positions of the buzzer and target were reversed so that the buzzer was immediately in front of the subject and the target was placed at various angular positions. Figure 5 shows the results. Speed and accuracy are consistently greater for the second experiment when the target was away from the subject. Not only that, but the angular position of about 60° optimizes the scores. In a third set of experiments, the distance of movement was

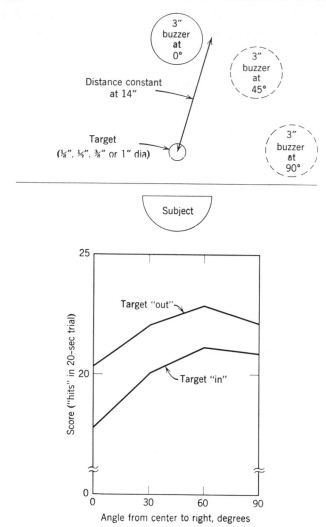

Figure 5. General experimental setup and results of positioning experiments Optimal angle was near 60°. Adapted from Briggs (4).

also varied, and angles to both the right and left of the subject were used. In general, scores were better when movement was to the right instead of to the left, and short distances were better than long.

Barnes and Mundel (3) showed that when the right- and left-hand work in simultaneous and symmetrical patterns, the accuracy of positioning is optimum when both hands are directly in front of the subject.

Blind positioning is sometimes either required or desirable, especially when the nature of the operation requires some simultaneous activities, or in some specialized activities which must be performed in the dark, such as certain phases of photographic film manufacture and processing. Experimental work by Fitts (10) indicates that blind positioning is the most accurate when it is directly in front of the subject.

Positioning through settings of dials, cranks, and handwheels. Movements to position dials, knobs, cranks, and handwheels are quite common as the means by which the human operator controls processes and machines. A number of studies have been made to determine factors which optimize the design of such devices. For example, when knob settings must be accomplished without visual control (blind), Chapanis (6) showed that average errors and variability of settings are minimized at the "twelve o'clock" position of the dial. Jenkins and Connor (13) showed that there is a large difference in the time to make a setting, depending on the ratio between knob movement and the movement of the pointer on the dial. Low ratios tend to minimize the time necessary to make final adjustments, but the time to bring the pointer to the approximate setting is fairly long. The reverse is true for high ratios. The optimum ratio is about 2 inches of pointer movement to one turn of the knob, as shown in Figure 6. Friction

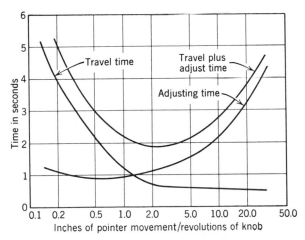

Figure 6. The time for setting indicators with different control ratios. Times are divided into two parts: the time of travel to get the pointer in the vicinity of the target, and the time for adjusting pointer accurately on the target. Note that there is an optimum at about 2 inches of pointer movement for each revolution of the knob. Adapted from Jenkins and Connor (13).

added to the system increases the travel time but has no effect on the final adjustment time.

Davis (8) performed a set of experiments to determine optimal sizes of cranks and handwheels under various conditions of frictional torque, position, and height. These types of cranks and handwheels are common devices used to move carriages and cutting tools to desired settings. Davis measured the time taken to make required settings for the various conditions. He found that for zero or very low frictional torque the small handwheels and cranks were best (3 to 5 inches in diameter). When it was necessary to crank against some frictional load, however, the larger diameters were better (10 to 16 inches). Cranks were superior to handwheels. Davis varied the height from the floor and the angular position of the wheel, since in practice these types of mechanisms might be found in various relative positions. The interesting general result was that location was not a serious factor for zero or low loads, but when a heavy frictional load was encountered the $-45°$ and $+45°$ positions were significantly better than the horizontal or vertical positions.

Information Displays

In many industrial operations workers must read dials and meters, receive auditory signals, or determine by sense of touch which knobs to turn to control their processes. Indeed, as we proceed in the direction of automation, business and industrial operations will emphasize these situations, where correct operation depends on proper interpretation of information displayed to one or more of the body sensory mechanisms. This raises the question of how information should be displayed to minimize errors and decision time.

Visual displays. Much of the postwar effort of experimental psychologists has been directed toward improving visual displays. Questions such as these have been raised: Which dial shapes are the most legible? What scale units should be used and how should they be marked on dials? Do people have number preference patterns that affect their interpretation of dial readings? What characteristics of numbers and letters make them most legible? Are black numbers on a white background superior to white on black? How big should letters and numerals be, and what proportions of line thickness, height, and width are best? How should systems of dials be arranged? Experimental work has been carried out on these and many other questions. We can get some idea of the problem from Figure 7 which shows a

Figure 7. Display panel in an automated engine block production line. Courtesy Ford Motor Company.

fairly complicated display panel in an automated engine block production line. Let us see some typical results of these studies.

Sleight (21) wondered about the shape of dials, so he constructed an experiment around five types of dials and had sixty subjects read seventeen settings from each dial in a random sequence. Figure 8 shows the results in terms of the percentage of errors recorded. A multitude of studies, of which the Sleight study is typical, has indicated the following fairly general guides on dial design, as summarized by Chapanis, Garner, and Morgan (7).

1. A dial about 2.75 or 3 inches in diameter is probably the best all-around size if we are going to read it at a distance of 30 inches or less.

2. Marks should be located at the 0, 5, 10, 15, 20, etc. (or 0, 50, 100, 150, 200, etc.) positions. The marks at the 0, 10, 20, . . . (or 0, 100, 200, . . .) positions should be longer than those at the 5, 15, 25, . . . (or 50, 150, 250, . . .) positions. Only the marks at 0, 10, 20, . . . should be numbered.

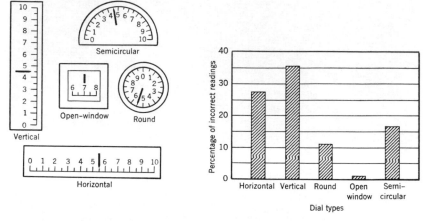

Figure 8. Five different dial shapes and the percentage of incorrect readings recorded for each. From Sleight (21).

3. The distance between the numbered markers should be about ½ inch as measured around the circumference of the dial.

4. The separation between scale markers should be the same all around the dial.

5. There should be a gap between the beginning and end of the scale.

6. Values on the scale should increase in a clockwise direction.

When there is a bank of dials to be read, it helps to orient them all in a pattern so that normal readings are in the 9 o'clock or 12 o'clock positions (see Figure 9). This makes it possible to tell at a glance if an abnormal reading is among the group instead of reading each dial individually. As a matter of fact, we often find that the operator is presented with too much information. He may not need to *read* the dial at all. Perhaps all that is required is simple recognition whether the reading is in the normal operating region or not. Or perhaps the real need is to know only if something is functioning or if it is not. Simple on-off lights may be satisfactory in such situations.

There is also the question of the letters and numbers that are used on visual displays. Studies have indicated that capital letters and numbers are read most accurately when the stroke width to height ratio is between 1 : 6 and 1 : 8, and when the overall width to height ratio is about 2 : 3.

Coding controls. In complex operations where a number of controls are used, coding by color, size, shape, or location helps dis-

Unpatterned dial display

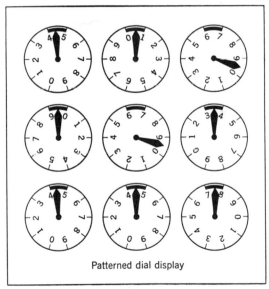

Patterned dial display

Figure 9. The dials in the upper diagram are unpatterned; those below are patterned. Patterning helps us see at a glance which ones are not indicating "normal" readings. From A. Chapanis, W. R. Morgan, and C. T. Garner, Applied Experimental Psychology, John Wiley and Sons, New York, 1949.

tinguish between them so that mistakes are minimized. Hunt (12) found that round knobs could be distinguished from each other when the smaller was five-sixths the size of the larger. The location of controls can be used to distinguish them from each other. For example, the clutch, brake, and accelerator pedals of automobiles are normally used without looking to see where they are. Hunt found that when switches were arranged in vertical columns, the errors in blind reaching to specified switches were lower than when the switches were arranged horizontally in rows. For switches arranged vertically, Hunt's results indicated that a 5-inch difference in location was desirable, but for horizontal arrangements this difference was about 8 inches. Hunt also investigated knob shapes that could be distinguished solely by touch. He classified the designs into three groups: multiple rotation knobs, fractional rotation knobs, and detent positioning (that is, where knob position is critical as, for example, a television channel

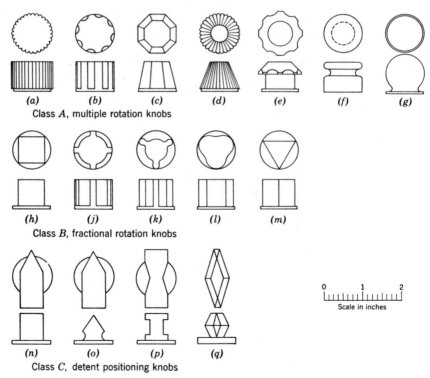

(a) (b) (c) (d) (e) (f) (g)

Class A, multiple rotation knobs

(h) (j) (k) (l) (m)

Class B, fractional rotation knobs

(n) (o) (p) (q)

Class C, detent positioning knobs

0 1 2
Scale in inches

Figure 10. Knob designs of three classes that are seldom confused by touch. Adapted from Hunt (12).

selector dial where each position "clicks" into place). The sixteen knob designs developed are shown in Figure 10.

Fatigue and Work Schedules

Scheduling the hours of work is a part of job design. For some very heavy industrial jobs a man might work 20 minutes and rest 20 minutes. This was the case for the "shake out" of poured iron castings at a well-known automotive foundry. It was a continuous operation which required the worker to break open the iron molding box containing the solidified but very hot casting. This was done over a vibrating grate, so that the molding sand could drop through to a recirculating conveyor, and the casting was conveyed to subsequent cleaning operations. The worker then placed the top half of the molding box on one overhead chain conveyor hook and the bottom half on another; each half weighed 50 pounds. It is evident that the work was done under conditions of high temperature, of dust from the molding sand, and of high noise intensity. The schedule of 20 minutes of work and 20 minutes of rest was probably none too generous. This type of very heavy work is not common today, but it occurs often enough so that there is a continuing interest in the subject of physical fatigue and rest allowances.

Unfortunately, we still lack an accepted framework for the establishment of rest allowances based on any rational or scientific measurements. In most instances, schedules of *fatigue allowances* for various types of work are used based on general acceptability, and are often the subject of agreements between labor and management.

A physiological basis for rest pauses. Recent research has indicated that physiological methods of measurement hold considerable promise for the determination of workloads and optimal environmental design. One application of physiological methods that goes to the heart of the long-standing question of fatigue allowances is the recent work of E. A. Müller in Germany (17).

Based on his studies, Müller proposes an energy expenditure standard of 4 large calories (kcal) per minute as the maximum that the average man can expend continuously without rest. (This is an expenditure above the basal metabolism rate which Müller takes as 1 kcal per minute.) This level of energy expenditure he calls the endurance limit (EL). If the task demands more than the EL, the man must tap his energy reserve, and therefore he must take a rest pause so that his muscles can recover. Müller suggests a standard energy reserve of 24 kcal. The rest or recovery time following work is necessary in order to continue, if the energy reserve of 24 kcal is used up.

Müller further relates work time and rest, or recovery time, by the statement that the average expenditure rate cannot exceed 4 large calories during the work plus resting time, if the effects of fatigue are not to be allowed to accumulate. For example, a task that demands 6 kcal per minute during work would require an average of 20 minutes of rest in an hour, or a fatigue allowance of 33⅓ per cent of the total work plus resting time. Figure 11 shows how this would work out for different levels of energy expenditure. Up to the 4 kcal rate, a man

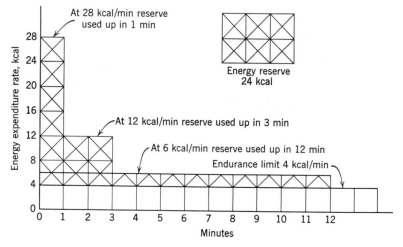

Figure 11. Various patterns of energy expenditure within the endurance limit or within the energy reserve limit. Adapted from E. A. Müller (**17**).

would be expected to be able to work continuously \without needing rest because of physical fatigue. At the 6 kcal rate, however, he could work for a maximum of 12 minutes, at which time he would have used up his 24 kcal energy reserve as indicated by Figure 11. To continue work, Müller suggests that he would have to have at least 6 minutes of rest so that the average energy expenditure for the work time plus rest time, or 12 + 6 = 18 minutes, does not exceed an average of 4 kcal per minute (72 kcal ÷ 18 = 4 kcal per minute).

Other energy expenditure levels are shown in Figure 11. For example, according to Müller's standards, a man could be expected to work at the 12 kcal rate for 3 minutes, at which point he would be exhausted, since his energy reserve would be used up. In order that

TABLE III. Energy Cost and Fatigue Allowance for Various Tasks

Activity	Energy Cost,* Kcal./min, above level basal	Fatigue Allowance, %
Men's Activities		
Miscellaneous office work, sitting	0.6	0
Miscellaneous office work, standing	0.8	0
Armature winding	1.2	0
Light assembly line work	0.8	0
Medium assembly line work	1.7	0
Sheet metal worker	2.0	0
Light machine work	1.4	0
Machinist	2.1	0
Plastic molding	2.3	0
Tool room worker	2.9	0
Loading chemicals into mixer	5.0	20.0
Shoveling 8 kg load, 1 m lift, 12/min	6.5	38.5
Push wheelbarrow, 57 kg load, 4.5 km/hr	4.0	0
Bricklaying	3.0	0
Mixing cement	3.7	0
Plaster lathing	2.1	0
Plastering walls	3.1	0
Coal mining:		
hewing	6.0	33.3
loading	6.1	34.4
timbering	4.7	14.9
drilling	4.8	16.7
pushing tubs	7.0	42.8
Women's Activities		
Machine sewing, foot operated	0.43	0
Typing, electric, 40 words/min	0.31	0
Typing, mechanical, 40 words/min	0.48	0
Tool setting	2.4	0
Gaging	3.0	0
General industrial labor	4.1	2.4

* Handbook figures were adjusted to energy cost above basal level by subtracting 1 kcal/min from each rate given to conform to Müller's formulation.

Source of activities and energy cost data, William S. Spector, editor, *Handbook of Biological Data*, WADC Technical Report 56–273, ASTIA Document No. AD 110501, Wright Air Development Center.

the energy expenditure level should not exceed 4 kcal, he would have to rest 6 minutes following the 3 minutes of work at 12 kcal per minute. This pattern of work 3 minutes, rest 6 minutes, would be required by the high energy expenditure level.

Physiologists have measured the energy costs of a large number of different activities, many of which are industrial tasks. Table III lists, for a few of these tasks, the energy cost and the fatigue allowance (per cent of total time that is rest), using Müller's concept. This list is not meant to be a recommendation for allowances of similar job titles in business and industry, since local job conditions and duties may vary considerably from plant to plant. But it does give an idea of how the Müller standard would work out for various widely known *types* of work. From Table III we see that the majority of activities listed require no fatigue allowance at all. This does not mean that these activities require no personal rest allowances of any kind; it merely means that no rest allowances are necessary in order to recover from *physical* fatigue. There may be psychological factors of boredom and work monotony that would make rest allowances desirable. The tasks that have energy costs above the *EL* require rest allowances for the recovery from physical fatigue or exertion beyond the *EL*. Thus we see that jobs such as shoveling, various coal mining tasks, and general industrial labor would require fatigue allowances according to Müller's standard. All types of office work, light assembly, and most types of light machine shop work, however, would require no allowances for physical fatigue.

At present, determinations of fatigue allowances are not based on measurements of energy expenditure as implied by the discussion of Müller's work, partly because suitable measurement devices for the practical business and industrial situations do not exist, and partly because there has been no acceptance of Müller's or anyone else's concept of the fatigue problem.

THE WORKING ENVIRONMENT

The working environment, which includes such factors as temperature, humidity, noise, and lighting, can produce marked effects on productivity, errors, quality levels, and employee acceptance, as well as on physiological well being. Therefore, we cannot measure the effectiveness of a job design without a knowledge of the working environment in which it will be placed. It is a part of the total picture.

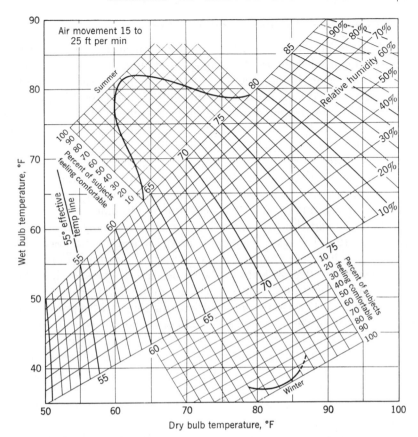

a. Note—Both summer and winter comfort lines apply to inhabitants of the United States only. Application of winter comfort line is further limited to rooms heated by central systems of the convection type. The line does not apply to rooms heated by radiant methods. Application of summer comfort line is limited to homes, offices, and the like, where the occupants become fully adapted to the artificial air conditions. The line does not apply to theaters, department stores and the like, where the exposure is less than 3 hours. The summer comfort line shown pertains to Pittsburgh and to other cities in the northern portion of the United States and Southern Canada, and at elevations not in excess of 1000 ft. above sea level. An increase of one degree *ET* should be made approximately per 5 degree reduction in north latitude.

b. Dotted portion of winter comfort line was extrapolated beyond test data.

Figure 12. Scale of effective temperature and comfort chart for still air. Reprinted from *1960 Heating, Ventilating, Air Conditioning Guide,* by permission of the American Society of Heating, Refrigerating and Air Conditioning Engineers, New York.

Temperature, Humidity, and Air Flow

We have all experienced the fact that our feeling of comfort is not determined solely by the thermometer reading. If there is a breeze we feel cooler even though the temperature has not changed, and on a stifling day we have all heard the comment, "It isn't the heat, it's the humidity." The sensation of warmth or cold is affected by each of these factors, which have been combined into a single psychological scale called *effective temperature*. Effective temperature is the temperature of still, saturated (100 per cent humidity) air, which gives the identical sensation of warmth or cold as the various combinations of air temperature, humidity, and air movement would. The American Society of Heating, Refrigerating, and Air Conditioning Engineers Laboratory performed the experiments that led to the effective temperature scale, and Figure 12 is based on their data for the average conditions of air movement at 20 feet per minute and conventionally clothed people doing light office work. The ASHRAE data, much more extensive than those shown here, give similar information for different air velocities and activity levels. The heavy diagonal lines in Figure 12 represent lines of equal effective temperature where the sensation of warmth or cold is the same, even though different values of air temperature and humidity are encountered. Comfort zones for winter and summer weather are also shown. One factor that the effective temperature scale does not take into account, however, is the temperature of objects in the environment which could radiate directly to the workers, such as furnaces.

The human body has automatic heat regulatory mechanisms which allow compensation for the environment over a certain effective temperature range. This compensation, of course, is also dependent on the activity level. Thus, a higher activity level can produce body comfort at a lower effective temperature.

Temperature and humidity effects on performance. Atmospheric conditions can have important effects on performance in both mental and physical tasks. Figure 13 shows, in summary form, (a) the effects of various levels of effective temperature on performance for Morse code receiving, and (b) for weight lifting. For Morse code receiving, the average number of errors goes up sharply as effective temperature goes beyond 90°F. For heavy work, represented by weight lifting, the total accomplished work in foot-pounds begins to fall off rapidly above 80°F effective temperature.

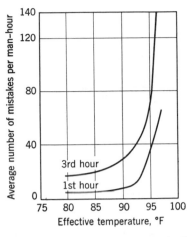
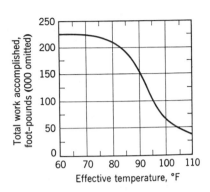

Figure 13. (*a*) Relationship of effective temperature and average number of mistakes per man hour in receiving Morse code. From N. H. Mackworth, "Effects of Heat on Wireless Telegraphy Operators Hearing and Recording Morse Messages," *British Journal of Industrial Medicine,* 1946, Vol. 3, pp. 143–158. (*b*) Foot-pounds of work performed by men under various effective temperatures. From E. J. McCormick, *Human Engineering,* McGraw-Hill Book Company, New York, 1957, p. 235, based on data from *Heating, Ventilating and Air Conditioning Guide,* American Society of Heating and Ventilating Engineers, New York, 1955.

Physiological cost of high effective temperature. Another measure of effectiveness of working in high effective temperature environments is physiological cost, or energy expenditure. Human energy expenditure can be measured by determining the amount of oxygen used during the task or can be approximated by heart rate measurements. It is not sufficient to measure only that oxygen consumed during the exercise or work itself, however, because additional oxygen is required after exercise for *recovery*.

Figure 14 shows the general pattern for a standard exercise for three different environmental conditions, using the heart rate measurement as a criterion of energy consumption. Note that all three curves follow the same general pattern, but at different levels. At the onset of exercise, the energy consumption goes up rapidly and reaches a steady level for the bottom curve of low heat stress. It then falls back to the resting level in about 5 minutes. Note that for the two upper curves representing higher effective temperatures, the resting level of energy consumption is higher and the curve never returns to the origi-

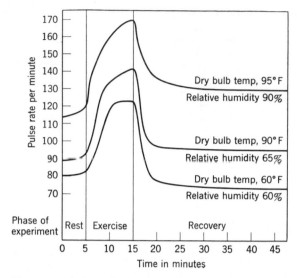

Figure 14. Heart rate before, during and after a standard exercise for various environmental conditions. From L. A. Brouha, "Physiological Approach to Problems of Work Measurement," *Proceedings, Ninth Annual Industrial Engineering Institute,* University of California, Berkeley-Los Angeles, 1957, pp. 12–20.

nal resting level in the time span of the graph. These effects indicate a buildup of physical fatigue, which has been drastically affected by higher effective temperatures.

Control of the thermal atmosphere. Dr. L. A. Brouha, working at E. I. du Pont de Nemours, has experimented with protective clothing for workers who must operate in very hot atmospheres, such as near industrial furnaces. He found that simple protective clothing actually increased the heat stress. However, a ventilated suit, through which a continuous air flow was maintained, reduced the heat stress considerably. Figure 15 shows how effective the suit was in reducing after-exercise fatigue effects. It is to be emphasized that this kind of protection is for extreme conditions.

Control for workers adjacent to hot areas such as furnaces, where heat radiation is the main problem, can be accomplished with shielding and by isolating the hot spot. General thermal control is accomplished through air conditioning, but is not universally practiced because for most United States climates and working conditions the zones of physiological compensation are effective, except for a few hot summer days.

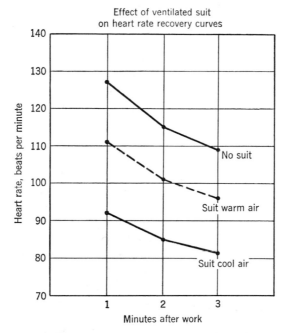

Figure 15. Average heart rate recovery curves of workers performing the same operation in very hot surroundings with their usual work clothes, with the suit ventilated with air at 90°F, and with the suit ventilated with air at 70°F. From L. A. Brouha, "Physiological Approach to Problems of Work Measurement," *Proceedings, Ninth Annual Industrial Engineering Institute,* University of California, Berkeley-Los Angeles, 1957, pp. 12–20.

The most frequent use of air conditioning to date has been in offices to provide attractive working conditions and to help control clerical errors in warm weather. Of course, winter heating has long been accepted as necessary by business and industry for inside tasks.

Noise

Unwanted sound is commonly called noise and there is growing evidence that it can produce damaging effects, especially when workers are exposed to it over a period of years. Sounds of all kinds, including noise, consist of variations in atmospheric pressure that are propagated in waves, similar to ripples on water. These variations in pressure are called *sound pressure*. We measure sound in decibels (db), but that measurement is not a measure of the pressure of sound; rather, it

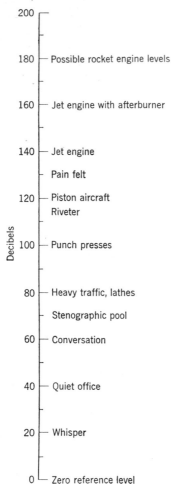

Figure 16. Decibel sound pressure levels of some typical noises.

is related to the ratio of the sound pressure of the source being measured to some reference sound pressure. Considerable confusion is possible here since more than one reference base is commonly used. Figure 16 helps to relate typical noise levels to the db scale. Another thing to note about noise measurements is that we must know something about the distribution of the sound energy over the range of tones, or frequencies, in order to know what will be the effects on man. Therefore, it is common to indicate the db levels in the various octave bands of frequencies. Figure 17 shows the distribution of db noise levels of three industrial operations.

Hearing loss due to noise exposure. Some of the most recent work in this general area has been done by the Research Center, Subcommittee on Noise in Industry, Los Angeles, California. We shall not attempt to report fully on their extensive research in this field, but we shall discuss the general nature of their results.* One study, based on data from 9145 audiograms from a large aircraft manufacturer, is typical of the hearing loss pattern which results from exposure to noise over a period of years. Figure 18 shows the contrast between the hearing loss for 2469 male factory employees (*a*), and 1190 male employees with riveting experience

* See William Grings, Ph.D., Anne Summerfield, Ph.D., and Aram Glorig, M.D., "Hearing Loss in Relation to Industrial Noise-Exposure," *Industrial Medicine and Surgery,* October 1957, pp. 451–458. Anne Summerfield, Aram Glorig, M.D., and D. E. Wheeler, "Is There a Suitable Industrial Test of Susceptibility to Noise-Induced Hearing Loss?" *Noise Control,* Vol. 4, No. 1, January 1958, pp. 40–46. Aram Glorig and Anne Summerfield, "Noise—Is it a Health Problem?" *The Journal of the American Medical Association,* Vol. 168, September 1958.

only (*b*). The first observation is that hearing loss is zero or small for the low frequencies and greatest at 4000 cycles per second (cps). Above 4000 cps the loss is small again. Second, we note that the riveters have experienced a much greater overall hearing loss than general factory workers. The conclusions indicated by Figure 18 are general; hearing loss progresses with years of exposure and is also dependent on the db intensity of the noise environment. The results for 4000 and 6000 cps were significant at the 1 per cent level for all age groups. Because hearing losses first show up there, and because the effects are most pronounced at this level, tests at 4000 cps are commonly used for screening purposes. Figure 19 shows comparative data for a container manufacturer and typical industrial exposure, plus general population data and a group termed *nonexposed* because the noise levels of their typical surroundings were very low. Here we see that hearing loss is characteristic of the general population, even of the nonexposed group, but the severity of loss depends on the intensity of exposure.

Noise effects on work performance. Industry, of course, has been interested in the possible direct effects that high noise levels may have on performance measures such as output, errors, and quality

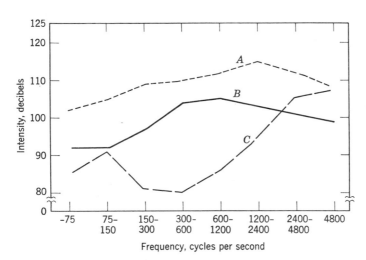

Figure 17. Distribution of noises of three industrial operations: *A* — riveting (overall noise level 115–120 db); *B* = speed hammers (112 db); *C* = compressed air drying (110 db). From W. P. MacLaren and A. L. Chaney, "An Evaluation of Some Factors in the Development of Occupational Deafness," *Industrial Medicine,* 1947, Vol. 16, pp. 109–115.

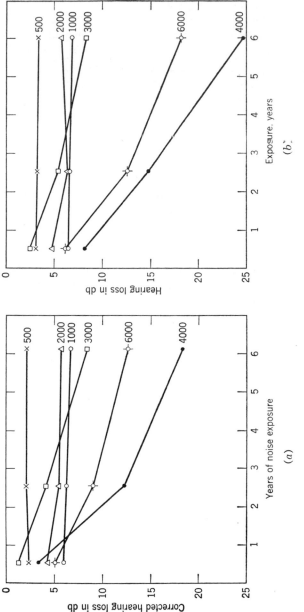

Figure 18. (a) Median hearing loss for 2469 male factory workers with different lengths of exposure. A correction for age has been applied. (b) Adjusted median hearing loss for 1190 male workers with riveting experience only, with different lengths of exposure. Right ear only. A correction for age has been applied. Adapted from W. Grings, A. Summerfield, and A. Glorig, "Hearing Loss in Relation to Industrial Noise-Exposure," *Industrial Medicine and Surgery*, October 1957, pp. 451–458.

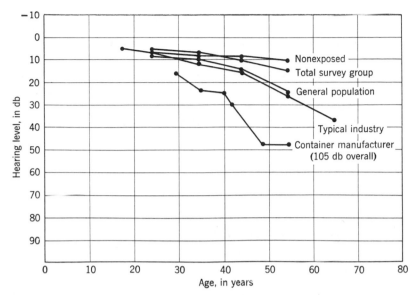

Figure 19. Comparative hearing loss in relation to age for different groups. Zero is a reference base of average normal hearing. Readings show the power level required to reach the average level. Readings were taken at 2000 cycles (speech range). Data courtesy of Research Center, Sub-Committee on Noise, Los Angeles.

levels. In a number of studies on this subject, the general result has been that if the injection of noise into the environment had any bad effects on performance, they were temporary.* We should note that good experimental design is difficult in such situations because the experiments usually must go on over a period of time, and it is difficult to know whether the results are attributable to noise effects or to other changes which may have taken place during the same time interval. The one sure reaction is that higher noise levels are annoying, but human beings seem to be able to adapt to them.

Noise control. Noise control can be accomplished in different ways, depending on the nature of the problem. Acoustical engineers often control noise at its source by redesigning the noise producing parts, by vibration isolation mountings of equipment, or sometimes by isolating the source of noise through the construction of proper enclosures so that the amount of noise transmitted beyond the enclo-

* See R. Lindahl, "Noise in Industry," *Industrial Medicine,* 1938, Vol. 7, pp. 664–669.

sures is reduced. In the last method, a knowledge of the physics of sound transmission is important, for the wrong enclosure design might transmit the noise with little or no loss, or might even amplify it.

Other forms of control are baffles, sound absorbers, and acoustical wall materials. Sound absorbers can be installed near or above noise sources to help reduce noise levels. Acoustical wall materials can be used to reduce noise levels within a room by reducing reverberation, the reflection of the sound waves back and forth in the room. Of course these wall materials have no effect on the original sound waves emanating from the source.

In severe noise situations, a properly fitted earplug can be effective. The maximum possible attenuation from earplugs is limited to about 50 db, because there are alternate paths to the eardrum through bone conduction. The more usual expected protection from earplugs would be an attenuation of 20 to 30 db.

Lighting

The conditions for seeing are an important aspect of the working environment. But no universally accepted standard for lighting is

TABLE IV. Levels of Illumination Recommended or Accepted
by Tinker Based on Critical Levels as a Criterion

Task or Situation	Recommended or Accepted Illumination Level, footcandles
Halls and stairways	5
Reception rooms and washrooms	10
Reading good-sized print (9 to 11 point) on good-quality paper	10–15
School classrooms, shops, and offices	15
Typical home tasks	15
Reading newsprint	15–20
Reading handwriting and comparable tasks	20–30
School sewing and drafting rooms	25
General office work, private office work, mail rooms	25
Most severe visual tasks in home	25–30
Tasks comparable to discrimination of 6-point type	30–40
Most severe tasks encountered in workday situations	40–50
Accounting, bookkeeping, drafting	50

From M. A. Tinker, Trends in illumination standards, *Transactions of the American Academy of Ophthalmology and Otolaryngology*, March–April 1949, pp. 382–394.

available, although there are recommended levels from many sources. Experimental data on illumination levels compared to some given criterion seem to indicate that many recommended standards are based on the view that "if 50 footcandles are good, then 100 footcandles of illumination are better." Part of the difficulty lies in the fact that various criteria have been used, such as visual acuity, blink rate, preference ratings, and critical illumination levels. From a business and industrial point of view, critical illumination levels make the most sense, since they are essentially performance types of criteria. The critical level of illumination for a given task is that level beyond which there is practically no increase in performance for increases in illumination intensity. Thus increases in intensity beyond these critical levels are assumed to be of no value. M. A. Tinker has constructed a table of recommended standards for different tasks based on the critical level criterion. Table IV summarizes his recommendations. Table V gives the recommendations of the Illuminating Engineering Society as a comparison. The recommended values of the Illuminating Engineering Society and the American Standards Association have the greatest circulation and use.

Illumination effects on work performance. There have been many laboratory studies of the effect of illumination level on some measure of performance of a task. In general, there is a rapid improvement in performance as illumination levels increase to the critical level, at which point performance measures level off and further increases in illumination produce little or no improvement in performance.

In many actual work situations where illumination levels have been increased, records of output and quality before and after the changes have indicated substantial improvements. Some studies report that output has gone up 4 to 35 per cent.* We should be wary of this type of support data, however. In the complex set of conditions existing in a business or industrial environment, variables other than just the illumination level could very well have changed, such as work methods, product designs, control procedures, supervision, and the weather, as well as the psychological climate. For example, in the famous Hawthorne studies at the Hawthorne Works of the Western Electric Company, lighting values were increased for an experimental work group and performance went up. Someone thought to check on the result by lowering intensities. The employees cooperated again by lowering performance, but performance increased again when employees

* For a summary of these studies, see E. J. McCormick, *Human Engineering,* McGraw-Hill Book Company, New York, 1957, pp. 61–64.

TABLE V. Industrial Lighting Practice—General Recommended
Values of Illumination Maintained in Service

Task	Footcandles (on task or 30 in. above floor)
Most difficult seeing tasks	200–1000
Finest precision work	
Involving: finest detail	
poor contrasts	
long periods of time	
Such as: extrafine assembly, precision grading; extrafine finishing	
Very difficult seeing tasks	100
Precision work	
Involving: finest detail	
fair contrasts	
long periods of time	
Such as: fine assembly; high-speed work; fine finishing	
Difficult and critical seeing tasks	50
Prolonged work	
Involving: fine detail	
moderate contrasts	
long periods of time	
Such as: ordinary benchwork and assembly; machine shop work; finishing of medium-to-fine parts; office work	
Ordinary seeing tasks	30
Involving: moderately fine detail	
normal contrasts	
intermittent periods of time	
Such as: automatic machine operation; rough grading; garage work areas; switchboards; continuous processes; conference and file rooms; packing and shipping	
Casual seeing tasks	10
Such as: stairways; reception rooms, washrooms, and other service areas; active storage	
Rough seeing tasks	5
Such as: hallways; corridors; passageways; inactive storage	

From *Industrial Lighting, American Standard Practice*, Illuminating Engineering Society, New York, 1952. At the time of publication of this book, the Illuminating Engineering Society was in the process of revising its standards based on new work by H. R. Blackwell.

were told that the light intensity had been increased, when actually it had been lowered, and then the smiles drained. It was finally realized that the employees were reacting to the psychological situation. They were experimental subjects, set aside from "ordinary" employees and unconsciously were simply being very cooperative for those "nice experimenters." When the situation was understood, the direction of the study changed to an evaluation of factors in morale. Very little concerning illumination was learned.

Glare effects.   Glare can reduce the effectiveness of the illumination provided. Glare is produced by some bright spot in the visual field, such as a bright light or reflected light from a polished surface, and can cause discomfort as well as reduce visual effectiveness. This reduction in visual effectiveness is summarized by Figure 20, based on

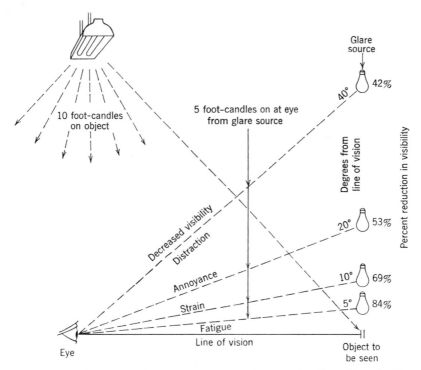

Figure 20.   Glare becomes worse as it comes closer to the direct line of vision. From M. Luckiesh, *Light, Vision, and Seeing,* copyright 1944, D. Van Nostrand Co., Princeton, N. J.

experimental results. Figure 20 shows that the effects of glare become acute when the sources are close to the line of sight.

Glare effects can be reduced by moving light sources where possible; by diffusing light sources that cannot be moved; or by increasing the general illumination level of the surroundings, so that the brightness contrast between the glare source and the surround is reduced. Reflection surfaces may sometimes be moved in relation to workplaces, or changed so that the surface diffuses light.

Criteria for the lighting environment. There is little doubt that it is worthwhile to provide at least the general critical levels of illumination. Although there is little evidence of any changes in performance above the critical levels, these levels may be exceeded without any known bad effects to allow for a safety factor. This idea seems to represent current practical philosophies. General illumination levels that are more than adequate are provided and the problem is forgotten. Often missed, though, is the need for special lights for fine detailed work and the elimination of glare.

Contaminants and Hazards in the Working Environment

A large number of fumes, dusts, gases, liquids, and solids have proved harmful to workers. These, together with the general mechanical hazards from machine moving parts, traffic from material transportation, falling objects, etc., form a part of the working environment.

Noxious substances. The number of industrial poisons is tremendous. Fortunately, however, in most situations only a few would be present and potentially dangerous. Industrial medicine is a special field which concerns itself with the diagnosing, treatment, and control of the noxious substances. Maximum allowable concentrations (MAC) have been determined for most of these substances as a basis for proper control. Table VI gives what are considered the MAC values for typical substances based on exposure of 8 hours per day.

Control procedures. Control procedures vary greatly because of the great variation of possible contaminants and their characteristics. In general, the control of the emissions of these substances in manufacturing processes poses engineering problems. Protection of workmen may require exhaust systems to collect dust, gases, and vapors to maintain concentrations below MAC. Personal protective gear such as respirators and gas masks supplement exhaust systems. Other protective clothing such as rubber aprons, coats, gloves, boots, and goggles, are available for various jobs that involve the handling of

**TABLE VI.   Table of Maximum Allowable Concentrations
of Common Industrial Substances***

(based on 8-hour work day)

Substance	Limit	Substance	Limit
Dusts		Gasoline	1000
Asbestos (0.5 to 10.0 μ)	5	Hydrogen cyanide	20
Cement	15	Hydrochloric acid	10
Organic	50	Hydrogen fluoride	3
Pottery	4	Hydrogen sulfide	20
Silica (25 to 35% Si O_2)	10	Methanol	200
(0.5 to 5.0 μ)		Methyl bromide	30
Silica ($>75\%$ Si O_2)	5	Methyl chloride	500
(0.5 to 5.0 μ)		Monochlorbenzine	75
Slate	15	Naptha (petroleum)	1000
Talc	15	Nitrobenzene	5
Nuisance dusts	50	Nitrogen oxides	10
		Ozone	1
Gases and Vapors		Phosgene	1
Acetone	200	Phosphine	2
Ammonia	400	Phosphorus trichloride	1
Amyl acetate	200	Sulfur dioxide	10
Analine	5	Tetrachlorethane	10
Arsine	1	Tetrachlorethylene	200
Benzol	100	Toluol	200
Butenol	50	Trichlorethylene	200
Butyl acetate	20	Turpentine	200
Carbon disulfide	20	Xylol (coal tar naphtha)	100
Carbon dioxide	5000		
Carbon monoxide	100	Metallic dusts and fumes	
Carbon tetrachloride	100	Cadmium	0.1
Chlorine	1	Chromic acid	0.1
Chloroform	100	Lead	0.15
Dichlorbenzene	75	Manganese	6.0
Dichlorethyl ether	15	Mercury	0.1
Ether (ethyl)	400	Zinc oxide	15
Ethyl alcohol	250	Chlorodiphenyl	1.0
Ethyl bromide	1700		
Ethyl chloride	70	Dusts, million particles /ft^3	
Ethylene dichloride	100	Gases and vapors, parts /million	
Formaldehyde	20	Metallic dusts and fumes, milligrams /m^3	

* From Patty, *Industrial Hygiene and Toxicology* (1948), pp. 195–197.
Values are those listed as commonly accepted or minimum.

chemicals and where the unprotected skin may leave the employee exposed to injury. In addition, vigilance through careful explanation of safe operating procedures and safety programs is common.

REFERENCES

1. Barnes, R. M., *Motion and Time Study*, John Wiley and Sons, New York, 4th ed., 1958.
2. Barnes, R. M., H. Hardaway, and O. Podalsky, "Which Pedal Is Best?" *Factory Management and Maintenance*, January 1942, Vol. C, pp. 98–99
3. Barnes, R. M., and M. E. Mundel, *A Study of Simultaneous Symmetrical Hand Motions*, University of Iowa Studies in Engineering, Bulletin 17, 1939.
4. Briggs, S. J., "A Study in the Design of Work Areas," unpublished doctoral dissertation, Purdue University, Lafayette, Ind., August 1955.
5. Buffa, E. S., "Toward a Unified Concept of Job Design," *Journal of Industrial Engineering*, 1960, Vol. XI, No. 4, pp. 346–351.
6. Chapanis, A., "Studies of Manual Rotary Positioning Movements: I. The precision of setting an indicator knob to various angular positions," *Journal of Psychology*, 1951, Vol. XXXI, pp. 51–64.
7. Chapanis, A., W. R. Garner, and C. T. Morgan, *Applied Experimental Psychology*, John Wiley and Sons, New York, 1949.
8. Davis, L. E., "Human Factors in Design of Manual Machine Controls," *Mechanical Engineering*, October 1949, Vol. LXXI, pp. 811–816.
9. Ellis, D. S., "Speed of Manipulative Performance as a Function of Work-Surface Height," *Journal of Applied Psychology*, 1951, Vol. XXXV, pp. 289–296.
10. Fitts, T. M., "A Study of Location Discrimination Ability," in T. M. Fitts (ed.), *Psychological Research on Equipment Design*, Army Air Force Psychology Program, Research Report 19, 1947.
11. Hunsicker, P. A., *Arm Strength at Selected Degrees of Elbow Flexion*, USAF, Wright Air Development Center, Technical Report 54–548, August 1955.
12. Hunt, D. P., *The Coding of Aircraft Controls*, USAF, Wright Air Development Center, Technical Report 53–221, August 1953.
13. Jenkins, W. L., and N. B. Connor, "Some Design Factors in Making Settings on a Linear Scale," *Journal of Applied Psychology*, 1949, Vol. XXXIII, pp. 395–409.
14. Karpovich, P. U., *Physiology of Muscular Activity*, Saunders, Philadelphia, 1953.
15. McCormick, E. J., *Human Engineering*, McGraw-Hill Book Company, New York, 1957.
16. Maynard, H. B., G. J. Stegemerten, and J. L. Schwab, *Methods Time Measurement*, McGraw-Hill Book Company, New York, 1948.
17. Müller, E. A., "The Physiological Basis of Rest Pauses in Heavy Work," *Quarterly Journal of Experimental Physiology*, Vol. XXXVIII, No. 4, 1953.
18. Mundel, M. E., *Motion and Time Study*, Prentice-Hall, Englewood Cliffs, N. J., 2nd ed., 1955.
19. Nadler, G., *Motion and Time Study*, McGraw-Hill Book Company, New York, 1955.
20. Nadler, G., *Work Design*, Richard D. Irwin, Inc., Homewood, Ill., 1963.

21. Sleight, R. B., "The Effect of Instrument Dial Shape on Legibility," *Journal of Applied Psychology*, 1948, Vol. XXXII, pp. 170–188.
22. Spector, W. L., editor, WADC Technical Report 56–273, ASTIA Document No. AD 110501, Wright Air Development Center, 1957.
23. Squires, P. C., *The Shape of the Normal Work Area*, Navy Department, Bureau of Medicine and Surgery, Medical Research Laboratory, New London, Conn., Report 275, July 23, 1956.
24. Woodson, W. E., *Human Engineering Guide for Equipment Designers*, University of California Press, Berkeley, 1954.

REVIEW QUESTIONS

1. Since labor is being progressively eliminated by automation, why is it important to consider the design of jobs and work methods?

2. In general, what functions can man perform in the work situation?

3. Compare man's capability with that of known machines.

4. Discuss the determinants of job content.

5. What are management's objectives in the design of jobs?

6. Of what use is anthropometric data in designing jobs? Outline the kinds of information available concerning the speed and accuracy of positioning elements.

7. Outline the guides for the design of dials.

8. If controls are to be coded solely by their location, what does experimental data indicate about their spacing? Discuss Müller's concept of the "endurance limit." Can it be applied in the business and industrial situation?

9. Using Müller's formulation for physical fatigue, what kinds of business and industrial jobs would require an allowance for recovery from physical fatigue? What elements of the working environment require consideration by job designers? What is the meaning of the term effective temperature? What factors does it take into account? What factors does it ignore?

10. What are the effects of high effective temperature on work performance? Summarize the control measures available for the thermal environment.

11. Discuss the performance and health effects of noise.

12. How can noise be controlled at the source and within a room? What are the factors which produce glare?

13. What is the meaning of the term, critical illumination level?

14. Why do industrial lighting standards apparently vary widely?

15. What is MAC?

16. What kinds of control procedures may be used for industrial poisons and contaminants?

5

Models of Man-Machine Systems (Continued)

ARRANGEMENT AND FLOW OF WORK

The psychophysiological data we have discussed consider various phases of human activity and attempt to give guides for job design—information such as recommended working heights, force to be applied by the hands and arms, placement of positioning elements, and display of information and code controls. All these data must be integrated into a logical pattern of work performance which uses the man, his machine, and mechanical aids to the best advantage. Here the principles of arrangement and work flow come into play.

Flow charts. Since jobs occur in such great variation, the activities of each one must be analyzed separately to see if efforts go to accomplish the job, or are wasted. Here is where the general schematic and graphic methods of analysis known as flow charts, operation charts, activity charts, man-machine charts, etc., are used to help design and improve the job.

Before any of the methods of analysis described here are used, the need for performing the activity at all should have been established. As previously discussed in Chapter 3 under product flow process charts, specific operations can often be eliminated, combined with other operations, or placed in a different sequential position to advantage. The general areas of application of the several analysis methods of this chapter are summarized in Table I.

TABLE I. Summary of Areas of Application of Different Man and Man-Machine Analysis Methods

Nature of Activity	Analysis Method
Repetitive short-cycle task, low to moderate production volume	Operation chart, or operation chart supplemented by motion-time standard data
Repetitive short-cycle task, high production volume	Micromotion analysis chart, motion-time standard data
Repetitive long-cycle tasks	Man flow process charts, activity charts
Repetitive tasks involving a crew and/or a machine	Activity charts
Jobs involving tasks occurring at irregular intervals	Activity classification

Repetitive short-cycle tasks. *Operation charts* are appropriate when the task has a fairly short cycle and the production volume is low to moderate. The operation chart analyzes the motions of the right and left hands into components of reach, grasp, transport, position, assemble, etc., and places the activities for each hand in parallel columns so that it can readily be seen how the two hands work together. Sometimes symbols are added, as in Figure 1, usually with large circles to indicate manipulative activity, small circles to indicate reaches and transports of material, and a simple connective line to indicate that the hand is idle. Using the symbols, Figure 1 shows a completed operation chart for the assembly of a bolt and three washers.

Sometimes the data of the operation chart are displayed against a time scale so that the relative value of the activities can be appraised. These time data may come from standard time values for motions such as reach, grasp, move, and position, or from detailed time studies of the operation being analyzed. The motion-time standard data discussed later in this chapter may be helpful particularly in evaluating the estimated effect of proposed changes.

Micromotion analysis breaks an operation down into elements called therbligs, which represent a finer breakdown than do the elements for the operation chart, and the results are plotted against a time scale so that the exact simultaneity of the two hands working together can be examined. The resulting chart is often called a "simo chart" because it shows this relationship. The data for the chart are gathered by means of motion pictures taken of a qualified operator. Time is measured either by placing a clock in the camera field that reads to a

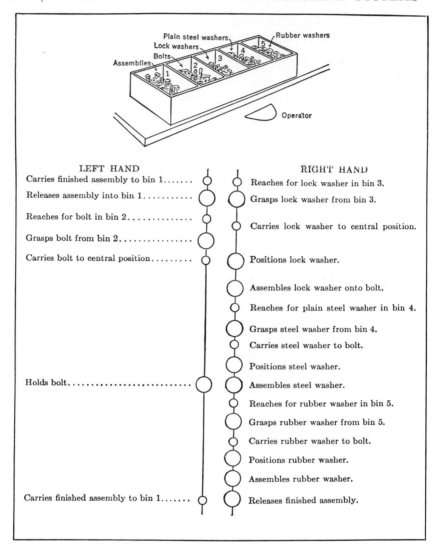

Figure 1. Operation chart of bolt and washer assembly—old method. From R. M. Barnes, *Motion and Time Study,* John Wiley and Sons, New York, 5th edition, 1963.

thousandth of a minute, or by using a synchronous motor drive on the camera so that each frame of the film represents one thousandth of a minute. (Faster camera speeds are sometimes used.) In either case, a special movie projector is used to analyze the film. This type of projector allows the analyst to advance the film one frame at a time to obtain the elapsed times for the therblig elements by the clock readings or from the frame counter on the projector. A simo chart for opening a corrugated case in a corn meal casing operation is shown in Figure 2 as an example.

Simo Chart

Sheet No.	Of						Film No.
Operation	*Open Case for Casing*				Date		
	$2\frac{1}{2}$# *Corn Meal*				Operation No.		
Part Name					Part No.		
Operator's Name and No.					Chart by *CBS*		

Left Hand Description	Symbol	Time	Thousanths of min.	Time	Symbol	Right Hand Description
Grasp case	G	5		5	G	Grasp case
Upright case	TL	5		6	TL	Upright case
R. to end flap	RL&TE	4		5	RL&TE	R. to end flap
Grasp flap	G	2		5	G	Grasp flap
Open case	TL	15	20	10	TL	Open flap & case
Fold over flap	TL	3		6	TL&RL	Fold over flap
R. to side flap	TE	3		5	TE	To side flap
Close flap	G&TL	3	40	2	TL	Close flap
Regrasp to close flap	G	6		14	TE&G	To case bottom
Case to conveyor	TL	23	60	14	TL	Case to conveyor
R. to end flap	RL&TE	5		2	RL&TE	To end flap
Bend over flap	TL	8	80	8	TL	Bend over flap
R. to side flap	TE	5		5	TE	To side flap
Bend over flap	G&TL	12		12	G&TL	Bend over flap
			100			

Figure 2. Micromotion analysis or "simo" chart for opening a corrugated case.

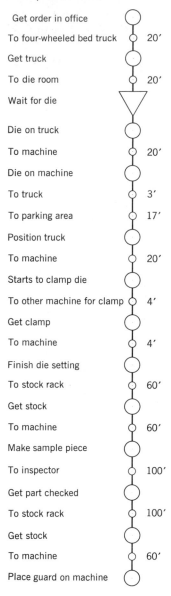

Get order in office	
To four-wheeled bed truck	20′
Get truck	
To die room	20′
Wait for die	
Die on truck	
To machine	20′
Die on machine	
To truck	3′
To parking area	17′
Position truck	
To machine	20′
Starts to clamp die	
To other machine for clamp	4′
Get clamp	
To machine	4′
Finish die setting	
To stock rack	60′
Get stock	
To machine	60′
Make sample piece	
To inspector	100′
Get part checked	
To stock rack	100′
Get stock	
To machine	60′
Place guard on machine	

Figure 3. Man flow process chart for setting a punch press die.

Owing to the extra time and cost required to use micromotion analysis, a simo chart is commonly limited to situations where a large number of workers are performing the same repetitive task, so the total saving may be great, even though the per cent reduction might be fairly small. It has also been found valuable in the design and development of new special production equipment. Here, a motion analyst and a machine designer working together often produce a superior design.

Repetitive tasks involving long cycles. *Man flow process charts* are commonly used to analyze long-cycle tasks in which the worker moves about considerably from place to place in the performance of his work. The same general type of analysis of the product flow process chart is used except that the analyst follows the worker, instead of a part, and classifies his activities sequentially into operations, transports (walking unloaded as well as when transporting material), storages (idleness), and inspections. Analysis of the resulting chart parallels product flow process charts, in that activities are examined with the objectives (a) of elimination, (b) of combination, and (c) of improved sequence, etc. Figure 3 is a man flow process chart for the task of setting a die in a punch press. Figure 4 shows the flow diagram of the activities of the die setter and emphasizes the amount of backtracking involved in the task as it was actually done. A common-sense analysis of the activity based on the process chart and flow diagram indicates that preplanning and maintaining a set of standard tools on the truck (such as the clamps) would reduce the amount of walking involved. Gang process charts are used where activities of a crew are studied, by using one column of symbols for each man in the crew.

Activity charts analyze operations into the time required to perform major manual and machine elements, or activities, and plot the elements on a time scale. Relationships between man and machine or between crew members can then be examined. Let us take the milling of a slot in a bracket as an example. Figure 5 shows a bracket and the activity chart for the milling of the slot. Here the major elements of the repetitive work of the man and the machine have been plotted side by side on a time scale, and the times are recorded in decimal hours. In this type of analysis the major objectives are commonly to maximize man and machine utilization. In the example of the milling of the bracket slot, we see that the machine is 100 per cent utilized, since it is either being loaded, unloaded, or actually taking a cut, and at no time is it idle. Nevertheless, machine effectiveness could be increased by improving the manual methods of loading and unloading, thus improving machine output per unit of time. The techniques for accomplishing this require a detailed study

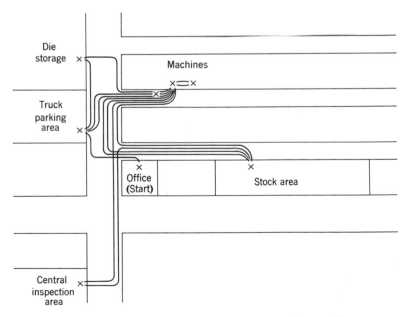

Figure 4. Flow diagram for setting a punch press die.

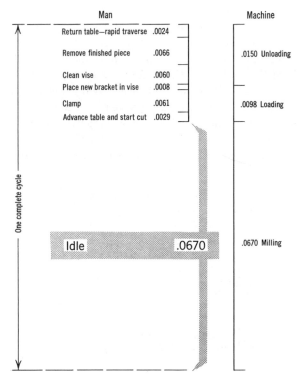

Figure 5. Activity chart of "mill slot in bracket." Courtesy Westinghouse Electric Corporation (11).

of the manual activity by means of the operation chart, etc., already discussed. On the other hand, the man is idle **73** per cent of the cycle while he waits for the milling machine to complete its cut. This general situation is common in many kinds of machine and process operations.

The question is, what to do with idle man time in such a situation. Perhaps the first consideration is whether the operator is really idle; some types of machine operations require operator vigilance and surveillance during the machine cycle, and an attempt to utilize such time could affect quality adversely. But it is often true that this is purely idle time. When such is the case on repetitive operations of considerable volume, it may be possible to have the man operate two or more machines. For the bracket slot milling operation, the operator could handle three machines doing the identical operation without introducing any idle machine time. Beyond that number, idle machine time develops, and an economy study would be required to determine whether idle man or machine time would be preferable.

Where the volume on the activity in question does not justify multiple machine operation, examination of the operation process chart for that part might reveal other elements which could be performed during the idle time. As an example, the operation that followed the slot milling on the bracket happened to be one of milling the lugs. Figure 6 is the activity chart for lug milling and Figure 7

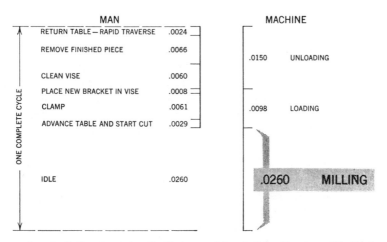

Figure 6. Activity chart for "mill lugs of bracket." Courtesy Westinghouse Electric Corporation (11).

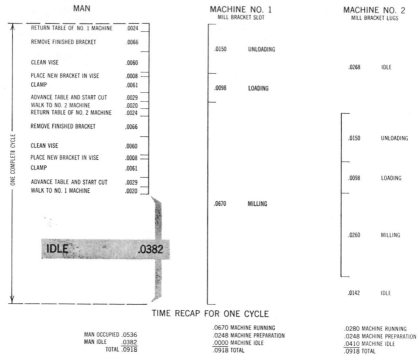

Figure 7. Activity chart for the composite operation, "mill slot and lugs of bracket." Courtesy Westinghouse Electric Corporation (11).

is the resulting composite operation of milling both the slot and the lugs. Note that the idle man time has now been reduced to about 40 per cent of the total cycle, but in so structuring the job, idle machine time has been introduced into the lug milling machine, amounting to about 45 per cent. Here again, the question comes up whether idle man or idle machine time is preferable. Note that if milling capacity were greater than demand, there would be incremental labor costs to do the two activities separately. On the other hand, if milling demand were at capacity or exceeded it, there would be created additional demand equal to the new machine idle time and there would be incremental labor costs equal to the overtime premium. But since the two operations are being performed in the labor time of the slot milling operation, there is still a net gain from combining the two operations. Table II summarizes the comparison for the conditions of demand below milling capacity and demand above milling capacity (forcing additional overtime). We see that multiple

TABLE II. Comparison of Man-Hours per Unit for Single Machine versus Multiple Machine Operation under Conditions of Demand under Capacity and Demand above Capacity

Condition	Single Machine Operation, Man-hours per unit		Multiple Machine Operation, Man-hours per unit	
Milling machine demand under capacity	Mill slot	0.0918	Mill slot and lugs	0.0918
	Mill lugs	0.0508		
		0.1426		
Milling machine demand above capacity	0.1426, same as "under capacity" condition		Mill slot and lugs	0.0918
			Extra labor cost is $\frac{1}{2}$ extra machine idle time = 0.0410/2 =	0.0205
				0.1123

machine operation is advantageous under either condition, for this example, since there is a labor cost advantage under either condition and there are no other obvious incremental costs.

Where it is impractical to combine two or more machining operations, it may be that other kinds of activity can be incorporated to reduce the idle time, for example, the removal of burrs produced by machining, or stacking otherwise jumbled parts so that they may be procured more easily in the following operation. Any useful work that can be accomplished during such idle times, of course, incurs no incremental labor cost.

Sometimes skilled workers object to running more than one machine, but where these idle times are long, workers often become bored and may welcome a more even distribution of load. It is common that other workers, such as inspectors, assemblers, and many who operate machines that do not have automatic or semiautomatic cycles, are loaded fairly steadily throughout the work day.

Crew or team activities which often appear complex to the observer are considerably simplified by activity charts. Because of the difficulty in observing the simultaneity of the operations, the motion picture camera is an excellent means for gathering the basic data. Figure 8 is an example of such a chart for a team of two women who are placing cereal boxes in corrugated cases for shipment. Note that operator 1 spends about half her time opening and forming the case. It was found that with the aid of a simple heavy wire fixture the case could be opened and formed very quickly so that one operator

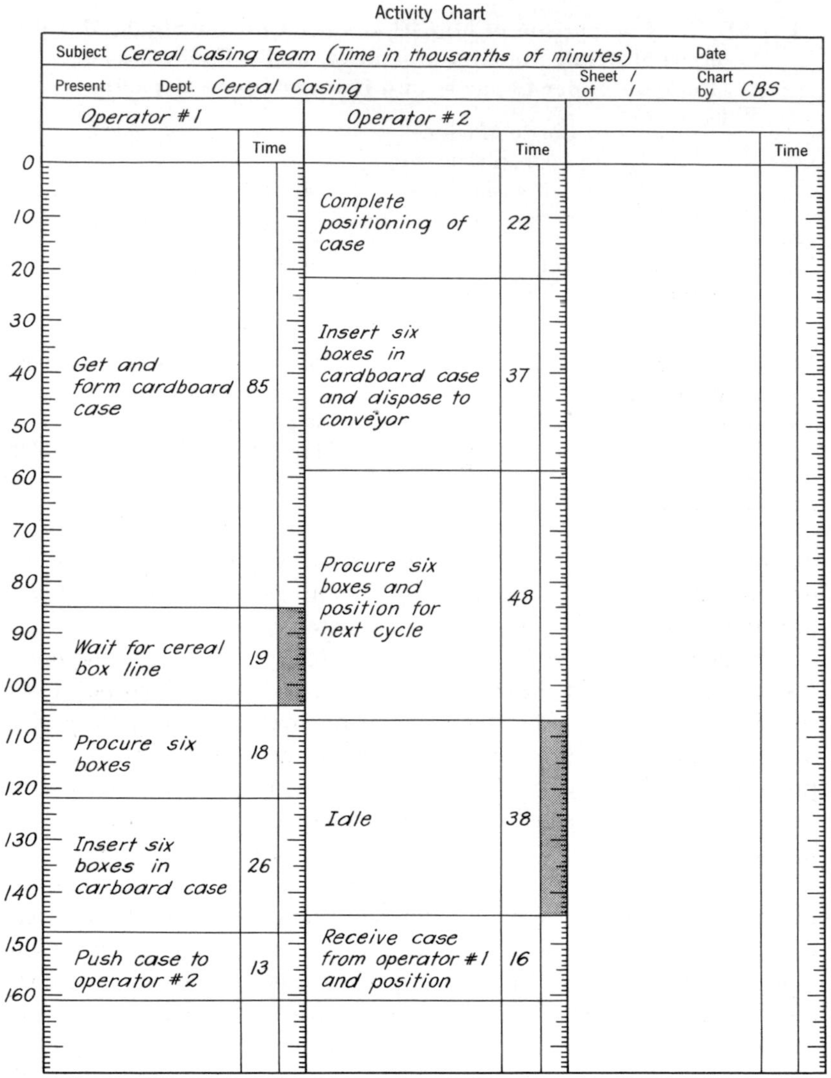

Activity Chart

Subject *Cereal Casing Team (Time in thousanths of minutes)*					Date		
Present	Dept. *Cereal Casing*				Sheet / of /	Chart by *CBS*	
Operator #1			*Operator #2*				
		Time		Time			Time

(Time scale at left: 0, 10, 20, 30, 40, 50, 60, 70, 80, 90, 100, 110, 120, 130, 140, 150, 160)

Operator #1:
- Get and form cardboard case — 85
- Wait for cereal box line — 19
- Procure six boxes — 18
- Insert six boxes in carboard case — 26
- Push case to operator #2 — 13

Operator #2:
- Complete positioning of case — 22
- Insert six boxes in cardboard case and dispose to conveyor — 37
- Procure six boxes and position for next cycle — 48
- Idle — 38
- Receive case from operator #1 and position — 16

Figure 8. Multiple activity chart for cereal casing.

could do the entire job and still keep pace with the feeding conveyor. Here is an instance where partial improvements only serve to increase operator idle time unless one entire operator can be eliminated, since the entire activity is paced by the conveyor line.

Analysis of tasks occurring at irregular intervals. *Activity classification* often provides valuable data for the analysis of jobs that have tasks (usually of wide variety) which occur at irregular intervals. An initial step in analysis is to determine the average proportion of time spent in each of several categories of activity. There are two valuable methods for gathering pertinent data for activity classification: work sampling and time-lapse movie camera techniques.

Work sampling involves a random sampling of activities so that the proportion of time spent in each activity can be estimated. Time-lapse movie cameras also can be used to obtain similar data. The camera, which takes pictures at slow speed intervals—one per second or slower, is set up to view the field of activity; it is driven by a synchronous motor so that each film frame represents a definite time unit. Since camera speeds can be slow, it is possible to obtain half-day or full-day records with a fairly modest film consumption.

Principles of motion economy. Over the years, industrial engineers have developed a set of general statements, called principles of motion economy, which concern work arrangement, the use of the human hands and body, and the design and use of tools. Table III summarizes the most widely circulated statement of these ideas. These guides to job design have general applicability and are supplemented, and in some cases corroborated, by some of the research into the speed and accuracy of motor activities that we have discussed.

Let us look at the operation chart of the bolt and washer assembly shown in Figure 1 from the point of view of the principles of motion economy. An examination shows that the left hand holds the bolt for a considerable part of the cycle while the right hand assembles parts on the bolt. This suggests the possibility of a fixture to relieve the left hand for useful work (No. 17, Table III). When the left hand is free, the possibility of making duplicate assemblies is suggested by numbers 1, 2, and 3. In addition, numbers 4, 8, 9, 11, 12, 13, 15, and 16 all contribute to the improved method for performing the bolt and washer assembly, which is shown in the operation chart of Figure 9.

Standard time values. An extremely useful tool, from the job designer's point of view, is a set of universal time values for fundamental types of motions that he can use to predict total cycle time for as many alternative structures of jobs as he may wish to consider. Fundamental time values of this nature could be used as building blocks to forecast the all-important time criterion, provided that the

TABLE III. Principles of Motion Economy

A Check Sheet for Motion Economy and Fatigue Reduction

These twenty-two rules or principles of motion economy may be profitably applied to shop and office work alike. Although not all are applicable to every operation, they do form a basis or a code for improving the efficiency and reducing fatigue in manual work.

Use of the Human Body

1. The two hands should begin as well as complete their motions at the same time.

2. The two hands should not be idle at the same time except during rest periods.

3. Motions of the arms should be made in opposite and symmetrical directions, and should be made simultaneously.

4. Hand motions should be confined to the lowest classification with which it is possible to perform the work satisfactorily.

5. Momentum should be employed to assist the worker wherever possible, and it should be reduced to a minimum if it must be overcome by muscular effort.

6. Smooth continuous motions of the hands are preferable to zigzag motions or straight-line motions involving sudden and sharp changes in direction.

7. Ballistic movements are faster, easier, and more accurate than restricted (fixation) or "controlled" movements.

8. Rhythm is essential to the smooth and automatic performance of an operation, and the work should be arranged to permit easy and natural rhythm wherever possible.

Arrangement of the Work Place

9. There should be a definite and fixed place for all tools and materials.

10. Tools, materials, and controls should be located close to and directly in front of the operator.

11. Gravity feed bins and containers should be used to deliver material close to the point of use.

12. Drop deliveries should be used wherever possible.

13. Materials and tools should be located to permit the best sequence of motions.

14. Provisions should be made for adequate conditions for seeing. Good illumination is the first requirement for satisfactory visual perception.

15. The height of the work place and the chair should preferably be arranged so that alternate sitting and standing at work are easily possible.

16. A chair of the type and height to permit good posture should be provided for every worker.

Design of Tools and Equipment

17. The hands should be relieved of all work that can be done more advantageously by a jig, a fixture, or a foot-operated device.

18. Two or more tools should be combined wherever possible.

19. Tools and materials should be pre-positioned whenever possible.

20. Where each finger performs some specific movement, such as in typewriting, the load should be distributed in accordance with the inherent capacities of the fingers.

21. Handles such as those used on cranks and large screwdrivers should be designed to permit as much of the surface of the hand to come in contact with the handle as possible. This is particularly true when considerable force is exerted in using the handle. For light assembly work the screwdriver handle should be so shaped that it is smaller at the bottom than at the top.

22. Levers, crossbars, and handwheels should be located in such positions that the operator can manipulate them with the least change in body position and with the greatest mechanical advantage.

From R. M. Barnes, *Motion and Time Study*, John Wiley and Sons, New York, 5th ed., 1963.

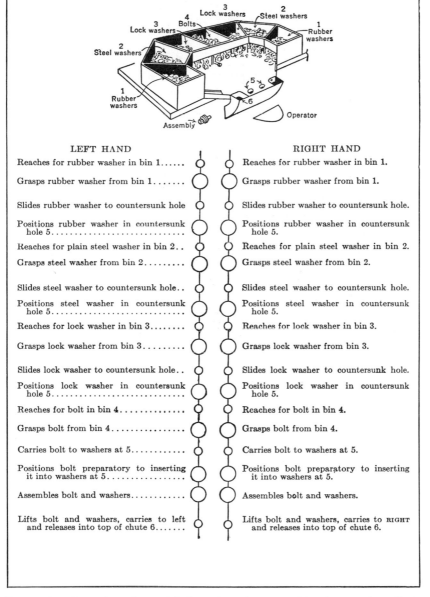

LEFT HAND

Reaches for rubber washer in bin 1......

Grasps rubber washer from bin 1.......

Slides rubber washer to countersunk hole

Positions rubber washer in countersunk hole 5...........................

Reaches for plain steel washer in bin 2..

Grasps steel washer from bin 2.........

Slides steel washer to countersunk hole..

Positions steel washer in countersunk hole 5...........................

Reaches for lock washer in bin 3........

Grasps lock washer from bin 3.........

Slides lock washer to countersunk hole..

Positions lock washer in countersunk hole 5...........................

Reaches for bolt in bin 4..............

Grasps bolt from bin 4................

Carries bolt to washers at 5............

Positions bolt preparatory to inserting it into washers at 5.................

Assembles bolt and washers............

Lifts bolt and washers, carries to left and releases into top of chute 6.......

RIGHT HAND

Reaches for rubber washer in bin 1.

Grasps rubber washer from bin 1.

Slides rubber washer to countersunk hole.

Positions rubber washer in countersunk hole 5.

Reaches for plain steel washer in bin 2.

Grasps steel washer from bin 2.

Slides steel washer to countersunk hole.

Positions steel washer in countersunk hole 5.

Reaches for lock washer in bin 3.

Grasps lock washer from bin 3.

Slides lock washer to countersunk hole.

Positions lock washer in countersunk hole 5.

Reaches for bolt in bin 4.

Grasps bolt from bin 4.

Carries bolt to washers at 5.

Positions bolt preparatory to inserting it into washers at 5.

Assembles bolt and washers.

Lifts bolt and washers, carries to RIGHT and releases into top of chute 6.

Figure 9. Operation chart of bolt and washer assembly—improved method. From R. M. Barnes, *Motion and Time Study,* John Wiley and Sons, New York, 5th ed., 1963.

TABLE I—REACH—R

Distance Moved Inches	Time TMU				Hand In Motion		CASE AND DESCRIPTION
	A	B	C or D	E	A	B	
¾ or less	2.0	2.0	2.0	2.0	1.6	1.6	**A** Reach to object in fixed location, or to object in other hand or on which other hand rests.
1	2.5	2.5	3.6	2.4	2.3	2.3	
2	4.0	4.0	5.9	3.8	3.5	2.7	
3	5.3	5.3	7.3	5.3	4.5	3.6	**B** Reach to single object in location which may vary slightly from cycle to cycle.
4	6.1	6.4	8.4	6.8	4.9	4.3	
5	6.5	7.8	9.4	7.4	5.3	5.0	
6	7.0	8.6	10.1	8.0	5.7	5.7	
7	7.4	9.3	10.8	8.7	6.1	6.5	
8	7.9	10.1	11.5	9.3	6.5	7.2	**C** Reach to object jumbled with other objects in a group so that search and select occur.
9	8.3	10.8	12.2	9.9	6.9	7.9	
10	8.7	11.5	12.9	10.5	7.3	8.6	
12	9.6	12.9	14.2	11.8	8.1	10.1	
14	10.5	14.4	15.6	13.0	8.9	11.5	**D** Reach to a very small object or where accurate grasp is required.
16	11.4	15.8	17.0	14.2	9.7	12.9	
18	12.3	17.2	18.4	15.5	10.5	14.4	
20	13.1	18.6	19.8	16.7	11.3	15.8	
22	14.0	20.1	21.2	18.0	12.1	17.3	**E** Reach to indefinite location to get hand in position for body balance or next motion or out of way.
24	14.9	21.5	22.5	19.2	12.9	18.8	
26	15.8	22.9	23.9	20.4	13.7	20.2	
28	16.7	24.4	25.3	21.7	14.5	21.7	
30	17.5	25.8	26.7	22.9	15.3	23.2	

TABLE II—MOVE—M

Distance Moved Inches	Time TMU				Wt. Allowance			CASE AND DESCRIPTION
	A	B	C	Hand In Motion B	Wt. (lb.) Up to	Factor	Constant TMU	
¾ or less	2.0	2.0	2.0	1.7	2.5	1.00	0	
1	2.5	2.9	3.4	2.3				
2	3.6	4.6	5.2	2.9	7.5	1.06	2.2	**A** Move object to other hand or against stop.
3	4.9	5.7	6.7	3.6				
4	6.1	6.9	8.0	4.3	12.5	1.11	3.9	
5	7.3	8.0	9.2	5.0				
6	8.1	8.9	10.3	5.7	17.5	1.17	5.6	
7	8.9	9.7	11.1	6.5				
8	9.7	10.6	11.8	7.2				
9	10.5	11.5	12.7	7.9	22.5	1.22	7.4	**B** Move object to approximate or indefinite location.
10	11.3	12.2	13.5	8.6				
12	12.9	13.4	15.2	10.0	27.5	1.28	9.1	
14	14.4	14.6	16.9	11.4				
16	16.0	15.8	18.7	12.8	32.5	1.33	10.8	
18	17.6	17.0	20.4	14.2				
20	19.2	18.2	22.1	15.6				
22	20.8	19.4	23.8	17.0	37.5	1.39	12.5	
24	22.4	20.6	25.5	18.4				**C** Move object to exact location.
26	24.0	21.8	27.3	19.8	42.5	1.44	14.3	
28	25.5	23.1	29.0	21.2				
30	27.1	24.3	30.7	22.7	47.5	1.50	16.0	

TABLE III—TURN AND APPLY PRESSURE—T AND AP

Weight	Time TMU for Degrees Turned										
	30°	45°	60°	75°	90°	105°	120°	135°	150°	165°	180°
Small— 0 to 2 Pounds	2.8	3.5	4.1	4.8	5.4	6.1	6.8	7.4	8.1	8.7	9.4
Medium—2.1 to 10 Pounds	4.4	5.5	6.5	7.5	8.5	9.6	10.6	11.6	12.7	13.7	14.8
Large— 10.1 to 35 Pounds	8.4	10.5	12.3	14.4	16.2	18.3	20.4	22.2	24.3	26.1	28.2

APPLY PRESSURE CASE 1—16.2 TMU.   APPLY PRESSURE CASE 2—10.6 TMU

Figure 10. Standard time values for various classifications of motions. (Times are recorded in a special time unit called a time measurement unit (TMU). 1 TMU = 0.0006 min.) Courtesy MTM Association for Standards and Research.

TABLE IV—GRASP—G

Case	Time TMU	DESCRIPTION
1A	2.0	**Pick Up Grasp**—Small, medium or large object by itself, easily grasped.
1B	3.5	Very small object or object lying close against a flat surface.
1C1	7.3	Interference with grasp on bottom and one side of nearly cylindrical object. Diameter larger than ½″.
1C2	8.7	Interference with grasp on bottom and one side of nearly cylindrical object. Diameter ¼″ to ½″.
1C3	10.8	Interference with grasp on bottom and one side of nearly cylindrical object. Diameter less than ¼″.
2	5.6	**Regrasp.**
3	5.6	**Transfer Grasp.**
4A	7.3	Object jumbled with other objects so search and select occur. Larger than 1″ x 1″ x 1″.
4B	9.1	Object jumbled with other objects so search and select occur. ¼″ x ¼″ x ⅛″ to 1″ x 1″ x 1″.
4C	12.9	Object jumbled with other objects so search and select occur. Smaller than ¼″ x ¼″ x ⅛″.
5	0	Contact, sliding or hook grasp.

TABLE V—POSITION*—P

CLASS OF FIT		Symmetry	Easy To Handle	Difficult To Handle
1—Loose	No pressure required	S	5.6	11.2
		SS	9.1	14.7
		NS	10.4	16.0
2—Close	Light pressure required	S	16.2	21.8
		SS	19.7	25.3
		NS	21.0	26.6
3—Exact	Heavy pressure required.	S	43.0	48.6
		SS	46.5	52.1
		NS	47.8	53.4

*Distance moved to engage—1″ or less.

TABLE VI—RELEASE—RL

Case	Time TMU	DESCRIPTION
1	2.0	Normal release performed by opening fingers as independent motion.
2	0	Contact Release.

TABLE VII—DISENGAGE—D

CLASS OF FIT	Easy to Handle	Difficult to Handle
1—Loose—Very slight effort, blends with subsequent move.	4.0	5.7
2—Close — Normal effort, slight recoil.	7.5	11.8
3—Tight — Considerable effort, hand recoils markedly.	22.9	34.7

TABLE VIII—EYE TRAVEL TIME AND EYE FOCUS—ET AND EF

Eye Travel Time $= 15.2 \times \frac{T}{D}$ TMU, with a maximum value of 20 TMU.

where T = the distance between points from and to which the eye travels.
D = the perpendicular distance from the eye to the line of travel T.

Eye Focus Time $= 7.3$ TMU.

Figure 10 (continued).

time values were properly gathered and that the various minute motion elements required by the tasks were perfectly analyzed. Taylor envisioned something comparable to this, and many alternative proposals have been made by management consultants who sell services consisting of installing systems based on their data and training client personnel in the use of these data. Some of these alternate time-value systems are known by the trade names: Methods-Time-Measurement (MTM), Work Factor, and Basic Motion Time Study.

Since MTM data and general instructions for use have received the greatest circulation, we shall refer to that system. Figure 10 summarizes the data for the various motions of reach, move, grasp, turn, apply pressure, position, release, disengage, and eye times. Times for various body motions also exist. These time standards are set so that the majority of the working population should be able to meet or exceed them. For each type of motion element, the standard time is dependent on certain physical variables, such as distance, and on classifications of sensory control required. For example, for the element reach, the *major* variable is distance, but there are five classifications of reach which specify the conditions of the object to which one is reaching, such as an object in a fixed location, an object jumbled with others in a group, etc. In developing the motion analysis for a task, the appropriate reaches, grasps, and moves are matched up to fit the general situation of required sensory control. For example, to obtain a part from a parts supply bin and place it in a fixture, we would first reach toward an object jumbled with others in the bin. In grasping the object, the table tells us that the grasp time will depend on the part size classification. In moving the part to the fixture, close control is required because the fixture is placed in an *exact location*. The time required to position the part in the fixture depends on the closeness of the fit between the part and fixture, the symmetry (how much orientation is required to align the mating parts), and the ease of handling (characteristics of the material, its size, and flexibility). Once positioned in the fixture, the part must be released. Figure 11 shows a possible workplace layout and MTM analysis for this simple manual task using the part shown.

How good are these systems of standard times? Do they show up the differences indicated by our sample of research studies? For example, in the study of cranks and handwheels by Davis reported in Chapter 4, would MTM values have signaled the fact that the $-45°$ and $+45°$ positions are superior for cranks and handwheels under conditions of heavy resistance? Would the system indicate that cranks are generally a little faster than handwheels? The answer

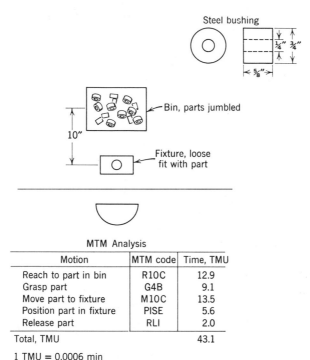

Figure 11. MTM analysis for a simple assembly task.

is no. These differences are too subtle for the standard data systems as they are presently constructed. In designing jobs it is necessary that research data be used as a background of knowledge for selecting certain kinds of mechanisms (such as cranks in preference to hand-wheels), for judging arm strength required, for using positioning stops and guides, and for arranging the workplace so that positioning elements occur in the best-known positions. In other words, the psycho-physiological data and the principles of motion economy serve as guides. Although MTM and like systems cannot substitute for this knowledge, MTM values can be used to compare and evaluate gross differences in method which represent alternatives to the job designer. These alternatives might represent manual labor versus degrees of mechanization, alternative machines, one-handed versus two-handed approaches to the task, etc. The degree of difference which can be distinguished is surprisingly great, especially in the hands of a trained man. It may be that a carefully planned standard data system, based on good experimental design and technique, will be able to reflect some of the more subtle differences based on the known results of present research.

Although we have discussed standard time data systems as a means of helping to develop job designs, they also serve to forecast expected output while the employee is working. This forecast is of considerable importance, for business and industrial management are always interested in the labor content of a given job design, and, therefore, an estimate of the work standard is desirable. These work standards, however, usually involve appraisals of work time, rest time, delay allowances, and allowances for personal time. The standard time values discussed give estimates for the *work time* only.

Summary

It is evident from the material presented in these two chapters that models of man-machine systems do not fit neatly into a mathematical formula. A model of a man-machine system with our present level of knowledge represents a description of various aspects of the system—the arrangement and work flow, the psychological and physiological demands, and the working environment. By drawing on the mass of known data, it is possible to design jobs that fairly well meet the restrictions imposed by the makeup of man and to take advantage of the known capabilities of man.

Job design is a blend of art and science. The content of most jobs is a result of restrictions imposed by existing machines, processes, and the overall mode of production that has been adopted, and very little has been done to determine the effectiveness of different basic approaches to the organization of work. Division of labor and job enlargement represent opposing points of view on the organization of work.

Given job content, job design is further determined by the detailed methods by which the tasks of the job are carried out within the working environment. In drawing on the mass of psychophysiological data, principles of work flow, and arrangement, the job designer creates a design which is partly scientific, but which depends a great deal on his ingenuity in utilizing the capabilities of the man, the machine, and mechanical aids, and in fitting the job in with the overall flow of work. Economic limitations go a long way in determining how good the result looks. For low-volume or short-run work, the most economical job design may involve rather crude methods, equipment, planning, and use of known data. On the other hand, high volumes of standardized items may justify the most careful design of jobs from every point of view, usually mechanizing many phases of the tasks and subjecting the remaining man-machine and environmental relationships to careful scrutiny so that the results are optimally designed jobs within the knowledge and skill of the job designer.

Finally, job design includes a forecast of output based on the content and methods. Motion standard data is useful here in forecasting output, as well as in comparing the expected output of alternative designs. To forecast output, however, requires an appraisal of fatigue and fatigue allowances, or rest time, as well as allowances for personal time or unavoidable delay factors.

REFERENCES

1. Abruzzi, A., *Work Measurement*, Columbia University Press, New York, 1952.
2. Barnes, R. M., *Motion and Time Study*, John Wiley and Sons. New York, 5th ed., 1963.
3. Barnes, R. M., *Work Sampling*, John Wiley and Sons, New York, 2nd ed., 1957.
4. Gustat, G. H., "Applications of Work Sampling Analysis," *Proceedings of Tenth Time Study and Methods Conference,* SAM-ASME, New York, April 1955.
5. Heiland, R. E., and W. J. Richardson, *Work Sampling*, McGraw-Hill Book Company, New York, 1957.
6. Lehrer, R. N., *Work Simplification*, Prentice-Hall, Englewood Cliffs, N. J., 1957.
7. Maynard, H. B., G. J. Stegemerten, and J. L. Schwab, *Methods-Time Measurement*, McGraw-Hill Book Company, New York, 1948.
8. Nadler, G., *Motion and Time Study*. McGraw-Hill Book Company, New York, 1955.
9. Nadler, G., *Work Design*, Richard D. Irwin, Homewood, Illinois, 1963.
10. Niebel, B. W., *Motion and Time Study*, Richard D. Irwin, Homewood, Illinois, 1955.
11. *Operation Analysis*, Westinghouse Electric Corp., Pittsburgh, Pa., 1948.

REVIEW QUESTIONS

1. Classify the various graphic tools of man-machine analysis according to the nature of activity to which they are applicable.

2. Contrast the operation chart and micromotion analysis in terms of the observation methods used and the usefulness of information resulting. What are the conditions under which micromotion analysis can perform a unique function?

3. What is the range of application of activity charts?

4. How many machines should one employee operate?

5. What methods may be used to analyze tasks which occur at irregular intervals?

6. Are the "principles of motion economy" really principles? Are there instances when they may seem contradictory?

7. Of what value are standard time values in constructing models of man–machine systems? What is the significance of the time values which result, that is, do they include pro rata allowances for rest time, delays, and for personal time?

PROBLEMS

1. *Job description of printed circuit tester:*
Inspects printed circuits for resistance, impedance, and heat emission rate by inserting the printed circuits in a testing device and reading the different indicator scales.

Sequence of operations (see workplace layout, Figure 12):

(1) The right hand picks up an untested circuit from the table on the right.

(2) Both hands insert the printed circuit in the testing device. (Requires 25 pounds of force to put in.)

(3) Right foot applies power to the testing device with the foot pedal. (Average pedal time is 1.5 seconds.)

(4) The eyes read the three indicators to determine if all dials indicate the proper amount. (See diagram of dial panel, Figure 13.)

(5) Both hands remove the circuit from the device. (Requires 25 pounds.)

(6) The left hand places the circuit either on the acceptable or unacceptable table to the left.

(7) Cycle starts over again.

Miscellaneous data:

(1) A minimum vertical insertion force of 15 pounds is required for placing the circuit in the testing device. This specification is needed to approximate a closed circuit after the printed circuit is in place.

(2) Power must be applied gradually to the testing device with a power pedal. The minimum time allowed for this power application is 0.9 second.

(3) The footcandle reading at the indicator panel was 10.

(4) Occasionally a small shock is felt by the tester when the printed circuit is removed from the testing device.

(5) The printed circuits weigh 0.5 pound.

Problem:

a. Recommend production equipment design changes and improved work methods based on:

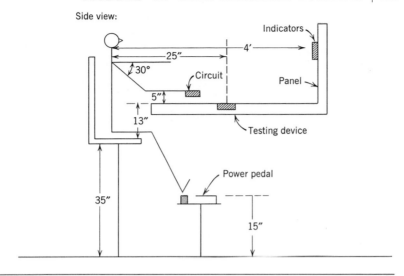

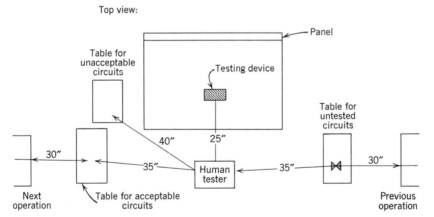

Figure 12.

1. principles of motion economy
2. anthropometric data
3. common sense
4. MTM analysis

b. Make an operation chart for your improved work methods and estimate the time needed for one cycle using MTM data.

2. Construct an operation chart for the assembly of some simple device such as a ball-point pen.

Indicator Display Panel

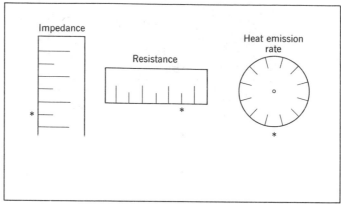

*Readings for an acceptable circuit

Figure 13.

3. A young couple has started a launderette. Their business, The Blue Monday Launderette, offers the following services:

    a. Washers for use by customers

    b. Drying service for customers' washes

    c. Dry cleaning and finished laundry

    d. Washing and fluff drying

The husband performs the "fluff dry" work (washing, extracting and fluff drying). The wife handles all other matters such as dealing with customers, aiding people who do their own washing, etc. She also folds and bundles the "fluff dry" work during slack periods in the day.

The "fluff dry" business has been unusually heavy and the couple has been forced to work evenings to get out work on time. It is their contention that five washers, if kept busy, can do the "fluff dry" work, but there are so many other things to be done such as semidrying the wet clothes in the extractor and loading and unloading the dryer that one person simply can not keep the washers loaded. The wife does not have time to assist the husband during normal working hours.

The following times are required to perform the various tasks:

	Time (minutes)
Washer (5 available for "fluff dry")	
(1) Load soiled clothes and soap, set water temperature, start machine	2
(2) Running time (automatically stops)	40
(3) Unload wet clothes into cart	2

Extractor (1 available for "fluff dry"; each holds one washer load only)

(1) Load wet clothes and start machine   2
(2) Running time (automatically stops)   5
(3) Unload semidry clothes into cart   2

Dryer (2 available for "fluff dry"; each holds one washer load only)

(1) Untangle and load clothes, start machine   3
(2) Running time (automatically stops)   20
(3) Unload dry clothes into cart   2

Miscellaneous

Travel times between equipment   Negligible

    a. With the data given, construct an activity chart for the best method of coordinating the work of one (1) man, five (5) washers, one (1) extractor, and two (2) dryers.

    b. What is the overall cycle time (time difference between identical points in the process) such as loading washer No. 1 on consecutive loads?

    4. Develop an MTM analysis for the bolt and washer assembly shown in Figure 1 of the text. Develop a contrasting analysis for the improved method shown in Figure 9.

part III

STATISTICAL METHODS

6

Statistical Analysis—Review
of Fundamental Concepts

Statistical analysis in operations management was introduced in 1924 by Walter Shewhart in a Bell Telephone Laboratories memorandum. In the years that followed, Shewhart, Dodge, and others also did early work in the concept of acceptance inspection. Much of Shewhart's thinking on these subjects was then published in 1931 in his book, *Economic Control of Quality of Manufactured Product.* In it, he introduced the basic concepts of statistical quality control, a field that has become an important and accepted part of production management. Industrial plants all over the country use the control chart methods which Shewhart introduced, and quality control has become a professional specialty. In the broader picture, the acceptance of statistical concepts of quality control represented a breakthrough in the way of thinking about many operations problems. Today there are many applications of statistical analysis in industry. *Work sampling* is becoming an accepted way of developing production standards. When an industrial engineer makes a time study, he is apt to consider how many readings are required in order to be confident of the result. The research worker in the operations field leans heavily on a branch of statistics called *experimental design,* in order to structure his experiments so that precise statements can be made about his results. *Correlation analysis* is used to develop occupational tests, which may help to select workers who have a higher than average probability of success on the job. These

* W. A. Shewhart, *Economic Control of Quality of Manufactured Product,* D. Van Nostrand Company, Princeton, N. J., 1931.

and other applications in production make a knowledge of statistical analysis important for today's operations management personnel. The continued rapid growth of the area makes it a must for tomorrow's personnel.

This chapter is no substitute for a course in statistics. Its purpose in this book is to provide a review of basic statistical terms, concepts, and techniques that are used in Chapters **7, 8, 9** and **10**, as well as in other sections of the book.

Universe and sample. A sample is drawn from a *universe* or *population,* and is, therefore, a subset of a universe or population. To draw the distinction, a *finite universe* might be a lot of 1000 parts produced on a lathe. Any of the dimensions produced might in themselves be considered a finite universe. If we measured the diameters of all 1000 parts, the result would be a distribution of the diameters of that universe. If we selected 100 parts from the 1000 and measured their diameters, we would have a sample distribution of diameters. If we let the selection of the sample of 100 parts be based strictly on chance, we have a *random sample.* An *infinite universe* might be represented by the time required for a worker to perform the lathe operation. If we timed a few cycles of the operation, we could form a *sequential sample* of the time required. If we timed these cycles at random intervals, we would have a random sample. If at each random interval we timed five cycles and averaged them, we would have a *sampling distribution* of averages of five.

It is often true that the entire universe data are difficult or laborious to obtain, or impossible as in the case of an infinite universe. Therefore, one of the important objectives of statistics is to infer from a sample distribution the characteristics of the universe distribution. Characteristics of the universe, such as the average, variance, and range (these terms will be defined later), are called *parameters.* These characteristics calculated from a sample are called *statistics.*

Notation. It is of some importance to retain the distinction just made between *parameters* and *statistics,* and we shall attempt to do this by using a system of notation. In general, when we are referring to the parameters of a universe, the symbol will be primed, and when we are referring to the statistics of a sample, the symbol will be unprimed. For example, the arithmetic average of a universe distribution is $\bar{x}'$, with a prime, and that of a sample distribution drawn from the universe is simply $\bar{x}$. In most instances, we will be dealing with statistics rather than parameters.

TABLE I.   Diameters of 200 Shafts Measured to the Nearest 0.001 Inch

1.0039	0.9956	1.0026	1.0004	1.0005
1.0014	0.9996	0.9994	0.9977	1.0023
0.9980	1.0025	1.0043	1.0004	0.9989
1.0000	1.0028	0.9954	0.9974	0.9992
0.9973	0.9994	1.0009	1.0033	1.0005
0.9996	0.9998	1.0026	1.0031	1.0034
1.0010	0.9995	0.9976	1.0009	0.9991
0.9999	0.9979	0.9983	0.9972	0.9998
1.0003	0.9968	1.0013	1.0007	1.0041
1.0037	1.0012	0.9985	1.0018	0.9987
1.0021	1.0008	1.0014	1.0000	1.0016
1.0006	1.0015	0.9971	1.0020	1.0046
0.9976	0.9988	1.0021	0.9990	1.0039
0.9978	0.9975	0.9988	1.0008	0.9986
1.0006	0.9984	1.0005	0.9948	1.0023
0.9943	1.0022	0.9985	0.9964	1.0005
0.9993	0.9967	1.0006	1.0008	0.9959
1.0016	0.9958	1.0056	0.9982	0.9999
0.9970	0.9996	0.9997	1.0009	0.9979
1.0005	0.9991	0.9989	1.0017	0.9993
1.0001	0.9997	0.9989	1.0020	0.9969
1.0049	1.0010	0.9981	1.0002	1.0001
0.9997	0.9963	0.9990	1.0031	0.9984
0.9992	0.9997	1.0000	1.0003	1.0027
1.0035	1.0002	0.9999	1.0016	1.0022
0.9998	0.9995	0.9997	0.9978	1.0007
0.9998	1.0009	1.0029	0.9996	1.0011
1.0012	0.9984	1.0033	0.9990	1.0013
1.0019	0.9992	1.0025	1.0002	0.9999
0.9981	0.9970	1.0011	1.0015	1.0013
1.0007	0.9985	0.9982	0.9980	1.0001
1.0000	0.9995	0.9984	1.0050	1.0003
1.0001	1.0010	0.9988	1.0008	0.9987
0.9983	1.0005	1.0028	0.9991	0.9993
1.0023	1.0004	1.0001	0.9989	0.9983
1.0015	0.9986	0.9993	1.0006	0.9982
0.9975	1.0010	0.0019	1.0000	0.9966
1.0030	0.9995	0.9987	0.9979	0.9999
0.9991	1.0019	0.9994	1.0017	1.0003
1.0018	1.0012	1.0015	0.9990	0.9996

Descriptive Statistics

One major area of the study of statistics has to do with precise and efficient ways of describing what otherwise would be a mass of data which would communicate very little worthwhile information. Table I illustrates this point. It lists measurements of the diameters of a sample of 200 shafts from a production lot of 10,000. By scanning the table we can pick out the maximum reading, 1.0056 inches, and the minimum reading, 0.9943 inches, but any generalization about the diameters of the 200 shafts is difficult. Similarly, inferences about the entire lot of 10,000 shafts are difficult.

Frequency distributions. The situation is improved by grouping the data into a frequency distribution. To do this we tabulate the number of shaft measurements that fall into certain class intervals, as in Table II. Immediately we observe some characteristics of the

TABLE II. **Frequency Distribution of the Data in Table I**

Class Limits, inches From To	Frequency, numbers of shafts	Class Limits, inches From To	Frequency, numbers of shafts
1.0053–1.0057	1	0.9993–0.9997	21
1.0048–1.0052	2	0.9988–0.9992	18
1.0043–1.0047	2	0.9983–0.9987	15
1.0038–1.0042	3	0.9978–0.9982	12
1.0033–1.0037	5	0.9973–0.9977	7
1.0028–1.0032	6	0.9968–0.9972	6
1.0023–1.0027	8	0.9963–0.9967	4
1.0018–1.0022	11	0.9958–0.9962	2
1.0013–1.0017	14	0.9953–0.9957	2
1.0008–1.0012	17	0.9948–0.9952	1
1.0003–1.0007	20	0.9943–0.9947	1
0.9998–1.0002	22		

data that were difficult to see before. For example, we see that the high and low readings represent a small minority of the cases, and that a large per cent of the shafts measured somewhere between 0.9982 inch and 1.0018 inch, with the largest number, 22, occurring around 1.000 inch. When the data are plotted in what is called a histogram, as in Figure 1, the general relationships show up clearly. We see that we have a fairly symmetrical bell-shaped distribution of the measurements, centering on 1.000 inch.

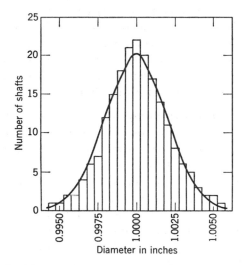

Figure 1. Histogram of the 200 shaft-diameter measurements.

The normal distribution. The smooth bell-shaped curve that has been superimposed on the histogram of Figure 1 is called the normal or Gaussian distribution. We see that the distribution of diameter measurements fairly well approximates normal distribution. The name *normal distribution* does not imply that distributions which do not approximate it are abnormal. The curve for the normal distribution has a specific mathematical function, so that for a distribution to approximate normality, the occurrence frequencies must follow closely the general pattern indicated in Figure 1. There are statistical tests which can be used to determine how closely a distribution approximates normality. If there is anything "normal" about the normal distribution, it is, perhaps, the fact that a great number of actual distributions in industry, science, and nature can be closely approximated by it. Thus a large part of statistical method is based on the normal distribution. Table I in Appendix *D* gives areas under a standardized normal curve.

Other distributions. There are a number of other important distributions which are useful in operation's management. For example, the Poisson and the negative exponential distributions are greatly used in waiting-line theory, as we shall see. The statistics dealing with proportions or fractions are of great importance in quality control by attributes; that is, where parts are classified into two groups, good and not good. The distributions that are applicable here are the binomial and the Poisson distributions. Techniques parallel to those discussed here for the normal distribution have been developed for these other distributions as well as for situations where no specific distribution is implied. We will review general statistical methods for the normal distribution and not attempt to review the details of analysis for the other distributions.

Measures of a distribution. There are several characteristics of distributions which can be used to describe or specify them. In Figure 1 we note that, first, the measurements tend to group around some central value; second, there is variability, that is, that no one value represents the whole; third, the distribution is symmetric; and fourth, there is one peak or mode. Therefore, to describe a distribution we need measures of central value, variability, symmetry, and an observation of the number of modes. Note that if a distribution can be assumed to be *normal*, only the first two measures will specify it, since a normal distribution is unimodal and symmetric. We shall discuss measures of central value and of variability, with only a minor reference to measures of symmetry.

Measures of central value. A measure of central value in the population is often made from a random sample drawn from the population. Suppose that the values for n individual items in a random sample are represented by $x_1, x_2, x_3, \cdots, x_i, x_n$. Then the arithmetic mean $\bar{x}$ of the sample can be computed by:

$$\bar{x} = \frac{\sum_{i=1}^{n} x_i}{n} = \frac{x_1 + x_2 + x_3 + \cdots + x_{n-1} + x_n}{n}$$

The Greek letter $\sum$ means "sum of," and the x_i are the individual observations which are numbered from 1 to n, the total number of observations.* Therefore, for our shaft diameter example, we can calculate $\bar{x}$ from Table I as follows:

$$\bar{x} = \frac{1.0039 + 1.0014 + 0.9980 + \cdots + 0.9996}{200} = 1.000$$

There are two other measures of the center of a distribution, the median and the mode. The *median* is that point on the horizontal scale which divides the area under the histogram into two equal parts. If the set of data were arranged in rank order from the lowest

---

* There is, of course, a short-cut method for calculating the mean based on the grouped data of Table II.

to the highest reading, the median would then be the middle value. For the data of Table II, the median can be determined by interpolating in the class interval, 0.9998–1.0002. Since there are **89** items on either side of this class interval and **22** items within it, the number within the class interval which divides the frequencies in half is exactly **1.000**.

The *mode* is the most frequently occurring value. On a histogram it is the midpoint of the class interval that has the greatest frequency of occurrence. For the data of Table II, represented by the histogram of Figure 1, the mode is 1.000. Note then, that for a symmetrical distribution, the mean, the median, and the mode will all be equal.

The *mean* is the commonly used measure of central value. When a distribution is strongly skewed (not symmetrical), however, it no longer represents the center of the distribution very well, because it is weighted heavily by the extreme values. Figure 2 shows the general effect of a skewed distribution on the three measures of central value. In such cases, the median is often used since it reflects

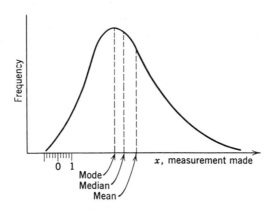

Figure 2. Effect of a skewed distribution on the mean, the median, and the mode.

the influence of the extreme values, but is not so sensitive to their presence in the distribution as is the arithmetic mean. The difference between the mean and the median is, therefore, one simple measure of skewness or symmetry. Other more precise measures exist. There are also techniques for *normalizing* the distribution in order that normal distribution statistical methods can be used. These methods are beyond our scope here.

Measures of variability or dispersion. The *range*, which is the simplest and most easily determined measure of variability, is the difference between the highest and lowest values in the distribution. For the data of Table I, it is $1.0056 - 0.9943 = 0.0113$ inch. It is not a very stable measure since it is based on only two values instead of on the entire set of data. Thus a very high or very low, but atypical, reading could increase the range considerably, but would not represent the variability of the entire set of data very well. The range is commonly used as a measure of variability in quality control because it is so easy to compute.

The *variance* is the most commonly used measure of variability in statistics because of its stability as a measure, and because of other valuable properties which we shall discuss. The variance is denoted by the square of the Greek letter sigma and is defined by:

$$\sigma^2 = \frac{\sum_{i=1}^{n} (x_i - \bar{x})^2}{n - 1}$$

It is simply the sum of the squares of the differences between the individual observations and the mean of a distribution, divided by one less than the total number of observations. For the data of Table I, where we have already computed $\bar{x} = 1.000$, the variance 0.00000407 is calculated as follows:

$$\sigma^2 = \frac{\left\{\begin{array}{l}(1.0039 - 1.0000)^2 + (1.0014 - 1.0000)^2 \\ \quad + (0.9980 - 1.0000)^2 + \cdots + (0.9996 - 1.0000)^2\end{array}\right\}}{199}$$

It is the estimate of the actual population variance of the parent distribution. A mathematically equivalent formula, which is much simpler for computational purposes, is:

$$\sigma^2 = \frac{\sum_{i=1}^{n} x_i^2 - \dfrac{\left(\sum_{i=1}^{n} x_i\right)^2}{n}}{n - 1}$$

Although this formula looks more complicated, it is simpler to use because it eliminates the successive subtraction of the mean from each observation and it uses data which must be assembled anyway to calculate the mean, that is, $\sum_{i=1}^{n} x_i$.

The *standard deviation* is the square root of the variance and is commonly denoted by σ. For the data of Table I, σ is:

$$\sqrt{\sigma^2} = \sqrt{0.00000407} = 0.002015 \text{ inch}$$

It has special properties which are useful to us.

If we consider a normal distribution with mean, $\bar{x}$, and standard deviation, σ, it is true that 68.27 per cent of the area under the curve (equivalent to the frequency of occurrence in the histogram) is included within the limits $\bar{x} \pm \sigma$; 95.45 per cent is included within the limits $\bar{x} \pm 2\sigma$; and 99.73 per cent is included within the limits $\bar{x} \pm 3\sigma$. See Figure 3. The significance of Figure 3 is that we can now make a probability statement about values that we presume come from the universe or population from which the sample distribution is drawn. Using the shaft diameter example, which had an $\bar{x} = 1.000$ inch and

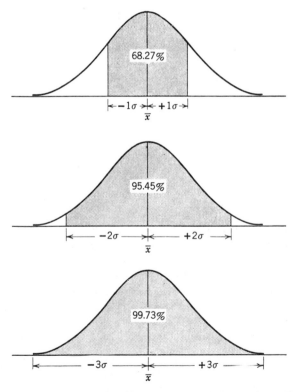

Figure 3. Areas under the normal curve for different sigma limits.

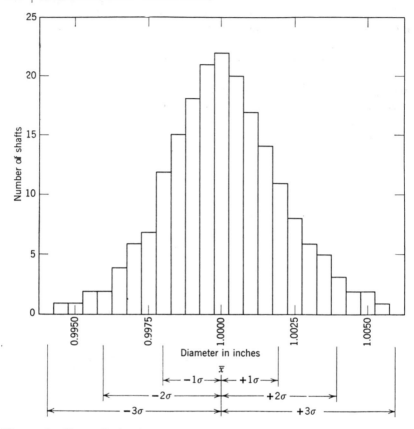

Figure 4. Sigma limits for the distribution of shaft-diameter measurements, based on Table II.

$\sigma = 0.0020$ inch, we can say that there is a 95.45 per cent probability that shafts coming from the lot or universe from which the distribution sample was drawn will have outside diameters measuring between 0.9960 and 1.0040 inches, and that there is only a 4.55 per cent probability that shafts will measure outside these limits. Similarly, virtually all shafts will measure between 0.9940 and 1.0060 inches, and there is only a 0.27 per cent chance that any shafts will measure outside these limits (see Figure 4). The latter probability is very small; although we are aware that it could happen, we might be suspicious that shafts measuring beyond these limits do not really come from the manufacturing process that produced the dimensions of the lot of 200 from which we established the distribution. In other words, the machine may be out of adjustment, or the cutting tool may have worn, etc. At least the probability is high that there is some assignable cause for the measurement that is greater or less than expected. These are ideas on which statistical quality control and control charts are based. See Table I in Appendix D for other values.

Control Charts

If, for the mean and standard deviation of a normally distributed variable, we have established standards that are based on the typical distribution resulting for normal conditions, we can use these data to construct a control chart. By plotting sample measurements on the chart, we can observe readily if the points are maintained within control limits, or if there is a tendency for drift to one limit or the other. We know that if the successive samples are representative of the original standard universe, the probability is very small that any sample measurements would fall outside the 3σ limits established. If sample measurements do fall outside these limits, we have reason to believe that something has changed which is producing nonstandard conditions, and the cause may be investigated and corrected. Thus a control chart signals when corrective action is required. Figure 5 shows a control chart for the shaft data based on our previous calculations of the mean and standard deviation.

Although other than the 3σ limits can certainly be used for control charts, these limits have actually been adopted as standard. With these limits, the probability is extremely small of labeling a point as out of control, when in fact the normal condition exists. Therefore, when the chart calls for action, it is probably warranted.

Control charts are constructed for different kinds of measures, such as the average measurement taken on samples of four or five, the proportion of defective items in a lot, etc. We shall elaborate on some applications of this basic idea in the chapter dealing with statistical control. Although control charts were originally used in quality control, we should recognize their value as analytical tools widely applicable to all kinds of control problems. They may apply to such things as accidents, costs, labor turnover, and labor standards, as well as to their traditional field of quality control. Statistical controls represent the epitome of managerial control by the exception principle. These types of controls require only minor attention by relatively unskilled personnel most of the time when conditions are normal. But when the probability is high that something has gone wrong, control charts summon the required high-level personnel to determine the causes of abnormal conditions and to take corrective action. When

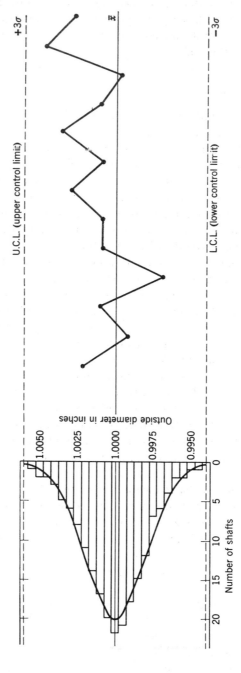

Figure 5. Control chart for the measurements of the diameters of the shafts.

normal conditions are obtained again, the high-level personnel can turn their attention to other problems that best utilize their talents.

Regression and Correlation

The statistical methods known as regression and correlation can help answer questions such as the following in the production and operations management field: What is the average line of relationship between wages paid and estimates of job difficulty? Is there a relationship between a test for finger dexterity and performance on a given manual job? If so, how good is the relationship? Is it good enough to help select personnel for the job? Suppose that we paint small metal parts by immersing them in the paint and then spinning them in a centrifuge to remove excess paint. Surface paint defects occur. Is there a relation between the occurrence of these defects and paint viscosity, time in the centrifuge, or lead content in the paint, etc.?

The *regression* line which best represents a set of points, (x_1, y_1), $(x_2, y_2) \cdots (x_i, y_i) \cdots (x_n, y_n)$, is often needed as a basis for an estimating function. Take the data represented by the scatter diagram of Figure 6. An estimate of job difficulty has been developed by a system of points which varies with the degree that jobs require certain

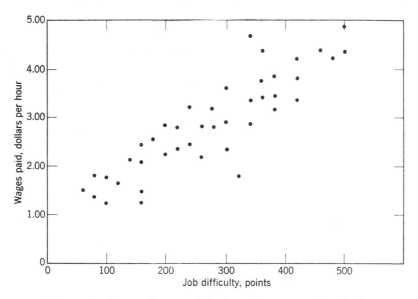

Figure 6. Scatter diagram, difficulty points versus wages paid.

TABLE III. Computation of Regression Line Coefficients, *a* and *b*,
for the Data from Figure 6

x Points	y Wages	xy	x^2	x Points	y Wages	xy	x^2
60	1.50	90	3,600	280	3.10	868	78,400
80	1.35	108	6,400	300	2.35	705	90,000
80	1.80	144	6,400	300	2.90	870	90,000
100	1.25	125	10,000	300	3.60	1,080	90,000
100	1.75	175	10,000	320	1.80	576	102,400
120	1.65	198	14,400	340	2.85	969	115,600
140	2.10	294	19,600	340	3.35	1,139	115,600
160	1.25	200	25,600	340	4.65	1,581	115,600
160	1.48	236.8	25,600	360	3.40	1,224	129,600
160	2.10	336	25,600	360	3.75	1,350	129,600
160	2.45	392	25,600	360	4.30	1,548	129,600
180	2.55	459	32,400	380	3.20	1,216	144,400
200	2.25	450	40,000	380	3.45	1,311	144,400
200	2.85	570	40,000	380	3.80	1,444	144,400
220	2.35	517	48,400	420	3.35	1,407	176,400
220	2.80	616	48,400	420	3.80	1,596	176,400
240	2.45	588	57,600	420	4.20	1,764	176,400
240	3.20	768	57,600	460	4.40	2,024	211,600
260	2.20	572	67,600	480	4.20	2,016	230,400
260	2.80	728	67,600	500	4.30	2,150	250,000
280	2.80	784	78,400	500	4.90	2,450	250,000
				$\sum x =$ 11,540	$\sum y =$ 120.58	$\sum xy =$ 37,638.8	$\sum x^2 =$ 3,801,600

$$N = 42; \quad \bar{x} = \frac{\sum x}{N} = \frac{11,540}{42} = 275.238; \quad \bar{y} = \frac{\sum y}{N} = \frac{120.58}{42} = 2.871$$

$$b = \frac{\sum xy - \bar{x}\sum y}{\sum x^2 - \bar{x}\sum x} = \frac{37,638.8 - 275.238(120.58)}{3,801,600 - 275.238(11,540)} = .00712$$

$$a = \bar{y} - b\bar{x} = 2.871 - 0.00712(275.238) = 0.911$$

Equation of least squares line is, $y = 0.911 + 0.00712x$.

factors of skill, education, experience, physical fitness, etc. In Figure 6 estimates of job difficulty have been plotted against existing wages on the jobs. In general, we can say that wages do vary with job difficulty, but there is considerable variation in wages paid for a given point rating. Obviously, no single line can be drawn which goes through all the points and makes any sense. But which line best represents the entire set of points? The line which best fits the points is commonly the linear regression line, that is, the line which minimizes the squares of the deviations from it, as well as setting the simple deviations to zero. This least squares line is the line:

$$y = a + bx$$

where: $b = \dfrac{\sum\limits_{i=1}^{n} xy - \bar{x} \sum\limits_{i=1}^{n} y}{\sum\limits_{i=1}^{n} \lambda - \bar{x} \sum\limits_{i=1}^{n} x}$

$a = \bar{y} - b\bar{x}$

y's = wages

x's = point ratings

This line can be computed easily with the aid of a desk calculator and plotted on the scatter diagram as the line of best fit for the given points. This is done for the data of Figure 6 in Table III. Since the resulting equation, $y = a + bx$, is a straight line, the value computed for a is the point where the line intersects the vertical axis, and the computed value for b is the slope of the line. For the data of Figure 6 the equation of the line is: $y = 0.911 + 0.00712x$.

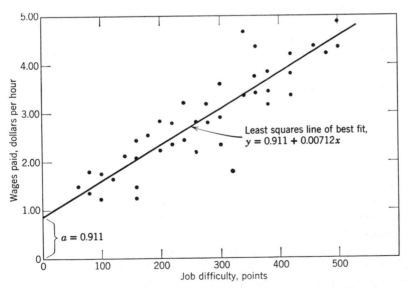

Figure 7. Scatter diagram and least squares line of best fit.

The line intersects the wages axis at $0.911, and for each point of job difficulty we add $0.00712. The line is superimposed on the scatter diagram in Figure 7.

Let us note further the assumed structure with which we are dealing in the regression equation. For each level of job difficulty there is a distribution of wages. The reasons for variation might be related to the people on the jobs, their skills, seniority, etc., and to errors made in appraising both jobs and people. The distributions are assumed to be normal. They each have a mean which falls on the regression line and they have equal variances. This is diagramed in Figure 8. Therefore, the regression equation is often used to

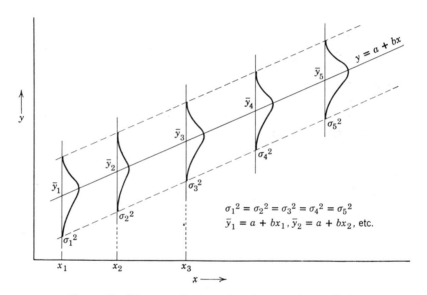

Figure 8. Diagram of assumptions in regression analysis.

estimate y within certain probability limits, given a value of x, since the value of x specifies a normal distribution with a mean and a variance. The probability that y will be beyond certain values is specified by the sigma limits, similar to the control chart concept.

There are other regression techniques that are appropriate when a straight line does not represent the data. Also, there are appropriate techniques for multiple regression—that is, where there are more than two variables to be related.

Correlation is a measure of the degree of relationship between two variables. Although many times we can suspect that a relationship exists by looking at a scatter diagram, a correlation coefficient tells us how close that relationship is. In our wages-job difficulty points example, we would have had a perfect correlation between wages and points if all the points had fallen on the regression line; that is to say, if the squares of the deviations from the line were zero, the correlation coefficient would be +1.00. Correlation is, then, a measure of the scatter or *dispersion* of the points in a scatter diagram. If the points are completely randomly scattered, the correlation is zero, and there is no relationship between the variables. If one variable increases generally while the other decreases, we have an inverse relationship, or a negative correlation.

Correlation coefficients vary from −1.00 to +1.00. Figure 9 illustrates this general picture. Thus a correlation coefficient, *r*, of 0.85 indicates a higher degree of relationship than 0.50, and similarly

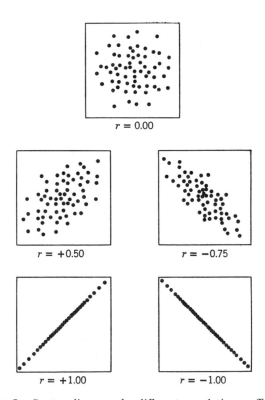

Figure 9. Scatter diagrams for different correlation coefficients.

an r of -0.85 indicates a higher degree of relationship than -0.50. It is important to note, however, that $r = 0.90$ does not imply twice as close a relationship as $r = 0.45$, since our ability to forecast y, given x, is better indicated by r^2, the square of the correlation coefficient. Therefore, $r = 0.90$ ($r^2 = 0.81$) is about twice as good as $r = 0.636$ ($r^2 = 0.405$).

How good is a correlation coefficient? Too often correlation coefficients are quoted without any indication of how much confidence we are justified in placing in them. There are statistical tests which allow us to make a probability statement about the r's which are observed. By adopting a significance level (similar to the three sigma limits of the control chart) we may be able to say, for example, that we are 95 per cent sure that the $r = 0.80$ which we observed is not less than 0.75. One easy check is to compare the observed value of r with the values given in Table IV. This table gives the critical values of r that must be exceeded for various numbers of observations, n, to be confident that r is not really zero. The critical values are given

TABLE IV. Critical Values of r for 95% and 99% Confidence.
These Values Must Be Exceeded for a Given Sample Size n to
Be Sure that the Observed Value of r Is not Really Zero

n	95%	99%	n	95%	99%	n	95%	99%
10	.632	.765	30	.361	.463	50	.279	.361
12	.576	.708	32	.349	.449	60	.254	.330
14	.532	.661	34	.339	.436	70	.235	.306
16	.497	.623	36	.329	.424	80	.220	.287
18	.468	.590	38	.320	.413	100	.197	.256
20	.444	.561	40	.312	.403	150	.161	.210
22	.423	.537	42	.304	.393	200	.139	.182
24	.404	.515	44	.297	.384	400	.098	.128
26	.388	.496	46	.291	.376	1000	.062	.081
28	.374	.479	48	.284	.368			

By permission from *Introduction to Statistical Analysis*, by W. J. Dixon and F. J. Massey, copyright, 1951, McGraw-Hill Book Company.

for both the 95 and 99 per cent confidence levels. This test assumes that both of the variables x and y are normally distributed.

Does r mean that there is a causal relation? It is sometimes implied that a high r indicates that a change in x causes y to change.

This is possible, but there is nothing in correlation analysis to make this situation a necessity. The existence of r merely indicates that x and y move together. Some other factor may control both of them. For example, it may be important that the tensile strength (the force per square inch of cross section required to pull it apart) of a steel part be at least 60,000 pounds per square inch. Since the tensile test requires the destruction of the part, we search for some test that is strongly correlated with tensile strength, and we come up with a hardness test that correlates $+0.90$ with tensile strength and does not destroy the part. Hardness does not cause tensile strength, nor is the reverse true. Rather, both hardness and tensile strength are controlled by the chemical composition of the steel, the rolling process it received at the steel mill, and the heat treatment processes it has received.

Calculation of correlation coefficients. The correlation coefficient may be calculated by the following formula:

$$r = \frac{\sum\limits_{i=1}^{n} (x - \bar{x})(y - \bar{y})}{n\sigma_x\sigma_y}$$

For each pair of measurements, the deviations from their means are multiplied. There are as many such multiplications as there are observations. The entire set is summed and divided by $n\sigma_x\sigma_y$. It is actually simpler computationally to use:

$$r = \frac{n\sum\limits_{i=1}^{n} xy - \sum\limits_{i=1}^{n} x \sum\limits_{i=1}^{n} y}{\sqrt{\left[n\sum\limits_{i=1}^{n} x^2 - \left(\sum\limits_{i=1}^{n} x\right)^2\right]\left[n\sum\limits_{i=1}^{n} y^2 - \left(\sum\limits_{i=1}^{n} y\right)^2\right]}}$$

The value of r can also be obtained from the constants of the regression equations.

AN EXAMPLE

In making steel, some of the major raw materials are pig iron, scrap iron, and limestone. The proportions of pig iron to scrap are commonly varied within limits to take advantage of price changes in scrap and pig iron. The limestone helps remove impurities during the steel making process. In Table V we have given data for 100 melts of steel. For each melt we have the per cent of pig iron (in proportion to scrap) and the limestone consump-

TABLE V. Percentage of Pig Iron and Limestone Consumption
(hundredweight per cast) in Steel Making

Pig	Lime-stone	Pig	Lime-stone	Pig	Lime-stone	Pig	Lime-stone	Pig	Lime-stone
23	164	35	156	37	216	43	210	47	310
25	141	35	165	38	145	43	212	48	170
26	140	35	176	38	157	44	176	48	205
29	156	35	193	38	164	44	215	48	241
30	165	35	194	38	175	45	174	48	242
30	177	36	124	38	225	45	184	49	193
30	178	36	132	38	281	45	187	49	204
30	182	36	146	39	190	45	194	49	206
30	184	36	174	39	201	45	216	50	158
31	172	36	180	40	138	45	219	50	195
32	159	36	195	40	200	45	219	50	196
32	185	36	201	40	223	46	205	50	198
33	138	37	126	40	241	46	235	52	208
33	155	37	140	41	212	47	193	52	219
33	170	37	170	42	166	47	197	52	262
33	192	37	176	42	182	47	206	53	170
33	228	37	182	42	194	47	218	53	188
34	161	37	191	42	213	47	218	53	193
35	133	37	194	42	246	47	220	53	219
35	146	37	198	43	207	47	274	53	240

From L. H. C. Tippett, *Technological Applications of Statistics*, John Wiley and Sons, New York, 1950, p. 147.

tion in hundredweight per melt. In Figure 10 the data is plotted as a scatter diagram and we can see the tendency for limestone consumption to increase with the percentage of pig iron in the melt. (This fact, of course, is well known in the steel industry.)

We also note that for a given pig iron percentage there is considerable variability in the consumption of limestone. How close is the relationship? It is calculated in Table VI as $r = 0.505$, which is not a high correlation ratio, but is felt to be highly representative of the degree of relationship in the population. Reference to the critical values of Table IV is one indication of our confidence in the calculated value of r.

Statistical Inference

The field of statistical inference helps us make decisions where we have incomplete information. We can often draw a sample from

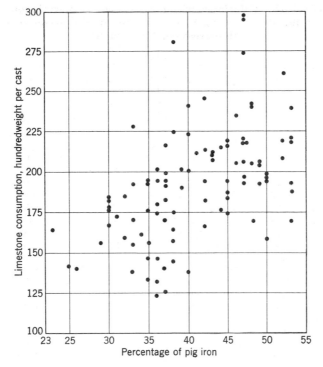

Figure 10. Scatter diagram of data in Table VI. From L. H. C. Tippett, *Technological Applications of Statistics,* John Wiley and Sons, New York, 1950, Fig. 18.

the population or universe about which we wish to make a decision, and from the sample we infer certain things about the characteristics of the universe; but, in addition, we want to know how good our inferences are, that is, what is the probability that they are right or that they are wrong? Suppose that we sample the time required for a worker to perform a proposed new method for a manual operation and, from ten readings, compute the average value to be 15 seconds per unit and the standard deviation to be 1 second. We have considerable data on the old method and accept 18 seconds as its average value. How do we know that the average of 15 seconds for the new method does not represent a chance variation; that is, we may just have happened to sample some especially low values. We can obtain helpful information by examining the distribution of our sample. Is the value of 18 seconds (old method mean) at all probable, given the data that we have? If it is, we would not have much confidence that the time

TABLE VI. Calculaton of the Coefficient of Correlation, r, for the Per Cent Pig Iron and Limestone Consumption (hundredweight per melt)

$N = 100$

x Pig Iron	y Lime-stone	xy	x^2	y^2	x Pig Iron	y Lime-stone	xy	x^2	y^2
23	164	3,772	529	26,896	38	145	5,510	1,444	21,025
25	141	3,525	625	19,881	38	157	5,966	1,444	24,649
26	140	3,640	676	19,600	38	164	6,232	1,444	26,896
29	156	4,524	841	24,336	38	175	6,650	1,444	30,625
30	165	4,950	900	27,225	38	225	8,550	1,444	50,625
30	177	5,310	900	31,329	38	281	10,678	1,444	78,961
30	178	5,340	900	31,684	39	190	7,410	1,521	36,100
30	182	5,460	900	33,124	39	201	7,839	1,521	40,401
30	184	5,520	900	33,856	40	138	5,520	1,600	19,044
31	172	5,332	961	29,584	40	200	8,000	1,600	40,000
32	159	5,088	1,024	25,281	40	223	8,920	1,600	49,729
32	185	5,920	1,024	34,225	40	241	9,640	1,600	58,081
33	138	4,554	1,089	19,044	41	212	8,692	1,681	44,944
33	155	5,115	1,089	24,025	42	166	6,972	1,764	27,556
33	170	5,610	1,089	28,900	42	182	7,644	1,764	33,124
33	192	6,336	1,089	36,864	42	194	8,148	1,764	37,636
33	228	7,524	1,089	51,984	42	213	8,946	1,764	45,369
34	161	5,474	1,156	25,921	42	246	10,332	1,764	60,516
35	133	4,655	1,225	17,689	43	207	8,901	1,849	42,849
35	146	5,110	1,225	21,316	43	210	9,030	1,849	44,100
35	156	5,460	1,225	24,336	43	212	9,116	1,849	44,944
35	165	5,775	1,225	27,225	44	176	7,744	1,936	30,976
35	176	6,160	1,225	30,976	44	215	9,460	1,936	46,225
35	193	6,755	1,225	37,249	45	174	7,830	2,025	30,276
35	194	6,790	1,225	37,636	45	184	8,280	2,025	33,856
36	124	4,464	1,296	15,376	45	187	8,415	2,025	34,969
36	132	4,752	1,296	17,424	45	194	8,730	2,025	37,636
36	146	5,256	1,296	21,316	45	216	9,720	2,025	46,656
36	174	6,264	1,296	30,276	45	219	9,855	2,025	47,961
36	180	6,480	1,296	32,400	45	219	9,855	2,025	47,961
36	195	7,020	1,296	38,025	46	205	9,430	2,116	42,025
36	201	7,236	1,296	40,401	46	235	10,810	2,116	55,225
37	126	4,662	1,369	15,876	47	193	9,071	2,209	37,249
37	140	5,180	1,369	19,600	47	197	9,259	2,209	38,809
37	170	6,290	1,369	28,900	47	206	9,682	2,209	42,436
37	176	6,512	1,369	30,976	47	218	10,246	2,209	47,524
37	182	6,734	1,369	33,124	47	218	10,246	2,209	47,524
37	191	7,067	1,369	36,481	47	220	10,340	2,209	48,400
37	194	7,178	1,369	37,636	47	274	12,878	2,209	75,076
37	198	7,326	1,369	39,204	47	310	14,570	2,209	96,100
37	216	7,992	1,369	46,656	48	170	8,160	2,304	28,900

TABLE VI (Continued). **Calculation of the Coefficient of Correlation, r, for the Per Cent Pig Iron and Limestone Consumption (hundredweight per melt)**

$$N = 100$$

x Pig Iron	y Lime-stone	xy	x^2	y^2	x Pig Iron	y Lime-stone	xy	x^2	y^2
48	205	9,840	2,304	42,025	50	198	9,900	2,500	39,204
48	241	11,568	2,304	58,081	52	208	10,816	2,704	43,264
48	242	11,616	2,304	58,564	52	219	11,388	2,704	47,961
49	193	9,457	2,401	37,249	52	262	13,624	2,704	68,644
49	204	9,996	2,401	41,616	53	170	9,010	2,809	28,900
49	206	10,094	2,401	42,436	53	188	9,964	2,809	35,344
50	158	7,900	2,500	24,964	53	193	10,229	2,809	37,249
50	195	'9,750	2,500	38,025	53	219	11,607	2,809	47,961
50	196	9,800	2,500	38,416	53	240	12,720	2,809	57,600
					$\sum x =$ 4,054	$\sum y =$ 19,104	$\sum xy =$ 786,668	$\sum y^2 =$ 169,430	$\sum y^2 =$ 3,764,318

$$r = \frac{N\sum xy - \sum x \sum y}{\sqrt{[N\sum x^2 - (\sum x)^2][N\sum y^2 - (\sum y)^2]}}$$

$$= \frac{100(786,668) - 4054(19,104)}{\sqrt{[100(169,430) - (4054)^2][100(3,764,318) - (19,104)^2}}$$

$$= \frac{78,666,800 - 77,447,616}{\sqrt{508,084 \times 11,468,984}}$$

$$= \frac{1,219,184}{\sqrt{5,827,207,266,656}} = \frac{1,219,184}{2,413,961} = 0.505$$

difference we have observed is real. If 18 seconds is highly improbable, we might be willing to accept the 3-second difference as valid. To formalize these ideas we proceed as follows:

1. Adopt a *hypothesis;* for example, we say that the mean time from our data could be 18 as well as 15. This is called the hypothesis to be tested, denoted by H_0. For our example, H_0: $\bar{x} = 18$.

2. We choose a *level of significance* or probability level to guide us in determining whether the hypothesis is true or false. This is always denoted by the Greek letter α. It is the chance or probability that if our test tells us that the hypothesis is not true, that is, that $\bar{x}$ is not 18, we may have erred. For example, in the control charts which we discussed, α was 0.27 per cent. If a point fell outside the 3σ limits, we concluded the chances were only 0.27 out of 100 that we were wrong in assuming that it was not in control. This is a very small value for α. In most instances outside the field of quality control, values of α are 1, 5, or 10 per cent.

Let us carry through a logical analysis of the previous example to see if it is at all probable that $\bar{x}$ could be as high as 18 seconds. We decide to adopt $\alpha = 5$ per cent. We have obtained estimates of $\bar{x} = 15$, and $\sigma = 1$, based on a sample of 10. Now we want to know if, in the sampling distribution of means of sample size 10, a mean of 18 would be probable. First we compute $\sigma_{\bar{x}} = \sigma/\sqrt{n} = 1/\sqrt{10} = 0.316$ second, the standard deviation of the sampling distribution of means of sample size 10. Then we plot the sampling distribution and see where H_0: $\bar{x} = 18$ falls in relation to it (see Figure 11). Our conclusion would surely be to reject H_0 since the probability that $\bar{x} = 18$ seconds for the new method is very remote. Actually we would have rejected any value for H_0 that was above 15.7 or less than 14.28. This was determined by $\alpha = 5$ per cent or the limits $\bar{x} \pm 2.26\sigma$.

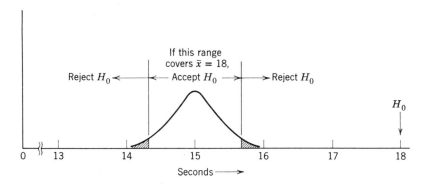

Figure 11. Relation of the estimated normal sampling distribution of means of sample size 10 to H_0. The value of 18 is highly improbable in the sampling distribution.

This example demonstrates some of the logical framework of the test of the hypothesis, but it is cumbersome to go through such an analysis each time. Instead, statisticians have determined the distribution of:

$$t = \frac{\bar{x} - \bar{x}_{H_0}}{\sigma/\sqrt{n}}$$

where $\bar{x}$ = the observed value of $\bar{x}$ (15 in our example)
$\bar{x}_{H_0}$ = the value of $\bar{x}$ specified by the hypothesis H_0
σ = the observed standard deviation of the sample
n = the number of observations in the sample

TABLE VII. Values of $t = \dfrac{\bar{x} - \bar{x}_{Ho}}{\sigma/\sqrt{n}}$

Degrees of Freedom	Significance Level		
	5%	2.5%	0.5%
1	6.31	12.70	63.70
2	2.92	4.30	9.92
3	2.35	3.18	5.84
4	2.13	2.78	4.60
5	2.01	2.57	4.03
6	1.94	2.45	3.71
7	1.89	2.36	3.50
8	1.86	2.31	3.36
9	1.83	2.26	3.25
10	1.81	2.23	3.17

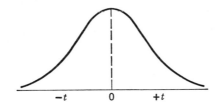

This is called the t distribution, and its values are tabled so that probability values are given directly. Table VII is a brief table of values of t for the first few degrees of freedom (df) and for three significance levels. The table is usually entered with the number of degrees of freedom, $n - 1$ for our case, and the significance level. Let us see how to utilize the t distribution.

Let us take as an example a machine that is set to turn out ball bearings with a radius of 1 inch. A sample of ten balls produced by the machine has a mean radius of 1.004 inches with a standard deviation of $\sigma = 0.003$. Is there reason to suspect that the machine is turning out ball bearings having a mean radius greater than 1 inch? We will make a step-by-step development.

1. Establish the *hypothesis*. We assume that the radius is still 1 inch, that is, that our sample represents a random variation, therefore, $H_0: \bar{x} = 1.000$.

2. Establish the *significance level*. We select $\alpha = 5$ per cent and split it between the two tails of the distribution as we did in the previous example.

3. Determine the *critical value of t* from the table. For our example, $df = n - 1 = 9$, and since we want 2.5 per cent in each tail, we look under that heading to find $t = 2.26$. Our critical values of t are, therefore, ± 2.26. This means that if the value of t which we compute from our sample data falls between -2.26 and $+2.26$, we accept the hypothesis that the overall mean radius is still 1.000 inch. If our computed t falls outside this range, however, we say that the chances are at least 95 out of 100 that the machine is no longer turning out balls of the proper average radius. The farther our computed t is beyond either limit, the surer we are of this conclusion.

4. *Compute t for the observed data.*

$$t = \frac{x - x_{H_0}}{\sigma/\sqrt{n}} = \frac{1.004 - 1.000}{0.003/\sqrt{10}} = \frac{0.004 \times 3.16}{0.003} = 4.22$$

5. *Compare the computed t with the critical values* and draw the conclusion indicated. Since $4.22 > 2.26$ (i.e., 4.22 is greater than 2.26), we reject H_0; the machine is producing oversized parts and it is quite unlikely that our sample mean represents a random variation.

Generality of these methods for testing statistical hypotheses. The basic ideas involved in the test of significance, which we have just completed, have general application. Where we are concerned with hypotheses concerning a mean value, or the comparison of two mean values, the t statistic is appropriate. If we wish to test hypotheses concerning variances, we use other distributions in a similar way, for example, the χ^2/df (chi square/degrees of freedom distribution) and the F distributions. The mechanics are different but the basic ideas are not. In general terms, testing statistical hypotheses involves the following:

1. *Establishing the hypothesis* to be tested, for example, $\bar{x}_1 = \bar{x}_2$, $\bar{x} = 10$, $\sigma^2 = 2$, $\sigma_1^2 = \sigma_2^2$, $\sigma_1^2 \geq \sigma_2^2$. These and others are possible specific hypotheses.

2. *Establishing the significance level α.* This is under the control of the experimenter and depends in part on the level with which he will be satisfied. If he wants to be very sure not to reject a hypothesis when actually it is true, he will make α very small, say 1 per cent. If he is more concerned about accepting a false hypothesis, he will select a larger value of α, perhaps 10 per cent.

3. *Selecting the appropriate probability distribution* to use as a basis for the test, for example, the t statistic to test for differences in means, the F statistic to test for the equality of two variances, etc.

4. *Establishing the critical values* (acceptance and rejection regions of the statistic for the test). These values normally come from tables and the values usually depend on the α selected and the degrees of freedom, which are related to the sample size.

5. *Drawing the sample* of the number previously decided on and computing the required statistics, that is, the observed t, χ^2/df, or F.

6. *Comparing the computed value with the critical values* and accepting or rejecting the hypothesis according to the acceptance and rejection regions established.

Examples of Hypotheses That Can Be Tested

I. Tests of mean values

   A. The average time to produce parts by a new method is the same as our present standard time, which is 10 seconds. $H_0 \colon \bar{x} = 10$.

   B. The average time to produce parts by a new method is less than our present standard time. $H_0 \colon \bar{x} < 10$.

   C. We are considering two alternate machines for a particular operation. We take sample time studies of the man-machine output. Machine 1 yields $\bar{x}_1$ and σ_1; and machine 2, $\bar{x}_2$ and σ_2. Are the average times different? $H_0 \colon \bar{x}_1 = \bar{x}_2$.

   D. We have five machines operated by five workers, which produce bushings. Differences in the mean outside diameter measurements that come from the different man-machine combinations have been noted. Are these differences due to the men or to the machines? We have two hypotheses. H_{0_1}: There are no significant differences in the mean diameters attributable to men, when the differences due to machines are removed. H_{0_2}: There are no significant differences in the mean diameters attributable to machines, when the differences due to men are removed. The technique known as analysis of variance would be used here.

II. Tests of variances

   A. A machine produces bushing diameters that are more uniform than the allowable variation, $\sigma^2 = 2$. $H_0 \colon \sigma^2 \leqq 2$.

   B. The diameters of bushings produced by machine 1 are more variable than those produced by machine 2. $H_0 \colon \sigma_1^2 > \sigma_2^2$.

III. Tests for proportions

   An automatic machine produces parts which are checked and classified as good and defective. The standard proportion of defectives has been set at $\bar{p} = 0.015$. Today's output yields $\bar{p} = 0.020$. Does this represent a random variation of p or is there cause for alarm? $H_0 \colon p = 0.015$.

Analysis of variance. One of the most powerful tools of statistical inference is analysis of variance. We cannot hope to give adequate coverage to that subject here; nevertheless, we can get an insight into the power of the technique and see the nature of problems for which it is appropriate.

AN EXAMPLE WHERE ANALYSIS OF VARIANCE CAN BE USED

We are producing steel shafts in large numbers, using several machines and operators. We observe differences in the diameters that come from the different man-machine combinations. Do the differences occur because the machines have slightly different characteristics, or are they due to the way the workers perform? We can find out by a simple experiment: four operators each produce a shaft on five different machines, and then we tabulate the data on shaft diameters in Table VIII. It is convenient in Table VIII to form the row and column totals and then compute the mean values for the diameters produced by each operator on the five machines and on each machine by the four operators.

TABLE VIII. Shaft Diameters in Inches Produced by Four Different Operators on Five Different Machines

Operator	Machine 1	2	3	4	5	$\sum$	$\bar{x}$
A	1.4970	1.4973	1.4982	1.4992	1.5000	7.4917	1.4983
B	1.5048	1.5038	1.5020	1.5016	1.5005	7.5127	1.5025
C	1.5005	1.5016	1.5031	1.5012	1.5002	7.5066	1.5013
D	1.4998	1.5003	1.4980	1.4999	1.4976	7.4956	1.4991
$\sum$	6.0021	6.0030	6.0013	6.0019	5.9983	30.0066	$\bar{\bar{x}} =$
$\bar{x}$	1.5005	1.5008	1.5003	1.5005	1.4996		1.5003

$$\sigma^2_{\text{total}} = \frac{\sum x_i{}^2 - \frac{(\sum x_i)^2}{n}}{n-1} = \frac{45.01988826 - \frac{900.39604356}{20}}{19} = 0.00000453$$

$$\sigma^2_{\text{operators}} = \frac{\sum \bar{x}_i{}^2 - \frac{(\sum \bar{x}_i)^2}{n}}{n-1} = \frac{9.00361164 - \frac{36.01440144}{4}}{3} = 0.00000376$$

$$\sigma^2_{\text{machines}} = \frac{\sum \bar{x}_j{}^2 - \frac{(\sum \bar{x}_j)^2}{n}}{n-1} = \frac{11.25510139 - \frac{56.27550289}{5}}{4} = 0.00000021$$

Now let us take a sidetrack for a moment to examine the *structure of variances* in this specific situation. Variability may often be attributed to several sources. In our situation, for example, we might attribute part of the variation to the fact that four different operators produced the shafts, part to the fact that five different machines were used, and part to random causes for which we cannot account, or for which we are not attempting to account.

In Table VIII we have computed three different variances. The first, σ^2_{total}, is based on the entire twenty observations in the table. The second variance, $\sigma^2_{\text{operators}}$, is based on the average shaft diameter produced by each of the operators. We compute a variance based on these four mean values, regarding each mean value as an observation. Finally, we compute the variance, $\sigma^2_{\text{machines}}$, based on the average shaft diameters produced by each of the five machines, regardless of which operator produced them. There are five such average values, one for each machine. Again, in computing this variance, we consider each of these five mean values as an observation.

Now let us examine the result. We see that $\sigma^2_{\text{operators}}$ is almost 18 times as large as $\sigma^2_{\text{machines}}$. In other words, the main source of variation in shaft diameters comes from differences between operators. The different machines contribute very little to the total variation that we observe. We can see this intuitively by examining the row and column mean values in Table VIII. By an analysis of variance of the data we could have determined more precisely the effect of different operators and different machines on the shaft diameters produced. As a matter of fact, such an analysis would show, in this case, that the differences in shaft diameters due to the different machines are simply random differences, that is, not significant.

Usefulness of analysis of variance. The experimental design that we used to demonstrate analysis of variance was a simple one. Other variables could have been incorporated, as well, to learn their effect on shaft size. The thing that seems most amazing about analysis of variance techniques is that two or more variables can be manipulated simultaneously, and yet the effect due solely to each variable can be isolated, as long as we know the state of each variable for every reading taken. This is in contrast to traditional methods of obtaining experimental data, in which the general procedure is to vary one factor at a time, and to observe the effect of each variation. The major advantages of modern experimental design are that experimental time and effort can be saved; but, in addition, when all pertinent variables are included in the experiment, information can be obtained on the interdependence of the variables. When variables are manipulated one at a time, this information may be lost. Another important feature of modern experimental design is that probability statements may be made about the conclusions.

Summary

How much does an operator produce? How big are the parts produced by a certain machine? How long does it take for an order to move through a sequence of fabrication and assembly operations? Such questions cannot be answered properly with the statement of a single number, because no single number is likely to represent a proper answer. In each instance, there is an average number, but the variability is usually great enough that it is as characteristic of the measurement as is an average figure. What is an accurate statement? Perhaps the best statement is a probability statement. For example, we might say: "Our best *estimate* of a particular operator's output is that he will produce between 102 and 130 pieces per day, 95 per cent of the time, with 116 pieces being the most likely output." This information would come from sample estimates of the mean and standard deviation of the operator's output. This type of statement recognizes the realities of the situation. First, it recognizes that any answer to the question is an estimate, and second, it recognizes that there will be considerable variability in output. It tells us what to expect in the way of variability, as well as what is the most likely value of output. Estimates of industrial output are not usually stated this way and, therefore, confusion often results. We state a single number without preparing the listener for the fact that considerable variation can be expected. When he observes the variation he may interpret our estimate as being just an educated guess, when actually we may have fairly precise knowledge about the measurement.

Statistical concepts are of great importance in operations management because nearly everything we try to measure and predict in operational systems display considerable variability. Variability is the rule, not the exception, and this often influences our concepts, as well as our solutions to specific problems. No machine, no matter how accurately made, turns out identical parts. When man enters the system the variability usually increases considerably. Therefore, to be most effective, measurements and controls need to be based on probability concepts.

REFERENCES

1. Chernoff, H., and L. E. Moses, *Elementary Decision Theory,* John Wiley and Sons, New York, 1959.
2. Dixon, W. J., and F. J. Massey, Jr., *Introduction to Statistical Analysis,* McGraw-Hill Book Company, New York, 1951.
3. Schlaifer, R., *Probability and Statistics for Business Decisions,* McGraw-Hill Book Company, New York, 1959.
4. Sprowls, R. C., *Elementary Statistics,* McGraw-Hill Book Company, New York, 1955.

REVIEW QUESTIONS

1. What sorts of problems in the field of production require a statistical point of view?

2. Define a universe or population, a finite universe, an infinite universe, a sample, a sampling distribution.

3. Differentiate between 'parameters and statistics.

4. What is meant by descriptive statistics?

5. What are the characteristics of a distribution? What statistics can describe a sample distribution?

6. What are the characteristics of the normal distribution? Are all unimodal, symmetrical distributions normal?

7. When are the various measures of central value all equal?

8. What are the various commonly used measures of variability in statistics? Are there any conditions under which they are all equal?

9. Why is the range commonly used in quality control as a measure of variability?

10. What is meant by statistical control?

11. If a sample measurement is outside control limits, does this automatically mean that the system is out of control and that an assignable cause exists?

12. What kinds of problems in operations management are appropriate for regression analysis? For correlation analysis?

13. Does a negative correlation indicate an extremely low correlation?

14. Does a high correlation between two variables indicate a causal relationship between the variables? If not, does correlation offer any predictive value?

15. Outline the basic structure for the formal testing of a hypothesis. Give examples of various types of hypotheses which can be tested.

16. What class of problems yields to analysis of variance? What is gained in modern experimental design as compared to traditional design where one factor at a time is varied?

PROBLEMS

1. Following is a set of data on the average daily output in units of a machine operation.
   (a) Determine and plot a frequency distribution for the data.
   (b) Compute the mean value, the median value and the modal value of the distribution.

(c) Compute the range, the variance, and the standard deviation.

Machine output, units per day

75	70	69	69	71	70	69	70
70	74	70	73	69	69	72	67
71	69	71	68	71	68	68	71
69	70	70	70	70	73	69	66
71	68	72	69	69	69	67	73
68	71	70	71	72	71	69	70
72	69	71	68	69	69	67	70
67	70	69	69	71	69	09	68
70	69	70	70	69	67	66	69
69	72	68	72	68	71	64	71

2. What would be the effect on the mean and standard deviation if all of the values in the data table of Problem 1 were multiplied by 4?

3. What would be the effect on the mean and standard deviation of adding 4 to each of the values in the data table of Problem 1?

4. Assuming that the data given in Problem 1 are drawn from a normal distribution, what is the probability of occurrence of the value 75 or greater (see Table I in Appendix D). What is the probability that a value will fall in the range 68–74?

5. A production manager maintains that the total flow time in days for an order through his shop is a function of the number of operations which must be performed. He offers the following sample data taken from past orders:

Number of operations required	2	2	3	4	4	5	6	6	7	7
Actual shop flow time, days	8	13	14	11	20	19	22	26	22	25

Determine the regression line for this data as an estimating function, that is, giving the number of operations to be performed, a function for estimating the flow time in days.

6. How good is the relationship between the number of operations required and resulting flow time, that is, calculate the correlation coefficient r for the data of Problem 5. Is the value significant at the 95 per cent confidence level? See Table IV in the text.

7. The production manager has kept records for a period of time on the flow time of orders, and he notes that the average flow time over a long period has been 20 days. Noting that his sample of $N = 10$ yielded an average flow time of only 18 days, he wonders if his sample actually reflects the population of flow times in his shop. Therefore, he wishes to test the hypothesis that his mean flow time of 18 days is not significantly different from the established value of 20 days. He chooses $\alpha = 5$ per cent. Set up the formal hypothesis and test it, using the t statistic and Table VII.

8. A manufacturer is experiencing some difficulty with quality of output and is attempting to determine the source of his difficulties. The foreman maintains that his four machines are not equally reliable, the superintendent accuses the operators of the machines on the theory that one simply cannot obtain qualified help these days, and the workers say that the raw material is sometimes faulty. To determine the major source of quality variation, the manufacturer rotates the four operators and has each operator use each machine, using raw material from each of two suppliers for one day, measuring the per cent of defective parts that result. The table below shows the result. Calculate variances attributable to each of the possible sources, as well as the total variance. What are your conclusions regarding the probable major sources of variation?

Daily Per Cent Defectives

		Machine			
Operator	Supplier	1	2	3	4
O_1	S_1	5.0	5.1	4.9	4.8
	S_2	5.4	5.2	5.1	5.0
O_2	S_1	4.2	4.8	4.5	5.0
	S_2	4.3	4.9	4.4	4.9
O_3	S_1	5.3	5.0	5.2	4.9
	S_2	5.3	5.2	5.3	5.2
O_4	S_1	4.8	5.0	5.1	5.2
	S_2	4.8	5.1	5.1	5.3

7

Models of Statistical Control

Any real process exhibits variation. In production processes, for example, variations occur in dimensions, in the per cent of parts that meet specifications, in chemical composition of materials, and in many other ways. In clerical operations we expect variation in the number of clerical errors produced. In shipping operations we would expect variation in transit time. In personnel we expect variation in absenteeism and in turnover. These and other situations are representative of what we expect. In most processes, a complex of causes of variation stemming from several sources contribute to what we would term the "normal" variation of the process. For example, in a production process, this complex of causes of variation stems mainly from differences in the performance of machines and workers, minor differences in work methods between workers, variations in materials, differences in atmospheric conditions of temperature and humidity, and others. The machine is not capable of perfection; it may contribute to variation because of "play" in its mechanical system and changes in atmospheric conditions may add to or subtract from this effect. Employees are subject to all sorts of pressures in their work and private life which may contribute to variations in work methods and performance. The materials used may vary in dimensions or composition and contribute to normal variation in the parameters of the output of the system. These normal variations are referred to by statisticians as stemming from random or "chance" causes. In general, we cannot do anything about these random variations without altering the system; that is, we may be able to design a new machine that is capable of greater normal precision, or perhaps control the temperature and humidity of the environments surrounding the production system. These kinds of changes would produce a new normal variation resulting from a new system of chance causes.

Statistical control theory is designed to separate relatively large causes of variation, due to some change in the normal pattern, from the variations due to chance causes. These larger individual sources of change are called "assignable" causes. For example, the common assignable causes in a production process are:

1. Differences among workers.
2. Differences among machines.
3. Differences among materials.
4. Differences due to interaction between any two or all three of these factors.

A comparable set of possible assignable causes could be developed for any process. For example, assignable causes for variation in absenteeism might be disease epidemics, changes in interpersonal relations at home or in an employee's work situation, and others.

When a process is in a state of control, variations that occur in the number of defects, the size of the dimension, chemical composition, turnover, absentee rates, etc., are due only to chance variations. With statistical control methods, we set up standards of expected normal variation due to chance causes so that when variations due to one or more of the assignable causes are superimposed, it becomes obvious that something basic has changed. It is then possible to investigate immediately to find the assignable cause of variation and correct it, before the nonstandard condition has gone on too long. These mechanisms of statistical control are called control charts.

Conceptual Framework for Control Charts

If we begin with a set of measurements taken in sequence, we may form the data into a distribution and compute the mean and standard deviation of the distribution. If we may assume that the data come from a normally distributed current distribution, recall from the discussion on pp. 149–151 that we may make precise statements about the probability of occurrence associated with measurements that are a given number of sigma units from the mean value. Specifically:

> 68.26% of the values normally fall within $\bar{x} \pm \sigma$
> 95.45% of the values normally fall within $\bar{x} \pm 2\sigma$
> 99.73% of the values normally fall within $\bar{x} \pm 3\sigma$

These percentage values represent the area under the normal curve between the given limits and, therefore, state the probability of occurrence for values that come from the current normal distribution. For example, the chances are 95.45 out of 100 that a measurement taken at random will fall within the 2σ limits and only 4.55 that it will fall outside these limits. These values, as well as decimal values of σ come from tables for the normal probability curve. Table I in Appendix D gives these values. The *natural tolerance* of a process is commonly taken as $\bar{x} \pm 3\sigma$.

The control chart represents established standards for the mean value and variation from the mean so that we may make more precise judgments about future measurements. If the future measurements fall within the stated probability limits in the proportions stated, it is reasonable to assume that the process is stable and generates measurements drawn from the original distribution on which the standards were based. If an abnormally large proportion of measurements fall outside these limits, it is reasonable to assume that something has changed; that is, there is an assignable cause of variation. (See our general discussion of control charts on pp. 151–153.)

What control limits? If we look at Figure 5 on p. 152, we note that the process generating the shaft diameter measurements appears to be in a state of statistical control by the criteria adopted there; that is, control limits of $\bar{x} \pm 3\sigma$. We could very well have adopted other standards for the control limits, however. For example, if the limits $\pm 2\sigma$ had been adopted, the next to the last point plotted would fall outside these limits. This would call for an investigation to determine if this "out of limits" observation did in fact signal that the process average measurement had shifted upward. If the investigation disclosed that the process had not changed, the investigation and the cost to make it would have been wasted. On the other hand, if the control limits had been $\pm 3\sigma$, as originally shown, and the process had in fact shifted, the observation in question would have been ignored and more scrap product would have been produced in the interim between the time of that sample and the time when a sample would fall outside the broader limits.

Thus we have a problem in setting control limits of balancing these two kinds of costs—the cost of investigation against the cost of losses when no investigation is made, but when in fact the process is out of control. In general terms, if the cost of investigation is high relative to possible losses if the process continues out of control, the limits should be relatively broad, perhaps $\pm 3\sigma$. Conversely, when the potential loss is high relative to the cost of investigation, we need more sensitive control limits, perhaps closer to $\pm 2\sigma$. All too commonly the balance of these costs are ignored in setting control limits, perhaps because the general practice in industrial quality control, where these techniques were originated, has been standardized at the limits of $\pm 3\sigma$. This may well have had the effect on management personnel of their not considering statistical controls in situations where possible losses were relatively great.

Kinds of control charts. Three basic kinds of control charts are commonly used for statistical control methods. They are: (1) control charts for variables when the parameter under control is some measurement of a variable, such as a dimension of a part or the time required for work or performance; (2) control charts for attributes when the parameter under control is a proportion or fraction, such as the fraction of defective parts in samples, the fraction of idle time for a machine, or the fraction of workers absent; and (3) control charts for the number of defects per unit, such as the number of blemishes on the surface of a unit area of glass.

Control Charts for Variables

Recall that the control chart shown as Figure 5 on page 152 was a "variables" chart since it was set up to control the outside diameter of the shaft, measured to the nearest 0.0001 inch. Note, however, that it was based on individual measurements (sample of one), and that the normality of the data had already been established. It is much more common, however, that control charts are constructed for averages of small samples rather than for individual measurements. One important reason for this is that *although a universe distribution may depart radically from normality, the sampling distribution of means of random samples will be approximately normal if the sample size is large enough.* This statement is of great importance, for it gives us some assurance that the probabilities associated with the control limits previously stated will apply. Figure 1 demonstrates that the deviation from normality can be fairly great, and yet, with the sampling distribution of the means of samples as small as $n = 5$, follow the normal distribution quite closely.

If we take samples of $n = 4$ from the shaft data distribution (Figure 4, p. 150) and determine an average for each sample, we have a new distribution. We regard each sample mean as an observation, and if we plot a frequency distribution of the sample means, it will have a mean and a standard deviation of its own. This distribution is called *a sampling distribution of means of $n = 4$* (the distributions of sample averages shown in Figure 1 are sampling distributions). To distinguish

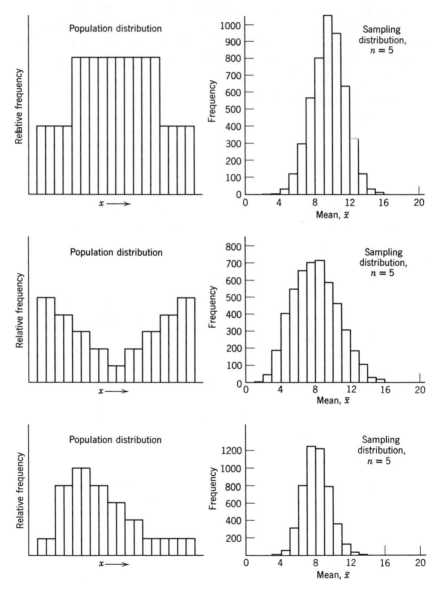

Figure 1. Normality of sampling distributions. The three distributions on the left are populations from which 5000 samples of $n = 5$ were drawn at random. The resulting sampling distributions are shown on the right.

the *statistics* from those of the distribution of individual observations, we use the notation $\bar{\bar{x}}$ for the grand mean of the sampling distribution and $\sigma_{\bar{x}}$ for the standard deviation of the sampling distribution. We expect that $\bar{x}$ and $\bar{\bar{x}}$ will be very nearly the same and that they will be equal in the limit as the number of subsamples increases. The standard deviation will be much smaller for the sampling distribution of means, however, since the variation is reduced by the averaging process within each sample. The resulting relationship between the two distributions for the shaft data is shown in Figure 2. Actually the relationship between σ and $\sigma_{\bar{x}}$ is given by:

$$\sigma_{\bar{x}} = \frac{\sigma}{\sqrt{n}}$$

where n is the size of the subsample.

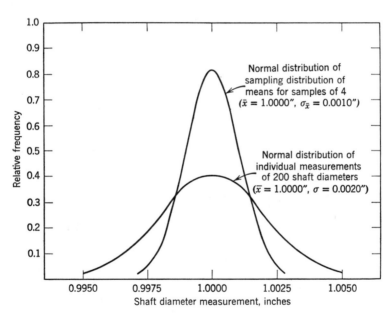

Figure 2. Relation between the distribution for individual observations and the sampling distribution of samples of 4 for the shaft-diameter data.

To construct a control chart for the means, we need first to establish standard values for $\bar{\bar{x}}$ and $\sigma_{\bar{x}}$. Means of subsequent samples are plotted again, and action would be called for if a sample mean should fall outside the control limits.

The reasons why sample means fall outside the control limits are, of course, related to the technology of the processes being controlled. For example, if parts were being produced on a lathe, they would tend to become oversized as the cutting tool became worn. Changes of this general nature tend to reflect themselves in the mean of the sampling distribution. If, however, the bearings of the lathe spindle had worn, it would be reflected by an increase in variability of the sampling distribution, and we would expect points to go outside of both control limits. The control chart can then show up changes in the mean of the distribution actually being generated, as well as

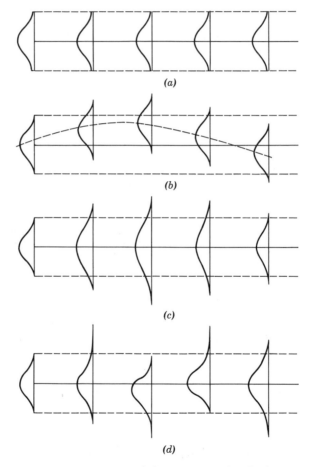

(a)

(b)

(c)

(d)

Figure 3. Changes in mean value, in variability, and in both measures in relation to specified process mean and control limits. (a) Process in control; (b) mean value out of control; (c) variability out of control; (d) both mean and variability out of control.

in the variability of the distribution, and combinations of changes in the mean and in the variability. Figure 3 summarizes these possible changes. Where changes in variability are particularly important, a special control chart on a measure of variability can be constructed, as we shall see.

$\overline{X}$ and R Control Charts

Setting standards for process average and control limits. Suppose we have taken a set of measurements on a process for which we wish to set up standards for the process average and for control limits, so that future measurements may be plotted on the control chart to determine if the process is remaining in a state of statistical control. How do we determine if the data that we propose to use for the determination of process average and control limits are themselves in control? It could well have happened that during the period over which the data were gathered, nonstandard conditions occurred resulting in a shift in either the process average, the standard deviation, or both. If the process average does shift, the resulting calculated estimate of the standard deviation will reflect this. To guard against this possibility, we may compute a separate σ for each of the small subsamples by the usual formula and average them. $\sigma_{\bar{x}}$ can then be calculated by,

$$\sigma_{\bar{x}} = \frac{\sum\limits_{i=1}^{N} \sigma_{x_i}}{N}$$

where N is the number of samples of size n, $\sigma_{\bar{x}}$ is the average standard deviation of the several subsamples, and σ_{x_i} is the calculated standard deviation for a subsample. The means of the subgroup samples can then be plotted on a control chart based on $\bar{x} \pm 3\sigma_{\bar{x}}$, to see whether or not changes in the process average have occurred during the period over which the preliminary data were gathered. The result is that the size of the subgroup should be relatively small and the period of time over which the preliminary data is gathered should be great enough so that changes in the process which occur between the sampling intervals may be recognized.

Practical procedures for $\overline{X}$ charts. As a practical matter, practitioners in the statistical control field use a short-cut method for calculating control limits, using the range as a measure of variability instead of the standard deviation. A table of factors is then used to calculate directly the upper and lower control limits. Table II in Appendix D gives these factors for the computation of the 3σ control limits commonly used. The procedure required is simply to determine the range for each of the subsamples and then to determine $\bar{R}$, the arithmetic mean of the ranges. The three sigma control limits are then calculated by:

$$\bar{x} \pm A_2 \bar{R}$$

where A_2 is a factor from Table II, Appendix D, depending on the size of the subsample.

Control charts on measures of variability. In developing the control chart for means, we used the sampling distribution of means and calculated control limits. We can as well take some measure of variability as the statistic, for example, the standard deviation or the range. For each subsample of size n, we can calculate a sample standard deviation. If we made a frequency distribution of these standard deviations, we would have a distribution which approximates the normal distribution. This distribution of sample standard deviations would itself have a mean and a standard deviation. We could, therefore, use this distribution of sample standard deviations to establish a control chart, which would tell us when the *variability* of the thing which is being controlled is greater or less than normal.

In statistical control work, the statistic chosen is usually the *range* instead of the standard deviation, because of the ease with which it can be computed for the successive samples. For each subsample the difference between the highest and lowest measurement is plotted on the control chart for ranges. The control chart for ranges represents the distribution of ranges for samples of size n. This distribution has an average $\bar{R}$ and a standard deviation σ_R. The $3\sigma_R$ limits have the same general significance as before. The probability that a sample range will fall outside the limits is only 0.27 per cent if it comes from the original universe. Therefore, when sample ranges do fall outside the control limits, we can presume that something has happened to cause greater than expected variability.

Practical procedures for constructing R charts. Just as with the $\bar{X}$ chart, a table of factors has been derived to simplify the calculation of the control limits for R charts. Using the data from Table II, Appendix D, for D_3 and D_4 listed for the appropriate sample size, the 3σ control limits for the R chart are:

$$UCL_R = D_4 \bar{R}$$

$$LCL_R = D_3 \bar{R}$$

An application of $\overline{X}$ and R charts. Suppose that we are involved in a study to determine the time required for an employee to perform a certain task. The job methods for the task have been studied carefully and standardized, and among other data gathered for the work measurement study are the 100 stopwatch readings of the actual time required for 100 cycles of the repetitive part of the task. Table I shows

TABLE I. 100 Stopwatch Readings for a Repetitive Task. Cycle Times, minutes

Sample Number

1	2	3	4	5	6	7	8	9	10
1.98	2.24	1.95	1.83	1.94	2.12	1.79	2.16	2.21	2.26
1.75	2.09	1.72	1.91	1.42	2.38	1.86	2.12	1.72	1.84
2.01	1.84	2.04	1.68	2.08	2.19	2.06	2.01	2.01	1.87
2.09	2.25	2.13	1.94	2.26	1.98	1.70	1.96	2.05	1.82
2.04	2.09	2.08	2.02	1.88	2.30	2.12	2.24	2.04	2.29

Sample Number

11	12	13	14	15	16	17	18	19	20
1.81	1.76	2.17	2.03	2.43	2.55	2.10	1.78	1.63	2.18
2.10	1.79	1.99	1.92	1.84	2.17	2.26	1.88	2.23	1.92
2.19	2.06	2.25	2.03	1.87	2.00	1.87	1.57	1.71	1.98
2.06	1.82	2.05	2.07	2.20	2.31	1.89	1.84	2.08	1.99
1.84	2.44	2.08	2.08	2.14	2.14	1.90	1.62	2.02	1.99

these 100 readings in minutes, divided into the subsamples of $n = 5$ by which they were gathered. Each sample of five readings were taken at random times in the order of the sample numbers as shown. Table II shows the sample means for each of the twenty samples, the grand mean of which is $\bar{x} = 2.01$ minutes. Table III shows the range in

TABLE II. Sample Means for Twenty Samples of Stopwatch Readings ($n = 5$, $\bar{x} = 2.01$) (Sequence of Samples is by Rows)

1.97	2.10	1.98	1.88	1.92	2.19	1.91	2.10	2.01	2.02
2.00	1.97	2.11	2.02	2.10	2.24	2.00	1.74	1.93	2.01

TABLE III. Ranges for Twenty Samples of Stopwatch Readings ($n = 5$). (Sequence of Samples is by Rows)
$\bar{R} = 0.43$ minutes

0.34	0.41	0.41	0.34	0.84	0.40	0.42	0.28	0.49	0.47
0.38	0.68	0.26	0.16	0.59	0.55	0.39	0.31	0.60	0.26

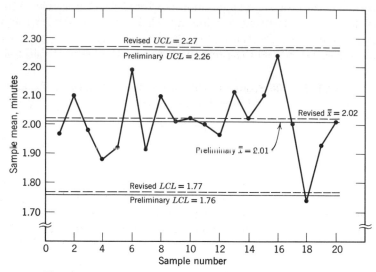

Figure 4. $\bar{X}$ Chart for the data of Table I showing preliminary control limits and revised limits after data for sample #18 has been eliminated. Values plotted from Table II.

minutes for each of the twenty samples, and the average of the ranges is calculated as $\bar{R} = 0.43$ minute. The preliminary control limits for the $\bar{X}$ chart are then calculated as follows:

$$UCL = \bar{x} + A_2\bar{R}$$
$$= 2.01 + 0.577 \times 0.43 = 2.26 \text{ minutes}$$
$$LCL = \bar{x} - A_2\bar{R}$$
$$= 2.01 - 0.577 \times 0.43 = 1.76 \text{ minutes}$$

These preliminary control limits and the preliminary center line for the grand mean are plotted in Figure 4 together with the twenty sample means shown in Table II. The chart seems to indicate that we have a stable data-generating system with the exception of sample No. 18 which falls below the lower control limit line. It is entirely possible, of course, that this sample mean represents one of the chance occurrences of a mean falling outside the three sigma limits. However, we also know that the chance that this will occur is only 0.27 per cent, and, therefore, an investigation to determine if a cause can be assigned is made immediately. The investigation reveals the fact that the operator had been following a nonstandard method at that time because of a material shortage. One small part had been left off the assembly to be added at a later time when the material was available. This resulted in a mean time value somewhat lower than expected. Since an assignable cause was determined, sample No. 18 was eliminated from the data and new revised grand mean and control limits computed as shown. The elimination of sample No. 18 also affects $\bar{R}$, which enters into the calculation of revised control limits.

The control limits for the R chart are determined in a similar way:

$$UCL_R = D_4\bar{R}$$
$$= 2.115 \times 0.43 = 0.91 \text{ minutes}$$

$$LCL_R = D_3\bar{R}$$
$$= 0 \times 0.43 = 0$$

Figure 5 shows the preliminary control limits for the R chart as calculated above. The center line for the R chart is the average of the sample

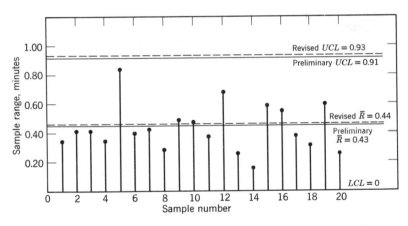

Figure 5. R Chart for data of Table I showing preliminary control limits and revised limits after data for sample #18 has been eliminated because of out-of-control mean. Values plotted from Table III.

ranges, $\bar{R} = 0.43$ minutes. The twenty sample ranges are shown in Figure 5, and we see that throughout the twenty samples variability within the samples remained stable within the control limits. Nevertheless, since sample No. 18 has been eliminated on the basis of the $\bar{X}$ chart, it must also be eliminated to calculate revised control limits for the R chart.

The revised center lines and control limits for the two charts of Figures 4 and 5 now represent reasonable standards for comparison of future samples. The basic calculations for determining the control limits and center lines for $\bar{X}$ and R charts remain the same, regardless of the variable being measured. In industrial product quality control, the measurement is commonly a dimension, in work measurement it is time, and in many cost control problems it would, of course, be dollars.

Control Charts for Attributes (p-Charts)

In control charts for attributes, the population is divided into two classifications: defective parts versus good parts in a production process, the number of errors versus the number of error-free calculations in a clerical operation, the number absent versus the number present for an absenteeism control, the proportion of idle time versus the proportion of working time in a work sampling study, etc. In each instance we may calculate the proportion or fraction that represents the parameter we wish to control. The probability distribution that is applicable in

TABLE IV. Record of the Number of Clerical Errors in Posting a Journal ($n = 200$). Calculation of $\bar{p}$ and Control Limits Shown Below

Sample Number	Number of Errors	Error Fraction	Sample Number	Number of Errors	Error Fraction
1	11	0.055	12	7	0.035
2	7	0.035	13	9	0.045
3	4	0.020	14	5	0.025
4	1	0.005	15	17	0.085
5	5	0.025	16	18	0.090
6	13	0.065	17	9	0.045
7	6	0.030	18	5	0.025
8	5	0.025	19	7	0.035
9	3	0.015	20	0	0.000
10	0	0.000	Total	131	
11	5	0.025			

$$\bar{p} = \frac{131}{20 \times 200} = 0.033$$

$$\sigma_p = \sqrt{\frac{0.033 \times 0.967}{200}} = 0.0126$$

$$3\sigma_p = 0.038$$

$$UCL = \bar{p} + 3\sigma_p = 0.033 + 0.038 = 0.071$$

$$LCL = \bar{p} - 3\sigma_p = 0.033 - 0.038 = 0$$

a situation such as those mentioned is the binomial distribution. The mean $\bar{p}$ and the standard deviation σ_p for the binomial distribution are given by:

$$\bar{p} = \frac{x}{n} = \frac{\text{number in classification}}{\text{total number observed}}$$

$$\sigma_p = \sqrt{\frac{\bar{p}(1 - \bar{p})}{n}}$$

where $n =$ the size of the subsample.

Following the general ideas for control charts which we have discussed, the control limits are normally set at the process average plus and minus three standard deviations; that is, they are set at $\bar{p} \pm 3\sigma_p$.

Let us take as an example of the application of a p-chart the control of the number of clerical errors that occur in the posting of a journal. Table IV shows a record of the number of errors that occurred in each of twenty samples of $n = 200$. For each sample the error fraction has been calculated as $p =$ number of errors/200. The average error fraction $\bar{p}$ is calculated by totaling the errors that occurred in the combined set of twenty samples divided by the total number of obser-

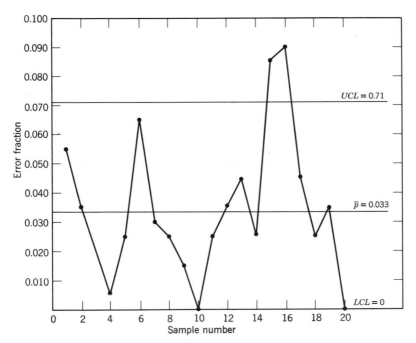

Figure 6. p-Chart for clerical errors in posting a journal. ($\bar{p}$ and control limits are preliminary; data and calculations from Table IV.)

vations, and is shown below Table IV. Also, below Table IV are shown the calculation of σ_p and the control limits adopted. Figure 6 shows the resulting control chart with the twenty sample points plotted. Note that samples 15 and 16 fall above the upper control limit. In this instance, investigation showed that at the time of those two samples construction work in the office was going on to remodel part of the area. Apparently the confusion and noise had affected the accuracy of the employee doing the posting, and this was regarded as an assignable cause of variation. In establishing the process average and the control limits, we would eliminate these two samples from our data to calculate a revised process average and control limits, just as we did with the data for Figures 4 and 5.

p-Charts for variable sample size. In the example of the control of clerical errors just shown, the sample size was constant. It often happens, however, that sample sizes vary from one sample to the

TABLE V. Record of the Number of Defective Parts in a Production Process, Variable Sample Size. Calculation of Variable Control Limits is Shown

Sample Number	Sample Size	Number of Defective Parts	Fraction Defective	$3\sigma_p =$ $\dfrac{3\sqrt{0.099 \times 0.901}}{\sqrt{n}}$	$UCL =$ $\bar{p} + 3\sigma_p$	$LCL =$ $\bar{p} - 3\sigma_p$
1	95	8	0.084	0.092	0.191	0.007
2	90	6	0.067	0.094	0.193	0.005
3	100	9	0.090	0.089	0.188	0.010
4	105	10	0.095	0.087	0.186	0.012
5	105	8	0.076	0.087	0.186	0.012
6	120	7	0.058	0.082	0.181	0.017
7	115	14	0.122	0.083	0.182	0.016
8	80	7	0.088	0.100	0.199	0
9	90	9	0.100	0.094	0.193	0.005
10	80	17	0.213	0.100	0.199	0
11	90	12	0.133	0.094	0.193	0.005
12	100	10	0.100	0.089	0.188	0.010
13	100	8	0.080	0.089	0.188	0.010
14	110	10	0.091	0.085	0.184	0.014
15	130	6	0.046	0.079	0.178	0.020
16	100	8	0.080	0.089	0.188	0.010
17	110	9	0.082	0.085	0.184	0.014
18	110	10	0.091	0.085	0.184	0.014
19	90	20	0.222	0.094	0.193	0.005
20	80	10	0.125	0.100	0.199	0
Totals	2000	198				

$$\bar{p} = \frac{198}{2000} = 0.0990$$

next. This is particularly true when 100 per cent inspection is being used and output volume varies from day to day. If the sample size varies only slightly, control limits may be computed, based on the average sample size. When there is wide variation in sample size, we may compute new control limits for each sample, or convert the deviations from process average into standard deviation units. Control charts based on the latter method are called stabilized p-charts.

Table V shows a record of twenty samples of the number of defective parts in a production process. Note that the sample size varies. In the last three columns of Table V we have calculated the data necessary for variable control limits. The value of $3\sigma_p$ is calculated for each sample. This may be done the most simply by computing the value of $3\sqrt{0.099 \times 0.901} = 0.894$, and dividing by $\sqrt{n}$ for each sample. Figure 7 shows the resulting control chart with the variable control limits and the sample points plotted.

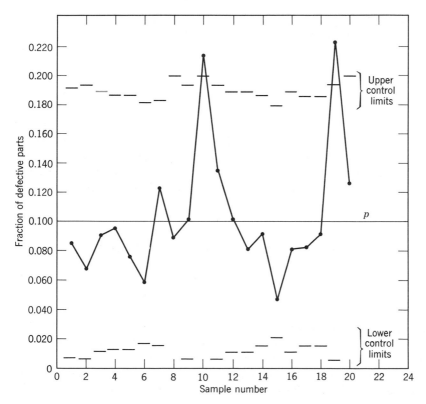

Figure 7. p-Chart with variable control limits. Data and calculations from Table V.

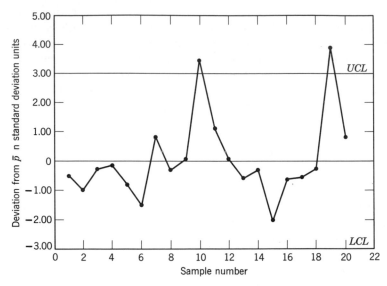

Figure 8. Stabilized p-chart. Sample points show deviation in standard deviation units from $\bar{p}$. Data and calculations are in Table VI.

A stabilized p-chart for the same data is shown in Figure 8, with supporting calculations shown in Table VI. In Table VI we have calculated σ_p for each of the samples, and determined the variation of p from $\bar{p}$, $(p - \bar{p})$, for each sample. In the last column, then, we determine the number of standard deviation units of variation from $\bar{p}$ for each sample by dividing the deviation by σ_p. The control chart plotted in Figure 8 shows the control limits at plus and minus three standard deviation units from $\bar{p}$.

Control Charts for Defects per Unit (c-Charts)

As we mentioned previously, sometimes the parameter to be controlled cannot be expressed as a simple proportion such as was true with p-charts. In weaving, for example, the number of defects per 10 square yards of material might be the parameter to be controlled. In such instances, each defect is in itself minor, but a large number of defects per unit might be objectionable. The probability distribution commonly applicable in this situation is the Poisson distribution. In the Poisson distribution the standard deviation σ_c is equal to the square

TABLE VI.   Calculation of Sample Points for a Stabilized p-Chart. Data for Sample Sizes and Defectives Are from Table V

Sample Number	Sample Size	Number of Defective Parts	Fraction Defective	$\sigma_p = \dfrac{\sqrt{0.099 \times 0.901}}{\sqrt{n}}$	$p - \bar{p}$	$\dfrac{p - \bar{p}}{\sigma_p}$
1	95	8	0.084	0.0306	−0.015	−0.49
2	90	6	0.067	0.0313	−0.032	−1.02
3	100	9	0.090	0.0296	−0.009	−0.30
4	105	10	0.095	0.0290	−0.004	−0.14
5	105	8	0.076	0.0290	−0.023	−0.79
6	120	7	0.058	0.0273	−0.041	−1.50
7	115	14	0.122	0.0276	+0.023	+0.83
8	80	7	0.088	0.0333	−0.011	−0.33
9	90	9	0.100	0.0313	+0.001	+0.03
10	80	17	0.213	0.0333	+0.114	+3.43
11	90	12	0.133	0.0313	+0.034	+1.09
12	100	10	0.100	0.0296	+0.001	+0.03
13	100	8	0.080	0.0296	−0.019	−0.64
14	110	10	0.091	0.0283	−0.008	−0.28
15	130	6	0.046	0.0263	−0.053	−2.02
16	100	8	0.080	0.0296	−0.019	−0.64
17	110	9	0.082	0.0283	−0.017	−0.60
18	110	10	0.091	0.0283	−0.008	−0.28
19	90	20	0.222	0.0313	+0.123	+3.93
20	80	10	0.125	0.0333	+0.026	+0.78
Totals	2000	198				

$$\bar{p} = \frac{198}{2000} = 0.099$$

root of the mean value $\bar{c}$. The result is that the calculation of control limits is extremely simple.

Let us take as an example the data in Table VII which shows a record of the number of paint defects per unit for metal desk equipment painted by a dipping process. The defects are all types of paint defects, such as dimples and blemishes. The calculation of $\bar{c}$, σ_c, and the control limits are shown below Table VII. The resulting c-chart is shown in Figure 9. If points were to have fallen outside the control limits, an investigation to determine if an assignable cause exists would proceed as before. Assignable causes in this example might be paint viscosity, mixture, drying temperatures, etc. Preliminary and revised control limits and mean value would be determined as before. Also, c-charts with varying control limits due to varying sample size may be constructed as was true for p-charts.

TABLE VII. Record of the Number of Paint Defects per Unit for Metal Desk Equipment Painted by Dipping

Item Number	Number of Defects per Unit	Item Number	Number of Defects per Unit
1	19	12	10
2	16	13	22
3	23	14	5
4	11	15	23
5	15	16	22
6	12	17	14
7	17	18	6
8	11	19	13
9	20	20	6
10	15	Total	293
11	13		

$$\bar{c} = \frac{293}{20} = 14.65 \text{ defects per unit}$$

$$\sigma_c = \sqrt{\bar{c}} = \sqrt{14.65} = 3.83$$

$$UCL = \bar{c} + 3\sigma_c = 14.65 + 3 \times 3.83 = 26.14$$

$$LCL = \bar{c} - 3\sigma_c = 14.65 - 3 \times 3.83 = 3.16$$

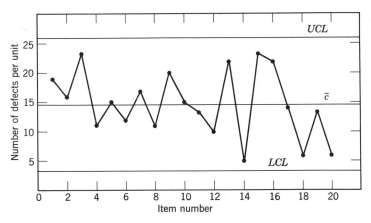

Figure 9. c-Chart for paint defects per unit. Data and calculations for control limits in Table VII.

Summary

The concept of statistical control represents the epitome of management control by the exception principle. Probability controls are set so that random variations, owing entirely to uncontrollable chance causes, are ignored. When a deviation that is larger than expected occurs, however, probability controls signal this fact immediately and call into play a corrective procedure. The result is that managerial personnel do not waste their time on the random variations, but their attention is called immediately when the probability is high that a real change in the process being controlled has occurred.

As we have pointed out, the selection of a control plan should be set so that there is a balance between the cost of investigation and the cost of letting a process that is out of control continue. The three factors which influence these costs and which may be set by the designer of the control system are the control limits, the sample size, and the interval between samples. Although it is not common to set the levels of these three factors by a careful investigation, models have been developed which have this objective (1).

Finally, although the basic ideas and procedures for statistical control have been developed in a framework for industrial quality control, we should recognize that the principles are broadly applicable to the control of any parameter which can be measured and sampled. Thus, whereas initial applications were in the field of statistical quality control, it is becoming much more common to find the use of these methods in work measurement, cost control, control of labor turnover, absenteeism, and so on.

REFERENCES

1. Bowman, E. H., and R. B. Fetter, *Analysis for Production Management,* Richard D. Irwin, Homewood, Ill., revised edition, 1961.
2. Duncan, A. J., *Quality Control and Industrial Statistics,* Richard D. Irwin, Homewood, Ill., 1955.
3. Grant, E. L., *Statistical Quality Control,* McGraw-Hill Book Company, New York, 2nd ed., 1952.
4. Shewhart, W. A., *Economic Control of Quality of Manufactured Product,* D. Van Nostrand Co., Princeton, N. J., 1931.
5. Tippett, L. H. C., *Technological Applications of Statistics,* John Wiley and Sons, New York, 1950.
6. Vance, L. L., and J. Neter, *Statistical Sampling for Auditors and Accountants,* John Wiley and Sons, New York, 1956.

REVIEW QUESTIONS

1. What are assignable causes and chance causes in a process?

2. What are the common assignable causes in production processes?

3. What is the probability that a measurement drawn from a normal distribution will fall within the 3σ limits?

4. What is the probability that a measurement drawn from some other distribution than normal will fall within the 3σ limits?

5. When the potential loss is high relative to the cost of investigation, should control limits be relatively broad, perhaps $\pm3\sigma$?

6. Which would be the more sensitive control limits, $\pm3\sigma$ or $\pm2\sigma$?

7. Why are variables control charts normally constructed for small samples rather than for individual measurements?

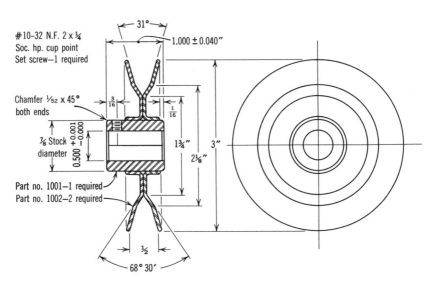

Figure 10. Drawing of a V-belt pulley.

Tolerance on wobble ±0.010 from center. Tolerance on concentricity ±0.010 from center. Fractional tolerances $\pm\frac{1}{64}$. Angular tolerances $\pm\frac{1}{2}°$. Finish: Cadmium plated all over 0.0003 ± 0.0001. *Notes:* 1. Press fit flanges to hub. 2. Spotweld flanges to hub, two spots each side. 3. Spotweld flanges together—four spots. 4. Flanges material: SAE #1010 deep-drawn steel. 5. Hub material: SAE #X1112 cold-finished screw stock.

8. What is the relationship between $\sigma_{\bar{x}}$, the standard deviation of the sampling distribution, and σ, the standard deviation of the population distribution?

9. Outline the procedures required to construct $\bar{X}$ and R control charts.

10. Can $\bar{X}$ and R charts be constructed for measures of variability?

11. What statistical distribution is appropriate for control charts for attributes (p-charts)?

12. Could a control chart be constructed that allowed for continuous variation of control limits, as in the situation where a tool might wear as a process progressed?

13. What is the appropriate statistical distribution for control charts for defects per unit (c-charts)?

14. What is the area of application of c-charts?

15. Discuss the concept of statistical control in relation to the general principle of "Management Control by the Exception Principle."

PROBLEMS

1. Figure 10 shows a drawing of a 3-inch V-belt pulley which is made up of two identical flanges, which are formed by presses, a hub which is produced on turret lathes, and a set screw which is purchased. The flanges are spot welded to the hub, and the two flanges are spot welded together, as specified. Finally, the entire pulley is cadmium plated. Trouble has been experienced in holding the tolerance specified for the length of the hub, $1.00'' \pm 0.040''$. Ten samples of four pulleys each yield the following data:

Sample No.	Sample Average $\bar{X}$	Sample Range R
1	1.007	0.013
2	1.008	0.022
3	0.991	0.018
4	0.993	0.014
5	0.998	0.019
6	1.008	0.026
7	0.996	0.024
8	0.995	0.011
9	0.999	0.021
10	0.995	0.024
Totals	9.990	0.192

a. Determine the natural tolerance of the process generating the hub length. Is the present turret lathe process capable of meeting the specified tolerance?

b. Assuming that toolware is the only predictable variable in the above process, at what average hub length should the process be centered when-

ever a tool change or adjustment is made? Sketch the distribution relationships and explain.

c. Determine preliminary control limits, based on data given, for $\bar{X}$ and
R charts to control the cutoff operation of the turret lathe, assuming samples
of $n = 4$.

d. Under normal conditions, the width of the cutoff tool wears at the
rate of 0.001 inch per hour of use. Determine the appropriate control limits
and trend of average hub length for the samples of $n = 4$ which reflect the
known rate of tool wear. Plot the results. How often should the tool be
sharpened and reset if the process is otherwise in control?

e. How will the tool wear affect the control limits and process average
for the R chart?

2. When assembling the pulleys by pressing the flanges on the hubs by
an arbor press, the flanges tend to split excessively in instances when the hub
is relatively large and the flange hole relatively small, and when the flange
material is relatively hard, even though all these factors are within their
stated tolerances. In addition, if the press fit between hub and flange is
loose, the spot-welding operation tends to pull the flanges off the axis of
rotation so that the pulley may be rejected because of excessive "wobble."
Inspection of daily production results in rejection of pulleys for these reasons.
The following is a record of 10 days' production and rejections. Construct
a p-chart with variable control limits. Is the process in control? Construct a
stabilized p-chart for the same data. Which distribution is applicable in
this case?

Day	Amount Produced	No. of Defectives
1	5,205	85
2	6,100	120
3	5,725	105
4	5,345	150
5	4,250	75
6	3,975	50
7	4,345	95
8	5,270	120
9	6,075	155
10	7,005	110
Totals	53,295	1,065

3. The plating process for the pulleys can produce defective parts either
because of too thick or too thin a plating, or because of defective appearance,
which shows up in surface defects. We shall assume that the plating thickness
is controlled by p-chart. We wish to establish control over surface defects by
means of a c-chart. Periodic samples of ten plated pulleys are drawn from
the output of the process, are inspected, and the number of surface defects
are counted. A record of ten samples follows; determine the preliminary
control limits for a c-chart, construct the chart, and plot the ten samples.
Is the process in control?

Sample No.	No. of Defects per sample
1	5
2	7
3	2
4	10
5	7
6	11
7	13
8	10
9	4
10	7
Total	76

8

Acceptance Sampling

Acceptance sampling is another statistical control technique which has proved to be of considerable value. The statistical control chart, which we discussed in Chapter 7, has the objective of controlling the process itself. The probability controls signal when adjustments and corrections to the process must be made, so that the condition does not continue for a considerable period of time. But suppose, however, that the parts already exist, or in a clerical operation, that the journals have already been posted. Is the lot of parts a good lot? Are the data in the journals accurate? We could re-examine each part, or recheck each entry and calculation to determine the answer; however, this inspection effort or audit may be expensive. On the other hand, if we accept the lot of parts without further inspection, or if we assume that the journal entries are correct, we may be faced with other kinds of costs. For example, if the parts were to be used in a subsequent production process, the occurrence of defective items could cause increased assembly costs and reworking. If the defective parts go out to customers, the costs of rehandling and replacement must be faced, to say nothing of a possible loss of customer good will. If the accounting data about which we spoke is assumed to be correct, but in fact contains errors, subsequent costly wrong decisions may be made on the basis of the information in the records. For example, an incorrect inventory balance record could lead to a decision not to reorder the material just yet, resulting in a material shortage. The material shortage in turn could cause a bottleneck in production, resulting in delays, idle labor, and possibly lost orders. In general then, we are faced with two kinds of costs which we wish to balance in proportion to the relative risks involved.

In the simplest case of acceptance sampling, we draw a random sample of size n from the total lot N, and decide whether or not to accept the entire lot based on the sample. If the sample signals a decision to reject the lot, it may then either be subject to 100 per cent inspection, sorting out bad parts, or finding errors in the entries of accounting records, as the case may be. Just as with the models of statistical control, acceptance-sampling techniques were developed in the field of industrial quality control. Nevertheless, we should generalize on the concepts presented because they are applicable to the acceptance or rejection of any kind of data, whether it be physical measurements of parts (such as in industrial quality control) or the occurrence of errors in an accounting system. In general, acceptance sampling is appropriate when:

1. Possible losses by passing defective items, or data, are not great, and the cost to inspect or audit is relatively high. In the limiting situation, this can mean no inspection at all.

2. Inspection requires the destruction of the product; for example, when it is necessary to determine the strength of parts by pulling them apart. Inferring the acceptability of an entire lot from a sample is necessary in these instances.

3. Further handling of any kind is likely to induce defects or errors; or when mental or physical fatigue is an important factor in the inspection or auditing process. In either instance, a sampling plan may actually pass fewer defective items than would 100 per cent inspection, and it also costs less.

Just as with statistical control, parallel acceptance sampling procedures are available for both the situation where we simply classify items as good or bad (sampling by attributes) and where we make actual measurements of some kind that indicate how good or bad the item is (sampling by variables).

ACCEPTANCE SAMPLING BY ATTRIBUTES

As with statistical control procedures, we shall consider here situations where the items being sampled may be classified into two groups, either acceptable or defective. In all instances, regardless of what we may be dealing with, some standard of acceptability has been established; and given those standards, the classification of acceptable and defective is made. If we are dealing with a manufactured part, a dimension may have a standard of acceptance of 1.000 ± 0.001 inches. If the part dimension falls within these tolerance limits, it is classified as acceptable. If it falls outside these tolerance limits, it is classified as defective. If we are dealing with accounting data, for example, the entries are either correct or in error. In any case, we wish to develop procedures whereby when we sample from the items of data available (the lot) the probability of acceptance by the sampling plan will be high, if in fact the entire lot is acceptable. On the contrary, if in fact the lot from which we sample is poor, we want the probability of acceptance to be relatively low. The curve of the actual quality of the lot plotted against the

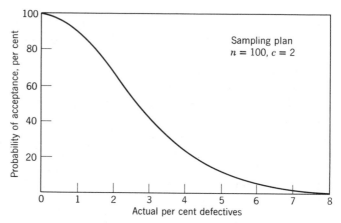

Figure 1. Operating characteristic (OC) curve for a sampling plan with $n = 100$ and $c = 2$. Plotted from data in Table I.

probability of acceptance by the sampling plan is called the operating characteristic curve.

Operating Characteristic (OC) Curves

The OC curve for a particular combination of sample size n and acceptance number c shows how well the plan discriminates between good and bad lots. The acceptance number c indicates the number of defectives in the sample if the entire lot from which the sample was drawn is to be accepted. Figure 1 is an OC curve for a sampling plan with a sample size $n = 100$ and acceptance number $c = 2$. In this plan, if 0, 1, or 2 defectives were found in the sample of $n = 100$, the lot would be considered acceptable. If more than two defectives were found, the lot would be rejected. For the plan, the *OC* curve of which is shown in Figure 1, if the actual lot quality were 1 per cent defectives, samples of $n = 100$ would accept the lot as satisfactory about 91.5 per cent of the time and reject it about 8.5 per cent of the time. In other words, the probability of finding 0, 1, or 2 defectives in random samples from such a lot is 91.5 per cent, whereas the probability of finding more than 2 defectives is only 8.5 per cent. Note, however, that if the actual quality of the lot were somewhat worse than 1 per cent defective—5 per cent—the probability of accepting these lots falls drastically to about 13 per cent. This is the situation that we would like to have in a sampling plan. If the

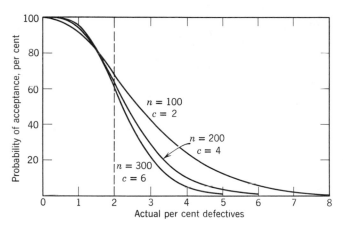

Figure 2. *OC* curves for different sample sizes with acceptance numbers in proportion to sample size.

actual quality is good, we want there to be a high probability of acceptance, but if the actual quality is poor, we want the probability of acceptance to be low. The *OC* curve, then, shows how well a given plan discriminates between good and poor lots.

The discriminating power of a sampling plan depends heavily on the size of the sample, as we might expect. Figure 2 shows the *OC* curves for sample sizes of 100, 200, and 300, with the acceptance number remaining in proportion to sample size. Note that the *OC* curve becomes somewhat steeper as the sample size goes up. If we compare the discrimination power of the three plans represented in Figure 2, we see that all three would accept lots of about 1.4 per cent defectives about 83 per cent of the time (the approximate crossover points of the three curves). If actual quality falls to 5.0 per cent defectives, however, the plan with $n = 100$ accepts lots about 13 per cent of the time, $n = 200$ about 3.0 per cent of the time, and $n = 300$ less than 1 per cent of the time. The plans with large sample sizes are definitely more effective.

What happens to the OC curve if only the acceptance number changes? Figure 3 shows OC curves for a sample of $n = 100$ and acceptance numbers of $c = 0, 1, 2,$ and 3. Note that the four curves

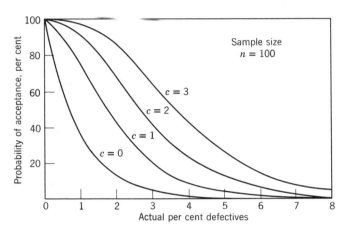

Figure 3. OC curves with different acceptance numbers for a sample size of $n = 100$.

remain approximately parallel in their middle ranges so that the effect is mainly to change the level of the OC curve so that lower acceptance numbers make the plan "tighter," that is, they hold outgoing quality to lower per cents defective. This is a generalization, of course, since there is some interaction between sample size and acceptance number in determining the discriminating power as well.

A plan that discriminates perfectly between good and bad lots would have an OC curve that was vertical, that is, it would follow the dashed line of Figure 2. For all lots having per cent defectives to the left of the dashed line, the probability of acceptance is 100 per cent. For all lots having per cent defectives to the right of the line, the probability of acceptance is zero. Unfortunately, the only plan that would achieve this discrimination is one requiring 100 per cent inspection. Therefore, the justification of acceptance sampling turns on a balance between inspection costs and the probable cost of passing defectives, as we have already noted. By making sampling plans more discriminating (increasing sample sizes) or tighter (de-

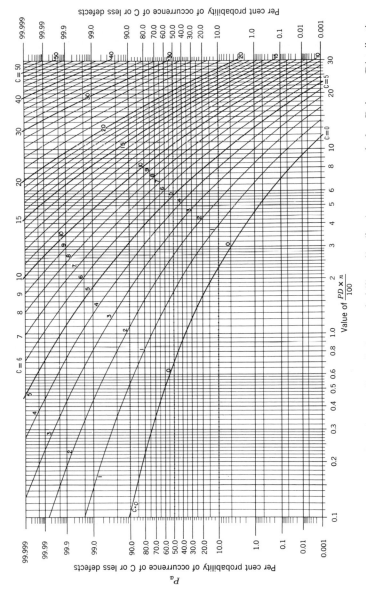

Figure 4. The Thorndike chart. Cumulative probability distribution curves of the Poisson Distribution. Adapted from H. F. Dodge and H. G. Romig, *Sampling Inspection Tables*, John Wiley and Sons, New York, 2nd ed., 1959.

creasing acceptance numbers), we can approach any desired level of outgoing quality that we please, but at increasing inspection costs. This increased inspection effort would result in lower probable costs of passing defective parts, and at some point the combination of these incremental costs is a minimum. This minimum point defines the most economical sampling plan for a given situation. Stated simply, then, to justify a 100 per cent sample, the probable losses due to passing of defectives would have to be large in relation to inspection costs. On the other hand, to justify no inspection at all, inspection costs would have to be very large in relation to probable losses due to passing defective parts or data. The most usual situation is between these extremes, where there exists a risk of not accepting lots which are actually good and a risk of accepting lots when actually they are bad. The first risk is called the producer's risk and the second, the consumer's risk. We shall discuss the definition of these risks more precisely in a moment.

Determining OC curves. The *OC* curve can be constructed easily from the normal or Poisson distributions. If lots are large, perhaps greater than ten times the size of the sample, probabilities for the *OC* curve are given by the binomial distribution. If samples are also large, however, the normal or Poisson distributions may be used. Specifically, the rules of thumb are as follows:

1. If $p'n > 5$, the probabilities can be determined from the normal distribution whose mean is p' and standard deviation $\sqrt{p'(1 - p')/n}$.
2. If $p'n < 5$, the Poisson distribution gives better results.

**TABLE I.   Calculation of Values of P_a, Probability of Acceptance
in Per Cent, from the Thorndike Chart for the Sampling
Plan $n = 100$, $c = 2$; OC Curve Shown in Figure 1**

PD, Actual Per Cent Defectives	$\dfrac{PD \times n}{100}$	Probability of Two or Less Defectives, in Per Cent = $100 \times$ Value from Figure 4 = P_a
0	0	100.0
1	1.0	91.5
2	2.0	68.0
3	3.0	42.0
4	4.0	24.0
5	5.0	13.0
6	6.0	6.0
7	7.0	3.0
8	8.0	1.5

In the most usual situation, the lot per cent defective is small and the lots themselves relatively large, so that the Poisson distribution is used to calculate the values for the probability of acceptance of the OC curve. For each value of the lot per cent defective, we may calculate $(PD \times n)/100$ and determine the probability of acceptance from the curves of the Thorndike chart shown in Figure 4. These curves are the cumulative probability curves of the Poisson distribution and give the probability of occurrence of c or less defectives in a sample of n selected from an infinite universe in which the per cent defective is PD. Thus these curves serve as a generalized set of OC curves for single sampling plans, when the Poisson distribution is applicable. Table I shows the calculation of eight points for the OC curve of Figure 1, using the Thorndike chart.

Producer's and Consumer's Risks

Let us now return to the definition of producer's and consumer's risks by referring to a typical OC curve. Figure 5 shows graphically the following four definitions:

AQL = Acceptable quality level. Good quality for which we wish to have a high probability of acceptance.

α = Producer's risk. The probability that lots of the quality level AQL will *not* be accepted. Usually $\alpha = 5$ per cent.

$LTPD$ = Lot tolerance per cent defective. The dividing line selected between good and bad lots. Lots at this level of quality are regarded as poor quality, and we wish to have a low probability for their acceptance.

β = Consumer's risk. The probability that lots of the quality level $LTPD$ will be accepted. Usually $\beta = 10$ per cent.

When we set levels for each of these four values we are determining two critical points on the OC curve which we desire, points a and b in Figure 5.

Specification of Single Sampling Plans

Although the specification of the four values AQL, α, $LTPD$, and β do specify the characteristics of the OC curve which is desired, the question we must now answer is, "What sample size n and acceptance number c will produce an OC curve approximating the one specified?"

Use of the Thorndike chart. Let us take as an example the following specifications: $AQL = 2$ per cent, $LTPD = 8$ per cent, $\alpha = 5$

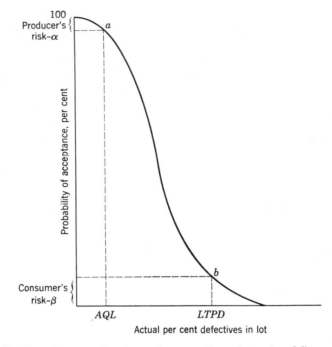

Figure 5. Complete specifications of a sampling plan. An *OC* curve which goes through the points *a* and *b* meets the requirements stated by α and *AQL*, and β and *LTPD*, thus specifying a sampling plan with a given *n* and *c*. (*AQL* = acceptance quality level; *LTPD* = lot tolerance per cent defectives.)

per cent, and β = 10 per cent. The values for the horizontal scale in the Thorndike chart are $PD \times n/100$, and we are interested in values at the points where the probability of acceptance P_a is 95 per cent (1 − α, and for β, 10 per cent). Therefore, let us tabulate the values of $PD \times n/100$ at these two points for each value of *c*. These values are listed in Table II. For example, if we locate the horizontal line β = 10 per cent and find its intersection with *c* = 0, we may read $PD \times n/100 = 2.30$. Similarly, we may check the values when *c* = 1, 2, etc., and for the 95 per cent line as well. The last column of Table II is then simply the ratio column 3:column 2 for each value of *c*. Now, of course, the value of *PD* that we have in mind for the 95 per cent level is our specification value of *AQL* = 2 per cent, and similarly at the 10 per cent level, our value of *LTPD* = 8 per cent. Since column 4 is the ratio of these two values, it is in fact the ratio of *LTPD*:*AQL* for the plan we seek. Our ratio is: $LTPD:AQL = \frac{8}{2} = 4$. Our value of 4 falls between 4.06 at *c* = 4 and

**TABLE II. Table for Determining Single Sampling Plans
with Specified *AQL* and *LTPD* and with α and β Near
5 Per Cent and 10 Per Cent Respectively***

(1) Accept- ance Number	(2) Value of $\dfrac{PD \times n}{100}$ at $P_a = 95\%$, from Figure 4	(3) Value of $\dfrac{PD \times n}{100}$ at $P_a = 10\%$, from Figure 4	(4) Ratio, Col. 3:Col. 2 $= LTPD/AQL$
0	0.051	2.30	45.10
1	0.355	3.89	10.96
2	0.818	5.32	6.50
3	1.366	6.68	4.89
4	1.970	7.99	4.06
5	2.613	9.28	3.55
6	3.285	10.53	3.21
7	3.981	11.77	2.96
8	4.695	12.99	2.77
9	5.425	14.21	2.62
10	6.169	15.41	2.50
11	6.924	16.60	2.40
12	7.690	17.78	2.31
13	8.464	18.96	2.24
14	9.246	20.13	2.18
15	10.04	21.29	2.12

* Adapted from F. E. Grubbs, "On Designing Single Sampling Inspection
Plans," *Annals of Mathematical Statistics*, Vol. XX, p. 256.

3.55 at $c = 5$. We must now decide whether to hold α and let β float,
or vice versa. If, for example, we set $c = 4$ and hold α at 5 per cent,
then $PD \times n/100 = AQL \times n/100 = 1.970$. We can then solve for
the sample size:

$$n = \frac{1.970 \times 100}{2} = 99$$

Our sampling plan is then $n = 99$, $c = 4$, based on the specifications
$AQL = 2$ per cent, $\alpha = 5$ per cent, and $LTPD = 8$ per cent (see
Table III). But what has happened to the value of β? We may
check easily by reference to the Thorndike chart. Since we have
now fixed $n = 99$ and $c = 4$, $LTPD \times n/100 = 8 \times 99/100 = 7.92$.
At this value of $PD \times n/100$ for $c = 4$, we read the actual value of
$\beta = 10.5$ per cent. Table IV shows the values of n, c, α and β for
each of the four plans that meet the basic requirements specified.

TABLE III. Sampling Plans for c = 4 and c = 5 When α Is Fixed and β Is Allowed to Float and When β Is Fixed, Allowing α to Float.
AQL = 2 Per Cent, LTPD = 8 Per Cent

c Fixed at 4		c Fixed at 5	
α Fixed at 5%, β Floats	β Fixed at 10%, α Floats	α Fixed at 5%, β Floats	β Fixed at 10%, α Floats
$n = \dfrac{1.970 \times 100}{2}$	$n = \dfrac{7.99 \times 100}{8}$	$n = \dfrac{2.613 \times 100}{2}$	$n = \dfrac{9.28 \times 100}{8}$
= 99	= 100	= 131	= 116

We see that plan 1 increases very slightly the probability of accepting lots of 8 per cent quality, while holding the other specifications. Plan 2 increases slightly the probability of rejecting lots of good quality; that is, $AQL = 2$ per cent while holding the ·specification

TABLE IV. Actual α's and β's for the Four Plans Derived.
AQL = 2 Per Cent, LTPD = 8 Per Cent

Plan Number	Sample Size, n	Acceptance Number, c	α Per Cent	β Per Cent
1	99	4	5	10.5
2	100	4	5.4	10
3	131	5	5	5
4	116	5	3	10

for $β$. Plan 3 holds $α$ at 5 per cent, but reduces the probability of accepting bad lots to the value of 5 per cent. Plan 4 decreases the probability of rejecting good lots while holding $β = 10$ per cent. In summary, plans 1 and 2 come the closest to meeting the original specifications, and the choice between them depends on which emphasis is desired.

Other values of α and β. Table II was constructed for the usual values of $α$ and $β$, but it is easy to see that a comparable table could be constructed from the Thorndike chart for any values of $α$ and $β$ that we may desire, so that the methods described are general.

Plans with specified LTPD, β, and minimum total inspection for a given average PD. Tables have been developed that give sampling plans with minimum total inspection for specified values of

TABLE V. Single Sampling Table* for Lot Tolerance Per Cent Defective (LTPD) = 5.0%

Lot Size	Process Average 0 to 0.05%			Process Average 0.06 to 0.50%			Process Average 0.51 to 1.00%			Process Average 1.01 to 1.50%			Process Average 1.51 to 2.00%			Process Average 2.01 to 2.50%		
	n	c	AOQL %	n	c	AOQL %	n	c	AOQL %	n	c	AOQL %	n	c	AOQL %	n	c	AOQL %
1–30	All	0	0	All	0	0	All	0	0	All	0	0	All	0	0	All	0	0
31–50	30	0	0.49	30	0	0.49	30	0	0.49	30	0	0.49	30	0	0.49	30	0	0.49
51–100	37	0	0.63	37	0	0.63	37	0	0.63	37	0	0.63	37	0	0.63	37	0	0.63
101–200	40	0	0.74	40	0	0.74	40	0	0.74	40	0	0.74	40	0	0.74	40	0	0.74
201–300	43	0	0.74	43	0	0.74	70	1	0.92	70	1	0.92	95	2	0.99	95	2	0.99
301–400	44	0	0.74	44	0	0.74	70	1	0.99	100	2	1.0	120	3	1.1	145	4	1.1
401–500	45	0	0.75	75	1	0.95	100	2	1.1	100	2	1.1	125	3	1.2	150	4	1.2
501–600	45	0	0.76	75	1	0.98	100	2	1.1	125	3	1.2	150	4	1.3	175	5	1.3
601–800	45	0	0.77	75	1	1.0	100	2	1.2	130	3	1.2	175	5	1.4	200	6	1.4
801–1000	45	0	0.78	75	1	1.0	105	2	1.2	155	4	1.4	180	5	1.4	225	7	1.5
1001–2000	45	0	0.80	75	1	1.0	130	3	1.4	180	5	1.6	230	7	1.7	280	9	1.8
2001–3000	75	1	1.1	105	2	1.3	135	3	1.4	210	6	1.7	280	9	1.9	370	13	2.1
3001–4000	75	1	1.1	105	2	1.3	160	4	1.5	210	6	1.7	305	10	2.0	420	15	2.2
4001–5000	75	1	1.1	105	2	1.3	160	4	1.5	235	7	1.8	330	11	2.0	440	16	2.2
5001–7000	75	1	1.1	105	2	1.3	185	5	1.7	260	8	1.9	350	12	2.2	490	18	2.4
7001–10,000	75	1	1.1	105	2	1.3	185	5	1.7	260	8	1.9	380	13	2.2	535	20	2.5
10,001–20,000	75	1	1.1	135	3	1.4	210	6	1.8	285	9	2.0	425	15	2.3	610	23	2.6
20,001–50,000	75	1	1.1	135	3	1.4	235	7	1.9	305	10	2.1	470	17	2.4	700	27	2.7
50,001–100,000	75	1	1.1	160	4	1.6	235	7	1.9	355	12	2.2	515	19	2.5	770	30	2.8

n = sample size; c = acceptance number.

"All" indicates that each piece in the lot is to be inspected.

AOQL = Average Outgoing Quality Limit in per cent.

* From H. F. Dodge and H. G. Romig, *Sampling Inspection Tables*, John Wiley and Sons, New York, 2nd ed., 1959.

LTPD, the process average of per cent defectives, and β. These are known as the Dodge-Romig *Sampling Inspection Tables* (3). The Dodge-Romig tables give the various plans that for selected values of incoming quality and various lot sizes have a minimum of total inspection, including the 100 per cent inspection of rejected lots. Table V shows one small part of these tables. The tables are organized according to the *LTPD*, with listings under 0.5, 1.0, 2.0, 3.0, 4.0, 5.0, 7.0, and 10.0 per cent. For each value of *LTPD*, the tables are organized as they appear in Table V. β is 10 per cent for all the tables.

As an alternate to the tables, we present Figures 6, 7, and 8 which may be used to determine sampling plans with minimum total inspection for a given process average per cent defectives, *LTPD*, and β. Let us construct an example with the following data: $LTPD = 8$ per cent, $\overline{PD} = 4$ per cent, $\beta = 10$ per cent, and $N = 1000$. The procedure is as follows:

1. Calculate the tolerance number of defectives in the lot = $LTPD \times N/100 = 8 \times 1000/100 = 80$.
2. Calculate the ratio $\overline{PD}/LTPD = \frac{4}{8} = 0.50$.
3. Enter Figure 6 with the values calculated in 1 and 2 to determine the acceptance number, c. The nearest value is $c = 11$.
4. Enter Figure 7 with the tolerance number of defectives in the lot $= 80$ and $c = 11$ to find on the vertical scale, $LTPD \times n/100 = 16$.
5. From the data determined in 4, calculate the sample size, $n = 16 \times 100/LTPD = 16 \times 100/8 = 200$.
6. Enter Figure 8 with the tolerance number of defectives in the lot $= 80$, and the ratio $\overline{PD}/LTPD = 0.50$ to find on the right-hand vertical scale, $LTPD \times I_{min}/100 = 23$.
7. With the data from 6, calculate the minimum average number inspected per lot, $I_{min} = 23 \times 100/LTPD = 23 \times 100/8 = 287.5$.

We have now determined a sampling plan with the following characteristics:

$$c = 11$$

$$n = 200$$

$$I_{min} = 287.5$$

$$\beta = 10 \text{ per cent}$$

The average number inspected per lot includes, of course, a pro-rata amount for the 100 per cent inspection of rejected lots. If *AQL* had been specified as 3 per cent, we could now go to the Thorndike chart

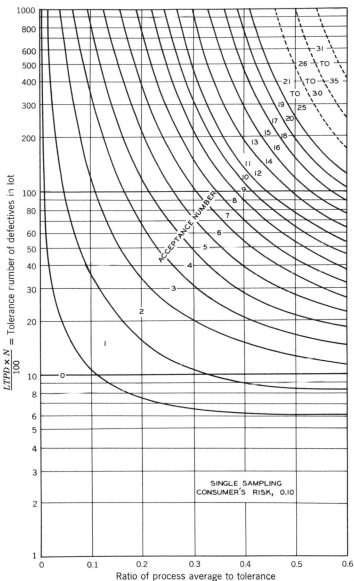

Figure 6. Chart for finding the acceptance number for minimum total inspection single sampling plans. *LTPD* and β specified $\overline{PD}$ given. Adapted from H. F. Dodge and H. G. Romig, *Sampling Inspection Tables*, John Wiley and Sons, New York, 2nd ed., 1959.

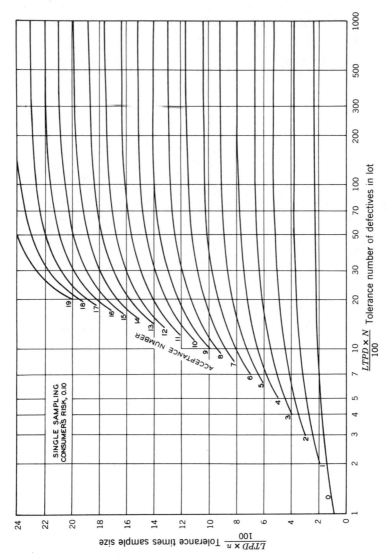

Figure 7. Chart for finding sample size for minimum total inspection single sampling plans. *LTPD* and β specified, $\overline{PD}$ given. Adapted from H. F. Dodge and H. G. Romig, *Sampling Inspection Tables,* John Wiley and Sons, New York, 2nd ed., 1959.

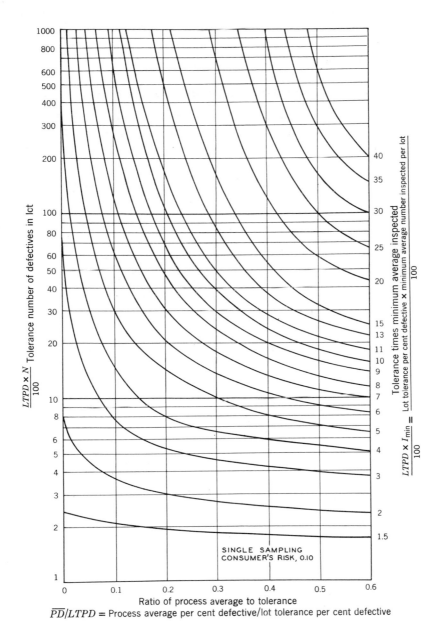

Figure 8. Chart for finding the minimum amount of inspection per lot for single sampling plans when $LTPD$ and β are specified and $\overline{PD}$ given. Adapted from H. F. Dodge and H. G. Romig, *Sampling Inspection Tables,* John Wiley and Sons, New York, 2nd ed., 1959.

to determine the value of α as before. Here it would be $\alpha = 2.5$ per cent. The Dodge-Romig charts furnish a convenient means of determining sampling plans with minimum total inspection over a wide range of conditions.

Average Outgoing Quality (AOQ) Curves

When a sampling plan rejects a lot, the most usual procedure is that the lot is subjected to 100 per cent inspection. It can be shown, then, that the sampling plan gives definite assurance that the average outgoing quality will not exceed a certain limit. Figure 9 shows the flow of good and rejected parts in a typical sampling plan

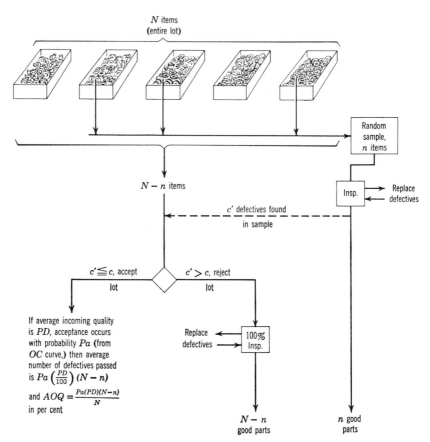

Figure 9. Flow of good and rejected parts in a typical acceptance sampling plan, showing the basis for calculating average outgoing quality.

and the basis for calculating the average outgoing quality, AOQ. The random sample of size n is inspected, and any defectives found in the sample are replaced by good parts so that the sample ends up with only good parts. Based on the number of defectives, c', found in the sample, the entire lot is accepted if $c' \leqq c$ and rejected if $c' > c$. If the lot is rejected, it is subjected to 100 per cent inspection and all defectives found are replaced by good parts. In this instance, the entire lot of N parts is free of defectives. If, however, the lot is accepted by the sample, we run the risk that some defective parts have passed. The average number of defectives is easy to calculate. If the average incoming quality percentage is PD, acceptance occurs with the probability P_a (taken directly from the OC curve for the per cent defective PD). The average number of defectives is then simply the product of the fraction defectives received, times the number remaining in the lot, weighted by the probability that acceptance occurs, or $(P_a/100)(PD/100)(N-n)$. The average outgoing quality AOQ in per cent is then:

$$AOQ = \frac{\text{Average number of defectives}}{\text{Number of parts in lot}} \times 100 = \frac{P_a(PD)(N-n)}{100N}$$

From the foregoing relationship we can now develop a curve for any given sampling plan which shows the AOQ for any level of incoming quality. Such a curve can be plotted by assuming different values of actual incoming quality, determining from the OC curve the probability of acceptance for that incoming quality P_a. These figures can then be substituted in the formula to compute AOQ. Each calculation for different incoming quality levels determines a point on the AOQ curve, as indicated in Figure 10. The AOQ curve of Figure 10 is based on a sampling plan with $n = 100$, $c = 2$, and $N = 1000$, the OC curve of which is shown in Figure 1.

Note the interesting characteristics of the AOQ curve. First, there is a maximum or limiting quality which can be passed, on the average. This peak of the curve is called the average outgoing quality limit ($AOQL$). There is an $AOQL$ for every sampling plan, which depends on the characteristics of the plan. We can reason why the AOQ curve takes the shape illustrated. When good quality is presented to the sampling plan, for example, 0 to 2 per cent, the probability of acceptance is relatively high, so that most of the defectives will be passed. As we go beyond 2 per cent incoming quality, however, the probability of acceptance is declining and, therefore, the probability of 100 per cent inspection is increasing, so that a larger share of defectives is screened out. This accounts for the

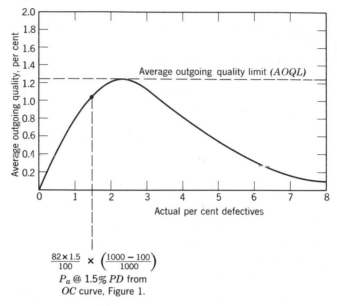

Average outgoing quality, per cent

Average outgoing quality limit *(AOQL)*

Actual per cent defectives

$$\frac{82 \times 1.5}{100} \times \left(\frac{1000 - 100}{1000}\right)$$

P_a @ 1.5% *PD* from
OC curve, Figure 1.

Figure 10. Average outgoing quality *(AOQ)* curve for a sampling plan with $n = 100$, $c = 2$, and lot size $N = 100$. *OC* curve shown in Figure 1.

fact that the outgoing quality improves as incoming quality becomes worse.

The essence of the characteristics of the sampling plan shown in Figure 10 is simply that average outgoing quality never exceeds approximately 1.25 per cent for the plan given, regardless of incoming quality. The amount of inspection required to maintain quality standards automatically adjusts to the situation. If incoming quality is very poor, perhaps 6 per cent, the sampling plan reacts by rejecting lots much more frequently, calling for 100 per cent inspection, so that average outgoing quality is about 0.32 per cent. On the other hand, if incoming quality is excellent, perhaps 1 per cent, the sampling plan more frequently passes the lots, and the amount of inspection required is small. Inspectors will usually be spending their time screening bad lots and not wasting their time going over good lots. The level of *AOQL* which should be selected for a given situation depends on the consequences of bad quality. If subsequent operations can catch further defectives without disrupting production, *AOQL* can be fairly loose. These probability controls over outgoing quality are ideal, especially since we can first specify the level of quality which is demanded by technical and economic considerations and then set up

TABLE VI. Single Sampling Table* for Average Outgoing Quality Limit (*AOQL*) = 1.5%

Lot Size	Process Average 0 to 0.03%			Process Average 0.04 to 0.30%			Process Average 0.31 to 0.60%			Process Average 0.61 to 0.90%			Process Average 0.91 to 1.20%			Process Average 1.21 to 1.50%		
	n	c	p_t %	n	c	p_t %	n	c	p_t %	n	c	p_t %	n	c	p_t %	n	c	p_t %
1–15	All	0	—	All	0	—	All	0	—	All	0	—	All	0	—	All	0	—
16–50	16	0	11.6	16	0	11.6	16	0	11.6	16	0	11.6	16	0	11.6	16	0	11.6
51–100	20	0	9.8	20	0	9.8	20	0	9.8	20	0	9.8	20	0	9.8	20	0	9.8
101–200	22	0	9.5	22	0	9.5	22	0	9.5	22	0	9.5	22	0	9.5	44	1	8.2
201–300	23	0	9.2	23	0	9.2	23	0	9.2	47	1	7.9	47	1	7.9	47	1	7.9
301–400	23	0	9.3	23	0	9.3	49	1	7.8	49	1	7.8	49	1	7.8	49	1	7.8
401–500	23	0	9.4	23	0	9.4	50	1	7.7	50	1	7.7	50	1	7.7	50	1	7.7
501–600	24	0	9.0	24	0	9.0	50	1	7.7	50	1	7.7	50	1	7.7	50	1	7.7
601–800	24	0	9.1	24	0	9.1	50	1	7.8	50	1	7.8	80	2	6.4	80	2	6.4
801–1000	24	0	9.1	55	1	7.0	55	1	7.0	85	2	6.2	85	2	6.2	85	2	6.2
1001–2000	24	0	9.1	55	1	7.0	55	1	7.0	85	2	6.2	120	3	5.4	155	4	5.0
2001–3000	24	0	9.2	55	1	7.1	90	2	5.9	125	3	5.3	160	4	4.9	200	5	4.6
3001–4000	24	0	9.2	55	1	7.1	90	2	5.9	125	3	5.3	165	4	4.8	240	6	4.4
4001–5000	24	0	9.2	55	1	7.1	90	2	5.9	125	3	5.3	205	5	4.6	280	7	4.2
5001–7000	24	0	9.2	55	1	7.1	90	2	5.9	165	4	4.8	205	5	4.6	325	8	4.0
7001–10,000	24	0	9.2	55	1	7.1	130	3	5.2	165	4	4.8	250	6	4.2	375	9	3.8
10,001–20,000	55	1	7.1	90	2	5.9	130	3	5.2	210	5	4.4	340	8	3.8	515	12	3.4
20,001–50,000	55	1	7.1	90	2	5.9	170	4	4.7	295	7	4.0	480	11	3.5	860	19	3.0
50,001–100,000	55	1	7.1	130	3	5.2	210	5	4.4	340	8	3.8	625	14	3.3	1120	24	2.8

n = sample size; c = acceptance number.

"All" indicates that each piece in the lot is to be inspected.

p_t = lot tolerance per cent defective with a consumer's risk (β) of 10%.

* From H. F. Dodge and H. G. Romig, *Sampling Inspection Tables*, John Wiley and Sons, New York, 2nd ed., 1959.

controls which guarantee the average performance needed, using inspection labor heavily when bad lots occur and only slightly when good lots occur.

We have shown the determination of the AOQ curve for the situation when defectives are replaced to maintain the lot size N; however, we could calculate in a parallel way AOQ assuming that all defectives are discarded, with rejected lots being 100 per cent inspected as before. In this situation, the average outgoing quality is calculated by:

$$AOQ = \frac{\text{Average number of defectives}}{\text{Number of parts in lot after defectives discarded}} \times 100$$

$$= \frac{(P_a/100)(PD/100)(N - n)}{N - (PD/100)[(n - PD)/100](1 - P_a/100)(N - n)} \times 100$$

which reduces to,

$$AOQ = \frac{P_a \times PD(N - n)}{100N - PD \times (n - PD)/100(100 - P_a)(N - n)}$$

Single Sampling Plans with Specified $AOQL$ and Minimum Total Inspection for a Given $\overline{PD}$

It is also possible to design single sampling plans that specify in advance $AOQL$ and, at the same time, minimize total inspection for a given process average $\overline{PD}$. Again, the Dodge-Romig *Sampling Inspection Tables* (3) provide us with a convenient means of selecting a sampling plan which fits requirements, just as was true with plans that specified $LTPD$, discussed previously. Table VI shows a section of the Dodge-Romig tables for $AOQL$ plans. All the plans shown in Table VI give $AOQL$ protection of 1.5 per cent with β set at 10 per cent. Comparable tables are given by Dodge-Romig for values of $AOQL$ of 0.1, 0.25, 0.5, 0.75, 1.0, 1.5, 2.0, 2.5, 3.0, 4.0, 5.0, 7.0, and 10.0. They also show the OC curves for all the $AOQL$ curves shown in the tables.

Single sampling plans with specified AOQL protection. Just as with $LTPD$ protection, the Dodge-Romig tables for $AOQL$ protection can be reduced to a chart with some side calculations necessary. We will summarize this procedure with the use of Figure 11 and Table VII. Let us assume that we have a lot of $N = 1800$ parts which come from a process where the average per cent defectives is known to be $\overline{PD} = 1$ per cent. We wish to determine a sampling plan

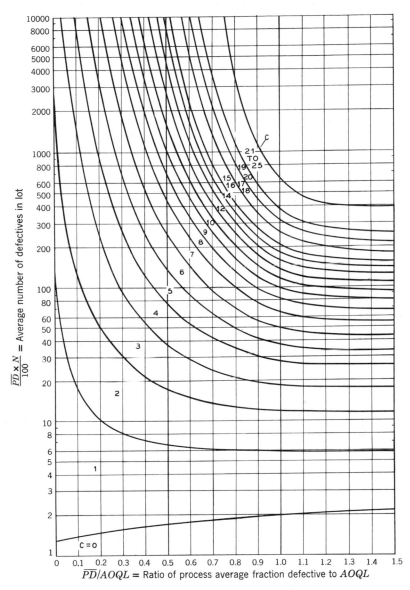

Figure 11. Chart for determining the acceptance number, c; $AOQL$ protection. Adapted from **H. F. Dodge** and **H. G. Romig**, *Sampling Inspection Tables*, John Wiley and Sons, New York, 2nd ed., 1959.

TABLE VII.* **Values of the Factor y for Given Values
of the Acceptance Number c.**
(*AOQL* protection)

Given c	y	Given c	y	Given c	y	Given c	y
0	0.3679						
1	0.8400	11	7.233	21	14.66	31	22.50
2	1.371	12	7.948	22	15.43	32	23.30
3	1.942	13	8.670	23	16.20	33	24.10
4	2.544	14	9.398	24	16.98	34	24.90
5	3.168	15	10.13	25	17.76	35	25.71
6	3.812	16	10.88	26	18.54	36	26.52
7	4.472	17	11.62	27	19.33	37	27.33
8	5.146	18	12.37	28	20.12	38	28.14
9	5.831	19	13.13	29	20.91	39	28.96
10	6.528	20	13.89	30	21.70	40	29.77

* Adapted from H. F. Dodge and H. G. Romig, *Sampling Inspection Tables*, John Wiley and Sons, New York, 2nd ed., 1959.

which will give protection of $AOQL = 3$ per cent. Our procedure is as follows:

1. Calculate $\overline{PD}/AOQL = \frac{1}{3} = 0.33$.
2. Calculate $(\overline{PD} \times N)/100 = (1 \times 1800)/100 = 18$.
3. From Figure 11, using the data from 1 and 2, the zone $c = 2$ is appropriate.
4. From Table VII, $y = 1.371$ for $c = 2$.
5. Calculate the sample size n by the formula,

$$n = \frac{yN}{AOQL/100 \times N + y}$$

$$= \frac{1.3710 \times 1800}{(0.03 \times 1800) + 1.371} = 45$$

From the foregoing procedure then, the sampling plan that will give the desired *AOQL* protection is $n = 45$ and $c = 2$.

Double Sampling

Double sampling, which has the advantage of lower inspection costs for a given level of protection, is accomplished by taking a smaller sample initially. Based on this sample, the lot is either accepted or rejected or results in no decision. In the latter instance a second sample is drawn and a decision finally made to reject or accept the lot, based on the combined sample. This basic structure is shown in Figure 12, where we see that two acceptance numbers, c_1 and c_2, have been chosen. If the number of defectives in the first sample is less than c_1, the lot is accepted at that point. If the number of defectives found exceeds the larger acceptance number c_2, the lot is immediately rejected and subjected to 100 per cent inspection. If, however, the number of defectives is between c_1 and c_2, a second sample is taken, and if the total number of defectives found in the *combined sample* exceeds c_2, the lot is rejected and subjected to 100 per cent inspection. If the number of defectives found at this point is less than c_2, the lot is accepted.

The advantage of double sampling lies in the possible reductions in the total amount of inspections required. This occurs because the

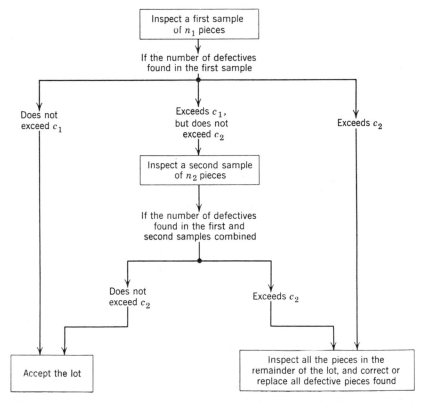

Figure 12. Double sampling inspection. From H. F. Dodge and H. G. Romig, *Sampling Inspection Tables,* John Wiley and Sons, New York, 2nd ed., 1959.

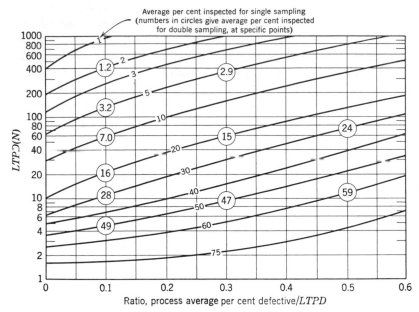

Figure 13. Relative amount of inspection, double and single sampling. Adapted from H. F. Dodge and H. G. Romig, *Sampling Inspection Tables,* John Wiley and Sons, New York, 2nd ed., 1959.

initial sample is smaller than that required by a comparable single sampling plan. If the lot can be accepted or rejected on the basis of the first sample, there will be a saving in total inspection. This saving in inspection is the greatest for large lot sizes and when incoming quality is normally quite good. Figure 13 shows a comparison of the amount of inspection required for single and double sampling. The curves in Figure 13 are marked to show the average per cent inspected for single sampling, with the circled numbers showing the average per cent inspected for double sampling at specific points on the curves. A study of the curves shows that the advantage of double sampling diminishes with smaller lot sizes. Also, there is a seeming advantage to the layman in the idea of "giving it a second chance." Actually this is illusory, because the probability of acceptance is determined by the OC curve for any plan, and a single sampling plan can be designed that yields greater discrimination between good and bad lots than a given double sampling plan. The disadvantage of double sampling is that the inspection load varies considerably. Figure 14 shows the OC curves for the first sample and for the

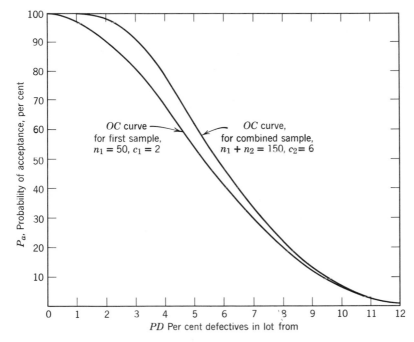

Figure 14. *OC* curves for a double sampling plan: $n_1 = 50$, $n_2 = 100$, $c_1 = 2$, $c_2 = 6$.

combined sample of a double sampling plan with $n_1 = 50$, $n_2 = 100$, $c_1 = 2$, and $c_2 = 6$.

As with single sampling, double sampling plans have been constructed for minimum total inspection where we wish to specify *LTPD* and where we wish to specify *AOQL*, for a given process average per cent defectives, $\overline{PD}$.

Double sampling plans with LTPD specified. The Dodge-Romig tables give double sampling plans that yield minimum total inspection for a given process average per cent defectives, $\overline{PD}$, with *LTPD* specified and β at 10 per cent. Table VIII shows a portion of the Dodge-Romig tables for *LTPD* = 5.0 per cent. Only half of the 5.0 per cent table is shown, there being tables for process averages running to 2.5 per cent. Separate tables are available for values of *LTPD* of 0.5, 1.0, 2.0, 3.0, 4.0, 5.0, 7.0, and 10.0 per cent. Dodge and Romig have also reduced to two charts the double sampling tables for *LTPD* protection, which make it possible to design sampling plans for a wide range of conditions of *LTPD*, $\overline{PD}$, and *N*. Figures 15 and

TABLE VIII. Double Sampling Table* for Lot Tolerance Per Cent Defective (LTPD) = 5.0%

Lot Size	Process Average 0 to 0.05%						Process Average 0.06 to 0.50%						Process Average 0.51 to 1.00%					
	Trial 1 n_1	c_1	Trial 2 n_2	n_1+n_2	c_2	AOQL in %	Trial 1 n_1	c_1	Trial 2 n_2	n_1+n_2	c_2	AOQL in %	Trial 1 n_1	c_1	Trial 2 n_2	n_1+n_2	c_2	AOQL in %
1–30	All	0	—	—	—	0	All	0	—	—	—	0	All	0	—	—	—	0
31–50	30	0	—	—	—	0.49	30	0	—	—	—	0.49	30	0	—	—	—	0.49
51–75	38	0	—	—	—	0.59	38	0	—	—	—	0.59	38	0	—	—	—	0.59
76–100	44	0	21	65	1	0.64	44	0	21	65	1	0.64	44	0	21	65	1	0.64
101–200	49	0	26	75	1	0.84	49	0	26	75	1	0.84	49	0	26	75	1	0.84
201–300	50	0	30	80	1	0.91	50	0	30	80	1	0.91	50	0	55	105	2	1.0
301–400	55	0	30	85	1	0.92	55	0	55	110	2	1.1	55	0	55	110	2	1.1
401–500	55	0	30	85	1	0.93	55	0	55	110	2	1.1	55	0	80	135	3	1.2
501–600	55	0	30	85	1	0.94	55	0	60	115	2	1.1	55	0	85	140	3	1.2
601–800	55	0	35	90	1	0.95	55	0	65	120	2	1.1	55	0	85	140	3	1.3
801–1000	55	0	35	90	1	0.96	55	0	65	120	2	1.1	55	0	115	170	4	1.4
1001–2000	55	0	35	90	1	0.98	55	0	95	150	3	1.3	55	0	120	175	4	1.4
2001–3000	55	0	65	120	2	1.2	55	0	95	150	3	1.3	55	0	150	205	5	1.5
3001–4000	55	0	65	120	2	1.2	55	0	95	150	3	1.3	90	1	140	230	6	1.6
4001–5000	55	0	65	120	2	1.2	55	0	95	150	3	1.4	90	1	165	255	7	1.8
5001–7000	55	0	65	120	2	1.2	55	0	95	150	3	1.4	90	1	165	255	7	1.8
7001–10,000	55	0	65	120	2	1.2	55	0	120	175	4	1.5	90	1	190	280	8	1.9
10,001–20,000	55	0	65	120	2	1.2	55	0	120	175	4	1.5	90	1	190	280	8	1.9
20,001–50,000	55	0	65	120	2	1.2	55	0	150	205	5	1.7	90	1	215	305	9	2.0
50,001–100,000	55	0	65	120	2	1.2	55	0	150	205	5	1.7	90	1	240	330	10	2.1

Trial 1: n_1 = first sample size; c_1 = acceptance number for first sample.

"All" indicates that each piece in the lot is to be inspected.

Trial 2: n_2 = second sample size; c_2 = acceptance number for first and second samples combined.

AOQL = Average Outgoing Quality Limit in per cent.

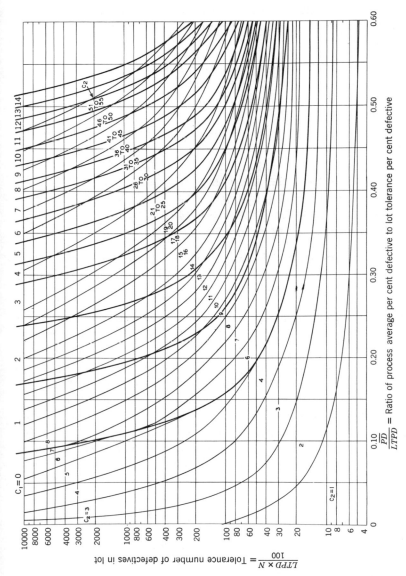

Figure 15. Chart for determining acceptance numbers c_1 and c_2; lot tolerance protection, Consumer's Risk, 10%. Adapted from H. F. Dodge and H. G. Romig, *Sampling Inspection Tables*, John Wiley and Sons, New York, 2nd ed., 1959.

16, which show these charts, make it possible to design a double sampling plan that yields minimum total average inspection, including the 100 per cent inspection of rejected lots. Let us design a plan for a process averaging 0.3 per cent defectives. $LTPD$ has been set at 5.0 per cent, and $N = 1500$. The procedure for using the two charts is as follows:

    1. Calculate $\overline{PD}/LTPD = 0.3/5.0 = 0.06$.
    2. Calculate $LTPD \times N/100 = 1500 \times 5.0/100 = 75$.
    3. Enter Figure 15 to find the applicable zones for c_1 and c_2. We find $c_1 = 0$ and $c_2 = 3$.
    4. Enter Figure 16 with the data from 2 and 3 and find the sample sizes for n_1 and n_2:
        For c_1, $LTPD \times n_1/100 = 2.8$
        And $n_1 = 2.8 \times 100/5.0 = 56$
        For c_2, $LTPD$ $(n_1 + n_2)/100 = 7.4$
        And $n_1 + n_2 = 7.4 \times 100/5.0 = 148$
        Therefore, $n_2 = 148 - 56 = 92$

The values obtained from the two charts for the example given may be compared with those found in Table VIII. Table VIII yields $n_1 = 55$, $c_1 = 0$, $n_2 = 95$, and $c_2 = 3$.

    Double sampling plans with AOQL protection. Paralleling single sampling plans, the Dodge-Romig tables give double sampling plans that minimize total inspection, including the 100 per cent inspection of rejected lots, specifying the desired level of $AOQL$. As before, the tables are set for $\beta = 10$ per cent and various given process averages, $\overline{PD}$. Table IX shows a section of the Dodge-Romig tables for double sampling plans with $AOQL = 1.0$ per cent. As before, the tables are given for a number of values of $AOQL$ ranging from 0.1 per cent to 10.0 per cent. The Dodge-Romig *Sampling Inspection Tables* also give OC curves for all the double sampling plans for $AOQL$ protection.

Sequential Sampling Plans

    Double sampling has the advantage of lower inspection costs for a given level of protection, accomplished by taking a smaller sample initially from which the lot is either accepted, rejected, or the decision is indeterminate. Why not carry this basic idea further? This is essentially what happens with sequential sampling. Samples are drawn at random, as before, but after each sample has been inspected,

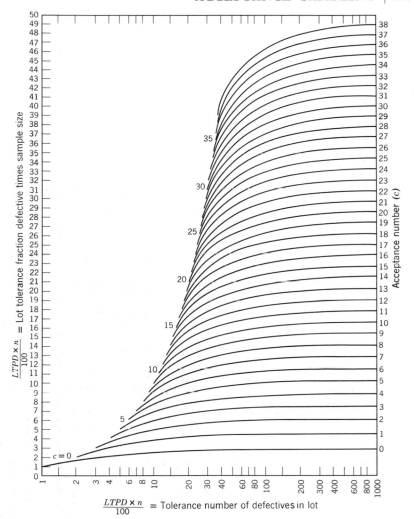

Figure 16. Chart for determining sample sizes n_1 and n_2; lot tolerance protection, Consumer's Risk, 10%. Adapted from H. F. Dodge and H. G. Romig, *Sampling Inspection Tables,* John Wiley and Sons, New York, 2nd ed., 1959.

the accumulated results are analyzed and a decision made to (1) accept the lot, (2) reject the lot, or (3) take another sample. The sequential sample sizes can be as small as $n = 1$. Figure 17 shows the graphical structure of a sequential sampling plan. The main advantage of sequential sampling is a further reduction in the total amount of inspection required to maintain a given level of protection

TABLE IX. Double Sampling Table* for Average Outgoing Quality Limit ($AOQL$) = 1.0%

Lot Size	Process Average 0 to 0.02%						Process Average 0.03 to 0.20%						Process Average 0.21 to 0.40%					
	Trial 1		Trial 2			p_t %	Trial 1		Trial 2			p_t %	Trial 1		Trial 2			p_t %
	n_1	c_1	n_2	n_1+n_2	c_2		n_1	c_1	n_2	n_1+n_2	c_2		n_1	c_1	n_2	n_1+n_2	c_2	
1–25	All	0	—	—	—	—	All	0	—	—	—	—	All	0	—	—	—	—
26–50	22	0	—	—	1	7.7	22	0	—	—	1	7.7	22	0	—	—	1	7.7
51–100	33	0	17	50	1	6.9	33	0	17	50	1	6.9	33	0	17	50	1	6.9
101–200	43	0	22	65	1	5.8	43	0	22	65	1	5.8	43	0	22	65	1	5.8
201–300	47	0	28	75	1	5.5	47	0	28	75	1	5.5	47	0	28	75	1	5.5
301–400	49	0	31	80	1	5.4	49	0	31	80	1	5.4	55	0	60	115	2	4.8
401–500	50	0	30	80	1	5.4	50	0	30	80	1	5.4	55	0	65	120	2	4.7
501–600	50	0	30	80	1	5.4	50	0	30	80	1	5.4	60	0	65	125	2	4.6
601–800	50	0	35	85	1	5.3	60	0	70	130	2	4.5	60	0	70	130	2	4.5
801–1000	55	0	30	85	1	5.2	60	0	75	135	2	4.4	60	0	75	135	2	4.4
1001–2000	55	0	35	90	1	5.1	65	0	75	140	2	4.3	75	0	120	195	3	3.8
2001–3000	65	0	80	145	2	4.2	65	0	80	145	2	4.2	75	0	125	200	3	3.7
3001–4000	70	0	80	150	2	4.1	70	0	80	150	2	4.1	80	0	175	255	4	3.5
4001–5000	70	0	80	150	2	4.1	70	0	80	150	2	4.1	80	0	180	260	4	3.4
5001–7000	70	0	80	150	2	4.1	75	0	125	200	3	3.7	80	0	180	260	4	3.4
7001–10,000	70	0	80	150	2	4.1	80	0	125	205	3	3.6	85	0	180	265	4	3.3
10,001–20,000	70	0	80	150	2	4.1	80	0	130	210	3	3.6	90	0	230	320	5	3.2
20,001–50,000	75	0	80	155	2	4.0	80	0	135	215	3	3.6	95	0	300	395	6	2.9
50,001–100,000	75	0	80	155	2	4.0	85	0	180	265	4	3.3	170	1	380	550	8	2.6

Trial 1: n_1 = first sample size; c_1 = acceptance number for first sample.

"All" indicates that each piece in the lot is to be inspected.

Trial 2: n_2 = second sample size; c_2 = acceptance number for first and second samples combined.

p_t = lot tolerance per cent defective with a consumer's risk (β) of 0.01.

* ... Engineering Tables, John Wiley and Sons, New York

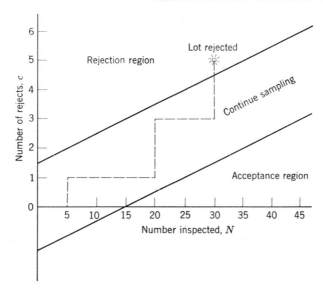

Figure 17. Sequential sampling plan.

as compared to double sampling. In the plan shown in Figure 17, a minimum of fifteen items must be inspected in order to accept a lot. If the number of rejects on the graph rises such that the point falls on or above the upper line, the lot is rejected. If the point should fall on or below the lower line, the lot is accepted. Until one of these events happens, sampling is continued. As with double sampling, the disadvantage is that inspection loads vary considerably. As with single and double sampling plans, a sequential plan is specified by the four requirements AQL, α, $LTPD$, and β, which in turn determine OC curves of sequential plans which meet the functional requirements. Detailed procedures for the construction of sequential sampling plans are given in references (4, 7, 9).

Comparison of Single, Double, and Sequential Sampling Plans

As we have noted, the relative advantages and disadvantages of single, double, and sequential sampling plans do not rest on the protection that can be achieved. The risks of both the producer and consumer type are determined by the OC curve of the plan, and the risk levels can be preset as desired for any of the three types of plans.

TABLE X.   Factors Influencing Choice of Single-, Double-,
or Group Sequential-Sampling Plan*

| | Type of Sampling Plan | | |
Factor	Single	Double	Sequential
Protection against rejection of lots of high quality and acceptance of lots of low quality		Approximately equal	
Total cost of inspection	Most expensive	Intermediate	Least expensive
Variability of inspection load	Constant	Variable	Variable
Sampling costs when all samples can be taken as needed	Most expensive	Intermediate	Least expensive
Sampling costs when all samples must be drawn at once	Least expensive	Most expensive	Intermediate
Accurate estimation of lot quality†	Best	Intermediate	Worst
Sampling costs when dependent on the number of samples drawn	Least expensive	Intermediate	Most expensive
Amount of record keeping	Least	Intermediate	Most
Psychological: "give supplier more than one chance"	Worst	Intermediate	Best

* U. S. Navy, Standard Sampling Inspection Procedures, D4.03.02/14.
† If estimate is based on a large number of lots, differences from one type of sampling to another may not matter.

Table X summarizes various factors which might influence the choice of the type of plan to use in a specific situation.

ACCEPTANCE SAMPLING BY VARIABLES

In acceptance samples by variables, we make and record actual measurements instead of simply classifying items as good or bad, as in attributes sampling.   This difference in procedure changes many of the details of determining a plan that meets specifications for acceptable quality, producer's risk, minimum acceptable quality, and consumer's risk, since the appropriate statistical distribution is now the *normal* distribution instead of distributions for proportions.   In addition, of course, inspection methods must change.   Conceptually, however, the basic ideas on which the control of outgoing quality is maintained remain the same.   The discriminating power of a plan is still represented by an *OC* curve, which shows the probability of acceptance for different levels of actual quality presented to the plan.

To specify a plan which gives the desired protection requires procedures parallel to those in acceptance sampling by attributes.

Kinds of Variables Acceptance Sampling Plans

Variables acceptance sampling plans are divided into two main categories which depend on our knowledge of the population standard deviation, σ'_x: where σ'_x is known and constant and where it is unknown and may be variable. Furthermore, the classification of variables sampling plans may be extended to the kind of decision criterion, that is, where the criterion is the average of measurements, and where the criterion is the per cent defectives which occur. To summarize, this classification is as follows:

1. Variables sampling plans where σ'_x is known and constant.
   (a) The decision criterion is expressed as the average of measurements, $\bar{x}_a$.
   (b) The decision criterion is expressed as the per cent defective items in the lot.
2. Variables sampling plans where σ'_x is unknown and may be variable.
   (a) The decision criterion is expressed as the average of measurements, $\bar{x}_a$.
   (b) The decision criterion is expressed as the per cent defective items in the lot.

To illustrate the concepts and procedures involved, we shall discuss variables sampling plans in which σ'_x is known and constant, and refer the reader to other sources for procedures in which σ'_x is unknown and may be variable (1).

Variables Sampling Plans in Which σ'_x Is Known and Constant

Let us take as an example the case of the testing of a certain steel bar stock which is being received in batches from a vendor. Because of the use to which the material is put, it has been determined that a tensile strength of 90,000 pounds per square inch (psi) is required and we wish the probability to be low, say 10 per cent, that lots of this tensile strength would be accepted. In addition, it has been determined that an average tensile strength of 95,000 psi is representative of good quality, and we wish there to be a high probability, say 95 per cent, that lots

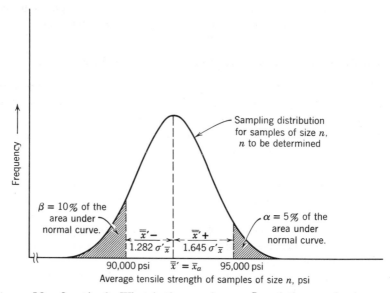

Figure 18. Question? What is the grand mean $\bar{\bar{x}}$, and the sample size, n, of a normal sampling distribution with the above characteristics, where $\sigma' = 6000$ psi, and, therefore, $\sigma'_x = 6000/\sqrt{n}$. The acceptance average, $\bar{x}_a$, of the plan we seek is the grand mean, $\bar{\bar{x}}$, of this sampling distribution, and the sample size of the plan is n.

of this tensile strength would be accepted. We have a long history with this material and supplier so that σ' is known to be 6000 psi, and the measurements normally distributed. In summary, we know that $AQL = 95,000$ psi, $\bar{x}_t = 90,000$ psi (equivalent to $LTPD$ in attributes sampling), $\alpha = 5$ per cent, and $\beta = 10$ per cent. We wish to determine a sampling plan that will indicate an acceptance average for sample tests $\bar{x}_a$ and a sample size n that will accept lots according to the specifications given. The acceptance average for sample tests $\bar{x}_a$ is equivalent to c, acceptance number, in attributes sampling plans. In other words, when $\bar{x}_a$ is less than the value we determine as being critical, the lot from which the sample was drawn will be rejected and presumably returned to the supplier. If the average tensile strength is equal to or greater than $\bar{x}_a$, we will accept such lots.

The standard deviation of the sampling distributions of means for samples of size n will be $6000/\sqrt{n}$. To be accepted 95 per cent of the time, $AQL = 95,000$ must be 1.645 σ' units above the grand mean, $\bar{\bar{x}} = \bar{x}_a$, since 5 per cent of the area under a normal curve is beyond $\bar{x}' + 1.645\ \sigma'$ (see Table I, areas of the normal curve, Appendix D).

Therefore, $\bar{x}_a - 95{,}000$ is 1.645 σ_x units. To be accepted 95 per cent of the time, then,

1. $\dfrac{\bar{x}_a - 95{,}000}{6000/\sqrt{n}} = -1.645$

Also, to ensure that lots of average tensile strength $\bar{x}_t = 90{,}000$ have only a 10 per cent chance of acceptance,

2. $\dfrac{\bar{x}_a - 90{,}000}{6000/\sqrt{n}} = +1.282$

We now have two independent equations with two unknowns, $\bar{x}_a$ and n. They may be solved simultaneously to yield the following values:

$$\bar{x}_a = 92{,}200 \text{ psi}$$

$$n = 12$$

Figure 18 attempts to show the relationship of the various elements of the problem.

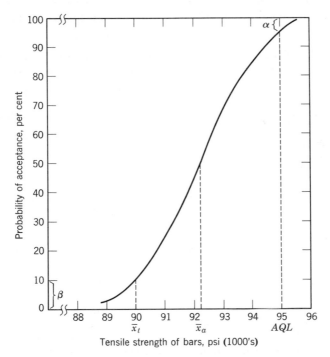

Figure 19. *OC* curve for a variables acceptance sampling plan for the tensile strength of steel bars.

The *OC* curve for the plan just described is determined by simply cumulating the normal distribution curve for the sampling distribution of sample size *n*. The *OC* curve for this plan is shown in Figure 19.

Upper and lower tolerance levels are often specified on measurements of part dimensions, chemical content, etc., as a part of variables sampling plans specifications. In these instances, the variables sampling plan must provide two-sided protection from defectives occurring because the measured characteristic may be too small or too large to be useful. A sampling plan would then specify a sample size and upper acceptance average and a lower acceptance average. Two equations must then be written for each limit. These equations would be solved for $\bar{x}_a$ upper, and $\bar{x}_a$ lower, and the integer value of *n* which most nearly satisfies α and β.

Criteria for acceptance can be expressed in per cent defective, as with attributes sampling, even though actual measurements are made. This merely requires a conversion of units within the plan. Also, *double sampling* is as applicable to acceptance sampling by variables as to sampling by attributes.

Field of application of variables sampling. Obviously, inspection, recording, and computing costs per unit will normally be higher with

TABLE XI. Reductions in Sample Size by Variables Sampling Plans as Compared to Attributes for Comparable Levels of Protection

Attributes Sample Size	Variables Sample Size	Reduction in Sample Size	
		Number	Percentage
10	7	3	30
15	10	5	33
20	13	7	35
30	16	14	47
40	20	20	50
55	25	30	55
75	35	40	53
115	50	65	57
150	60	90	60
225	70	155	69
300	85	215	72
450	100	350	78
750	125	625	83
1500	200	1300	87

Adapted by permission from *Sampling Inspection by Variables*, by A. H. Bowker and H. P. Goode, copyright, 1952, McGraw-Hill Book Company, Table 3.1, p. 33.

variables sampling inspection plans than with attributes plans. Then why use variables plans? The most important reason is that for a given level of protection, variables plans will require smaller samples and less total inspection than do attributes plans. Table XI shows this contrast. The differences are smaller for small sample size levels, but if a plan required a sample size of 750 for attributes sampling, comparable protection could be obtained with a sample of only 125 with variables sampling. These smaller sample sizes can be very important where the inspection process destroys the part. From an economic point of view, then, variables inspection should be used where the smaller sample size tips the balance of costs of inspection, recording, and computing. In addition to the possible cost advantages, the data generated by variables inspection ($\bar{x}$ and σ) provide more valuable diagnostic information in controlling production processes.

ECONOMICS OF DECISIONS BASED ON ACCEPTANCE SAMPLING

The bulk of the material presented here has had to do with the derivation of plans for acceptance sampling that meet specified values of risks for passing lots of specified quality. But what should these risks and quality levels be? Should the standard be tight or loose? The answer, of course, depends on relative values for costs of inspection and the costs or consequences of passing defective items. If, for example, we were searching for an economical single sampling plan, we could use the Dodge-Romig tables to find several plans at different $LTPD$ levels of protection, determining an I_{min}, the average minimum total inspection required, and AOQ. The balance of costs for a lot of size N for each plan would be

(Inspection cost per unit) $\times$ (I_{min} per lot)
+ (cost of passing a defective) $\times$ ($AOQ/100$) $\times$ (N).

The plan for which the sum of these two costs is minimum would in general satisfy requirements. More general economic models for sampling plans allow the σ and the β risks to vary (2). Where the inspection process affects yield, the cost of production must also be accounted for.

The implications on managerial decision making of the principles of acceptance sampling are that the long-run effect of such a decision process will be decisions that are correct. The plain fact is that a manager is constantly faced with making decisions on the basis of incomplete or sampled data. When he can apply the principles of acceptance sampling, he can determine the risks involved, or conversely, he may assess the risks of a given decision.

REFERENCES

1. Bowker, A. H., and H. P. Goode, *Sampling Inspection by Variables*, McGraw-Hill Book Company, New York, 1952.
2. Bowman, E. H., and R. B. Fetter, *Analysis for Production Management*, Richard D. Irwin, Homewood, Ill., revised edition, 1961.
3. Dodge, H. F., and H. G. Romig, *Sampling Inspection Tables*, John Wiley and Sons, New York, 2nd ed., 1959.
4. Duncan, A. J., *Quality Control and Industrial Statistics*, Richard D. Irwin, Homewood, Ill., 1955.
5. Grant, E. L., *Statistical Quality Control*, McGraw-Hill Book Company, New York, 2nd ed., 1952.
6. Statistical Research Group, Columbia University, *Sampling Inspection*, McGraw-Hill Book Company, New York, 1948.
7. Statistical Research Group, Columbia University, *Sequential Analysis of Statistical Data*, Columbia University Press, New York, 1945.
8. Tippett, L. H. C., *Technological Applications of Statistics*, John Wiley and Sons, New York, 1950.
9. Wald, A., *Sequential Analysis*, John Wiley and Sons, New York, 1947.
10. Vance, L. L., and J. Neter, *Statistical Sampling for Auditors and Accountants*, John Wiley and Sons, New York, 1956.

REVIEW QUESTIONS

1. What is the function of acceptance sampling and how is it distinguished from the application areas of statistical control, discussed previously?

2. Summarize the conditions under which acceptance sampling is appropriate.

3. What are the general conditions under which a 100 per cent sample is justified?

4. What information does the OC curve convey?

5. What is the effect on the OC curve of increasing sample size? Of increasing acceptance number?

6. For acceptance sampling by attributes, what is the statistical distribution which is most commonly appropriate? If $p'n$ is greater than 5, what distribution is used?

7. Outline the use of the Thorndike chart in determining OC curves for sampling by attributes.

8. Define AQL, α, $LTPD$, and β, and show their relationships on a typical OC curve.

9. Is it possible to specify exactly the levels of $LTPD$, AQL, α, and β in determining an acceptance sampling plan for attributes?

10. What is the function of the AOQ curve? Can we specify $AOQL$ as one of the design specifications for a plan?

11. Describe the structure of a double sampling plan.

12. What are the advantages of double sampling over single sampling? What are the disadvantages?

13. Describe the structure of sequential sampling plans. What are their advantages and disadvantages?

14. Outline the general procedures necessary to construct an acceptance sampling plan for variables.

15. Under what conditions would a variables sampling plan be used?

PROBLEMS

1. Referring to the V-bolt pulley discussed in the problem section of Chapter 7, the bar stock from which the hubs are fabricated has the diameter specification of $0.875'' \pm 0.002''$. This specification is related to the problem of flange splitting and "wobble" described in Problem 2 at the end of Chapter 7. It is felt that if 98 per cent of the bars meet specifications, this would be excellent quality. Also, it has been decided that the company should not accept shipments in which as many as 10 per cent of the bars do not meet specifications. If $\alpha = 5$ per cent, and $\beta = 10$ per cent, what single sampling plan will meet the stated requirements? Bars are ordered in lots of 400. Records indicate that the average number of bars which do not meet specifications in a lot is 12.

2. Determine the OC curve for the plan derived in Problem 1, and make a graph of it.

3. What is the $AOQL$ of the plan derived in Problem 1?

4. What single sampling plan would hold the $LTPD$ and β specifications given in Problem 1 and minimize total inspection?

5. What sampling plan would result if we determined that $AOQL$ should be held to 2 per cent, $\beta = 10$ per cent?

6. What double sampling plan will provide the $LTPD$ and β protections specified in Problem 1?

7. The flange material for the V-belt pulley must be relatively soft to carry out the press forming operations. Therefore, the material is specified with a Rockwell hardness of 55, and a hardness of 60 is regarded as unacceptable. The scrap rate goes up so fast when material with a hardness index above and beyond 60 is used that β has been set at 5 per cent rather than the usual 10 per cent. Alpha has been set at 5 per cent. Determine the Rockwell hardness sample average for acceptance, x_a, and the sample size needed for the requirements stated. The material is received in 100-feet rolls, $3\frac{1}{4}$ inches wide, 100 rolls per shipment. We have had considerable experience with the current supplier of the material so that the standard deviation of hardness for individual samples has been well established as $\sigma' = 2$.

8. What plan would result if we set $\beta = 10$ per cent?

9. Determine the OC curve for the plan in Problem 7.

part **IV**

WAITING LINE MODELS

9

Basic Waiting Line Models

Many types of production problems are described by the buildup of waiting lines (queues) of some input to the production system, or subsystem. Processing takes place within the system and the interplay of the timing of the *arrivals* and the required time for processing determines such important characteristics of the situation as the probable length of the waiting line, the average number in the line including the one being serviced, the average time that an input waits, and the average time that an input spends both waiting and being processed. If this information can be determined, we are often in a position to construct special models of the balance of costs which will serve as guides to decision making.

The original work in waiting line, or queuing theory was done by A. K. Erlang, a Danish telephone engineer. Erlang started his work in 1905 in an attempt to determine the effect of fluctuating service demand (arrivals) on the utilization of automatic dial equipment. It has been only since the end of World War II that work on waiting line models has been extended to other kinds of problems. There are a wide variety of seemingly diverse problem situations which are now recognized as being described by the general waiting line model. In all instances, we have an input that arrives at some facility for service or processing. The time between the arrival of individual inputs at the service facility is commonly random. Similarly, the time for service or processing is commonly a random variable. Table I shows the waiting line model elements for a number of commonly known situations.

There are four basic structures of waiting line situations which describe the general conditions at the servicing facility. The simplest situation is where arriving units form a single line to be serviced by a

TABLE I. **Waiting Line Model Elements for Some Commonly Known Situations**

	Unit Arriving	Service or Processing Facility	Service or Process Being Performed
Ships entering a port	Ships	Docks	Unloading and loading
Maintenance and repair of machines	Machine breaks down	Repair crew	Repair machine
Assembly line, not mechanically paced	Parts to be assembled	Individual assembly operations or entire line	Assembly
Doctor's office	Patients	Doctor, his staff and facilities	Medical care
Purchase of groceries at a supermarket	Customers with loaded grocery carts	Checkout counter	Tabulation of bill, receipt of payment and· bagging of groceries
Auto traffic at an intersection or bridge	Automobiles	Intersection or bridge with control points such as traffic lights or toll booths	Passage through intersection or bridge
Inventory of items in a warehouse	Order for withdrawal	Warehouse	Replenishment of inventory

single processing facility, for example, a one-man barber shop. This is called the single-channel, single-phase case. If the number of processing stations is increased (two or more barbers), but still draws on the one waiting line, we have a multiple-channel, single-phase case, since a customer can be serviced by any one of the barbers. A simple assembly line has a number of service facilities in series or tandem and is the single-channel, multiple-phase case. Finally, we have the multiple-channel, multiple-phase case which might be illustrated by two or more parallel production lines. Figure 1 shows the four cases diagrammed and labeled. Variations in the four basic structures may be in the queue discipline, that is, the order in which inputs are taken out of the waiting line. We have implied a first come–first served queue discipline in the diagrams, but obviously priority systems could be used. Also, combinations of the basic structures could exist.

An example

A simple example will serve to help us gain some insight into the nature of the waiting line problem. Assume that we are observing and recording

(a) Single channel, single phase case.

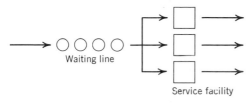

(b) Multiple channel, single phase case.

(c) Single channel, multiple phase case.

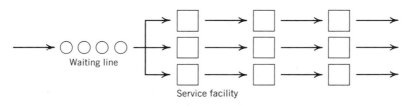

(d) Multiple channel, multiple phase case.

Figure 1. Four basic structures of waiting line situations.

the activities of a mechanic who is maintaining a large bank of automatic machines. When a machine breaks down or needs service, the mechanic is called. He services the machines in the order of breakdown (first come–first served). The mechanic is the equivalent of the service facility and machine breakdowns represent arrivals. We have the structure of the single-channel, single-phase case as diagrammed in Figure 1. We begin our record at 8:00 AM, Monday, recording the time when machines break down, when service begins and ends and thereby produce the history for twenty break-downs shown in Table II. The time at which machines break down is of course random, and therefore the time between arrivals is random. In Table II the average time between arrivals is approximately 2 hours. The

TABLE II. Record of Twenty Machine Breakdowns with Service History. Average Time between Breakdowns is Approximately 2 Hours, Average Service Time is Approximately 1 Hour

Time of Machine Breakdown	Time Required for Service, minutes	Service Begins at	Service Ends at	Idle Time of Mechanic, minutes	Waiting Time of Machine, minutes	Number of Machines Waiting for Service
Mon., 8:16 AM	20	Mon., 8:16 AM	Mon., 8:36 AM	16	20	0
11:28	9	11:28	11:37	172	9	0
3:03 PM	64	3:03 PM	4:07	206	64	1
3:53	1	4:07	4:08	0	15	0
6:03	21	6:03	6:24	115	21	0
9:28	56	9:28	10:24	184	56	1
9:32	30	10:24	10:54	0	82	0
11:02	198	11:02	Tues., 2:20 AM	8	198	2
Tues., 1:07 AM	30	Tues., 2:20 AM	2:50	0	103	1
1:15	10	2:50	3:00	0	105	0
5:31	58	5:31	6:29	151	58	1
5:46	41	6:29	7:10	0	84	0
10:26	120	10:26	12:26 PM	196	120	1
11:53	40	12:26 PM	1:06	0	73	0
3:28 PM	75	3:28	4:43	142	75	0
6:25	120	6:25	8:25	102	120	0
9:22	68	9:22	10:30	57	68	1
10:14	180	10:30	Wed., 1:30 AM	0	196	2
11:13	78	Wed., 1:30 AM	2:48	0	215	1
11:25	2	2:48	2:50	0	205	0
Totals	1221			1349	1887	

Time machines wait for service to begin

$$= \text{(total machine waiting time)} - \text{(total machine service time)}$$
$$= 1887 - 1221 = 666 \text{ minutes}$$

mechanic begins service immediately, or as soon as possible if he is already servicing another machine. The time per service varies considerably, depending on the nature of the trouble. It may be that a minor adjustment is needed requiring only 1 or 2 minutes. On the other hand, a part failure may require 2 or 3 hours for repair.

The record of Table II shows the typical pattern of such a situation. Sometimes the mechanic has nothing at all to do. In three instances these periods of idleness exceed three hours. But sometimes, owing to the pattern of machine breakdowns in relation to required service times, the mechanic has a backlog of work, that is, a waiting line of machines needing service.

Let us now change one of the important conditions to see the effect on the idle time of the mechanic, the machine waiting time, and the waiting line of machines to be repaired. Table III shows a typical record for the new condition where the average time between arrivals has been reduced from 2

TABLE III. Record of Twenty Machine Breakdowns and Service History with Average Time between Breakdowns Reduced to Approximately 1.5 Hours. Average Service Time Remains Unchanged at Approximately 1 Hour

Time of Machine Breakdown	Time Required for Service, minutes	Service Begins at	Service Ends at	Idle Time of Mechanic, minutes	Waiting Time of Machine, minutes	Number of Machines Waiting for Service
Mon., 9:31 AM	24	Mon., 9:31 AM	Mon., 9:55 AM	91	24	0
10:41	194	10:41	1:55 PM	46	194	2
11:16	11	1:55 PM	2:06	0	170	2
11:24	60	2:06	3:06	0	222	1
2:04 PM	136	3:06	5:22	0	198	1
4:59	81	5:22	6:43	0	104	0
9:19	22	9:19	9:41	156	22	0
10:16	35	10:16	10:51	35	35	1
10:33	60	10:51	11:51	0	78	1
11:28	58	11:51	Tues.,12:49 AM	0	81	0
Tues., 3:44 AM	38	Tues., 3:44 AM	4:22	175	38	1
3:48	17	4:22	4:39	0	51	0
6:23	15	6:23	6:38	104	15	1
6:27	110	6:38	8:28	0	121	2
7:38	22	8:28	8:50	0	72	2
8:06	87	8:50	10:17	0	131	1
8:39	126	10:17	12:23 PM	0	224	2
10:23	12	12:23 PM	12:35	0	132	1
11:18	20	12:35	12:55	0	97	0
1:48 PM	74	1:48	3:02	53	74	0
Totals	1202			660	2083	

Time machines wait for service to begin

= (total machine waiting time) − (total machine service time)
= 2083 − 1202 = 881 minutes

hours to 1.5 hours, with the average service time remaining at about 1 hour. The increased arrival rate has had a dramatic effect. The mechanic's idle time is less than half of the previous figure. In addition, the time that machines waited for service to begin, and the average waiting line length have both increased. The relative changes in these measures of effectiveness are somewhat greater than the increase in arrival rate.

Tables II and III both reflect the nature of the typical waiting line situation. Because of the random nature of arrivals, we may at times have long periods between breakdowns, but sometimes two or three breakdowns may occur almost simultaneously. Similarly, since the time required for service varies considerably and is a random process, long service times may occur at the time that several machines are down, causing long waiting times, or, the reverse pattern may be true. The resulting length of waiting line and waiting time, and the idle time of the service facility depend on the distribution of arrivals and of service times.

DISTRIBUTION OF ARRIVALS AND SERVICE TIMES

The common basic waiting line models have been developed on the assumption that *arrival rates* follow the Poisson distribution and that *service times* follow the negative exponential distribution. This situation is commonly referred to as the Poisson arrival–exponential holding time case. These assumptions are often quite valid in operating situations.

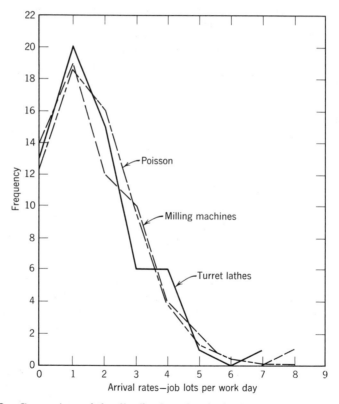

Figure 2. Comparison of the distribution of arrival rates at two machine centers in a jobbing machine shop with the Poisson distribution. Adapted from Ross T. Nelson, "An Empirical Study of Arrival, Service Time and Waiting Time Distributions in a Job Shop Production Process," Research Report No. 60, *Management Sciences Research Project*, June 1959, UCLA.

Poisson Arrival Rates

The Poisson distribution of arrival rates occurs frequently in the real world. Figures 2, 3, and 4 are examples of cases that have been validated by statistical analysis. Figure 2 is based on a broad study by Nelson (5) of the distributions of arrival rates and processing times in a Los Angeles jobbing machine shop. The frequency of arrivals of job orders at fifteen machine centers for a period of three months was tabulated. Table IV summarizes the data on the distribution of arrival rates, and Figure 2 shows the graphs for two of the machine groups compared to the theoretical distribution of the Poisson. The distributions for the entire set of fifteen machine centers were subjected to careful statistical tests in comparison to the Poisson, using the chi square goodness of fit test. It was concluded that the distributions of arrival rates for all fifteen machine centers were not significantly different from the Poisson distribution.

TABLE IV. Distributions of Arrival Rates of Job Orders to Fifteen Machine Centers in a Jobbing Machine Shop, over a 3-Month Period*

Machine Group	Number of Machines in Group	Total Arrivals in 3 Months	Mean Arrival Rate, Arrivals per Work Day	Distribution of Arrivals— Job Lots per Work Day								
				0	1	2	3	4	5	6	7	8
Engine lathes	7	120	1.935	11	14	21	4	9	2	1	—	—
Turret lathes	6	104	1.677	13	20	15	6	6	1	—	1	—
Automatic lathes	3	6	0.097	57	4	1	—	—	—	—	—	—
Hollow spindle lathes	1	27	0.435	40	18	3	1	—	—	—	—	—
Milling machines	6	107	1.726	14	19	12	10	4	2	—	—	1
Saws	2	77	1.242	25	14	11	9	1	2	—	—	—
Drill presses	3	95	1.532	15	18	18	6	3	1	1	—	—
Punch presses	2	37	0.597	39	12	8	3	—	—	—	—	—
Boring machines	2	33	0.532	39	16	4	3	—	—	—	—	—
Slotters	1	14	0.226	51	9	1	1	—	—	—	—	—
Hydrostatic pipe tester	1	33	0.532	37	19	5	—	1	—	—	—	—
Upsetters	2	57	0.919	25	22	10	5	—	—	—	—	—
Shapers	2	5	0.081	59	1	2	—	—	—	—	—	—
Wheelabrator	1	24	0.387	44	14	3	—	1	—	—	—	—
Pipe threading machine	1	30	0.484	37	20	5	—	—	—	—	—	—

* Adapted from Ross T. Nelson, "An Empirical Study of Arrival, Service Time, and Waiting Time Distributions of a Job Shop Production Process," Research Report No. 60, *Management Sciences Research Project*, UCLA, June 1959.

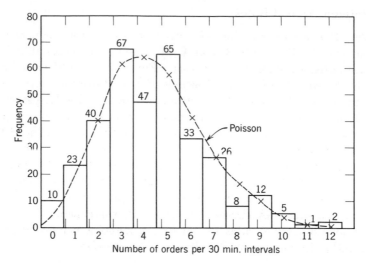

Figure 3. Distribution of order rates for mixed chemicals compared to the Poisson distribution. From O. J. Feorene, "The Gentle Art of Simulation," *Proceedings, Twelfth Annual Industrial Engineering Institute,* University of California, Berkeley-Los Angeles, 1960, pp. 15–22.

Figure 3 shows the comparison between the actual distribution of order rates and the Poisson distribution. This study took place at the Kodak Park Works of the Eastman Kodak Company, and the distribution represented the rate at which orders for mixed chemicals needed by several production departments in the company were received at a storeroom. Statistical tests again indicate that the actual distribution was described adequately by the Poisson. Figure 4 shows comparisons of actual distributions of arrival rates with the Poisson and normal distributions in traffic studies.

Although we cannot say with finality that distributions of arrival rates are always described adequately by the Poisson, there is much evidence to indicate that this is often the case. We might have reasoned that this should be true, because the Poisson distribution corresponds to completely random arrivals, since it is assumed that an arrival is completely independent of other arrivals as well as of any condition of the waiting line.

The commonly used symbol for average arrival rate in waiting line models is the Greek letter lambda (λ), arrivals per time unit. It can be shown that when the arrival rates follow a Poisson process with mean arrival rate λ, the time between arrivals follows a negative

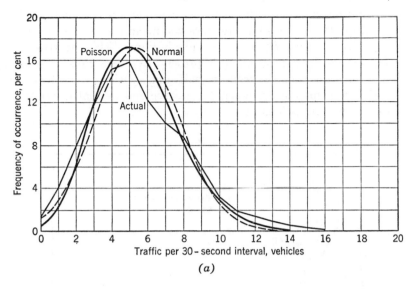

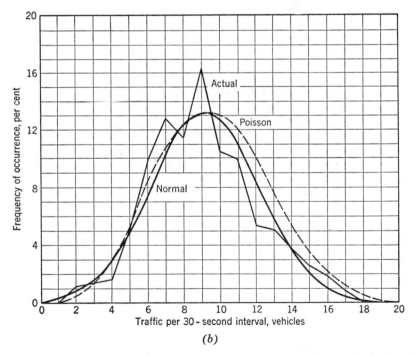

Figure 4. Arrival rates in traffic studies. From C. W. Churchman, R. L. Ackoff, and E. L. Arnoff, *Introduction to Operations Research,* John Wiley and Sons, New York, 1957, p. 424.

exponential distribution with mean time between arrivals of $1/\lambda$. This relationship between mean arrival rate and mean time between arrivals does not necessarily hold for other distributions. The negative exponential distribution, then, is also representative of a Poisson process, but describes the time between arrivals, and specifies that these time intervals are completely random. Negative exponential distributions are shown in Figures 5 and 6.

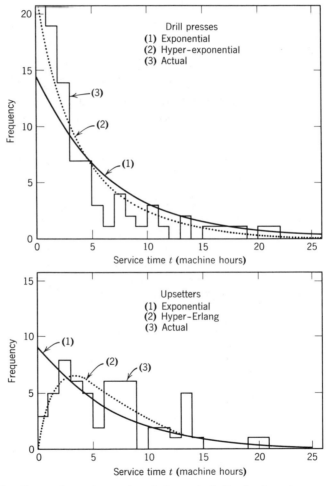

Figure 5. Comparison of actual and theoretical distributions for two machine groups. From R. T. Nelson, "An Empirical Study of Arrival, Service Time and Waiting Time Distributions in a Job Shop Production Process," Research Report No. 60, *Management Sciences Research Project*, June 1959, UCLA.

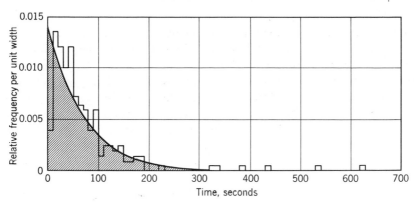

Figure 6. Service time at a tool crib. From G. Brigham, "On a Congestion Problem in an Aircraft Factory," *Operations Research,* Vol. 3, No. 4, 1955, pp. 412–428.

Exponential Service Times

The commonly used symbol for average service rate in waiting line models is the Greek letter mu (μ), the number of services completed per time unit. As with arrivals, it can be shown that when service rates follow a Poisson process with mean service rate μ, the distribution of service times follows the negative exponential distribution with mean service time $1/\mu$. The reason for the common reference to *rates* in the discussion of arrivals and *times* in the discussion of service is simply a matter of practice. We should hold it clearly in mind, however, for both arrivals and service, that in the general Poisson models rates follow the Poisson distribution and times follow the negative exponential distribution.

The evidence that real world service distributions commonly follow the Poisson process is not nearly as strong as it was for arrivals. Nevertheless, in some instances the assumption appears to be valid. Nelson's study of the distributions of arrivals and service times in a Los Angeles jobbing machine shop cited previously in our discussions of arrivals did *not* indicate that the exponential model fit the actual distributions adequately for all of the machine centers. The machine centers where service time distributions seemed adequately described by the negative exponential were turret lathes, milling machines, boring machines, and the wheelabrator. In general, the instances where the exponential hypothesis was reasonable occurred in the machine centers with the largest mean processing time.

Nelson's study indicated that other mathematical distributions such as the hyperexponential and the hyper-Erlang were better descriptions of the actual distributions. Figure 5 shows the distributions and fitted curves for the drill presses and the upsetters. A visual comparison indicates that the negative exponential distribution does not yield the best fit, and this was also indicated by statistical analysis.

Other evidence indicates that in some cases the negative exponential distribution fits. Figure 6, for example, shows that service time at a tool crib was nearly exponentially distributed. The duration of local telephone calls not made from a pay station has been shown to be exponential.

The net result of our discussion is that we cannot assume without a careful check that service distributions are described by a Poisson process. We may expect some instances where the negative exponential fits, but in many instances service times have been shown to be approximated by some unimodal distribution, usually somewhat positively skewed.

We might ask at this point, why the interest in establishing the validity of the Poisson and negative exponential distributions? The answer is that where the assumptions hold, the resulting waiting line formulas are quite simple. The Poisson and negative exponential distributions are single parameter distributions, that is, they are completely described by one parameter, since the mean and variance are equal. The result is that the mathematical derivations and resulting formulas are not complex. Where the assumptions do not hold, the mathematical development may be rather complex, or we may resort to other techniques for solution, such as simulation. We will discuss these techniques at a later point; however, our present objective is to discuss waiting line models based on the Poisson process for arrivals and service, that is, the situation commonly referred to as Poisson arrival rates and exponential holding times.

INFINITE WAITING LINE MODELS

We must now make another distinction in the classifications of waiting line models, that is, between situations where the waiting line may theoretically become infinite and where the maximum length of the waiting line is finite. In practice we would apply infinite waiting line models where the number in line could grow very large. From Figure 4 we see that the high average rate of arrivals of 1100 autos per hour does indeed imply the potential of the very large waiting line. In contrast, consider the case of maintaining a bank of ten automatic machines. The breakdown of a machine is considered to be an arrival. Obviously, the maximum possible waiting line of machines to be serviced is ten. It is finite and requires a different analysis resulting in a different model compared to the infinite waiting line problem.

Single-Channel, Single-Phase Case

We assume that the following conditions are valid: (1) Poisson arrival rates; (2) exponential service times; (3) first come–first served queue discipline; (4) the mean service rate μ is greater than the mean arrival rate λ. Under these conditions, the following equations apply:

Mean number in waiting line

$$L_q = \frac{\lambda^2}{\mu(\mu - \lambda)} \tag{1}$$

Mean number in system, including the one being serviced

$$L = \frac{\lambda}{\mu - \lambda} = L_q + \frac{\lambda}{\mu} \tag{2}$$

Mean waiting time

$$W_q = \frac{\lambda}{\mu(\mu - \lambda)} = \frac{L_q}{\lambda} \tag{3}$$

Mean time in system, including service

$$W = \frac{1}{\mu - \lambda} = W_q + \frac{1}{\mu} = \frac{L}{\lambda} \tag{4}$$

Probability of n units in the system

$$P_n = \left(1 - \frac{\lambda}{\mu}\right)\left(\frac{\lambda}{\mu}\right)^n \tag{5}$$

At first glance, it might seem that the difference between the mean number in the system and the mean number in the waiting line $(L - L_q)$ should be 1, the unit being served. A check of the formulas, however, indicates that this is not true; the difference is less than 1. A moment's reflection indicates the intuitive reason. Sometimes, because of the random nature of arrivals and service times, the service facility is idle so that the average number being served per unit of time must be less than 1. Also, note that the difference between the mean time in the system and the mean waiting time $(W - W_q)$ is simply the average time for service.

If we take the ratio between the mean arrival rate and the mean service rate, we have an index of the utilization of the service facility. The ratio is commonly called the utilization factor and is denoted by the Greek letter rho (ρ). If the two rates are equal, $\rho = 1$, and theoretically the service facility could be used 100 per cent of the time. But let us see what actually happens to the queue as ρ varies from zero to one. Figure 7 summarizes the result of computing L_q for different values of ρ. As ρ approaches unity, the number waiting in line increases rapidly and approaches infinity. We can also see that this is true by examining equations 1, 2, 3, and 4. In

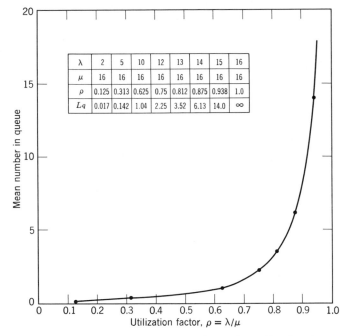

Figure 7. Relationship of queue length to the utilization factor ρ.

all cases, $\mu - \lambda$ appears in the denominator. When λ and μ are equal, $\mu - \lambda$ is zero and the value of L, L_q, W, or W_q becomes infinitely large. In practical situations, this never really happens because arrivals may not choose to wait if the line is already very long, or someone takes action either to reduce the arrival rate or increase the processing rate in order to remedy the situation. We see now one of the requirements of any practical system: μ must always exceed λ, otherwise we cannot have a stable system. If units are arriving faster on the average than they can be processed, the waiting line will be continuously increasing and no steady state will be achieved.

When conditions of arrival and service rate are such that the average length of the waiting line increases as noted in Figure 7, we can reason that the probability that the service facility will be idle must become rather small. Equation 5 allows us to calculate this probability rather easily. The probability of 0 units in the system (service facility idle), P_0, is

$$P_0 = \left(1 - \frac{\lambda}{\mu}\right)\left(\frac{\lambda}{\mu}\right)^0$$

and, since $\left(\dfrac{\lambda}{\mu}\right)^0 = 1$,

$$P_0 = \left(1 - \frac{\lambda}{\mu}\right) = (1 - \rho)$$

This is the probability that the service facility will be idle, and checks our intuition that utilization of the facility plus idleness should total 100 per cent.

An example

Let us illustrate the usefulness of the basic equations in a typical decision problem. Suppose that we have a tool crib in a factory where mechanics come to check out special tools needed for the completion of a particular task assigned to them. A study is made of the time between arrivals and of the time required for service. Both distributions are found to be adequately described by the negative exponential. The average time between arrivals was found to be 60 seconds and the average time for service 50 seconds. The arrival and service rates per minute are:

$$\lambda = \tfrac{1}{60} \times 60 = 1 \text{ arrival per minute}$$

$$\mu = \tfrac{1}{50} \times 60 = 1.2 \text{ services per minute}$$

Let us determine the magnitude of waiting line lengths, waiting time and the per cent of idle time of the attendant, using equations 1, 2, 3, 4, and 5.

$$L_q = \frac{\lambda^2}{\mu(\mu - \lambda)} = \frac{1^2}{1.2(1 - 1.2)} = \frac{1}{1.2 \times 0.2} = 4.17 \text{ mechanics in line}$$

$$L = \frac{\lambda}{\mu - \lambda} = \frac{1}{1.2 - 1.0}$$

$$= 5 \text{ mechanics in line, including the mechanic being served}$$

$$W_q = \frac{\lambda}{\mu(\mu - \lambda)} = \frac{1}{1.2(1.2 - 1.0)} = \frac{1}{1.2 \times 0.2}$$

$$= 4.17 \text{ minutes per mechanic}$$

$$W = \frac{1}{\mu - \lambda} = \frac{1}{1.2 - 1.0} = 5 \text{ minutes waiting time, including service}$$

Idle time $= 1 - \rho = 1 - \dfrac{1}{1.2} = 0.1667$, or 16.67% idle time of attendant

If the attendant is paid $2 per hour and the mechanics are paid $4 per hour, what policy or service should be established? What cost function do we wish to minimize? If we add more attendants, the waiting line and mechanics' waiting time will be reduced, but the idle time of the attendants will be increased. Therefore, what we wish to do is to determine the number of attendants that will minimize the combined cost of attendants' idle time, plus the cost of mechanics' waiting time. For one attendant, the cost of idle time is:

$$8 \times 0.1667 \times 2.00 = \$2.67 \text{ per day}$$

If mechanics arrive at the rate of 1 per minute, then 480 are served in an 8-hour day, and the daily cost of waiting time is

480 (waiting time per mechanic in hours)(hourly pay rate)

$$= 480 \times \frac{W_q}{60} \times 4.00 = 480 \times \frac{4.17}{60} \times 4.00 = \$133.50 \text{ per day}$$

Obviously, with one attendant, we are incurring a very large waiting time cost ($33\frac{1}{3}$ hours per day) in relation to the cost of the attendants' idle time, and more attendants to step up the effective service rate will be justified. But before we can proceed with our analysis we must have information about the next most complex situation, because if we add a second, third, or fourth attendant, we are dealing with the multiple-channel, single-phase situation.

Constant service times modify the formulas for the mean number in the waiting line and mean waiting time only slightly. The formulas are:

Mean number in waiting line

$$L_q = \frac{\lambda^2}{2\mu(\mu - \lambda)} \tag{6}$$

Mean waiting time

$$W_q = \frac{\lambda}{2\mu(\mu - \lambda)} \tag{7}$$

Whereas constant service time does not represent a large number of real situations, it is reasonable in cases where a machine processes arriving items by a fixed time cycle.

Multiple-Channel, Single-Phase Case

In the multiple-channel case we assume the same conditions of Poisson arrivals, exponential service times, and first come–first served queue discipline. The effective service rate $M\mu$ must be greater than the arrival rate λ, where M is the number of channels. First, it is necessary to calculate P_0, the probability that there are zero units in the system (service facility idle), since the basic formulas all involve P_0 in their simplest forms.

$$P_0 = \frac{1}{\left[\sum_{n=0}^{M-1} \frac{(\lambda/\mu)^n}{n!}\right] + \left[\frac{(\lambda/\mu)^M}{M!\left(1 - \frac{\lambda}{\mu M}\right)}\right]}$$

and substituting $r = \lambda/\mu$,

$$P_0 = \frac{1}{\left[\sum_{n=0}^{M-1} \frac{r^r}{n!}\right] + \left[\frac{r^M}{M!\left(1 - \frac{r}{M}\right)}\right]} \tag{8}$$

where n is an index for the number of channels, the calculation of the term $\sum_{n=0}^{M-1} \frac{r^r}{n!}$ being the sum of $\frac{r^r}{n!}$ for all of the numbers of channels ranging from $n = 0$ to $n = M - 1$. The notation $n!$ means to multiply the declining series of numbers beginning with the value of n, declining to 1. For example, $6! = 6 \cdot 5 \cdot 4 \cdot 3 \cdot 2 \cdot 1 = 720$.

Then the formulas parallel to the single channel case are:

Mean number in waiting line

$$L_q = \frac{(r)^{M+1}}{(M - 1)!(M - r)^2} \cdot P_0 \tag{9}$$

Mean number in system, including those being serviced

$$L = L_q + r \tag{10}$$

Mean waiting time

$$W_q = \frac{r^{M+1}}{\lambda(M-1)!(M-r)^2} \cdot P_0$$

$$= \frac{L_q}{\lambda} \tag{11}$$

Mean time in system, including service

$$W = W_q + \frac{1}{\mu}$$

$$= \frac{L}{\lambda} \tag{12}$$

Although the relationships are somewhat more complex, especially for a large number of channels, we can see that we need calculate only one of the conditions, L_q, L, W_q, or W, and all of the others may be calculated quite simply through the interrelationships that exist.

The effect of increasing the number of channels. To compare the effects of increasing the number of channels, it is useful to plot curves for line lengths and waiting times versus the utilization factor which may now be generalized as $\rho = \lambda/M\mu$, where M is the number of channels. Figures 8 and 9 show line lengths and waiting times for $M = 1, 2, 3, 4, 5$, and 10. If, for example, we were faced with a situation where $\rho = 0.9$ for the single-channel case, then L_q is approximately 8 from Figure 8. Adding a second channel reduces the utilization factor to $\rho = 0.9/2 = 0.45$, which results in $L_q = 0.23$ from Figure 9. The effects are surprisingly large, that is, we can obtain disproportionate gains in waiting time by increasing the number of channels. We can see intuitively that this might be true from Figure 7 since queue length (and waiting time) begins to increase very rapidly at about $\rho = 0.8$. A rather small increase in the capacity of the system (decrease in ρ) at these high loads can produce a large decrease in line length and waiting time.

Let us return now to the tool crib example. If a second tool crib attendant were added, the utilization factor becomes $\rho = 1/2 \times 1.2 = 0.417$, whereas previously it was 0.833. Reading approximate values from the curves of Figure 8, $L_q = 0.175$ and $W_q = 0.175/\lambda = 0.175/1 = 0.175$ minute per mechanic. The cost of mechanics' waiting time is now reduced to:

$$480 \times \frac{0.175}{60} \times 4 = \$5.60 \text{ per day}$$

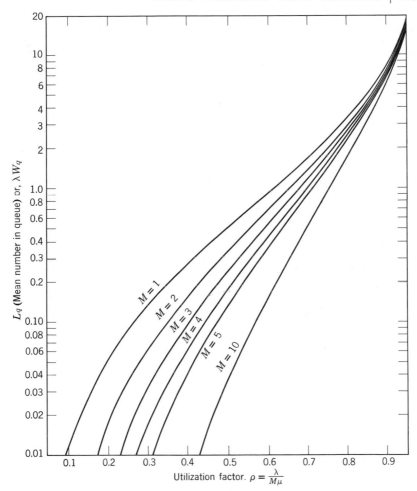

Figure 8. L_q (Mean number in queue) or λW_q for different values of M, versus the utilization factor ρ. $L_q = \lambda W_q$.

The idle time of the attendants has increased by 8 hours, however, since there is no more work to be done than before—it is simply distributed between two attendants. The new idle time cost is then,

$$\$2.67 + \$2 \times 8 = \$18.67 \text{ per day}$$

The combined cost of waiting plus idle time is much less ($\$24.27$) when two attendants are available than when only one was available ($\$136.17$). We can also see without further detailed analysis that it would not be economical to add a third attendant, since the incremental

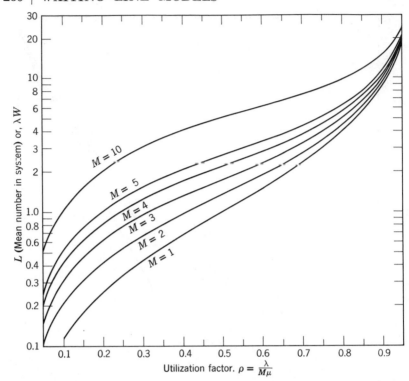

Figure 9. L (Mean number in system) or λW for different values of M, versus the utilization factor ρ. $L = \lambda W$.

cost of doing so would be $16.00 per day and the waiting time cost with two attendants is only $5.60 per day.

The effect of pooling facilities. This effect can also be seen from Figure 8. Suppose, for example, that since we find a second attendant is warranted following our previous analysis, the proposal is made to decentralize and have two separate tool cribs. What effect will this have on waiting time costs? With two separate tool cribs we will assume that half the mechanics go to each, so that the average arrival rate at each crib is now 0.5 arrival per minute. The utilization factor is then $\rho = 0.417$ and waiting time per mechanic is $L_q/\lambda = 0.3/0.5 = 0.6$ minute from Figure 8. This translates into a waiting time cost for the two tool cribs of

$$\frac{0.6}{60} \times 480 \times 4 = \$19.20 \text{ per day}$$

This compares to $5.60 per day waiting time cost for the single facility with two attendants previously calculated. The result is clear. One large facility can give better service than an equivalent number of small facilities. This, of course, accounts only for the waiting time costs. In the case of the tool crib a centralized facility would have other economic advantages and disadvantages such as reduced total investment in tools and increased transportation time by mechanics.

FINITE WAITING LINE MODELS

Many practical waiting line problems which occur in production systems have the characteristics of finite waiting line models. This is true whenever the population of machines, men, or items which may arrive for service is limited to a relatively small finite number. The result is that we must express arrivals in terms of a unit of the population rather than as an average rate. In the infinite waiting line case the average length of the waiting line is effectively independent of the number in the arriving population, but in the finite case the number in the queue may represent a significant proportion of the arriving population, and therefore the probabilities associated with arrivals are affected. The resulting mathematical formulations are somewhat more difficult computationally than for the infinite queue case. Fortunately, however, *Finite Queuing Tables* (6) are available which make problem solution very simple. Although there is no definite number that we can point to as a dividing line between finite and infinite applications, the finite queuing tables have data for populations from 4 up to 250, and this may be taken as a general guide. We have reproduced these tables for populations of 5, 10, 20, and 30 in Appendix D, Table III, to illustrate their use in the solution of finite queuing problems. The tables are based on a finite model for exponential times between arrivals and service times.

Use of the Finite Queuing Tables

The tables are indexed first by N, the size of the population. For each population size, data are classified by X, the service factor (comparable to the utilization factor in infinite queues), and by M, the number of parallel channels. For a given N, X, and M, two factors are listed in the tables, D (the probability of a delay; that is, if a unit calls for service, the probability that it will have to wait) and F (an efficiency factor, used to calculate other important data).

To summarize, we define the factors just expressed plus those which may be calculated as follows:

N = population (number of machines, customers, etc.)

T = mean service time (repair time, length of telephone conversation, process time, etc.)

U = mean run time, or time between calls for service

X = service factor = $\dfrac{T}{T + U}$

M = number of service channels

D = probability of delay (probability that if a unit calls for service, it will have to wait)

F = efficiency factor

L_q = mean number in waiting line = $N(1 - F)$

W_q = mean waiting time = $L_q(T + U)/(N - L_q)$

H = mean number of units being serviced = FNX

J = mean number of units running = $NF(1 - X)$

The procedure for a given case is as follows:

1. Determine the mean service time T, and the mean running time U, based on data or measurements of the system being analyzed.

2. Compute the service factor $X = T/(T + U)$.

3. Locate the section of the tables listing data for the population size N.

4. Locate the service factor calculated in 2 for the given population.

5. Read the values of D and F for the number of channels M, interpolating between values of X when necessary.

6. Compute values for L_q, W_q, H, and J as required by the nature of the problem.

AN EXAMPLE

Let us take as an illustrative example the case of tire curing. After tires have been assembled, they go to curing presses where the various layers of rubber and fiber are vulcanized into one homogeneous piece and the final shape including the tread is molded. Different tires require somewhat different curing times which may range up to 90 minutes or more. The press operator can unload and reload a press in 3 minutes, so that one operator would normally service a bank of curing presses, and each press may be molding tires of a different design, so that presses are "arriving" for service at nearly random times. The presses automatically open when the preset cure time is complete.

In servicing a bank of thirty presses, the operator is ranging over a wide area of approximately 90 feet by 200 feet. Indicator lights flash on, signifying that the press is ready for service, and the operator walks to the open press, unloading and reloading it. Sometimes, of course, the position of the open press may be quite close to the operator so that his walk is fairly short. In rare instances the operator is at one extreme end of the area and the press requiring service is at the other extreme end, requiring a fairly long walk. Thus the operator's tasks in rendering service are made up of walking plus unloading and reloading the presses. The average time for the operator's activity is 3 minutes and is approximated by the negative exponential distribution.

When a press is idle, waiting to be serviced, the only costs which continue are the services to the press, mainly heat supply. The cost of supplying this heat is $4.00 per hour per press. Operators are paid $3.50 per hour and marginal profit per tire is $5.00.

Let us determine the number of operators (number of channels) to be used when the average cure time of tires being produced is 80 minutes for conditions when market demand is less than plant capacity and when it is above plant capacity.

THE SOLUTION

To state our objective we wish to determine the number of servicing operators which will minimize the combined costs of downtime due solely to waiting for service and the operators' idle time. The downtime costs due to queuing effects are of two types, the cost of heat supplied to the presses while waiting and the loss of marginal profit when demand is above capacity and any additional output can be sold. When demand is below capacity, we assume that management is adjusting the number of presses in operation, hours worked, or even the number of shifts worked to match output to demand. We will calculate costs for 24 hours of operation.

1. *Value of wasted heat due to presses waiting for service.* Since $T = 3$ minutes and $U = 80$ minutes,

$$X = \frac{T}{T + U} = \frac{3}{3 + 80} = 0.036$$

for $N = 30$, and $X = 0.036$ we have the following values from the tables:

M	F
3	0.998
2	0.988
1	0.853

and, we compute L_q and W_q,

M	$L_q = N(1 - F)$	$W_q = \dfrac{L_q(T + U)}{N - L_q}$
3	0.06 presses	0.167 min./press/cycle
2	0.36 presses	1.007 min./press/cycle
1	4.42 presses	14.20 min./press/cycle

Since the presses are running, being serviced, or waiting to be serviced, the per cent of time that they are waiting is

$$\frac{W_q}{U + T + W_q} \times 100$$

and we may calculate the cost of waiting time for thirty presses and 24 hours of operation:

M	Per Cent Waiting Time $-\dfrac{W_q}{U + T + W_q} \times 100$	Cost for Thirty Presses and 24 Hours of Operation at $4/hr.
3	0.2%	\$ 5.76
2	1.2%	34.50
1	14.6%	420.00

2. *Value of operator's idle time.* Recall that $H = FNX$ is the average number of units being serviced at any one time. If there are M channels, there are $M - H$ channels idle at any one time, so we may calculate easily the value of operator idle time for 24 hours of operation:

M	$H = FNX$	Average Number of Operators Idle $= M - H$	Cost of Idle Time for 24 Hours at Pay Rate, \$3.50/hr.
3	1.077	1.923	\$161.30
2	1.067	0.933	78.30
1	0.92	0.08	6.73

When demand is less than capacity, our decision is based on the balance of costs of wasted heat due to presses waiting and of operators' idle time:

M	Cost of Wasted Heat Due to Presses Waiting	Cost of Operator's Idle Time	Total
3	\$ 5.76	\$161.30	\$167.30
2	34.50	78.30	111.80
1	420.00	6.73	426.73

The use of two operators to service the thirty presses is indicated since this situation produces the lowest combined cost of wasted heat and operator idle time. Now let us see if conditions change sufficiently when demand exceeds capacity to warrant a change of operating policy.

3. *Value of lost marginal profit due to presses waiting for service, when demand exceeds capacity and additional tires can therefore be sold.* If there were no waiting time the average output from the thirty presses would be $30(60/83) = 21.7$ tires per hour. Also, we may calculate the average num-

ber of presses running at any point in time by $J = NF(1 - X)$. Every 80 minutes of run time produces a tire on the average, therefore:

M	Average Number of Presses Running = $J = NF(1 - X)$	Average Output per Hour $= J\left(\dfrac{60}{80}\right)$	Output Lost per Hour Due to Waiting = 21.7 − Average Output	Cost of Output Lost = (output lost) ($5)(24)
3	28.85	21.65 tires	0.05 tires	$ 6.00
2	28.55	21.4	0.3	36.00
1	24.65	18.5	3.2	384.00

Finally, the total of downtime costs due to waiting plus the cost of operator idle time is:

M	Value of Wasted Heat Due to Presses Waiting	Cost of Output Lost	Cost of Operator's Idle Time	Total
3	$ 5.76	$ 6.00	$161.30	$173.06
2	34.50	36.00	78.30	148.80
1	420.00	384.00	6.73	810.73

Therefore, two operators is the best number to service the bank of thirty machines when demand exceeds capacity.

There are a number of other important phases of the preceding problem which we are not attempting to deal with here, but which could be analyzed from the data in the *Finite Queuing Tables* and the relationships which were developed on page 262. For example, is the decision to use two operators sensitive to the number of presses in operation? How sensitive is it to changes in average cure time (a different product mix)? Curves could easily be developed for average output versus average cure time for different numbers of presses operating, indicating the zones for using 1, 2, 3, etc. operators to serve the presses. Other elements of the operation of the press room, which in themselves are finite queuing problems, are the changeover of presses to different tire sizes, and the mechanical maintenance of the presses. We can see that these problems interact with the overall problem of production programming the output of the press room.

Summary

Waiting line models are among the most used of quantitative methods today. The common assumptions of Poisson arrivals and exponential holding times are reasonable in quite a number of instances. In many cases where they are not appropriate we have a non-homogeneous situation, where two or more basic conditions are mixed— for example, the service times of a punch press department that handled both repair work (very small orders) and production work (large orders). In such a case the resulting distribution of service times really reflects two basic distributions.

Note that we did not cover any of the multiple-phase cases, situations involving arrival and/or service distributions other than the Poisson, and queue disciplines other than first come–first served. It is felt that these more complex structures are best handled through the technique of computer simulation, which will be covered later. Also, because of work done by P. M. Morse (4) and others, there is considerable knowledge about the machine maintenance problem which will be covered separately in Chapter 10.

REFERENCES

1. Brigham, F., "On a Congestion Problem in an Aircraft Factory," *Operations Research,* Vol. 3, No. 4, 1955, pp. 412–428.
2. Churchman, C. W., R. L. Ackoff, and E. L. Arnoff, *Introduction to Operations Research,* John Wiley and Sons, New York, 1957.
3. Malcolm, D. G., "Queuing Theory in Organization Design," *Journal of Industrial Engineering,* November–December 1955, pp. 19–27.
4. Morse, P. M., *Queues, Inventories, and Maintenance,* John Wiley and Sons, New York, 1958.
5. Nelson, R. T., "An Empirical Study of Arrival, Service Time, and Waiting Time Distributions of a Job Shop Production Process," Research Report No. 60, *Management Sciences Research Project,* UCLA, 1959.
6. Peck, L. G., and R. N. Hazelwood, *Finite Queuing Tables,* John Wiley and Sons, New York, 1958.
7. Saaty, T. L., *Elements of Queuing Theory,* McGraw-Hill Book Company, New York, 1961.
8. Saaty, T. L., "Resume of Useful Formulas in Queuing Theory," *Operations Research,* Vol. 5, No. 2, 1957.
9. Sasieni, M., A. Yaspan, and L. Friedman, *Operations Research,* John Wiley and Sons, New York, 1959.

REVIEW QUESTIONS

1. Outline and compare the four alternate structures of waiting line situations discussed. Suggest a physical example of each.

2. If arrival rates follow the Poisson distribution, what would the distribution of the times between arrivals be?

3. What evidence is there that arrival rates in actual situations do in fact follow the Poisson distribution?

4. What evidence is there that service times follow the negative exponential distribution in actual processing situations?

5. Contrast infinite and finite waiting line models. What is the characteristic of the situation which makes the distinction between the two kinds of waiting line models?

6. Why is it not true that the difference between the mean number in the system L and the mean number in the waiting line L_q is simply the number of items being served?

7. Explain in physical terms why the waiting line may become infinitely long when the utilization factor is 1.

8. What are the effects on waiting time costs of pooling facilities?

PROBLEMS

1. Trucks arrive at a dock in a Poisson manner at the rate of 8 per hour. Service time distribution is closely approximated by the negative exponential. The average service time is 5 minutes.
  a. Calculate the mean number in the waiting line.
  b. Calculate the mean number in the system.
  c. Calculate the mean waiting time.
  d. Calculate the mean time in the system.
  e. Calculate the probability of six units being in the system.
  f. Calculate the utilization factor.

2. People arrive at a theater ticket booth in a Poisson distributed arrival rate of 25 per hour. Service time is a constant 2 minutes.
  a. Calculate the mean number in the waiting line.
  b. Calculate the mean waiting time.
  c. Calculate the utilization factor.

3. A taxi cab company has 4 taxi cabs at a particular location. Customer arrival rates and service rates are Poisson distributed. The average arrival rate is 10 per hour. The average service time is 20 minutes.
  a. Calculate the utilization factor.
  b. From Figure 8 determine the mean number in the waiting line.
  c. From Figure 9 determine the mean number in the system.
  d. Test the answers to b and c by the formula $L = L_q + r$.
  e. Determine the mean waiting time.
  f. Determine the mean time in the system.

4. Using the data in Problem 3:
  a. What would the utilization factor be if the number of taxi cabs was increased from 4 to 5?
  b. What would be the effect of this change on the mean number in the waiting line as determined by Figure 8?

c. What would be the effect of this change on the mean number in the system as determined by Figure 9?

d. What would be the effect of reducing the number of taxi cabs from 4 to 3?

5. A stenographer has five persons for whom she performs stenographic services. Arrival rates are Poisson distributed and service times follow the negative exponential distribution. The average arrival rate is 5 jobs per hour. The average service time is 10 minutes.

a. Calculate the mean number in the waiting line.

b. Calculate the mean waiting time.

c. Calculate the mean number of units being serviced.

d. Calculate the mean number of units running.

6. A trucking company has docking facilities with Poisson distributed arrival and service rates. Trucks arrive at the rate of 10 per hour and the unloading rate is 2 trucks per man hour. The time to unload a truck is inversely proportional to the number of workers unloading. The docking facility permits either one or two trucks to be unloaded at the same time. Under the present system, the entire crew works on the same truck until unloading is completed. Each man on the dock crew is paid $2.00 per hour. The cost of an idle truck and driver is estimated to be $15.00 per hour.

a. Determine the optimal number of workers for this docking facility and the average hourly cost.

b. What would be the effect of a 10 per cent increase in arrival rate on the optimal number of men? On the utilization factor?

c. What change in average hourly cost would result if the men were split into two crews?

d. What advantages would be gained by such a split?

e. Is such a split analogous to the facilities pooling as exemplified in the chapter?

7. A hospital has thirty beds in one particular section. Calls from patients follow a Poisson process and the distribution of the times required is approximated by the negative exponential. The mean call rate is 20 calls per hour and the mean service time is 8 minutes. The hospital believes that patients should have immediate service at least 80 per cent of the time because of possible emergencies. Qualified nurses of this type are paid $3.00 per hour.

a. Determine the optimal number of nurses for this section and the hourly cost.

b. Determine the average idle time and the cost of this idle time.

c. Assuming a nonprofit organization, how much extra must a patient pay for the 80 per cent criterion than if the immediate service level were placed at 50 per cent?

8. A hotel beauty shop has Poisson process arrival and service rates of 3 per hour and 1.25 per hour respectively. Beauty operators are paid $1.75 per hour plus tips, time and one half for over 40 hours per week. Incremental profit averages $1.00 per customer; fixed expenses are $100.00 per week, and the shop operates on a 6 day 48 hour week. Because of competitive factors, the management does not want customers to wait more than 15 minutes on the average.

a. Determine the optimal number of beauty operators.
b. Determine the weekly profit.
c. Evaluate the possibility of remaining open an extra hour each night if the average demand would be 10 per cent less than normal.
d. How much can the shop afford to pay per week for advertising that will increase business 5 per cent?

10

Waiting Lines and
Maintenance

With the rapid and continuous development of mechanization and automation, the problem of machine maintenance has become one of particular interest to production and operations management. We can view the problem as one of maintaining the reliability of the entire production system. In general, this reliability can be maintained and improved by the following:

1. *Increasing the size of repair facilities and crews* so that average machine downtime is reduced because maintenance crews are less likely to be busy when a breakdown occurs, or in some cases because a larger crew may be able to repair a machine more quickly.

2. *Utilizing preventive maintenance* where practical so as to replace critical parts before they fail. It is often possible to do this on second and third shifts and thereby not interfere with normal production schedules. Whether preventive maintenance is worthwhile or not depends on the distribution of breakdowns, the relation of preventive maintenance time to repair time, as we shall see, and the relative importance of downtime costs.

3. *Providing for slack in the system* at critical stages so that we have parallel paths available. This means excess capacity so that some machines can be down without affecting the delay costs to any great degree.

4. *Making individual components within a machine or the machines within the system more reliable* through improvements in engineering design. For example, special lubrication systems that may extend the life of working parts.

5. *Decoupling successive stages of the production system by inventories* between operations. The resulting independence of operations localizes the effect of a breakdown so that operations preceding and following the machine that is down are less likely to be affected.

To accomplish increased reliability by any of these means is costly, and therefore we can justify it only insofar as the costs of attaining it are offset by cost reductions in idle labor, scrap, lost business, etc. Number 4 in the preceding list may be regarded as an engineering design problem coupled with economic analysis. Number 5 interacts with problems of facility layout and inventory control, which are in themselves separate subjects. Numbers 1, 2, and 3, however, represent ideas which may be approached through the general methodology of waiting line models, and hence they will be the focus of our interest in this chapter.

Breakdown-Time Distributions

Breakdown-time distribution data are basic if we hope to be able to formulate any general policies concerning maintenance through the mechanism of waiting line models. The basic data might be gathered in the form of the number of hours or days that machines operate free of breakdowns. This data then could be formed into distributions which show the frequency with which a machine has a given free run time. These distributions take different shapes, depending on the nature of the equipment with which we are dealing. For example, a simple machine with few moving parts would tend to break down at nearly constant intervals following the last repair. That is, they exhibit minimum variability in their distribution of free run times. Curve *a* of Figure 1 would be fairly typical of such a situation. A large per cent of the breakdowns occur near the average breakdown time U, and only a few occur at the extremes. Obviously, we are in a rather good position to deal with such a situation, because the relatively small variability in the distribution makes it possible for us to predict with reasonable accuracy when the bulk of breakdowns will occur, and, therefore, we can anticipate the breakdown with some preventive maintenance policy.

If a machine is more complex, having many parts, each part has a failure distribution. When all these are grouped together in a single distribution of the free run time between breakdowns for any cause, we expect to find greater variability because the machine can break down for any one of a number of reasons. Some breakdowns could occur shortly after the last repair, or any time. Therefore, for the

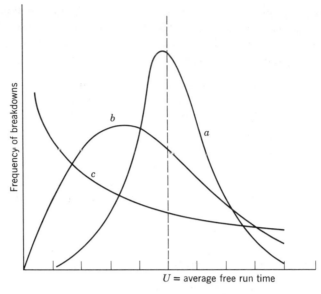

Figure 1. Frequency distributions of run time free of breakdowns representing three degrees of variability in free run time.

same average breakdown time U, we would find much wider variability of breakdown time as in curve b of Figure 1. Curve b has the same average free run time U as does curve a, but the probability of breakdown is more evenly distributed throughout the range.

To complete the picture of representative distributions of free run time, curve c is representative of a distribution with the same average breakdown time U, but with very wide variability. A large proportion of the breakdowns with a distribution such as curve c occur just after repair, and, on the other hand, a large proportion have a long free running time. Curve c may be typical of machines that require "ticklish" adjustments. If the adjustments are made just right, the machinery may run for a long time, but if not, readjustment and repair may be necessary almost immediately.

In waiting line models for maintenance, we normally deal with distributions of the percentage of breakdowns that exceed a given run time, such as Figure 2. They are merely transformations of the distributions of free run time typified by those in Figure 1. Taking curve a of Figure 1 as an example, we may convert it to the breakdown-time distribution of curve a in Figure 2 in the following way. If the vertical scale of Figure 1 is converted to the percentage of breakdowns that occur instead of the frequency of breakdowns, we can then easily plot the percentage of breakdowns that exceed a given run time. First, we know that all the breakdowns, or 100 per cent, exceed an average run time of zero. To obtain curve a in Figure 2, we simply subtract successively the percentages that occur at different free run times. We can see by examination of Figure 1 that almost 60 per cent of the breakdowns exceeded the average breakdown time U, and that very few of the breakdowns occurred after $2U$.

In practice, actual breakdown-time distributions can often be approximated by standard distributions, three of which are shown in Figure 2. Curve b is actually the exponential distribution which we discussed in connection with waiting line theory. From this point on, our reference will be to the breakdown-time distributions plotted in Figure 2, recognizing that the basic data for breakdown-time distributions would be accumulated as a distribution of the frequency of free run time as in Figure 1.

Preventive Maintenance versus Repair (Single Machine)

Let us assume a preventive maintenance policy that provides for an inspection and perhaps replacement of certain critical parts after

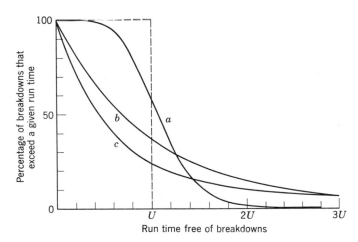

Figure 2. Breakdown time distributions. Curve a exhibits low variability from the average breakdown time U. Curve b is the exponential distribution and exhibits medium variability. Curve c exhibits high variability, and the dashed line represents a constant breakdown-time. Adapted from P. M. Morse, *Queues, Inventories and Maintenance,* John Wiley and Sons, New York, 1958.

the machine has been running for a fixed time, called the preventive maintenance period. The maintenance crew takes an average time T_m to accomplish the preventive maintenance. This is the preventive maintenance cycle. A certain proportion of the breakdowns will occur before the fixed cycle has been completed, and for these cases the maintenance crew will repair the machine, taking an average time T for the repair. This is the repair cycle. These two patterns of maintenance are diagrammed in Figure 3. The probability of occurrence of the two different cycles depends on the specific breakdown-time distribution of the machine and the length of the standard preventive maintenance period. If the distribution has low variability and the

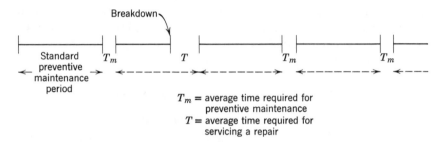

Figure 3. Illustrative record of machine run time, preventive maintenance time T_m, and service time for actual repairs T.

standard preventive maintenance period is perhaps only 80 per cent of the average free run time U, actual breakdown would occur rather infrequently, and most of the cycles would be preventive maintenance cycles. If the distribution were more variable for the same standard preventive maintenance period, more actual breakdowns would occur before the end of the standard period. Shortening the standard preventive maintenance period would obviously result in fewer actual breakdowns and lengthening it would have the opposite effect for any distribution. Assuming that either a preventive maintenance or a repair puts the machine in shape for a running time of equal probable length, the percentage of time that the machine is working can be plotted as the ratio of the standard maintenance period and the average run time U for the breakdown-time distribution. Figure 4 shows the relation of the percentage of time that the machine is working and the ratio of the standard period to the average run time U for the three distributions of breakdown-times shown in Figure 2. Note that, in general, when the standard period is short, say less than

50 per cent of U, the machine is working only a small fraction of the time. This is because the machine is down so often owing to preventive maintenance. As the standard period is lengthened, more actual breakdowns occur which require repair. For curves b and c this improves the fraction of time the machine is running because the combination of preventive maintenance time and repair time produces a smaller total of downtime.

Curve a, however, has a peak in it, or an optimum preventive maintenance period which maximizes the percentage of machine working time. What is different about curve a? It is based on the low variability breakdown-time distribution from Figure 2. For curve a, lengthening the maintenance period beyond about 70 per cent of U reduces the fraction of machine working time because actual machine breakdowns are more likely. For the more variable distributions of curves b and c this is not true, because breakdowns are more likely throughout their distributions than they are in curve a.

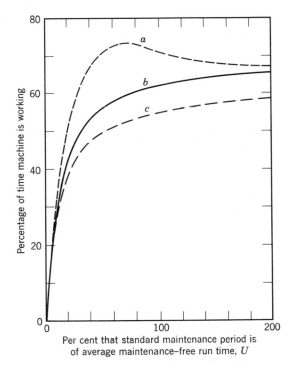

Figure 4. Percentage of time a machine is working for the three distributions of breakdown time shown in Figure 2. Preventive maintenance time T_m is 2 per cent of U, and repair time is 5 per cent of U. Adapted from P. M. Morse, *Queues, Inventories and Maintenance*, John Wiley and Sons, New York, 1958.

Guides to a Preventive Maintenance Policy

Some generalizations about preventive maintenance policy can be made through the concepts which we have developed. First, preventive maintenance is generally applicable to machines with breakdown-time distributions that have low variability, exemplified by curve a of Figure 2. In general, distributions with less variability than the exponential, curve b, are in this category. The reasons are that low variability means that we can predict with fair precision when the majority of breakdowns will occur. A standard preventive maintenance period can then be set which anticipates breakdowns fairly well.

Equally important, however, is the relation of preventive maintenance time to repair time. If it takes just as long to perform a preventive maintenance as it does to repair the machine, there is no advantage in preventive maintenance, which has the effect of reducing the amount of time that the machine can work. Thus if we are attempting to maximize machine running time, the machine spends a minimum amount of time being down for maintenance if we simply wait until it breaks down. This is shown by Figure 5, where we compare the percentage of the time a machine is working when repair time is greater than preventive maintenance time and when the two times are equal. Both curves are based on the low variability distribution of curve a, Figure 2. Note that curve d exhibits an optimum, but curve e does not. For curve e, the percentage of time that the machine works continues to increase as the standard maintenance period is lengthened, which results in more repairs and fewer maintenance cycles. Clearly, there is no advantage in preventive maintenance when $T_m = T$ from the point of view of maximum machine working time. To sum up, preventive maintenance is useful when breakdown-time distributions exhibit low variability and when the average time for preventive maintenance is less than the average time for repair after breakdown.

The effect of downtime costs can modify the conclusions just stated, however. Suppose that we are dealing with a machine in a production line. If the machine breaks down, the entire line may be shut down, with very high idle labor costs resulting. In this situation, preventive maintenance is more desirable than repair *if* the preventive maintenance can take place during second or third shifts, vacations, or lunch hours, when the line is normally down, anyway. This is true even when $T_m = T$. The determination of the standard preventive maintenance period would require a different, but

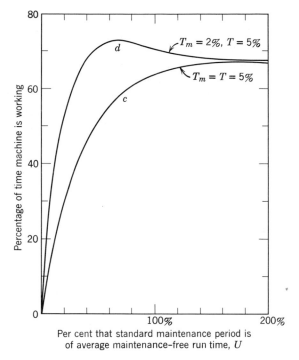

Figure 5. Comparison of percentages of machine working time when preventive maintenance time is less than repair time, curve d, and when they are equal, curve e. Curve d is identical with curve a, Figure 4. T_m and T are expressed as percentages of the average breakdown time U.

similar, analysis in which the percentage of machine working time was expressed as a function of repair time only, since preventive maintenance takes place outside of normal work time. An optimal solution would be one that minimized the total of downtime costs, preventive maintenance costs plus repair costs. The effect of the downtime costs would be to justify shorter standard preventive maintenance periods and to justify making repairs more quickly (at higher cost) when they do occur. There are many situations, however, where extra manpower on a repair job would not speed it up. In such cases, total repair time might be shortened by overtime on multiple shifts and weekends, with attendant higher costs. Optimal solutions would specify the standard preventive maintenance period, the machine idle time, and the repair crew idle time, which strike a balance between downtime costs and maintenance costs.

A special case exists when sales are such that the plant must operate at full capacity to meet demand. Under these circumstances, reduced machine working time due to repair and preventive maintenance reduces the number of units which can be sold and, therefore, affects income. Optimal maintenance policy is then even more heavily weighted in favor of shortening standard preventive maintenance periods and pouring in more effort to repair machines quickly when breakdowns occur. Morse [(4), pp. 165–166] has developed basic models that fit this special case in which an income-less-maintenance cost function is maximized.

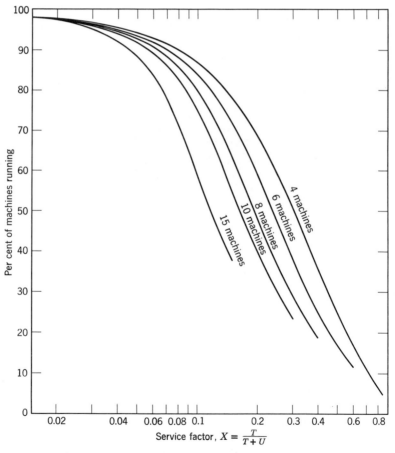

Figure 6. Per cent of machines running versus the service factor.

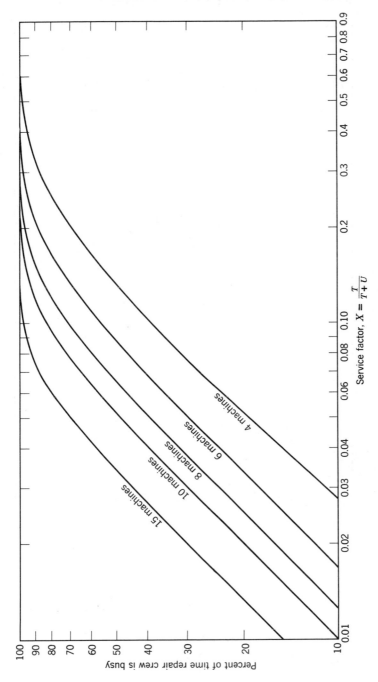

Figure 7. Per cent of time repair crew is busy versus the service factor.

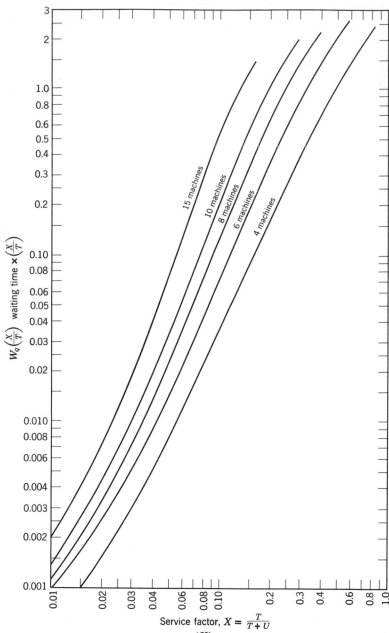

Figure 8. Waiting time $x\left(\dfrac{X}{T}\right)$ versus the service factor.

Maintaining Several Machines (Single Repair Crew)

The single machine situation that we have been discussing contains basic elements of general policy which can be carried over into the multimachine case. When several machines must be serviced, however, our problem more closely resembles the usual finite waiting line model. If we assume that all the machines have the same breakdown-time distribution, breakdowns are comparable to arrivals in the finite waiting line model, and the repair crew is the service station. As machines break down, the crew services them in the average time T as before. If the crew is already working on a machine, successive machines that break down must wait for service, and the costs associated with downtime will grow with the delay. We can reduce the chance that this will happen by increasing the size of the crew in some instances, but this solution also costs money and will increase the cost of crew idle time, waiting for breakdowns to occur. The problem, then, is one of striking a balance between the downtime costs of the machines and the idle time costs of the maintenance crew as before.

When the breakdown times and the repair times follow the exponential distribution, we may use the *Finite Queuing Tables* (5) to obtain solutions to a wide variety of specific problems. Figures 6, 7, and 8 show data computed from the *Finite Queuing Tables* for 4, 6, 8, 10, and 15 machines.

The curves for Figures 6, 7, and 8 give the per cent of machines running, the per cent of time that the repair crew is busy, and a factor related to the waiting time, all plotted in relation to the service factor X, as defined for use in the *Finite Queuing Tables*. Recall that the service factor is $X = T/(T + U)$, where T is the average time for service and U is the average free run time. We could compute from Figure 6, for example, the average output expected from a given bank of machines and a given service factor. Figure 7 gives directly the per cent of time that the repair crew is busy for a given service factor. Figure 8 allows us to calculate waiting time for a given service factor. For example, if $X = 0.1$, then from Figure 8, $W_q(X/T) = 0.125$ for eight machines. If $T = 1$ hour, then $W_q = 0.125 \times 1/0.1 = 1.25$ hours. If T were expressed in working days, then W_q is waiting time in working days.

Multiple Machine–Multiple Repair Crews

The multiple machine–multiple repair crew case is, of course, simply an extension of the single repair crew case. Figures 9, 10,

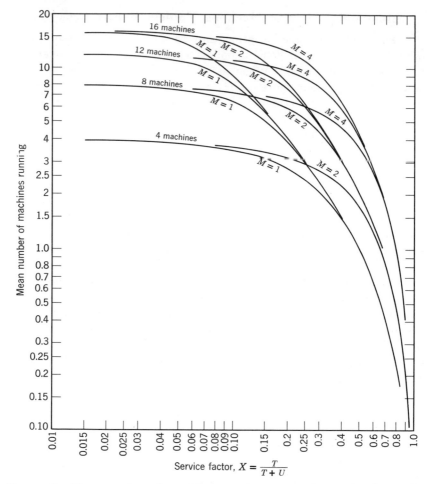

Figure 9. Mean number of machines running versus the service factor for different numbers of machines and repair crews, M.

and 11 present data on the average number of machines in running order, the per cent of time that the repair crew is busy, and a factor related to the waiting time, plotted in relation to the service factor for different numbers of machines and repair crews. Again, these charts will allow us to make calculations for specific cases.

Interpretation of the charts requires some care. For example, what would be the effect on the mean number of machines in running order, and on the combined waiting plus maintenance time, if one large repair crew could service a machine in half the time of two

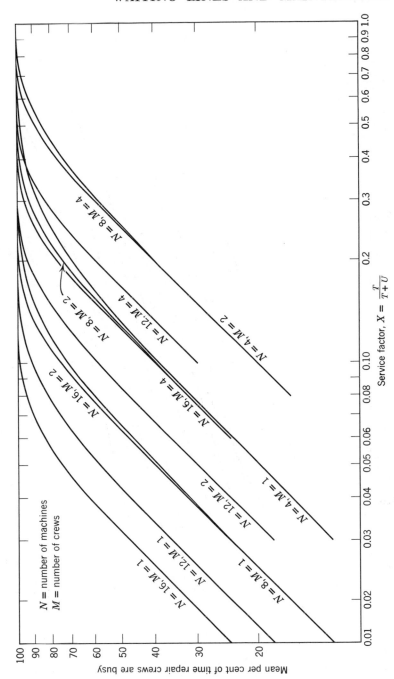

Figure 10. Mean per cent of time repair crews are busy versus the service factor for different numbers of machines and repair crews.

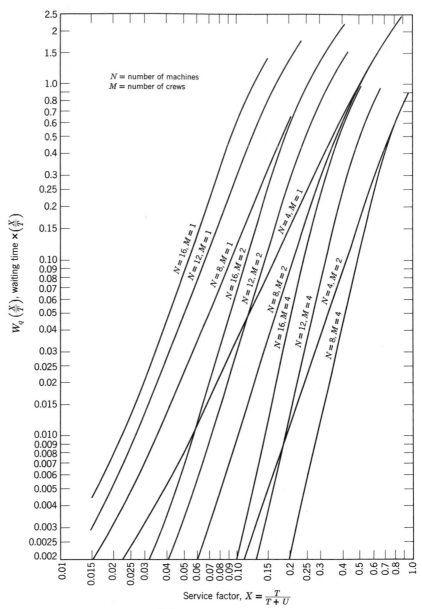

Figure 11. Waiting time $\times \left(\dfrac{X}{T}\right)$ versus the service factor for different numbers of machines and repair crews.

separate but smaller repair crews working independently? If we assume sixteen machines to be maintained, with an average exponential breakdown time of $U = 95$ hours, and if the service time $T = 5$ hours for two crews, the service factor is $X = 0.05$. From Figure 9, the average number of machines in running order would be fifteen. If one large crew were used which could service a machine in half the time, $T = 2.5$ hours, the service factor $X = 0.026$, and from Figure 9 an average of 15.4 machines would be kept in running order. The single fast repair crew is better than the two slower crews. Of course, the average time that a machine must wait for service is increased by the single crew from 0.7 hour to 1.42 hours as may be calculated from Figure 11. There is, however, a net reduction of time spent in maintenance of 2.5 hours per machine which results in a net reduction in the combined time of waiting plus maintenance and a net improvement in the number of machines in working order. Normally, of course, it would not be true that one large crew of twice the size could carry out repairs twice as fast; however, Figures 9, 10, and 11 and the *Finite Queuing Tables* may be used to evaluate whatever specific alternatives exist.

Summary

With the material in this chapter we have been able to formulate some general policies concerning preventive maintenance and present data which make it possible to formulate specific operational models. Where the assumption of exponential breakdown and service time are valid, the *Finite Queuing Tables* provide the means for quick solution to practical problems. There are many conditions where the assumptions of exponential breakdown and service time are not appropriate, and where other conditions of the problem require a somewhat more complex model. These cases are best handled through the techniques of simulation.

REFERENCES

1. Barlow, R., and L. Hunter, "Optimum Preventive Maintenance Policies, *Operations Research*, Vol. 8, pp. 90–100, 1960.
2. Bovaird, R. L., "Characteristics of Optimal Maintenance Policies," *Management Science*, Vol. 7, No. 3, pp. 238–254, April 1961.
3. Fetter, R. B., "The Assignment of Operators to Service Automatic Machines," *Journal of Industrial Engineering*, September–October 1955, pp. 22–29.
4. Morse, P. M., *Queues, Inventories, and Maintenance*, John Wiley and Sons, New York, 1958.

5. Peck, L. G., and R. N. Hazelwood, *Finite Queuing Tables,* John Wiley and Sons, New York, 1958.
6. Weiss, G. H., "A Problem in Equipment Maintenance," *Management Science,* Vol. 8, No. 3, pp. 266–278, April 1962.

REVIEW QUESTIONS

1. What kinds of incremental costs are associated with machine breakdown and repair?

2. Discuss the general methods by which the reliability of production systems can be maintained.

3. What is a breakdown-time distribution? How can it be derived?

4. Discuss the types of situations of machine breakdown which are typified by curves *a, b,* and *c,* respectively, in Figure 2.

5. What are the general conditions for which preventive maintenance is appropriate for a *single* machine?

6. If it takes just as long to perform a preventive maintenance as it does a repair, is there an advantage to preventive maintenance? How can high downtime costs modify this? What is the effect if preventive maintenance can be achieved during off hours when the machine is normally not working?

7. Compare the problem of maintaining a bank of machines to the general waiting line model.

8. What would be the effect on the mean number of machines in running order, and on the combined waiting plus maintenance time, if one large repair crew could service a machine in half the time of two separate but smaller repair crews working independently, assuming the multiple machine case?

PROBLEMS

1. A group of twenty machines is serviced by 6 repairmen. Breakdown and service rates follow the Poisson distribution. The average breakdown rate is 3 per 8-hour shift for each machine and the mean repair time is $1\frac{1}{2}$ hours.

    a. Determine the average number of machines running.

    b. Determine the average waiting time of a machine.

    c. What is the probability that a machine will be repaired as soon as it breaks down?

    d. What is the cost per shift of repairman idle time? (Repairman average earnings = $3.50 per hr.)

2. A lathe department with 8 machines has mean Poisson process breakdown for each machine and repair rates of 2.4 and 8.7 per 8-hour shift respectively.

    a. From Figure 6, determine the per cent of machines running.

    b. From Figure 7, determine the per cent of time the repair crew is busy.

    c. From Figure 8, determine the average waiting time.

    d. What is the average number of machines waiting for service?

    3. An automatic screw machine department has 16 machines. Service is required on these machines at random as approximated by the Poisson distribution. The distribution of service times follows the negative exponential. The mean number of calls for service is 3 per hour for each machine. The mean service time is 2.8 minutes per call.

        a. From Figure 9, determine the average number of machines running for 1, 2, and 4 operators.

        b. From Figure 10, determine the per cent of time the operators are busy for 1, 2, and 4 operators.

        c. From Figure 11, determine the average amount of waiting time for 1, 2, and 4 operators.

    4. A milling machine department has 10 machines. Breakdowns follow the Poisson process and average 0.4 per 8-hour shift for each machine. The service rate is 2.1 per 8-hour shift and also follows the Poisson process. Repairmen are paid $4.50 per hour and work individually. Machine downtime is estimated to cost $7.00 per hour. What is the optimal number of repairmen for this department?

    5. A steel rolling mill is operated 24 hours a day by a crew of 30 men with the following cost structure:

Average hourly wage	$4.00 per hour
Fringe benefits	10 per cent of labor cost
Fuel expense (not stopped for short periods)	$50.00 per hour
Power expense	$15.00 per hour
Heat and lights expense	$5.00 per hour
Water expense	$0.50 per hour
Expendable tools expense	$1.50 per hour
Depreciation expense	$8.00 per hour
Factory burden	$200.00 per hour

The breakdown rate follows the Poisson process and is 2 per hour. The distribution of repair times is approximated by the negative exponential; the mean service rate is 5 minutes if done by one repairman and varies inversely with the number of repairmen. Repairmen are paid $10 per hour (including fringe benefits).

        a. Determine the optimal number of repairmen for this rolling mill.

        b. What proportion of the time will repairmen be idle?

        c. What would be the effect of assigning some value to fill-in work done by repairmen in their idle time?

    6. A group of thirty machines has Poisson process breakdown rates of 2 per hour for each machine and a Poisson process service rate of 10 per hour. If preventive maintenance is done on these machines at night while they are idle, the daytime breakdown rates can be reduced by 40 per cent. The cost of downtime is estimated to be $8 per hour and capable repairmen are paid $5 per hour. The cost of second-shift preventive maintenance is estimated to be $500 per week. What cost advantage or disadvantage would be realized by adopting this plan? (5-day, 40-hour week.)

7. A group of twenty machines has Poisson process breakdown rates of three per hour for each machine and a Poisson service rate of 20 per hour. Management is considering the installation of a system of preventive maintenance. It is believed that by instituting various levels of preventive maintenance, breakdown rates can be decreased. To do this, however, repair time and the cost of repair parts will necessarily increase because of parts being replaced before they are completely worn out. After a study of maintenance records and machine design, the following estimates of various preventative maintenance levels have been prepared:

Level	Breakdown Rate	Service Time	Repair Parts
L_1	—30%	+20%	+50%
L_2	—40%	+35%	+80%
L_3	—50%	+75%	+120%

Downtime is estimated to cost $9 per hour. Capable repairmen are paid $6 per hour. Present repair part cost averages $1 per breakdown. Determine the optimal number of repairmen and preventive maintenance level.

8. A building materials yard loads trucks with a payloader-type tractor. Because of the varying travel distances, the distribution of truck loading times follows the negative exponential. The truck arrival rate follows the Poisson process. The mean service time is 6 minutes, and the arrival rate is 8 per hour. The waiting time per hour for a truck and driver is estimated to be $10. How much could the company afford to pay per day for an overhead hopper system that could fill any truck in 2 minutes? (Assume that the present tractor could adequately service the conveyors loading the hoppers.)

part **V**

PROGRAMMING MODELS

11

Linear Programming—
Distribution Methods

Linear programming is one of the most recent and far reaching developments in management science methodology. Many of the other model types have had their beginnings some time ago, and current efforts represent evolution and development based on relatively old fundamental ideas. This is true of inventory models, waiting line models, statistical models, and others. Linear programming, however, is a creation of the present era, dealing with some of the problems of allocating the resources of an enterprise. Perhaps the most general statement of objective of programming is that *we wish to allocate some kind of limited resource to competing demands in the most effective way.* These kinds of problems are some of the most fundamental to the effective operation of an enterprise.

Typical Allocation Problems

Following is a description of a number of typical problems which have been approached by linear programming methods. They are diverse in their settings and in the methods required for their solution, and should spark our imagination to think of related or different problems that might be approached in the same general way. Some are stated generally and others represent specific studies.

1. *Distribution of products from a set of origin points to a number of destinations* in a way which satisfies the demand at each destination and the supplies available at the origins, and minimizes total transportation cost.

2. *Distribution of products from factories to warehouses,* similar to 1, but minimizing combined production and distribution costs; or if the products have different revenues in the various marketing areas, maximizing a function of revenue minus production-distribution costs.

3. *Multiple plant location studies,* where common products are produced with a decentralized complex of plants. Here we wish to evaluate various alternate locations for the construction of a new plant. Each different location considered produces a different allocation matrix of product from the factories to the distribution points because of differing production-distribution costs. The best new location is the one that minimizes total production-distribution costs for the entire system, and this, of course, is not necessarily the location which seems to have the lowest production cost. (3, page 377)

4. *Locational dynamics for multiple plants.* Here, the problem is somewhat similar to 3, but the question is, which plants to operate at what levels for a given total demand. Since additional capacity at each location can normally be obtained through overtime, and since certain overhead costs can be saved by shutting down a plant, there are conditions when total costs are minimized by shutting down a plant and supplying the total demand from the other plants, even though overtime costs are incurred. The plant to be shut down is not necessarily the high production cost plant—this depends on the relative importance of production and distribution costs. (3, page 383)

5. *Redistribution of empty freight cars* from their existing locations to the points where they are needed in a way that minimizes transportation costs.

6. *Allocation of limited raw materials used in a variety of products* so that total profit is maximized, meeting market demands insofar as is possible. (10, page 65)

7. *Allocation of production facilities when alternate routings are available.* Given the unit machine time for the alternate machine routes, total hours available on the different machine classes, requirements for the number of each product, and unit revenue for each product, linear programming can give a solution that maximizes some profit function, minimizes incremental cost, or meets some other management objective. (10, page 53)

8. *Blending problems.* As an example, a paint manufacturer may need to prepare paint vehicles that are a blend of several constituents. The constituents, such as oil, thinner, etc., are available in limited quantity and in commercial blends of fixed proportions. Costs per gallon of the various possible raw materials are known. The problem

is to determine the amount of each raw material such that the required amounts for the new blends are obtained at minimum cost. Another similar problem is the blending of animal feed to provide certain minimum nutrient values at minimum cost. (8, page 156)

9. *Maximizing material utilization.* Many times different stock sizes must be stamped or cut from standard raw material sizes. The problem is to determine the combination of cuts that will meet requirements for the amounts of the different sizes with a minimum trim loss. (8, Chapter 8)

10. *Development of a program for production, when demand is seasonal.* Here we are attempting to allocate available capacity to various production periods for the products to be produced in such a way that requirements for all products are met and combined incremental inventory and production costs are minimized. The incremental production costs may include overtime premium, turnover costs, and extra subcontracting costs. (2, 4, 8, 10)

11. *Product mix problems.* Here we have a general class of problems of considerable interest. If we have production facilities that can be used to produce several different items which may have different costs, revenues, and market demands, we wish to know how best to allocate the available capacity to various products within the limitations of market demand. (4, 5, 10)

12. *Long-range planning.* The general capacity planning problem has been treated as being met by ownership, leases, or short-term contracts. A model cast in a linear programming framework may help in answering questions such as, (a) the effect of a given demand forecast on capacity plans, (b) the effects of changes in ownership costs, (c) the effect of changes in the costs of leased capacity, and (d) the sensitivity to forecast error of various decisions and costs (6).

STEPPING-STONE METHOD FOR DISTRIBUTION PROBLEMS

We begin our survey of linear programming with distribution (transportation) type problems using methods for solution commonly termed, "stepping-stone methods." These methods are discussed because the nature of the problems and solution makes close contact with all phases of the solution possible and one obtains a "feel" for what he is doing and why. This will also provide insights into the more complex, but more general, simplex solution to allocation problems which we shall cover in Chapter 12.

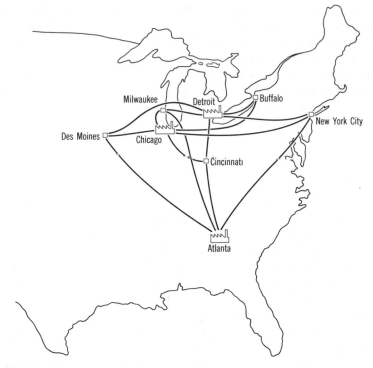

Figure 1. Geographical locations of factories and distribution points.

As a setting for an illustrative problem, let us assume the distribution situation indicated by Figure 1. Here we see that we have three factories located in Chicago, Detroit, and Atlanta, which produce some identical products. The distribution system of the organization has established five major distribution points that serve various market areas in Milwaukee, Cincinnati, Des Moines, Buffalo, and New York City. The three factories have capacities which determine the availability of product, and the market demand in the five major areas determine the requirements to be met. The problem in general, then, is one of determining an allocation of the available product at the three factory locations to the five distribution points in a way that meets the demands and minimizes the cost of distribution for the entire system. Data for our illustrative problem are shown in Table I. We see that there are 19,000 units available at the Detroit plant, 28,000 at Chicago, and 25,000 at Atlanta, or a total of 72,000. Similarly, demands in the five market areas are indicated in the

TABLE I. Summary of Quantities of Product Available and Required, and Distribution Costs per Thousand.

(Distribution or Transportation Matrix)

To Dist. Points / From Factories	Milwaukee (V)	Cincinnati (W)	Des Moines (X)	Buffalo (Y)	New York City (Z)	Available, at Factories 1000's
Detroit (A)	42	42	44	40	44	19
Chicago (B)	34	42	40	46	48	28
Atlanta (C)	46	44	42	48	46	25
Required, at Dist. Points 1000's	11	13	7	17	24	72

bottom row of the table, and also total 72,000 units, although, as we shall see later, this is not a necessary requirement for solution.

These figures of units available and required are commonly termed the "rim conditions." We have also shown in Table I the distribution costs per thousand units for all combinations of factories and distribution points. These figures are shown in the small boxes, for example, the distribution cost between the Chicago plant and the Milwaukee distribution point is $34 per thousand units. For convenience in notation, we have labeled the plants A, B, and C and the distribution points V, W, X, Y, and Z. Table I is commonly termed the "distribution or transportation matrix." Our measure of effectiveness is distribution cost, and we wish to distribute our 72,000 units available from the factories A, B, and C to the distribution points V, W, X, Y, and Z in such a way that the total distribution cost is at a minimum, within the restrictions imposed by units available and required.

An Initial Solution

We shall make a beginning by assigning the various units available in an arbitrary way, ignoring the distribution costs. We begin in the upper left-hand corner of the matrix (the so-called northwest corner) and we note that A has 19 (thousand) units available and V needs 11. We assign the 11 from A to V. (See Table II; circled numbers represent assigned product, for example, 11 in box AV means 11,000 units to go from A to V.) We have not yet used up A's supply, so we move to the right under column W and assign the balance of A's supply, 8, to W. Looking at the requirements for W, we note that it has a total requirement of 13, so we drop down to row B and assign the balance of W's requirements, 5, from B's supply of 28. We then move to the right again and assign the balance of B's supply of 7 to X. We continue in this way, stair-stepping down the matrix until all the arbitrary assignments have been made, as in Table II. The total distribution cost, $3176, is calculated in Table II below the matrix. Note that we have 7 squares with assignments and 8 open squares, that is, squares without assignments.

TABLE II. Northwest Initial Solution

To \ From	V	W	X	Y	Z	Available 1000's
A	42 ⑪	42 ⑧	44	40	44	19
B	34	42 ⑤	40 ⑦	46 ⑯	48	28
C	46	44	42	48 ①	46 ㉔	25
Required, 1000's	11	13	7	17	24	72

Total distribution cost:

$$AV, \quad 11 \times 42 = \quad 462$$
$$AW, \quad 8 \times 42 = \quad 336$$
$$BW, \quad 5 \times 42 = \quad 210$$
$$BX, \quad 7 \times 40 = \quad 280$$
$$BY, \quad 16 \times 46 = \quad 736$$
$$CY, \quad 1 \times 48 = \quad 48$$
$$CZ, \quad 24 \times 46 = \quad \underline{1104}$$
$$\$3176$$

Improving the Initial Solution

Is the initial northwest corner solution shown in Table II the best possible? We can answer this by successively examining the open squares to see if total distribution cost is reduced by shifting assignments to them. When all possible shifts in assignments of this nature have been made, we can be certain that we have an optimum solution. Let us examine such a procedure. First, we want to be sure that any shift made conforms to the restrictions of available and required units as shown in the rim conditions of the distribution matrix. Let us select the first open square in the first column, square BV. If we were to add 1 (thousand) unit each to BV and AW and subtract the same amount from AV and BW, we would still satisfy the restrictions of availability and requirements. Table III shows us that such a

TABLE III. Evaluation of Square BV for Possible Improvement

From \ To	V	W	X	Y	Z	Available 1000's
A	(−) 42 (11)→	42 (8)(+)	44	40	44	19
B	34 (+)←	42 (5)(−)	40 (7)	46 (16)	48	28
C	46	44	42 (1)	48 (24)	46	25
Required, 1000's	11	13	7	17	24	72

Evaluation of square BV: for shifting one unit to BV, change in cost is:

$$+34 - 42 + 42 - 42 = -8.$$

Since this is a net improvement in cost, increase the assignment for BV to the maximum possible. This is limited by the assignment for BW which can be reduced by only 5. Maximum improvement at BV is, therefore, $5(-8) = -40$. New total distribution cost $= 3176 - 40 = \$3136$.

shift would be advantageous because we would be shifting from higher cost routes to lower cost routes. We would be adding 1000 units each to routes BV and AW at a cost of $34 + 42 = \$76$ and subtracting 1000 units each from AV and BW at a saving of $42 + 42 = \$84$, or a net decrease of $84 - 76 = \$8$ per 1000 units. Since we have found an advantageous shift, we want to take advantage of it by increasing the assignment at BV to the maximum. The shift in assignments is limited to 5 units, however, because that is the existing assignment at BW, and we cannot reduce it below zero. Therefore, the maximum improvement in the solution that we can effect at BV is 5000 units at a distribution cost saving of \$8 per thousand, or \$40. The new total

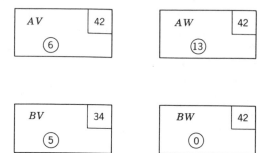

Figure 2. Resulting assignments to the four squares affected by the evaluation of square *BV*.

distribution cost is now $3136. We make the changes in assignment indicated and the resulting assignments to the four squares affected are indicated in Figure 2.

We now proceed systematically through the table, column by column, evaluating each open square, making shifts in assignments when they are advantageous. The pattern required to evaluate a given open square is not necessarily a rectangular one as in Tables III and IV, however. We must have a closed path starting at the square to be evaluated, with right angle turns only at squares that

TABLE IV.   Evaluation of Square *CV* for Possible Improvement

To From	V	W	X	Y	Z	Available 1000's
A	⑥ 42	⑬ 42	44	40	44	19
B	(−) ⑤ 34	42	⑦ 40	⑯ (+) 46	48	28
C	(+) 46	44	42	① (−) 48	㉔ 46	25
Required, 1000's	11	13	7	17	24	72

Evaluation of square *CV*: for shifting one unit to *CV*, change in cost is:

$$+46 - 34 + 46 - 48 = +10.$$

This would result in a net increase in total cost and therefore the changes are not made.

already have assignments, proceeding either clockwise or counter-clockwise. Squares may be skipped to get to the corners as illustrated in Table IV. No diagonal movement is permitted. Beginning at the square being evaluated, we assign a plus sign, since we propose to add a load, and alternate with minus and plus signs as we go around the closed path. There is ordinarily only one closed path to evaluate for a given open square if the initial arbitrary solution has been properly established. By adhering to the closed path idea which we have expressed, we insure that proposed shifts in assignments do not violate the restrictions of the rim conditions of availability and requirements, since in each row and column we add and subtract the same amount so that the totals are unaffected by the shifts in assignments that we make.

We proceed systematically through the table evaluating each open square, column by column or row by row, making shifts and assignments when they are advantageous. The next open square for evaluation in column V is CV. Square CV is evaluated in Table IV, and we see that if we were to make the shift in allocations indicated, there would be a net increase in total distribution cost. Therefore, the changes are not made. Proceeding to column W we pass over square BW, since the evaluation of square BV by Table III indicates immediately that BW will only increase total cost. The next open square is CW which is evaluated in Table V. Here we see an illus-

TABLE V.   Evaluation of Square CW for Possible Improvement

To / From	V	W	X	Y	Z	Available 1000's
A	42 (+)(6)	(−) 42 (13)	44	40	44	19
B	34 (−)(5)	42	40 (7)	46 (16)(+)	48	28
C	46	44 (+)	42	48 (1)(−)	46 (24)	25
Required, 1000's	11	13	7	17	24	72

Evaluation of square CW: for shifting one unit to CW, change in cost is:

$$+44 - 48 + 46 - 34 + 42 - 42 = +8.$$

This would result in a net increase in total cost and therefore the changes are not made.

tration of a more complex closed path for the evaluation of an open square. Note that in each row and column affected there is a plus sign and a minus sign so that the rim restrictions are not violated by the proposed change in assignments. Table V indicates that CW would also result in a net increase in total costs; therefore, the changes are not made. As we proceed systematically through the table, evaluating each open square, we may find that squares which previously indicated no improvement may later yield improvement because of subsequent changes made. This process is continued until all open squares show no further improvement.

An optimal solution. At this point, an optimal solution has been obtained and is shown in Table VI. The total distribution cost required by the optimal solution is \$2746, which is \$430 less than

TABLE VI. An Optimal Solution. Evaluation of All Squares without Assignments in This Table Results in no Further Improvement

To \\ From	Milwaukee (V)	Cincinnati (W)	Des Moines (X)	Buffalo (Y)	New York City (Z)	Available, 1000's
Detroit (A)	42 +8	42 ②	44 +4	40 ⑰	44 0	19
Chicago (B)	34 ⑪	42 ⑩	40 ⑦	46 +6	48 +4	28
Atlanta (C)	46 +10	44 ①	42 0	48 +6	46 ㉔	25
Required, 1000's	11	13	7	17	24	72

Total distribution cost = \$2746.

the original northwest corner solution. This reduction in total distribution cost can be accomplished by the column-by-column evaluation of thirteen open squares, five of which yield improvement. The first time through the table, no improvement is obtained from CV, BW, CW, CX, AZ, and BZ, but squares BV, AX, and AY yield improvement. The second time through the table, BW and CW yield improvement. At this point the solution is optimal, because reevaluation of all open squares shows no further improvement possible. Table VI shows the resulting optimal solution and indicates the evaluations of the open squares by the small figures in the lower left-hand corner of the squares. Note that all open squares show that distribution costs would either increase or not change at all by further shifts in assignments.

Alternate optimal solutions. The fact that open squares CX and AZ in Table VI have zero evaluations is important and gives us flexibility in determining the final plan of action because these zero evaluations allow us to generate other solutions which have the same total distribution cost as the optimal solution generated in Table

TABLE VII. Alternate Basic Optimum Solution

From \ To	V	W	X	Y	Z	Available 1000's
A	42 +8	42 (2)	44 +4	40 (17)	44 0	19
B	34 (11)	42 (11)	40 (6)	46 +6	48 +4	28
C	46 +10	44 0	42 (1)	48 +6	46 (24)	25
Required, 1000's	11	13	7	17	24	27

VI. To take an example, since open square CX has a zero evaluation we may make the shifts in allocations indicated by its closed path and generate the alternate basic optimal solution shown in Table VII. Similarly, we could generate another basic optimal solution by shifting assignments to open square AZ as shown in Table VIII. Also

TABLE VIII. Second Alternate Basic Solution

From \ To	V	W	X	Y	Z	Available, 1000's
A	42 +8	42 0	44 +4	40 (17)	44 (2)	19
B	34 (11)	42 (10)	40 (7)	46 +6	48 +4	28
C	46 +10	44 (3)	42 0	48 +6	46 (22)	25
Required, 1000's	11	13	7	17	24	72

note that we could derive a different basic optimal solution from Table VII by taking advantage of the fact that open square AZ has a zero evaluation; or following a similar procedure, we could derive a fourth alternate basic optimum solution from Table VIII by taking advantage of the fact that open square CX has a zero evaluation. We have discovered for this example an entire family of solutions that are all equally good, and optimal.

But we are not yet finished, for we can generate literally dozens of other optimal solutions from each of the five basic optimal solutions we have just discussed. Let us go back to our original optimal solution shown in Table VI. Recall that we derived a second optimal solution shown in Table VII by shifting 1000 units to open square CX which had a zero evaluation. But it was not necessary for us to shift the entire 1000 units to CX. We could have shifted only 500 units, or 400, or 300, or any fractional amount of the 1000 units. Table IX shows one of these solutions where 500 units have been shifted to

TABLE IX. Alternate Optimum Solution Derived from Table VI

From \ To	V	W	X	Y	Z	Available, 1000's
A	42 +8	42 (2)	44 +4	40 (17)	44 0	19
B	34 (11)	42 (10½)	40 (6½)	46 +6	48 +4	28
C	46 +10	44 (½)	42 (½)	48 +6	46 (24)	25
Required, 1000's	11	13	7	17	24	72

CX. This solution as well as any of the others which would involve shifting fractional amounts of 1000 units to CX has the same total distribution cost as the original optimal solution. We see that where we have optimal solutions containing open squares with zero evaluations we have great flexibility in distribution at minimum cost. Where fractional shifts are permitted, we have in fact an infinite number of alternate optimal solutions. This may often make it possible to satisfy nonquantitative factors in the problem and still retain a minimum distribution cost solution.

Degeneracy in distribution problems. Another aspect of the mechanics of developing a solution is the condition known as degeneracy. Degeneracy occurs in distribution problems when, in shifting assignments to take advantage of a potential improvement, more than one of the existing assignments go to zero, as has been true in our previous examples. Degeneracy can also occur in an initial solution which does not meet the requirements stated below. Examination of the problem in Table X shows that degeneracy is about to

TABLE X. Evaluation of Square *AX* Produces Degeneracy

To\From	V	W	X	Y	Z	Available, 1000's
A	42 (-) 6 —	42 (13) —→	44 (+)	40	44	19
B	34 (+) 6 ←	42	40 6 (-)	46 (16)	48	28
C	46	44	42 (1)	48 (24)	46	25
Required, 1000's	12	13	6	17	24	72

happen. Note that the problem in Table X is only slightly different from the example we have been using, that is, the requirements for *V* and *X* have been changed. This problem was set up in the usual way, and an initial northwest corner solution was established. The open squares were evaluated column by column as before, and changes in assignments were made when they indicated potential improvement. In Table X we are evaluating square *AX* by the closed path pattern shown. Potential improvement is indicated, since a unit of allocation reduces transportation costs by $4 per thousand. We wish to press this advantage to the maximum by shifting as much as possible to *AX*. We are limited, however, by both squares *AV* and *BX*, each of which has an allocation of 6000 units assigned to them. When the shift in assignment is made, both *AV* and *BX* go to zero. This is shown in the resulting matrix of Table XI. We now have only six allocations instead of seven as before and we do not meet the restriction on the stepping-stone method of solution which we stated earlier, that is, that the number of allocations must be

TABLE XI.   Problem Now Degenerate, Squares *AV*, *BW*, *CW*, *BX*, *CX*, *AY*, and *AZ* Cannot Be Evaluated

From \ To	V	W	X	Y	Z	Available, 1000's
A	42	42 ⑬	44 ⑥	40	44	19
B	34 ⑫	42	40	46 ⑯	48	28
C	46	44	42	48 ①	46 ㉔	25
Required, 1000's	12	13	6	17	24	72

$m + n - 1$. The practical effect of this is that several of the open squares, namely, *AY*, *DW*, *CW*, *BX*, *CX*, *AY*, and *AZ*, cannot be evaluated in the usual way because a closed path cannot be established for them.

The degeneracy can be resolved, however, by regarding one of the two squares where allocations have disappeared as an allocated square with an extremely small allocation, which we shall call an ϵ allocation. This is illustrated in Table XII. Conceptually, we shall regard the ϵ allocation as being infinitesimally small so that it does not affect the totals indicated in the rim. The ϵ allocation, however, does make it possible to meet the $m + n - 1$ restriction on the number of allocations so that evaluation paths may be established for all

TABLE XII.   Degeneracy Resolved by Use of the ϵ Allocation

From \ To	V	W	X	Y	Z	Available, 1000's
A	42 ⓔ	42 ⑬	44 ⑥	40	44	19
B	34 ⑫	42	40	46 ⑯	48	28
C	46	44	42	48 ①	46 ㉔	25
Required, 1000's	12	13	6	17	24	72

TABLE XIII. Shift of ϵ Allocation when it Is Limiting

From \ To	V	W	X	Y	Z	Available, 1000's
A	42 (−)(ε)	42 (13)	44 (6)	40	44 (ε)(+)	19
B	34 (+)(12)	42	40	46 (−) (16)	48	28
C	46	44	42	48 (+)(1)	46 (24)(−)	25
Required, 1000's	12	13	6	17	24	72

open squares.   The ϵ allocation is then simply manipulated as though it were no different from the other allocations.

If in subsequent manipulations the ϵ allocation square is the one that limits shifts in assignments, it is simply shifted to the square being evaluated and the usual procedure is then continued.   This is illustrated in Table XIII where we are attempting to evaluate square AZ by the closed path shown.   A potential improvement of $8 per 1000 units is indicated, but the limiting allocation at a negative square is the ϵ allocation.   The net effect of adding and subtracting the ϵ allocation around the closed path is to move the ϵ allocation from square AV to AZ.   The procedure is then continued as before until an optimal solution is obtained.

TABLE XIV.   Disappearance of the ϵ Allocation when it Falls at a Positive Corner of an Evaluation Path

From \ To	V	W	X	Y	Z	Available, 1000's
A	42	42 (13)	44 (−) (6)	40	44 (+)(ε)	19
B	34 (12)	42	40	46 (16)	48	28
C	46	44	42 (+)	48 (1)	46 (24)(−)	25
Required, 1000's	12	13	6	17	24	72

As the procedure continues it may happen that the ϵ allocation disappears. This is illustrated in Table XIV where we are evaluating the open square CX. Potential improvement of $4 per 1000 units is indicated, and here we are limited not by the ϵ allocation but by the allocation of 6000 units at AX. In making the adjustments we add and subtract 6000 units around the closed path according to the signs indicated, and the result is that the ϵ allocation at AZ becomes 6000 units. We now have seven squares with positive allocations and the ϵ allocation is no longer needed. In carrying through the solution of larger scale problems, degeneracy could appear and disappear in the routine solution of a problem, or we might sometimes have more than one ϵ allocation. Also, optimal solutions may be degenerate.

Unequal Supply and Demand

We may now bring up the question of the handling of a problem where supply and demand are not equal. Suppose, for example, that supply exceeded demand. This situation is shown in Table XV

TABLE XV. Distribution Matrix with Supply Exceeding Demand

To / From	V	W	X	Y	Z	Dummy	Available
A	10	3	2	5	7	0	10
B	9	8	5	6	6	0	15
C	4	8	7	8	7	0	25
Required	4	10	7	14	12	3	50

where there is available a total of 50 units from the three points of origin at A, B, and C. Demand at the five distribution points V, W, X, Y, and Z, however, totals only 47 units. This situation can be handled in the problem by creating a dummy distribution point to receive the extra three units. The nonexistent distribution point is assigned zero distribution costs, since the product will never be shipped. The optimal solution then assigns 47 of the 50 available units in the most economical way to the five real distribution points and assigns the balance to the dummy department.

When demand exceeds supply, we can resort to a modification of the same technique. In this instance, we create a dummy factory to take up the slack. Again zero distribution costs are assigned for the dummy factory, since product will never be shipped. The solution then assigns the available product to the distribution points in the most economical way. The solution then shows which distribution points should receive "short" shipments in order that total distribution costs are minimized.

TECHNIQUES FOR SIMPLIFYING PROBLEM SOLUTION

First, we can simplify the arithmetic complexity considerably by two methods. A little thought about the illustrative example we used will convince us that it is the cost differences that are important in determining the optimal allocation rather than their absolute values. Therefore, we can reduce all costs by a fixed amount and the resulting allocation will be unchanged. In our illustrative example, we may subtract 34 from all distribution cost values so that the numbers with which we must work are of such magnitude that many evaluations can be accomplished by inspection. Another simplification in the arithmetic may be accomplished by expressing the rim conditions in the simplest terms. For example, in our illustrative problem we expressed the rim conditions in thousands of units so that we were able to work with two digit numbers only.

Getting an advantageous initial solution. The northwest corner initial solution is actually not used a great deal in practice, since it is ordinarily a rather poor solution which will involve a number of steps to develop an optimal solution. The usual procedure is to start with some solution by inspecting the most promising routes, entering allocations which are consistent with the rim conditions. In establishing such an initial solution, the only rules to be observed are that there must be exactly $m + n - 1$ allocations, and it must be possible to evaluate all open squares by the closed path methods previously discussed. If the initial solution turns out to be degenerate, it is a simple matter to increase the allocations to the exact number required by resorting to the ϵ allocation. There are a number of short-cut methods which are commonly used such as row minimum, column minimum, matrix minimum, and VAM. They all have merits; but we shall discuss VAM in some detail because it seems particularly valuable for hand computation of problems of fairly large scale.

Vogel's Approximation Method (VAM) (9)

VAM makes possible a very good initial solution which in fact is usually the optimal solution. The technique is a simple one and reduces considerably the amount of work required to develop a solution. We shall use as an example the same problem used to illustrate the stepping-stone method. Table XVI shows the distribution matrix

TABLE XVI. Distribution Matrix with Initial VAM Row and Column Differences Shown

	↓8	0	2	6	2	
To \ From	V	W	X	Y	Z	Available
A	8	8	10	6	10	19	2
B	0	8	6	12	14	28	6
C	12	10	8	14	12	25	2
Required	11	13	7	17	24	72

with the distribution costs all reduced by the constant amount, $34. The steps in determining an initial VAM solution are as follows:

1. *Determine the difference between the two lowest distribution costs for each row and each column.* This has been done in Table XVI, and the figures at the heads of columns and to the right of the rows represent these differences. For example, in column V the three distribution costs are **8**, **0**, and **12**. The two lowest costs are **8** and **0**, and their difference is **8**. In row A the two lowest distribution costs are **6** and **8**, or a difference of **2**. The other figures at the heads

of the columns and to the right of the rows have been determined in a similar way.

2. *Select the row or column with the greatest difference.* For the example we are using, the row or column with the greatest difference is column *V* which has a difference of 8.

3. *Assign the largest possible allocation within the restrictions of the rim conditions to the lowest cost square in the row or column selected.* This has been done in Table XVII. Under column *V* the

TABLE XVII. First VAM Assignment Satisfies *V*'s Requirement. Row and Column VAM Differences are Recalculated

To \ From	V	W	X	Y	Z	Available	
	↓ 8	0	2	6	2		
A	8 X	8	10	6	10	19	2
B	0 (11)	8	6	12	14	28	6 2
C	12 X	10	8	14	12	25	2
Required	11	13	7	17	24	72	

lowest cost square is *BV* with a cost of 0, and we have assigned 11 units to that square. The 11-unit assignment is the largest possible because of the restriction imposed by the number required at distribution point *V*.

4. *Cross out any row or column completely satisfied by the assignment just made.* For the assignment just made at *BV*, the requirements for *V* are entirely satisfied, so we may cross out the other squares in that column, since we can make no future assignments to them. This is shown in Table XVII.

5. *Recalculate the differences as in Step 1, except for rows or columns that have been crossed out.* This has been done in Table XVII where row *B* is the only one affected by the assignment just made.

6. *Repeat Steps 2 to 5 until all assignments have been made.*

a. Column Y now exhibits the greatest difference; therefore, we allocate 17 units to AY, since it has the smallest distribution cost in column Y. Since Y's requirements are completely satisfied, the other squares in that column are crossed out. Differences are recalculated. This entire step is shown in Table XVIII.

TABLE XVIII. Second VAM Assignment Satisfies Y's Requirement. Row and Column VAM Differences are Recalculated

	8̶	0	2	↓ 6̶	2	
To \ From	V	W	X	Y	Z	Available
A	8 X	8	10	6 ⑰	10	19 2
B	0 ⑪	8	6	12 X	14	28 6̶2
C	12 X	10	8	14 X	12	25 2
Required	11	13	7	17	24	72

b. The recalculated differences now show all remaining columns and rows with a difference of **2**. The lowest cost square in any column or row is BX which has a cost of 6. We assign **7** units to BX which completely satisfies the requirements at X. Table XIX shows the allocation of **7** units at BX, the crossing out of the other squares in column X, and the recalculation of cost differences for the remaining rows and columns.

c. Again we see that the remaining rows and columns have a cost difference of **2**. The lowest cost remaining squares are AW and BW, both of which have a cost of **8**. By making the assignments in rows A and B, we completely use up the supplies at A and B. Table XX shows these two allo-

TABLE XIX. Third VAM Assignment

| | 8̶ | 0 | 2̶ ↓ | 6̶ | 2 | |
	V	W	X	Y	Z	Available	
A	8 X	8	10 X	6 (17)	10	19	2
B	0 (11)	8	6 (7)	12 X	14	28	6̶2
C	12 X	10	8 X	14 X	12	25	2
Required	11	13	7	17	24	72	

cations, the crossing off of the remaining squares in rows A and B, and the recalculation of cost differences in the remaining row C.

TABLE XX. Fourth and Fifth VAM Assignments

| | 8̶ | 0 | 2̶ | 6̶ | 2 | |
	V	W	X	Y	Z	Available	
A	8 X	8 (2)	10 X	6 (17)	10 X	19	2̶ ←
B	0 (11)	8 (10)	6 (7)	12 X	14 X	28	6̶2̶ ←
C	12 X	10	8 X	14 X	12	25	2
Required	11	13	7	17	24	72	

d. The last two allocations at *CW* and *CZ* are made by inspection of the rim conditions. This is shown in Table XXI. An evaluation of the open squares in Table XXI shows that this solution is optimal, being identical to the optimal solution shown in Table VI.

TABLE XXI. **Final Assignments at *CW* and *CZ* Balance with Rim Restrictions and Yield VAM Initial Solution Which Is Optimal**

To / From	*V*	*W*	*X*	*Y*	*Z*	Available
A	8 X	8 (2)	10 X	6 (17)	10 X	19
B	0 (11)	8 (10)	6 (7)	12 X	14 X	28
C	12 X	10 (1)	8 X	14 X	12 (24)	25
Required	11	13	7	17	24	72

Modified Distribution Method (MODI)

The MODI method for improving an initial solution is an alternate to the stepping-stone method. The main difference is that the MODI method selects the particular open square that will yield the most improvement by a set of index numbers calculated for the rows and columns. The shifts in allocation are then made for that square, according to the usual rules of a closed path. Revised index numbers then indicate the next best open square, and the procedure is repeated until an optimal solution is obtained. The index numbers are referred to as R for row index numbers and K for column index numbers. In the MODI method, the beginning solution may be the northwest corner solution, or some other feasible solution, as before. The VAM initial solution is preferable since it will probably involve fewer steps to an optimal solution.

Calculating R and K values. Given some initial solution, an index number is calculated for each row and column. These numbers, together with the "costs" associated with each square, are used to evaluate open squares. We will let R and K represent the row and column numbers and use subscripts to identify the rows and columns, that is, R_A is the row number for row A, etc. The costs associated with each square will be denoted by C, therefore C_{AX} is the cost for square in AX. Then for a *square with an assignment*, and only for squares with assignments, we establish the following formula:

$$R + K + C = 0$$

We will begin with the northwest corner initial solution for the illustrative example used in the stepping-stone method to illustrate the procedure. Table XXII shows the initial northwest corner solution. We assume that $R_A = 0$ to get started; therefore based on square AV, we can calculate K_V as follows:

$$K_V = -R_A - C_{AV} = 0 - 8 = -8$$

TABLE XXII. Northwest Corner Initial Solution with R and K Values Entered to Evaluate Open Squares by MODI

From \ To	$K_V = -8$	$K_W = -8$	$K_X = -6$	$K_Y = -12$	$K_Z = -10$	Available
$R_A = 0$	8 ⑪	8 ⑧	10	6	10	19
$R_B = 0$	0	8 ⑤	6 ⑦	12 ⑯	14	28
$R_C = -2$	12	10	8	14 ①	12 ㉔	25
Required	11	13	7	17	24	72

Square	Calculation	Improvement
BV	$0 + (-8) + 0 = -8$	Yes
CV	$(-2) + (-8) + 12 = 2$	No
CW	$(-2) + (-8) + 10 = 0$	No
AX	$0 + (-6) + 10 = 4$	No
CX	$(-2) + (-6) + 8 = 0$	No
AY	$0 + (-12) + 6 = -6$	Yes
AZ	$0 + (-10) + 10 = 0$	No
BZ	$0 + (-10) + 14 = 4$	No

Also, knowing that $R_A = 0$, we can calculate K_W:

$$K_W = -R_A - C_{AW} = 0 - 8 = -8$$

Now that we have K_W we can calculate R_B at the square BW as follows:

$$R_B = -K_W - C_{BW} = 8 - 8 = 0$$

Stepping down the squares with assignments in this fashion, we can calculate the balance of R and K values as follows:

$$K_X = -R_B - C_{BX} = 0 - 6 = -6$$

$$K_Y = -R_B - C_{BY} = 0 - 12 = -12$$

$$R_C = -K_Y - C_{CY} = 12 - 14 = -2$$

$$K_Z = -R_C - C_{CZ} = 2 - 12 = -10$$

These values are entered in the headings of rows and columns in Table XXII.

Evaluating Open Squares by MODI

The open squares are evaluated by adding algebraically the R, K, and C values associated with them. This is done for all the open squares of our example in Table XXII, below the matrix. Squares that yield negative numbers are squares that would result in improvement if the assignments were shifted to them, according to the closed path patterns which we have used before. The square that yields the largest negative number would result in the greatest improvement, and we should select that square to make shifts in assignments. In Table XXII the largest negative number is -8 for square BV. We therefore make the changes in assignment to the maximum possible, according to its closed path as we did in our previous procedure. These changes are shown in the matrix of Table XXIII. Since the assignments are now changed, some of the R and K values will change. Table XXIII also shows the new R and K values based on the set of squares with assignments in the new matrix. Open squares are then evaluated by the new R, K, and C values as before. In this instance, however, we have simply shown the evaluations as small numbers in the lower left-hand corners of the open squares. The largest negative number again identifies the open square which would result in the greatest improvement. In this instance, it is square AY.

TABLE XXIII. Assignment Changes Indicated by Table XXII Are Made. New MODI R and K Values and the Evaluation of Open Squares are Shown

To From	$K_V=-8$	$K_W=-8$	$K_X=-14$	$K_Y=-20$	$K_Z=-18$	Available
$R_A=0$	8 (6)	8 (13)	10 −4	6 −14	10 −8	19
$R_B=8$	0 (5)	8 8	6 (7)	12 (16)	14 4	28
$R_C=6$	12 10	10 8	8 0	14 (1)	12 (24)	25
Required	11	13	7	17	24	72

The Optimal Solution by MODI

This procedure is continued until a matrix of assignments is obtained where the R, K, and C values yield positive evaluations for all open squares. Table XXIV shows the optimal solution which is

TABLE XXIV. Optimal Solution with MODI R and K Values and Open Square Evaluations

To From	$K_V=0$	$K_W=-8$	$K_X=-6$	$K_Y=-6$	$K_Z=-10$	Available
$R_A=0$	8 0	8 (2)	10 4	6 (17)	10 0	19
$R_B=0$	0 (11)	8 (10)	6 (7)	12 6	14 4	28
$R_C=-2$	12 10	10 (1)	8 0	14 6	12 (24)	25
Required	11	13	7	17	24	72

identical with that obtained by the stepping-stone method in Table VI. The MODI evaluations in lower left-hand corners of the open squares are now all positive, indicating that no further improvement can be obtained.

Mathematical Formulation of Distribution-Type Models

A mathematical formulation of our distribution problem is now in order. The following are three word statements which we wish to express with mathematical symbolism, using our distribution example for illustrative purposes:

1. The sum of units sent to distribution points V, W, X, Y, and Z equals the amount available at each of the supplying factories. For example, for factory A, we say that the sum of units sent to V, W, X, Y, and Z equals 19. We will have three equations like this, one for A, one for B, and one for C.

2. The sum of units received from factories A, B, and C equals the amount required for each of the receiving distribution points. For example, for distribution point V, the sum of units received from A, B, and C equals 11. We will have five equations like this, one each for V, W, X, Y, and Z.

3. Our objective is to minimize the sum of the products of units allocated times distribution costs for all routes. There will be one such equation.

To state these ideas mathematically, let us call the assigned loads x. The subscripts will identify which x we mean. Therefore, the first three equations that identify the distribution of product available are for A, B, and C, respectively:

$$x_{AV} + x_{AW} + x_{AX} + x_{AY} + x_{AZ} = 19 \tag{1}$$

$$x_{BV} + x_{BW} + x_{BX} + x_{BY} + x_{BZ} = 28 \tag{2}$$

$$x_{CV} + x_{CW} + x_{CX} + x_{CY} + x_{CZ} = 25 \tag{3}$$

Also, the five equations that identify the units of product received by V, W, X, Y, and Z respectively are:

$$x_{AV} + x_{BV} + x_{CV} = 11 \tag{4}$$

$$x_{AW} + x_{BW} + x_{CW} = 13 \tag{5}$$

$$x_{AX} + x_{BX} + x_{CX} = 7 \tag{6}$$

$$x_{AY} + x_{BY} + x_{CY} = 17 \tag{7}$$

$$x_{AZ} + x_{BZ} + x_{CZ} = 24 \tag{8}$$

Finally, the *objective function* is:

$$42x_{AV} + 42x_{AW} + 44x_{AX} + 40x_{AY} + 44x_{AZ}$$

$$34x_{BV} + 42x_{BW} + 40x_{BX} + 46x_{BY} + 48x_{BZ}$$

$$46x_{CV} + 44x_{CW} + 42x_{CX} + 48x_{CY} + 46x_{CZ} = \text{minimum} \qquad (9)$$

The first eight equations represent our model. The ninth formulates our objective. The method of solution is linear programming, and a specific solution is represented by the optimum assignment matrix in Table VI.

Zeros in the Matrix

We note that in our optimal solution, represented by Table VI, there are only seven routes that end up with assignments. Therefore, there are eight others where the x's are zero. This is not an accident. As we pointed out previously, it is true that if we have m sources and n destinations in our problem, then *no more than* $m + n - 1$ of the routes will have a positive value of x. In our case, there will be at least $15 - (3 + 5 - 1) = 8$ zeros. This is fundamental to linear programming.

Now let us see if the knowledge of the number of zeros in the matrix can help us to understand something about linear programming. Recall that basic algebra taught us that two unknowns and two independent equations can be solved simultaneously. In our case we have fifteen unknowns and only eight problem equations plus an objective function, but we know that at least eight of the unknowns are zero, so in reality we have one more equation than we need. As a matter of fact, what we did to solve our problem was start with an arbitrary solution in which we assumed that 8 x's were zero. The other 7 x's were assigned values that were consistent with the rim conditions. We then proceeded systematically to improve our solution, which involved changing our minds several times as to which of the x's should be zero. We could have taken a trial-and-error approach to solving the problem, each time calculating the total time for the solution. To do so, we would have to take all combinations of zero assignments, solve for the remaining x's to determine their values, and finally compute the total distribution cost by means of the objective function. By tabulating the total distribution cost associated with each combination of assignments, we could finally select the optimum solution by finding the one with the lowest total distribution cost; however, we would have to have computed for all possible combinations to be sure that the combination we had selected was the best possible. Linear programming takes us to the optimum solution much more directly and gives us a test for knowing when we have it, so that we need not put in additional effort.

Linear programming determines which of the variables are zero and gives the value of those that are not zero for the optimum solution. If someone had told us which of the x's were zero to begin with, our problem would have been very simple. Let us see that this is true. From Table VI, our optimum solution, we can see where these zeros should be. They are:

$$x_{AV}, \; x_{AX}, \; x_{AZ}, \; x_{BY}, \; x_{BZ}, \; x_{CV}, \; x_{CX}, \; \text{and} \; x_{CY}$$

If we substitute the value of zero for each of these eight variables in our first eight equations, we have:

$$\overset{0}{x}_{AV} + x_{AW} + \overset{0}{x}_{AX} + x_{AY} + \overset{0}{x}_{AZ} = 19 \tag{1a}$$

$$x_{BV} + x_{BW} + x_{BX} + \overset{0}{x}_{BY} + \overset{0}{x}_{BZ} = 28 \tag{2a}$$

$$\overset{0}{x}_{CV} + x_{CW} + \overset{0}{x}_{CX} + \overset{0}{x}_{CY} + x_{CZ} = 25 \tag{3a}$$

$$\overset{0}{x}_{AV} + x_{BV} + \overset{0}{x}_{CV} = 11 \tag{4a}$$

$$x_{AW} + x_{BW} + x_{CW} = 13 \tag{5a}$$

$$\overset{0}{x}_{AX} + x_{BX} + \overset{0}{x}_{CX} = 7 \tag{6a}$$

$$x_{AY} + \overset{0}{x}_{BY} + \overset{0}{x}_{CY} = 17 \tag{7a}$$

$$\overset{0}{x}_{AZ} + \overset{0}{x}_{BZ} + x_{CZ} = 24 \tag{8a}$$

From this we obtain directly the fact that $x_{BV} = 11$ (from $4a$), $x_{BX} = 7$ (from $6a$), $x_{AY} = 17$ (from $7a$), and $x_{CZ} = 24$ (from $8a$). Then from ($1a$) we know that $x_{AW} = 2$ since $x_{AY} = 17$. From ($2a$) we know that $x_{BW} = 10$, since $x_{BV} = 11$ and $x_{BX} = 7$. Finally, from ($3a$) we know that $x_{CW} = 1$ since $x_{CZ} = 24$. We still have equation $5a$ which we have not used, although we now have all the values of our unknowns. We can check some of our values with it, and we find that $x_{AW} + x_{BW} + x_{CW} = 13$. Of course, these values also check with the values obtained previously and displayed in our optimal distribution matrix.

We can see that the distribution methods of linear programming make a great contribution to the *practical* solution of these types of problems. If linear programming did not exist, we could only guess at solutions, perhaps finding an improved solution from time to time based on some individual's insight. To consider the trial-and-error approach, however, would be impractical or even impossible for problems of the magnitude encountered in business and industrial practice.

Summary

Now that we have covered the basic methodology for distribution problems of linear programming, there are some important variations and conditions which follow easily and extend the range of application of distribution methods. The first is the inclusion in our objective of minimizing combined production plus distribution costs. In the illustrative example that we used, it is probable that the production costs at the three factory locations were not identical. The addition of these different production costs in the matrix would undoubtedly result in a different allocation of capacity to demand.

In problems where we wish to determine which plants to operate and at what levels, we may wish to determine whether or not it would be more economical to use overtime capacity with attendant higher costs in one location, and produce less at other factory locations. This can be handled easily by regarding the overtime production at each location as a separate source of supply. The production cost at these overtime sources is of course somewhat higher than it would be for regular time production; however, the expanded production-distribution matrix will handle this with no difficulty.

It would be realistic to consider problems where the revenue obtained for products distributed in different marketing areas varies. In this instance, we wish to deal not with a cost matrix, but with a marginal profit matrix, that is, revenue–production costs–distribution costs. Our objective now will be to maximize marginal profit rather than to minimize costs. This requires only a minor change in our usual procedure. Since the figures in the matrix now represent a measure of profit rather than costs, we would make changes in allocation when using the stepping-stone method where such a change would result in an increase in profit. In making shifts in allocations, however, we are still limited by the smallest allocation at a negative square in the closed path. In establishing an initial solution by the VAM method for a profit matrix, we would compute differences for the two highest marginal profit figures in a given row or column, instead of the two smallest cost figures as we had indicated when dealing with a cost matrix. In the MODI method for improving a solution, maximizing a profit function means simply that squares that yield positive numbers are squares that would result in improvement if the assignments were shifted to them, according to the closed path patterns. The square that yields the largest positive number would yield the greatest improvement. Otherwise the procedure is identical.

REFERENCES

1. Bertoletti, M., "Planning Continuous Production by Linear Programming," *Management Technology, No. 1,* January 1960, pp. 75–81.
2. Bowman, E. H., "Production Scheduling by the Transportation Method of Linear Programming," *Operations Research,* Vol. 4, No. 1, 1956, pp. 100–103.
3. Buffa, E. S., *Modern Production Management,* John Wiley and Sons, New York, 1961, Chapter 8.
4. Charnes, A., and W. W. Cooper, *Management Models and Industrial Applications of Linear Programming,* 2 Volumes, John Wiley and Sons, New York, 1961.
5. Ferguson, R. O., and L. F. Sargent, *Linear Programming,* McGraw-Hill Book Company, New York, 1958.
6. Fetter, R. B., "A Linear Programming Model for Long Range Capacity Planning," *Management Science,* Vol. 7, No. 4, 1961, pp. 372–378.
7. Henderson, A., and R. Schlaifer, "Mathematical Programming," *Harvard Business Review,* May–June 1954.
8. Metzger, R. W., *Elementary Mathematical Programming,* John Wiley and Sons, New York, 1958.
9. Reinfeld, N. V., and W. R. Vogel, *Mathematical Programming,* Prentice-Hall, Englewood Cliffs, N. J., 1958.
10. Vazsonyi, A., *Scientific Programming in Business and Industry,* John Wiley and Sons, New York, 1958.

REVIEW QUESTIONS

1. What is the general nature of problems for which linear programming provides a general model?

2. What is the structure of the northwest corner initial solution to distribution-type problems?

3. How do we know whether or not a shift in assignments is advantageous in the stepping-stone method? How do we know when an optimal solution has been obtained?

4. Is it possible to have more than one optimal allocation in a distribution problem? What is the practical significance of this?

5. If fractional assignments are allowed and alternate optima exist, how many alternate optimal solutions could be generated?

6. What conditions produce degeneracy in distribution problems? In initial solutions?

7. How can the condition of degeneracy be resolved in a distribution problem?

8. How can unequal supply and demand be handled in the distribution matrix?

9. Outline Vogel's Approximation Method (VAM). Does it result in an optimal solution?

10. Why does the Modified Distribution Method (MODI) provide a more efficient means of improving an initial solution? How many variables will result from a 4 × 5 distribution matrix? How many of the variables will have a zero allocation?

11. How would an objective function proportional to profits rather than to costs affect the practical procedures of solving distribution-type problems?

PROBLEMS

1. A company has factories at A, B, and C which supply warehouses at D, E, F, and G. Monthly factory capacities are 70, 90, and 115 respectively. Monthly warehouse requirements are 50, 60, 70, and 95 respectively. Unit shipping costs are as follows:

From	To			
	D	E	F	G
A	$17	$20	$13	$12
B	$15	$21	$26	$25
C	$15	$14	$15	$17

Determine the optimum distribution for this company to minimize shipping costs.

2. A company with factories at A, B, and C supplies warehouses at D, E, F, and G. Monthly factory capacities are 20, 30, and 45 respectively. Monthly warehouse requirements are 10, 15, 40, and 30 respectively. Unit shipping costs are as follows:

From	To			
	D	E	F	G
A	$6	$10	$6	$8
B	$7	$9	$6	$11
C	$8	$10	$14	$6

Determine the optimum distribution for this company to minimize shipping costs.

3. A company has factories at *A*, *B*, and *C* which supply warehouses *D*, *E*, *F*, and *G*. Monthly factory capacities are 300, 400, and 500 respectively. Monthly warehouse requirements are 200, 240, 280, and 340 respectively. Unit shipping costs are as follows:

From	To			
	D	*E*	*F*	*G*
A	$7	$9	$9	$6
B	$6	$10	$12	$8
C	$9	$8	$10	$14

Determine the optimum distribution for this company to minimize shipping costs.

4. A company has factories at *A*, *B*, and *C* which supply warehouses at *D*, *E*, *F*, and *G*. Monthly factory capacities are 160, 150, and 190 respectively. Monthly warehouse requirements are 80, 90, 110, and 160 respectively. Unit shipping costs are as follows:

From	To			
	D	*E*	*F*	*G*
A	$42	$48	$38	$37
B	$40	$49	$52	$51
C	$39	$38	$40	$43

Determine the optimum distribution for this company to minimize shipping costs.

5. A company has factories at *A*, *B*, *C*, and *D* which supply warehouses at *E*, *F*, *G*, *H*, and *I*. Monthly factory capacities are 200, 225, 175, and 350 respectively. Monthly warehouse requirements are 130, 110, 140, 260, and 180 respectively. Unit shipping costs are as follows:

From	To				
	E	*F*	*G*	*H*	*I*
A	$14	$19	$32	$9	$21
B	$15	$10	$18	$7	$11
C	$26	$12	$13	$18	$16
D	$11	$22	$14	$14	$18

Determine the optimum distribution for this company to minimize shiping costs. (*Hint.* Use VAM for initial solution and MODI to evaluate.)

6. A company has factories at *A*, *B*, and *C* which supply warehouses at *D*, *E*, *F*, and *G*. Monthly factory capacities are 250, 300, and 200 respectively for regular production. If overtime production is utilized, the capacities can be increased to 320, 380, and 210 respectively. Incremental unit overtime costs are $5, $6, and $8 per unit respectively. The current warehouse requirements are 170, 190, 230, and 180 respectively. Unit shipping costs between the factories and warehouses are at the top of page 323.

| | To | | | |
From	D	E	F	G
A	$8	$9	$10	$11
B	$6	$12	$9	$7
C	$4	$13	$3	$12

Determine the optimum distribution for this company to minimize costs.

7. A company with factories at *A*, *B*, *C*, and *D* supplies warehouses at *E*, *F*, *G*, and *H*. Monthly factory capacities are 100, 80, 120, and 90 respectively for regular production. If overtime production is utilized, the capacities can be increased to 120, 110, 160, and 140 respectively. Incremental unit overtime costs are $5, $2, $3, and $4 respectively. Present incremental profits per unit excluding shipping costs are $14, $9, $16, and $27 respectively for regular production. The current monthly warehouse requirements are 110, 70, 160, and 130 respectively. Unit shipping costs are as follows:

| | To | | | |
From	E	F	G	H
A	$3	$4	$5	$7
B	$2	$9	$6	$8
C	$4	$3	$8	$5
D	$6	$5	$4	$6

Determine the optimum distribution for this company.

12

Linear Programming—Simplex Methods*

Simplex methods of linear programming are more general in scope and application than the distribution-transportation methods. Distribution problems may be solved by the simplex method, but usually with some additional time and effort. The simplex method, however, can be used where distribution methods cannot; hence, the field of application for simplex is considerably broader. In developing the conceptual framework for the simplex method, we will first use a graphical example to introduce the nature of the problem restrictions and objectives, show an algebraic solution, and finally present the detailed procedure for solution of more complex problems. The problems set up for illustrative purposes are necessarily simple; however, this is not a limitation of simplex methods or of linear programming. Actually, one of the great advantages of linear programming is the complexity of problems that can be handled.

GRAPHIC INTERPRETATION

For simple problems we can show graphically how the restrictions of the linear programming problem limit the possible solution and how the objective function determines the optimum solution for a problem. This will help in the interpretation of the algebraic and procedural aspects of the simplex method.

As an example let us consider the facilities of a company which

---

* The simplex methods of solution were developed by Professor George B. Dantzig, University of California, Berkeley.

manufactures a line of refrigerators and air conditioners. The major manufacturing departments are the machine shop, the stamping department, the "unit" department, which makes the refrigeration units for both products, and separate final assembly lines for the refrigerators and air conditioners. The monthly capacities of the five departments are as follows:

Department	Capacity for Refrigerators		Capacity for Air Conditioners
Machine shop	7500	or	6000
Stamping	5000	or	9000
Unit	6000	or	7000
Refrigerator assembly	4000		—
Air conditioner assembly	—		5000

The first three departments produce both refrigerator and air conditioner parts in the proportions scheduled within the capacity restrictions indicated. For example, the machine shop could devote all of its capacity to the production of refrigerator parts—7500 refrigerator parts per month. Alternately, it could produce parts for 6000 air conditioners, or proportionate combinations of the two products. The final assembly facilities for the two products are specialized and separate, as indicated by the capacity figures.

The marginal contribution (sales value less variable cost) is $50 per refrigerator and $60 per air conditioner. We wish to know how many of each product to produce to maximize marginal contribution, assuming we can sell what we make. We will remove this assumption of a sellers' market at a later point.

Let us set up the restrictions of the problem. We shall denote the number of air conditioners by x and the number of refrigerators by y. The simplest restrictions are those imposed by the two final assembly lines. They indicate that the number of air conditioners produced per month must be less than or equal to 5000 and that the number of refrigerators must be less than or equal to 4000. These restrictions are plotted in Figure 1. The shaded areas of Figure 1 indicate the parts of the graph that are eliminated as feasible solutions to the problem by the limitations of assembly line capacity. Any feasible solution to the problem must be a combination of air conditioners and refrigerators which falls within the area abcd.

The other restrictions are only slightly different. The machine shop capacity limits production to either 6000 air conditioners, 7500 refrigerators, or comparable combinations of both. This restriction is shown in Figure 2 as a straight line which goes through the points $(x = 0,\ y = 7500)$ and $(x = 6000,\ y = 0)$. This line further restricts the area of feasible solutions. The only combinations of air conditioner and refrigerator production which would not exceed the capacity of the machine shop are those that fall on or below the line.

Figure 2 also shows the limitations imposed by the capacities of the stamping and unit departments. The stamping department restriction is represented by a straight line that goes through the two points $(x = 0,\ y = 5000)$ and $(x = 9000,\ y = 0)$. Combinations of air conditioner and refrigerator production which are equivalent fall on this straight line, for example, 900 air conditioners and 4500 refrigerators, or 4500 air conditioners and 2500 refrigerators. Finally, the unit department restriction is represented by a straight line that goes through the two points $(x = 0,\ y = 6000)$ and $(x = 7000\ y = 0)$, which is shown also in Figure 2. The only combinations of air conditioner and refrigeration production that do not exceed the capacity

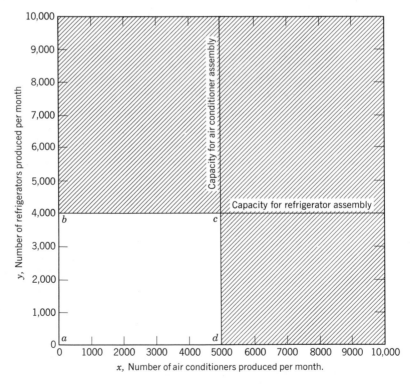

Figure 1. Graphic illustration of the limitations imposed by the final assembly capacity of air conditioners and refrigerators.

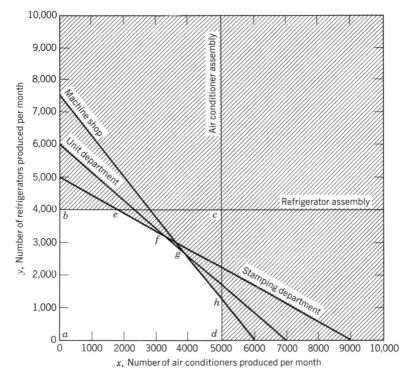

Figure 2. Remaining limitations imposed by capacities of the machine shop, unit department, and stamping department. The area enclosed by *abefghd* includes all feasible solutions to the problem.

of the unit department are those that fall on or below its line. Note that all the restrictions have been expressed as straight lines, that is, linear relationships. The term, "linear programming," is derived from the fact that all relationships within the model are linear.

Figure 2 shows clearly that the feasible solutions to our problem fall within the white area in *abefghd*. All combinations that fall in the shaded area exceed the capacity of one or more departments. The remaining question is then: Which of the feasible combinations will maximize marginal contribution?

Maximizing Marginal Contribution

Recall that marginal contribution was earned at the rate of $50 per refrigerator and $60 per air conditioner. Our objective function is then:

$$60x + 50y = \text{maximum}$$

Our objective is to produce the combination of air conditioners and refrigerators that is feasible and at the same time maximizes marginal contribution. Let us select arbitrarily some marginal contribution figure to see how the objective function looks graphically. At a total marginal contribution of $180,000, for example, the objective function becomes:

$$60x + 50y = 180,000$$

when $x = 0$, $y = 3600$, and $y = 0$, $x = 3000$

The line passing through these two points is shown as the $180,000 line in Figure 3. This line defines all combinations of air conditioner and refrigerator production that yield a total marginal contribution of $180,000.

Now let us choose a larger value of marginal contribution, perhaps $240,000. The objective function becomes:

$$60x + 50y = 240,000$$

when $x = 0$, $y = 4800$, and $y = 0$, $x = 4000$

The line passing through these two points is also shown in Figure 3 as the $240,000 line. It defines all combinations of air conditioner and refrigerator production that yield a total marginal contribution of $240,000. Note that it is parallel to the $180,000 line. If we increase the marginal contribution to $300,000, we have the $300,000 line shown in Figure 3. We can see now that we will be limited in the size of the total marginal contribution by the point g. It defines the combination of air conditioner and refrigerator production that produces the largest possible marginal contribution within the space of feasible solutions. Reading from the graph, the point g is approximately at the coordinate $x = 3800$, $y = 2700$. Since the point g is the intersection of the two lines which define the machine shop capacity and the unit department capacity, we can determine the point g exactly by solving the equations of these two lines simultaneously. These two equations are of the form $y = mx + b$, where m is the slope of the line and b is the y intercept. The two equations are:

Machine shop capacity,

$$y = -1.25x + 7500$$

Unit department capacity,

$$y = -\tfrac{6}{7}x + 6000$$

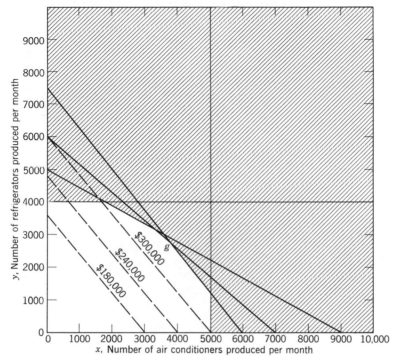

Figure 3. Marginal contribution lines plotted to show the effect of larger and larger marginal contributions. The maximum possible marginal contribution within the polygon is defined by a marginal contribution line through the point g.

solving simultaneously, we have

$$7500 - 1.25x = 6000 - \tfrac{6}{7}x$$

$$2.75x = 10{,}500$$

$$x = 3825 \text{ air conditioners}$$

using $x = 3950$ in the first equation, we have

$$y = -1.25(3825) + 7500$$
$$= 2725 \text{ refrigerators}$$

the marginal contribution of this solution is:

marginal contribution $= 60(3825) + 50(2725) = \$365{,}750$

Of course, this agrees with the values of the production program read approximately from the graph.

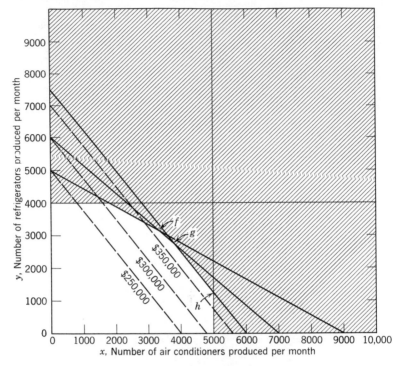

Figure 4. Effect of change of relative profitability on objective function produces a family of optimum solutions along the line segment *gh*.

The graphical interpretation of linear programming can also be extended to three-dimensional space. For example, we could have shown three products, perhaps air conditioners, refrigerators, and stoves. The lines which represent restrictions on the problem would becomes planes. Feasible solutions would appear in a volume instead of an area, and optimal would occur at the intersections of planes instead of lines. Beyond three-dimensional problems, there is no direct geometric presentation.

The Effect of Changes in Objective Function

Let us assume for a moment that the objective function is slightly different, perhaps reflecting an increase in the profitability of air conditioners. Assume that the marginal contribution from air conditioners has increased to $62.50 per air conditioner and that the marginal contribution for refrigerators has remained at $50. The new objective function is $62.5x + 50y =$ maximum. We have shown plotted in Figure 4 Iso-Revenue lines for total marginal contributions of $250,000, $300,000, and $350,000. We can see that the slope of the revenue lines is identical to the slope of the machine shop restriction line. We will now have an entire family of alternate optimum solutions described by the line segment gh. All combinations of air conditioner and refrigerator production which fall on this line segment have the maximum possible total marginal contribution. This solution is geometrically equivalent to the alternate optimum solutions that we obtained in our discussion of distribution methods of linear programming.

Market Restrictions

Let us now examine what happens if we remove the assumption stated earlier that we were operating in an unlimited market. Suppose that market studies have indicated that we cannot expect to sell more than 4500 air conditioners and 3000 refrigerators per month. These

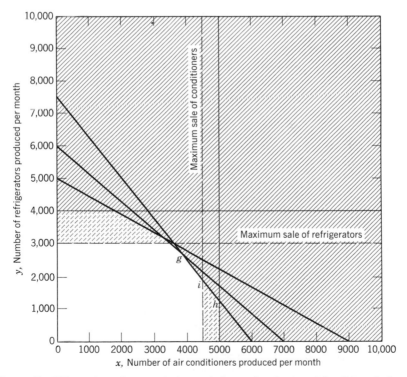

Figure 5. Effect of market restrictions on the enclosed area of feasible solutions.

may be plotted as additional restrictions to feasible solutions, as indicated in Figure 5. Note that if we are considering our first objective function to be valid, the market restrictions have not changed the optimal solution, which is still indicated by the point g. That is, the controlling limitation is still determined by the capacities in the machine shop and in the unit department. If we are considering the second objective function, the family of alternate optimum solutions has been reduced to the line segment gi because of the limitations of the market for air conditioners. More severe market limitations would of course change this. If, for example, the market studies indicated a maximum sale of 4000 air conditioners and only 2000 refrigerators, all the plant capacities become irrelevant and the maximum total marginal contribution is achieved by producing to meet market requirements, as may be verified by an examination of the graphical relationships.

ALGEBRAIC INTERPRETATION

Let us take a slightly different problem and develop an algebraic solution, attempting to relate our methods to the graphic interpretation as well as to the distribution methods discussed previously.

Let us assume the conditions of a plant which manufactures two products, which we designate by x and y. Each product is manufactured by a two-step process which involves machines A and B. The process time for the two products on the two machines is as follows:

Product	Machine A	Machine B
x	2 hours	3 hours
y	4 hours	2 hours

For the period ahead, machine A has available 80 hours and machine B has available 60 hours.

The marginal contribution (sales value minus variable cost) for product x is $60 per unit, and for y it is $50 per unit. The company faces a situation where it can sell as much as it can produce for the immediate planning period ahead, and therefore wishes to know how many units of each of the two products it should produce to maximize its marginal contribution.

Formulation of the Problem

Since we are limited only by the available hours on the two machines, we wish to make symbolically the common-sense statement that, for each of the two machines, the total time spent in the manufacture of product x and of product y cannot exceed the total time available. For machine A then, since product x requires two hours per unit and y four hours per unit, 2 (units of product x) + 4 (units of product y), must be less than or equal to 80 hours. Symbolically, this is:

$$2x + 4y \leqq 80 \qquad\qquad (A\text{–}1)$$

And for machine B,

$$3x + 2y \leqq 60 \qquad\qquad (B\text{–}1)$$

In addition, since the total marginal contribution depends only on the amounts of the two products produced, the objective function is:

$$\text{Marginal contribution} = 60x + 50y = \text{maximum} \qquad (C\text{–}1)$$

Let us pause for a moment to see how the problem looks graphically. Figure 6 shows the restrictions for the capacity of the two machines plotted for the limiting cases when the productive hours

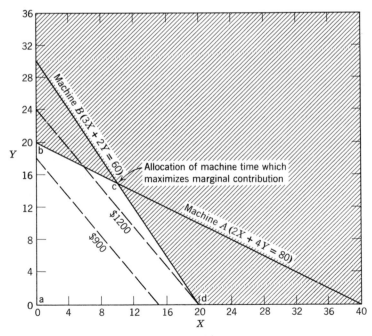

Figure 6. Graphical solution of example used for algebraic interpretation of the simplex method.

allocated to products x and y total 80 hours and 60 hours for machines A and B respectively. The objective function is also plotted for the two levels of total marginal contribution, \$900 and \$1200, and it is easy to see that point c defines the combination of products x and y for which we will obtain maximum marginal contribution.

Slack Variables

Formulations A–1 and B–1 are inequalities, that is, they state that the total time on machine A, for example, allocated to products x and y might not be as much as 80 hours. There could be some idle time. If we let W_A represent this idle time, we convert (A–1) to an equation with W_A taking up the slack:

$$2x + 4y + W_A = 80 \qquad (A\text{–}2)$$

And for machine B,

$$3x + 2y + W_B = 60 \qquad (B\text{–}2)$$

The only permissible values for the unknowns are zero, or some positive value, that is, we cannot produce negative amounts of the products or have negative idle time on the machines.

We now have two equations with four unknowns for which we wish to determine the values x, y, W_A, and W_B. It can be shown that there is a solution to such a system, such that at least two of the unknowns are zero. The practical effect of this statement is that our problem becomes one of determining which two of the variables should be zero in order that marginal contribution is maximum.

Initial Solution

To start, we first develop a trivial solution, which is nonetheless feasible and which we may then improve by a procedure that will take us, step by step, toward the optimum solution. This initial solution is comparable to the northwest corner initial solution we discussed under Distribution Methods. Let us start with the worst possible solution, from the point of view of our objective function, in which W_A and W_B are assumed to be the variables with positive values, and x and y are zero. In other words, all the available machine time is idle, since there is no production. First, we solve for W_A and W_B by transposing (A–2) and (B–2) as follows:

$$W_A = 80 - 2x - 4y \qquad (A\text{–}3)$$

$$W_B = 60 - 3x - 2y \qquad (B\text{–}3)$$

If x and y are zero, the values of W_A and W_B are

$$W_A = 80 - 2(0) - 4(0) = 80$$

$$W_B = 60 - 3(0) - 2(0) = 60$$

The value of the objective function is

$$\text{Marginal contribution} = 60x + 50y = 60(0) + 50(0) = 0 \quad (C\text{–}3)$$

which is the marginal contribution expected when nothing is produced. Note that this initial solution is point a in Figure 6.

Improving the Initial Trivial Solution

Obviously, we can improve this initial solution by decreasing either W_A or W_B to zero and selecting either x or y as a variable with a positive value. The question is, however, which variable, x or y, should we choose first? The answer is that we wish to introduce the variable that will improve the marginal contribution by the greatest amount. This step is comparable to selecting the open square with the greatest negative evaluation in MODI, in order to improve the solution by the greatest amount.

Selecting the key variable. Which variable, x or y, would improve the total marginal contribution most? We can tell by looking at the objective function. Each unit of x earns \$60 as compared to only \$50 for each unit of y. Therefore, it is x that we wish to increase from zero to some positive value.

Increasing x to the maximum possible. We know that allocating productive time to x will increase marginal contribution. For each unit of x produced, we obtain a marginal contribution of \$60. How many x's should we produce, 1, 2, 10, 20, $\cdots$? Since we have found an advantageous shift in the allocation of available machine time, why not produce as many as possible? Recall the comparable step in Distribution Methods. When we found an advantageous shift in allocations, we shifted as many units as possible to the open square in question, being limited by the smallest allocation at a negative square. Here we will do essentially the same thing. We will increase the value of x to the maximum possible without violating the restrictions of the problem. Equation A–2 shows us that if y and W_A were zero, the maximum value of x is

$$x = \frac{80 - 4 \times 0 - 0}{2} = 40 \qquad (A\text{–}4)$$

Equation B–2 tells us that if y and W_B are zero, the maximum value of x is

$$x = \frac{60 - 2 \times 0 - 0}{3} = 20 \qquad (B\text{–}4)$$

Key equation. Equation B–2 is controlling, since in it a value of x greater than **20** is not permitted. This means then that we will increase x to the maximum and reduce W_B to zero. The two variables to have positive values are now x and W_A, y and W_B being zero. Equation B **2** is then the key equation, so we solve it for x:

$$x = \frac{60 - 2y - W_B}{3}$$
$$= 20 - \frac{2y}{3} - \frac{W_B}{3} \qquad (B\text{–}5)$$

Since this expression of x limits it to the maximum possible, we will substitute this expression for x in $(A\text{–}2)$ and in the objective function.

$$W_A = 80 - 2\left(20 - \frac{2y}{3} - \frac{W_B}{3}\right) - 4y$$

which simplifies to

$$W_A = 40 - \tfrac{8}{3}y + \tfrac{2}{3}W_B \qquad (A\text{–}5)$$

The objective function then becomes

$$\text{Marginal contribution} = 60(20 - \tfrac{2}{3}y - \tfrac{1}{3}W_B) + 50y$$
$$= 1200 + 10y - 20W_B \qquad (C\text{–}3)$$

Letting y and W_B become zero results in the following values of the four variables:

$$x = 20, \quad \text{from } (B\text{–}5)$$
$$W_A = 40, \quad \text{from } (A\text{–}5)$$
$$y = 0$$
$$W_B = 0$$

$$\text{Marginal contribution} = 1200, \quad \text{from } (C\text{–}3)$$

This is an obvious improvement over the first solution, since the value of the objective function has now increased from zero to $1200. We can see from Figure 6 that the second stage of our solution is represented by point d.

Repeating the procedure. Is it possible to improve on the solution just presented? Our test is a simple one. We look at the last statement of the objective function, $(C\text{-}3)$. Here we see that the total value of the objective function would increase if we could increase the value of y above zero. For every unit of y produced, we would add \$10 to the total marginal contribution. Also, we can see from $(C\text{-}3)$ that total marginal contribution would increase if we could decrease W_B; however, we know that W_B is already zero so that it is impossible to reduce it any more. Therefore we select y as the variable to increase.

How much can y be increased? As before, we look to the equations that represent the current stage of solution, $(A\text{-}5)$ and $(B\text{-}5)$. From $(A\text{-}5)$, the maximum value of y occurs when W_A and W_B are zero, or $y = 15$. From $(B\text{-}5)$ the maximum value of y occurs when x and W_B are zero, or $y = 30$.

Equation $A\text{-}5$ is the more restrictive and is, therefore, selected as the *key equation*. We solve $(A\text{-}5)$ for y:

$$y = 15 + \tfrac{1}{4}W_B - \tfrac{3}{8}W_A \qquad (A\text{-}6)$$

Substituting this value of y in $(B\text{-}5)$ and the last statement of the objective function, $(C\text{-}3)$, we obtain

$$x = 10 + \tfrac{1}{4}W_A - \tfrac{1}{2}W_B \qquad (B\text{-}6)$$

$$\text{Marginal contribution} = 1350 - \tfrac{15}{4}W_A - \tfrac{35}{2}W_B \qquad (C\text{-}6)$$

When W_A and W_B are zero, the values of the variables and of the objective function are as follows:

$$x = 10$$

$$y = 15$$

$$W_A = 0$$

$$W_B = 0$$

$$\text{Marginal contribution} = 1350$$

We see that this is point c in Figure 6, and we have noted before that this was the optimal solution by inspection of Figure 6. How can we tell that this is true from the algebraic interpretation? We look at the last statement of the objective function $(C\text{-}6)$ to see if it can be increased without violating any of the restrictions of the problem. We note that the only possible way that marginal contribution could increase is by decreasing either W_A, W_B, or both. Since the solution at this stage already specifies that W_A and W_B are at their minimum values of zero, and since none of the variables can take on negative values, there is no way to increase marginal contribution. We have the optimal solution.

Value of the Simplex Method

It seems as though we have performed a great deal of computation and manipulation to solve so simple a problem, one which was obvious by graphical methods. The value of the simplex method, however, is for large-scale problems where there is no graphic equivalent. In these complex cases, the simplex method saves time and effort by taking us to the optimal solution in a finite number of steps, each step bringing us closer to the optimum. Note that the initial solution was at point a of Figure 6, the second solution at d, and the third at c, all corners of the polygon a, b, c, d. There were many combinations of the four variables that we did not even consider as we converged on the optimal solution. For example, in proceeding from a to d, we considered none of the many feasible solutions along the line ad, which would have yielded progressively larger values of marginal contribution, as the value of x increased. Instead, we jumped from a to d. Similarly, we did not consider any of the feasible solutions along the line dc, although each one would have progressively yielded a larger marginal contribution as we converged on the optimum. For example, the point ($x = 16$, $y = 6$) results in $W_A = 24$, $W_B = 0$, and marginal contribution = \$1260. Also, we did not consider any of the feasible solutions that fell inside the polygon. We should note that all these other solutions which we did not consider are feasible solutions that involve more than two of the four variables as positive values. By requiring that we deal only with solutions where two, and only two, variables could be positive, we can jump from corner to corner, rather than move more slowly in more steps along the lines of the polygon. The solutions that involve only two of the four variables are called *basic solutions*. There are only four such basic solutions in our example, at points a, b, c, and d. In larger scale problems, we are doing the same sort of thing, that is, moving from one basic solution to a better one, leaping over an entire set of other feasible solutions that are in-between. These basic solutions are always at the corners of two- and three-dimensional problems, and conceptually at the equivalent of the corners of multidimensional problems in hyperspace.

Now let us consider the effect of a slightly different objective function in the example. Suppose that the marginal contribution of y is only \$40 instead of \$50. The objective function becomes:

$$60x + 40y = \text{maximum}$$

The objective function line is now parallel to the line segment cd in Figure 6 so that we have an entire family of optimum solutions. Two of these optima would be basic solutions (points c and d) with total marginal contribution of \$1200. All the combinations of x and y that fall along the line segment cd also give the maximum marginal contribution of \$1200, but they are not basic solutions because they will involve some idle machine time—that is, more than two of the variables x, y, W_A, and W_B have positive values. If we take the point ($x = 16$, $y = 6$), $W_A = 24$ and $W_B = 0$, as noted before. We call the optimum solutions of this type, "derived optima." Recall that we found a similar situation in our discussion of alternate optimum solutions for distribution problems. Tables VI, VII, and VIII in Chapter 11 were all basic optimum solutions because they involved only seven allocations ($m + n - 1$). Table IX, however, was a derived optimum solution and involved eight allocations.

This procedure is the simplex method. The basic procedure can be used with problems of great complexity. To apply the procedure to complex problems, it will be useful to reduce it to a set of rigorous rules which can be applied rather mechanically to save time and to reduce the computation required to a minimum. In such a procedure, it is important to retain contact with the meaning of each step so that we have more than just a mechanical procedure. We shall attempt to do this by using the same example as was used for the algebraic interpretation, and by relating our manipulations to what we did in the algebraic procedure.

THE SIMPLEX PROCEDURE

Recall that after the addition of the slack variables to account for idle time, our two restricting equations for machines A and B were respectively:

$$2x + 4y + W_A = 80$$

$$3x + 2y + W_B = 60$$

and the objective function was

$$60x + 50y = \text{maximum}$$

Since idle time contributes nothing to marginal contribution, we could also write the objective function as follows, without changing its value:

$$60x + 50y + (0)W_A + (0)W_B = \text{maximum}$$

To minimize the recopying of x, y, W_A, and W_B, let us rearrange the two restricting equations with the variables at the heads of columns and the coefficients of these variables in rows to represent the equations.

	x	y	W_A	W_B
80	2	4	1	0
60	3	2	0	1

The usual form is to reverse the right- and left-hand sides of the equations so that the constants 80 and 60 now appear on the left, with the equal sign now dropped. For machine A, we have entered the coefficient 0 under column W_B, since it does not apply to machine A, and similarly for W_A in the equation for machine B. Next we place the coefficients from the objective function above the variables, and to the left we place beside the constants 80 and 60 two columns which identify the variables in the solution and their contribution rates in the objective function. This is shown in Table I. Table I also

TABLE I.   Initial Simplex Matrix

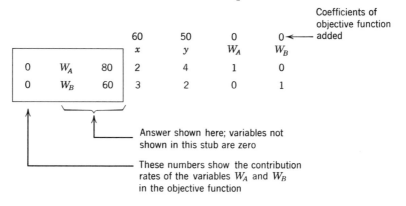

shows the condition of the matrix for the initial solution. Recall that in the algebraic interpretation we started with an initial trivial solution where all the available machine time was idle. The stub of the matrix identifies the variables in the solution which are nonzero and shows their values, as well as showing in the far left column

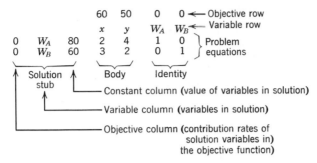

Figure 7. Nomenclature of the simplex matrix.

the contribution to the objective function that each of these variables makes.

Before proceeding, let us name the various parts of the matrix. Figure 7 shows the nomenclature of the various parts of the matrix. The objective row contains the coefficients which show the contribution rates of each of the variables in the objective function at any particular stage of solution. For example, the contribution of each unit of x is $60 per unit, y is $50, etc. The variable row simply identifies the variable associated with each of the coefficients in the various columns. The solution stub will always contain three columns. The variable column shows the variables that have positive values at a given stage of solution, and variables not shown in the stub have a value of zero. The constant column shows the value of each of the variables in the solution. The objective column shows the contribution rates of the solution variables and these coefficients come from the objective row. For example, in the initial solution shown, the coefficients above W_A and W_B are zeros. The body and identity will vary in size, depending on the particular problem. The identity will be that portion of the matrix showing the coefficients for slack variables.

Improving the Initial Solution

To improve the initial solution, we must have a measure of the potential improvement that we would make in the objective function by bringing some of the variables which are now zero into the solution, instead of the variables that are now in the solution. This step is comparable to the evaluations of the open squares in the distribution and in MODI methods. To determine measures of potential improvement for the simplex method, we will develop an *index row* which will be placed just below the present initial matrix. These index numbers will appear under the constant column, the body, and the identity. They are calculated from the formula:

Index number = $\sum$ (numbers in column) $\times$ (corresponding number in objective column) $-$ (number in objective row at head of column).

Recall that the numbers in the objective column represent the contribution rates of the variables which are in the solution represented by the matrix. The numbers in the column are the coefficients of the variable for which the index number is being computed. What we have then, essentially, is a measure of the contribution of the present variables in the solution weighted by the coefficients of a variable we propose to introduce. We then subtract from this the contribution rate for that variable at the head of the column. If the algebraic sum is negative, the practical meaning is that the variable in question would contribute more to the objective than one or more of the variables now in the solution. We can see, then, that negative numbers in the index row will indicate variables which are good candidates for changes in allocation.

For our problem, the index row numbers are as follows:

1. Index number for constant column,
$$= (80 \times 0 + 60 \times 0) - 0 = 0$$

2. Index number for first column of body,
$$= (2 \times 0 + 3 \times 0) - 60 = -60$$

3. Index number for second column of body,
$$= (4 \times 0 + 2 \times 0) - 50 = -50$$

4. Index number for first column of identity,
$$= (1 \times 0 + 0 \times 0) - 0 = 0$$

5. Index number for second column of identity,
$$= (0 \times 0 + 1 \times 0) - 0 = 0$$

We now place the index numbers in the initial simplex matrix, as indicated in Table II. We see that the index row is merely the

TABLE II. Initial Simplex Matrix with Index Row Included

			60	50	0	0	
			X	Y	W_A	W_B	
0	W_A	80	2	4	1	0	
0	W_B	60	3	2	0	1	
		0	-60	-50	0	0	←Index row

objective row preceded by minus signs. *This occurs when the objective column contains all zeros.*

Just as it was true that the most negative index number in the MODI method indicated where the greatest improvement could be made, so it is also true here. The larger the negative number, the greater the potential improvement. If all the numbers under the body and identity of the index row were zero or positive, no further improvement could be obtained, which would indicate that the solution presented in the stub was an optimal solution.

Selecting the key column and key row. We see from Table II that the column headed by the variable x has the greatest improvement potential, so we select it as the *key column*. This selection means that the variable x will be introduced into the solution in favor of W_A or W_B. To determine whether x will replace W_A or W_B, we must select a key row. To do this, *we divide each number in the constant column by the corresponding positive nonzero number in the key column.* The resulting quotients are compared and the *key row* is selected as the row yielding the smallest nonnegative quotient. For our problem, the quotients are:

$$\text{First row,} \quad \frac{80}{2} = 40$$
$$\text{Second row,} \quad \frac{60}{3} = 20 \text{ (key row)}$$

Through the selection of the key row, we are determining which of the two problem equations will limit the value of x. See equations A–4 and B–4 to verify that we have performed exactly the same computation as we did at that point.

Since the second row limits the value of x, it is designated the key row, and the number at the intersection of the key row and key column is designated the *key number*. Table III shows the initial matrix with the key column, key row, and key number identified.

TABLE III. Initial Simplex Matrix with Key Column, Row, and Number Identified

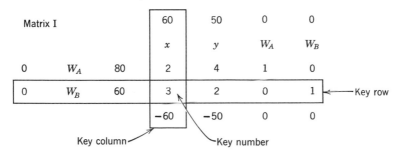

Developing an Improved Solution

With the key column and key row selected, we can now prepare a new table representing an improved solution. The first step in developing the new table is to calculate the coefficients for the *main row*. This main row appears in the relative position in the new table as the key row in the preceding table. It is computed by dividing the coefficients of the key row by the key number. Table IV shows

TABLE IV. Simplex Matrix with Main Row of New Table

Matrix I			60	50	0	0
			x	y	W_A	W_B
0	W_A	80	2	4	1	0
0	W_B	60	3	2	0	1
			-60	-50	0	0

Matrix II

		20	1	$\frac{2}{3}$	0	$\frac{1}{3}$ ← Main row

this development. The variable and its objective number from the head of the key column, that is, x and 60, are placed in the stub of the main row replacing W_B and 0 from the previous table. The balance of the objective and variable columns in the stub is copied from the previous table, and the new table developed to this point now appears as Table V.

TABLE V. Simplex Matrix with Variable and Objective Columns Completed

Matrix I			60	50	0	0
			x	y	W_A	W_B
0	W_A	80	2	4	1	0
0	W_B	60	3	2	0	1
			-60	-50	0	0

Matrix II

0	W_A					
60	x	20	1	$\frac{2}{3}$	0	$\frac{1}{3}$

Now all of the remaining coefficients in the new table, including the constant column, the body, identity, and index row can be calculated by the following formula:

$$\text{New number} = \text{old number} - \frac{\left(\begin{array}{c}\text{corresponding}\\ \text{number of}\\ \text{key row}\end{array}\right) \times \left(\begin{array}{c}\text{corresponding}\\ \text{number of}\\ \text{key column}\end{array}\right)}{\text{key number}}$$

1. First row, constant column,

$$\text{new number} = 80 - \frac{60 \times 2}{3} = 40$$

2. First row, first column of body,

$$\text{new number} = 2 - \frac{3 \times 2}{3} = 0$$

3. Index row, constant column,

$$\text{new number} = -60 - \frac{3 \times (-60)}{3} = 0$$

The remaining coefficients can be calculated in the same way and the completed improved solution is shown in Table VI.

Let us pause for a moment to determine what we have accomplished by this manipulation and to relate it to the previous

TABLE VI. Simplex Matrix with First Iteration Completed

Matrix I			60	50	0	0
			x	y	W_A	W_B
0	W_A	80	2	4	1	0
0	W_B	60	3	2	0	1
			-60	-50	0	0
Matrix II						
0	W_A	40	0	$2\frac{2}{3}$	1	$-\frac{2}{3}$
60	x	20	1	$\frac{2}{3}$	0	$\frac{1}{3}$
		1200	0	-10	0	20

algebraic solution. First, in generating the main row for the second table, we have done the equivalent of solving the equation for machine B for the variable x as was done by equation B–5. Note that the coefficients for each of the variables in the main row are the same as those in equation B–5, ignoring sign. In generating the balance of the numbers to complete the table by the formula for "new numbers," we are doing the equivalent of substituting the value of x determined by equation B–5 in the equation for machine B and in the objective function. To check this, note that the coefficients, ignoring sign, for the row above the main row are the same as those in equation A–5, and those in the row below the main row are the same as those in equation C–3.

The solution at this stage is:

$$W_A = 40$$

$$x = 20$$

$$y = 0$$

$$W_B = 0$$

The values in the constant column of the stub indicate this, y and W_B being zero since they are not in the stub at all. The value of the objective function (marginal contribution) for this solution is $1200, given in the constant column, index row. Table VI, however, shows that the solution can still be improved since a -10 appears in the index row under the variable y.

Since the index row has only one negative number under the variable y, it is selected as the key column for the next iteration. The key row is selected in the same way as before. The two quotients are:

First row, $40/\frac{8}{3} = 15$ (key row)

Second row, $20/\frac{2}{3} = 30$

The first row has the smallest nonnegative quotient, so it is selected as the key row. A new main row is calculated as before, by dividing the coefficients in the main row by the key number. The new variable y and its objective number are entered in the stub, and the new numbers in the body, identity, and index row are computed as before. The remaining variable and its objective number are copied from the preceding iteration table; Table VII shows the new solution.

TABLE VII. Simplex Matrix, Second and Final Iteration Completed

Matrix I

			60	50	0	0
			x	y	W_A	W_B
0	W_A	80	2	4	1	0
0	W_B	60	3	2	0	1
			−60	−50	0	0

Matrix II

0	W_A	40	0	$2\frac{2}{3}$	1	$-\frac{2}{3}$
60	x	20	1	$\frac{2}{3}$	0	$\frac{1}{3}$
		1200	0	−10	0	20

Matrix III

50	y	15	0	1	$\frac{3}{8}$	$-\frac{1}{4}$
60	x	10	1	0	$-\frac{1}{4}$	$\frac{1}{2}$
		1350	0	0	$3\frac{3}{4}$	$17\frac{1}{2}$

The new solution in Table VII is optimal since no further improvement is indicated in the index row. The values of the variables for the optimal solution are:

$$x = 10$$
$$y = 15$$
$$W_A = 0$$
$$W_B = 0$$

The value of the objective function for the optimal solution is shown as $1350. Of course, all these values check with our previous algebraic solution and with the graphical solution.

Procedure Summary.

1. *Formulate the problem and the objective function.*
2. *Develop the initial simplex matrix,* including the initial trivial solution and the index row numbers. The index row numbers in the initial matrix are calculated by the formula:

$$\text{Index number} = \sum \begin{pmatrix} \text{numbers} \\ \text{in} \\ \text{column} \end{pmatrix} \times \begin{pmatrix} \text{corresponding} \\ \text{number in} \\ \text{objective} \\ \text{column} \end{pmatrix} - \begin{pmatrix} \text{number in} \\ \text{objective} \\ \text{row at head} \\ \text{of column} \end{pmatrix}$$

3. *Select the key column,* the column with the most negative index number in the body or the identity.

4. *Select the key row,* the row with the smallest nonnegative quotient obtained by dividing each number of the constant column by the corresponding positive, nonzero number in the key column.

5. *The key number* is at the intersection of the key row and key column.

6. *Develop the main row of the new table.*

$$\text{Main row} = \frac{\text{key row of preceding table}}{\text{key number}}$$

The main row appears in the new table in the same relative position as the key row of the preceding table.

7. *Develop the balance of the new table.*

A. The variable and its objective number at the head of the key column are entered in the stub of the new table to the left of the main row, replacing the variable and objective number from the key row of the preceding table.

B. The remainder of the variable and objective columns are reproduced in the new table exactly as they were in the preceding table.

C. The balance of the coefficients for the new table are calculated by the formula:

$$\text{New number} = \text{old number} - \frac{\left(\begin{array}{c}\text{corresponding}\\\text{number of}\\\text{key row}\end{array}\right) \times \left(\begin{array}{c}\text{corresponding}\\\text{number of}\\\text{key column}\end{array}\right)}{\text{key number}}$$

8. Repeat (iterate) steps 3 through 7C until all the index numbers (not including the constant column) are positive. An optimal solution then results.

9. The interpretation of the resulting optimum solution is as follows: The solution appears in the stub. The variables shown in the variable column have values shown in the corresponding rows of the constant column. The value of the objective function is shown in the constant column, index row. All variables not shown in the stub are equal to zero.

Checking the work. The simplest and most effective check of the work in progress is to establish a check column to the right of the simplex matrix. The numbers in the check column are simply the algebraic sum of all the numbers in a given row, beginning with the constant column and adding all the coefficients to the right. This check column can be established for each row, including the index row. All transformations of the numbers in the check column are the same as for any of the other numbers in the table. After transformation, the algebraic sum of the row coefficients should equal the transformed number in the check column. If it does not, an error has been made and it should be traced and corrected before proceeding. Table VIII shows the three iterations of our illustrative problem with the check column included.

TABLE VIII. Completed Solution from Table VII with Check Column

Matrix I

			60	50	0	0	
			x	y	W_A	W_B	Check
0	W_A	80	2	4	1	0	87
0	W_B	60	3	2	0	1	66
			-60	-50	0	0	-110

Matrix II

0	W_A	40	0	$2\frac{2}{3}$	1	$-\frac{2}{3}$	43
60	x	20	1	$\frac{2}{3}$	0	$\frac{1}{3}$	22
		1200	0	-10	0	20	1210

Matrix III

50	y	15	0	1	$\frac{3}{8}$	$-\frac{1}{4}$	$16\frac{1}{8}$
60	x	10	1	0	$-\frac{1}{4}$	$\frac{1}{2}$	$11\frac{1}{4}$
		1350	0	0	$3\frac{3}{4}$	$17\frac{1}{2}$	$1371\frac{1}{4}$

Degeneracy in the simplex solution. Degeneracy in the simplex solution can be recognized at the time that the key row is being selected. If a tie exists between two or more rows for the smallest nonnegative quotient at that time, the problem is degenerate. Table IX shows this situation. Dividing the constant column by the corresponding number in the key column, we have:

$$\text{Row 1: } \tfrac{40}{4} = 10$$

$$\text{Row 2: } \tfrac{30}{3} = 10$$

A tie exists, and there is the possibility that if the wrong row is selected as the key row, the variable in the stub of the other row

**TABLE IX. Degeneracy in the Simplex Matrix.
Rows 1 and 2 are Tied for Key Row**

			12	10	0	0	0
			A	B	W_1	W_2	W_3
0	W_1	40	4	2	1	0	0
0	W_2	30	3	1	0	1	0
0	W_3	20	1	3	0	0	1
		0	-12	-10	0	0	0

may disappear. The problem may begin to cycle at this point and
an optimum solution could not be obtained. The degeneracy is resolved
by the following procedure:

1. Divide each element in the tied rows by the key column number
in that row.
2. Compare the resulting ratios, column by column, from left
to right, first in the identity and then in the body.
3. The first comparison that yields unequal ratios breaks the tie.
4. The key row is the row that has the algebraically smaller ratio.

Applying this procedure to the degenerate problem of Table IX,
we begin our paired comparison in the left-hand column of the
identity. The ratios in column W_1 are:

$$\text{Row 1: } \tfrac{1}{4}$$

$$\text{Row 2: } 0$$

The second row yields the algebraically smaller ratio and therefore
is selected as the key row. The regular simplex procedure may then
be resumed. This procedure for resolving degeneracy is general and
can be applied at any stage of the solution to any size matrix.

The problem of Table IX may be taken as an exercise, including
a check column. (Answer: $A = 8$, $B = 4$, $W_2 = 2$)

Exercises Involving Variations and Other Objective Functions

Cost of idle equipment. In our illustrative example we assumed
that there was no cost attached to idle equipment. This, of course,
is not necessarily true. There may be standby heating or lighting
costs, routine maintenance or machine rental. Any incremental costs

incurred by a machine, department, or other productive unit, while it is idle should be included.

Idle equipment costs appear in the objective function. They are represented by negative coefficients of the slack variables. For example, let us assume that the idle costs for our previous illustrative problem were \$30 per hour for machine A and \$25 per hour for machine B. The new objective function would be:

$$60x + 50y - 30W_A - 25W_B = \text{maximum}$$

EXERCISE

Determine the optimum allocation of machine time when idle equipment costs stated above are included. Use a check column to insure accuracy.

Maximizing the number of units produced. Our previous illustrative problems have been concerned with maximizing a profit function. We may, however, reconstruct our objective to maximize the total number of units of x and y produced. The objective of maximum number of units of output might be appropriate where a delivery date must be met which involves a large penalty for default. Also, wartime conditions often produce maximum production goals, cost being only a secondary objective.

In our illustrative example, if we had wished to maximize the total number of units of x and y produced, the objective function would be

$$x + y = \text{maximum}$$

The basic relationships restricting capacity for machines A and B would of course remain the same.

EXERCISE

Develop an optimum solution to the problem of maximizing the number of units produced, using the restricting equations for our previous illustrative example.

Minimizing an objective function. The procedure with which we have been dealing is a maximizing one. Suppose that we had wished to maximize the time that the equipment was in use. Using the same illustrative example as a background, the objective function would have been

$$W_A + W_B = \text{minimum}$$

This of course has the effect of maximizing the time that the equipment was being used. Since the procedure we have developed is for maximizing an objective function, we simply multiply the foregoing statement through by -1 and obtain

$$-W_A - W_B = \text{maximum}$$

This does not alter the objective function, but makes it possible for us to use the maximizing procedure that we have developed.

We may also achieve the objective of minimizing a given objective function by changing one simple rule in the simplex procedure. When selecting the *key column*, the largest *positive* number in the index row is selected, rather than the largest negative number. All other steps remain exactly the same. Recall that in the distribution method of linear programming, we could reverse objectives in a similar way.

Requirements

To this point, we have dealt only with restrictions to a problem. In our illustrative example, both machines A and B had maximum amounts of time available. There may be situations, however, where we are given a requirement that some combination of the variables must be greater than or equal to a given number. For example, the inequality

$$3x + 2y \geqq 12$$

has a requirement of at least 12. To convert this statement to an equation, we must *subtract* a slack variable, and the result is

$$3x + 2y - W_1 = 12$$

As it stands, however, this equation cannot be used in the simplex matrix, because the coefficient for W_1 is -1. *The simplex method requires that each equation have one (and only one) nonzero entry in the identity and that this entry must have a coefficient of $+1$.* We can accomplish this by adding an artificial variable U, which will appear in the identity. Our equation becomes

$$3x + 2y - W_1 + U_1 = 12$$

The slack variable W_1 will now appear in the body of the simplex matrix and the artificial variable U_1 appears in the identity, satisfying the requirement of only one nonzero entry in the identity with a coefficient of $+1$. The artificial variable was included simply as a computational device that permits us to stay within the rules of the simplex method. Consequently, the artificial variable is not wanted in an optimum solution. To be sure that the artificial variable will always be zero in the optimum solution, we may assign an arbitrarily large negative contribution to it in the objective function which we shall call $-M$. The $-M$ is in reality an overwhelming cost in relation to the positive contributions in the objective function, so that as the objective function is maximized through the usual procedure, the artificial variable is driven to zero.

Equations

A problem may state that a certain combination of variables must total some exact quantity. To fit this into the requirements of the simplex matrix we must have a variable for the identity, which can be accomplished through the use of an artificial variable. For example, the equation

$$2x + 3y = 90$$

can be modified to fit into the simplex format by adding an artificial variable U, and the equation becomes

$$2x + 3y + U = 90$$

As with the handling for requirements, a $-M$ contribution is assigned to the artificial variable U in the objective function so that the artificial variable is always zero in the optimum solution.

Approximations

It may be that a particular problem requires only that some combination of the variables involved should be approximately equal to some number, so that some flexibility is allowed. For example, we may state this as

$$2x + 4y \approx 40$$

(The symbol $\approx$ means "approximately equal to.") This statement may be prepared for the simplex matrix by both adding and subtracting slack variables:

$$2x + 4y - W_1 + W_2 = 40$$

The two slack variables permit $2x + 4y$ to be either slightly larger or slightly smaller than 40. The slack variable W_1 represents the amount by which $2x + 4y$ exceeds 40, and the slack variable W_2 represents the amount by which $2x + 4y$ is less than 40. We wish to minimize the value of the slack variables so that $2x + 4y$ will be as close as possible to 40 and this may be accomplished in the objective function by assigning the coefficient -1 to both slack variables in the objective function. In this example, the objective function might be

$$60x + 50y - W_1 - W_2 = \text{maximum}$$

The approximation, modified by the two slack variables, is now prepared for inclusion in the simplex matrix. The slack variable W_1 will appear in the body, and the slack variable W_2 will appear in the identity.

EXAMPLE

To summarize the way in which different types of relationships are prepared for inclusion in the simplex matrix, let us take an example that involves the four types of relationships which we have discussed—restrictions, requirements, equations, and approximations. Assume that our objective function is

$$30x + 25y = \text{maximum}$$

subject to

$$4x + 2y \leqq 60$$
$$2x + 3y \geqq 50$$
$$3x + 9y = 65$$
$$5x + 2y \approx 40$$

Adding and subtracting the appropriate slack and artificial variables, we have the following four equations for inclusion in the simplex matrix:

$$4x + 2y + W_1 = 60$$
$$2x + 3y - W_2 + U_1 = 50$$
$$3x + 9y + U_2 = 65$$
$$5x + 2y - W_3 + W_4 = 40$$

We now modify the objective function to include the slack and artificial variables:

$$30x + 25y + 0W_1 - 0W_2 - W_3 - W_4 - MU_1 - MU_2 = \text{maximum}$$

Rearranging the objective function so that the sequence of the variables is divided between the body and the identity, we can develop the initial simplex matrix for this problem as shown in Table X.

TABLE X. Initial Simplex Matrix for a Problem Involving Restrictions, Requirements, Equations, and Approximations

			30	25	0	-1	0	$-M$	$-M$	-1
			x	y	W_2	W_3	W_1	U_1	U_2	W_4
0	W_1	60	4	2	0	0	1	0	0	0
$-M$	U_1	50	2	3	-1	0	0	1	0	0
$-M$	U_2	65	3	9	0	0	0	0	1	0
-1	W_4	40	5	2	0	-1	0	0	0	1

The Dual Problem

Simplex problems formulated in the way that we have illustrated in the previous examples are called *primal* problems. It is interesting to note that the same basic problem may be solved in a different way, essentially by reversing the rows and columns. Turning the problem around in this way results in what is called the *dual* problem. A solution to the dual problem can easily be converted into a solution of the original problem, that is, the primal. This is useful when we have a problem with a large number of rows and a small number of columns. In such a case, if we solved the dual problem, instead of the primal, there would be less total work and effort involved. The rules of thumb are as follows:

1. Select the way of formulating the simplex matrix that presents the smaller number of rows.

2. If both the primal and the dual have the same number of rows, select the simplex matrix that presents the smaller number of columns.

Let us illustrate the formulation of the dual problem, using as an example our previous illustrative problem, augmented by two additional restrictions. The problem may be stated as:

Maximize: $60x + 50y$, subject to,

$$2x + 4y \leq 80$$

$$3x + 2y \leq 60$$

$$x \leq 15$$

$$2y \leq 36$$

If we were going to solve the problem as before, that is, the primal problem, we might begin by arranging the coefficients in rows and columns as follows:

	60	50
	x	y
$80 \geq$	2	4
$60 \geq$	3	2
$15 \geq$	1	0
$36 \geq$	0	2

We have not, as yet, added in the necessary slack variables. We can now convert the problem to a dual problem by the following five steps:

1. *Assign a new variable to each row*

		60	50
		x	y
V_1	$80 \geqq$	2	4
V_2	$60 \geqq$	3	2
V_3	$15 \geqq$	1	0
V_4	$36 \geqq$	0	2

2. *Write the constant column of the primal as the objective row of the dual, reversing the algebraic signs.* The objective row for the dual of our problem is then:

$$-80 \quad -60 \quad -15 \quad -36$$

3. *Write the objective row of the primal as the constant column of the dual, reversing the inequality signs.* The constant column of the dual of our problem is then:

$$-80 \quad -60 \quad -15 \quad -36$$
$$60$$
$$50$$

4. *Write the remainder of the rows of the primal problem as the columns of the dual.* This results in:

	-80	-60	-15	-36
	V_1	V_2	V_3	V_4
60	2	3	1	0
50	4	2	0	2

5. *Add slack and artificial variables as required by the restrictions or requirements of the dual problem.* Since the conversion of the

problem from primal to dual changed our original restrictions to requirements, the resulting initial dual matrix is as follows:

	-80	-60	-15	-36	0	0	$-M$	$-M$
	V_1	V_2	V_3	V_4	W_A	W_B	A_1	A_2
60	2	3	1	0	-1	0	1	0
50	4	2	0	2	0	-1	0	1

This is a simplex matrix and may be solved in the usual way. Table XI shows the final optimal solution of the dual problem. For comparison Table XII shows the optimal solution for the primal.

TABLE XI. Optimum Solution for Dual Simplex Problem

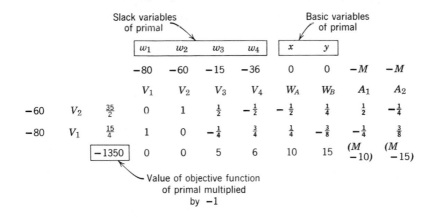

			Slack variables of primal				Basic variables of primal			
			w_1	w_2	w_3	w_4	x	y		
			-80	-60	-15	-36	0	0	$-M$	$-M$
			V_1	V_2	V_3	V_4	W_A	W_B	A_1	A_2
-60	V_2	$\frac{35}{2}$	0	1	$\frac{1}{2}$	$-\frac{1}{2}$	$-\frac{1}{2}$	$\frac{1}{4}$	$\frac{1}{2}$	$-\frac{1}{4}$
-80	V_1	$\frac{15}{4}$	1	0	$-\frac{1}{4}$	$\frac{3}{4}$	$\frac{1}{4}$	$-\frac{3}{8}$	$-\frac{1}{4}$	$\frac{3}{8}$
		-1350	0	0	5	6	10	15	$(M-10)$	$(M-15)$

Value of objective function of primal multiplied by -1

TABLE XII. Optimum Solution for Primal of Dual Problem Shown in Table XI

			60	50	0	0	0	0
			x	y	W_1	W_2	W_3	W_4
0	W_3	5	0	0	$\frac{1}{4}$	$-\frac{1}{2}$	1	0
50	y	15	0	1	$\frac{3}{8}$	$-\frac{1}{4}$	0	0
60	x	10	1	0	$-\frac{1}{4}$	$\frac{1}{2}$	0	0
0	W_4	6	0	0	$-\frac{3}{4}$	$\frac{1}{2}$	0	1
		1350	0	0	$\frac{15}{4}$	$\frac{35}{2}$	0	0

Let us now compare the two tables so that we may see where to find in either table the answers to either the primal or dual problems.

1. *Values for the basic variables of the primal are found in the dual solution under the slack variables columns, index row.* The basic variables of the primal are x and y; in Table XI we find their optimal values in the index row under the slack variables. Their values are 10 and 15, respectively. This may be verified by looking in Table XII, constant column.

2. *The values for the slack variables of the primal are found in the dual solution under the columns for basic variables, index row.* The dual solution of Table XI shows the values in the index row for the four basic variables to be 0, 0, 5, and 6. Therefore, we know that the optimal values in the primal problem are, $W_1 = 0$, $W_2 = 0$, $W_3 = 5$, and $W_4 = 6$. Checking with the primal solution of Table XII, we see that this is true.

3. *The value of the objective function is in the same location in both the primal and dual matrixes, but of opposite sign.* Therefore, in the dual solution we find the value of the objective function to be -1350, whereas in the primal it is $+1350$.

To summarize, let us repeat the steps required to convert a primal problem to its equivalent dual. The steps are:

1. Assign a new variable to each row.
2. Write the constant column of the primal as the objective row of the dual, reversing algebraic signs.
3. Write the objective row of the primal as the constant column of the dual, reversing the inequality signs.
4. Write the remainder of the rows of the primal problem as columns of the dual.
5. Add slack and artificial variables as required by the restrictions or requirements of the dual and solve by the usual simplex methods.

Summary

The range of application of the linear programming technique is, of course, limited by the requirement that all the mathematical functions involved be linear in form. Quite often, however, the functions may not actually be linear, but can be reasonably approximated by a straight line. Also, although a function may be nonlinear over its entire range, it may be approximated by a straight line in the operating portion of the curve, that is, the portion of the curve that is of practical significance in the problem at hand. There are other programming techniques which can be used in the nonlinear cases, however, and these are dealt with in some of the references listed. Dynamic programming makes it possible to solve multistage programming problems where the decisions generated by stage 1 become the conditions of the problem for stage 2, etc. For example, in scheduling production the amount we plan to produce this month is dependent partially on how much we produced last month, because of the possible accumulation or reduction of inventories or back orders.

The examples we have used to illustrate the basic steps óf the simplex method have been trivial ones. Linear programming, however, is not restricted to these trivial problems, and as mentioned earlier, part of the great power of the technique is that very complex situations can be handled. In larger scale problems the real difficulty is a computational one; that is, the number of man-hours required to develop a solution. The digital computer is, of course, the final answer to this problem, and library programs for linear programming models are commonly available.

REFERENCES

1. Bertoletti, M. E., J. Chapiro, and H. R. Rieznik, "Optimization of Investment—A Solution by Linear Programming," *Management Technology, No. 1,* January 1960, pp. 64–75.
2. Charnes, A., and W. W. Cooper, *Management Models and Industrial Applications of Linear Programming,* 2 Volumes, John Wiley and Sons. New York, 1961.
3. Charnes, A., W. W. Cooper, and R. Ferguson, "Optimal Estimation of Executive Compensation by Linear Programming," *Management Science,* Vol. 1, No. 2, January 1955, pp. 138–151.
4. Charnes, A., W. W. Cooper, and R. Ferguson, "Blending Aviation Gasolines — A Study in Programming Interdependent Activities," *Econometrica,* Vol. 20, No. 2, April 1952, pp. 135–159.
5. Eisemann, K., and W. N. Young, "Study of a Textile Mill with the Aid of Linear Programming," *Management Technology, No. 1,* January 1960, pp. 52–63.
6. Fabian, T., "A Linear Programming Model of Integrated Iron and Steel Production," *Management Science,* Vol. 4, No. 4, July 1958, pp. 415–449.
7. Ferguson, R. O., and L. F. Sargent, *Linear Programming,* McGraw-Hill Book Company, New York, 1958.
8. Fetter, R. B., "A Linear Programming Model for Long-Range Capacity Planning," *Management Science,* Vol. 7, No. 4, July 1961, pp. 372–378.
9. Greene, J. H., K. Chatto, C. R. Hicks, and C. B. Cox, "Linear Programming in the Packing Industry," *Journal of Industrial Engineering,* Vol. X, No. 5, 1959, pp. 364–372.

10. Hanssmann, F., and S. W. Hess, "A Linear Programming Approach to Production and Employment Scheduling," *Management Technology, No. 1,* January 1960, pp. 46–52.
11. Henderson, A., and R. Schlaefer, "Mathematical Programming," *Harvard Business Review,* May–June 1954.
12. Metzger, R. W., *Elemental Mathematical Programming,* John Wiley and Sons, New York, 1958.
13. Metzger, R. W., and R. Schwarzbek, "A Linear Programming Application to Cupola Charging," *Journal of Industrial Engineering,* Vol. XII, No. 2, March–April 1960, pp. 87–93.
14. Vajda, S., *Readings in Linear Programming,* John Wiley and Sons, New York, 1958.
15. Vajda, S., *The Theory of Games and Linear Programming,* John Wiley and Sons, New York, 1956.
16. Vazsonyi, A., *Scientific Programming in Business and Industry,* John Wiley and Sons, New York, 1958.

REVIEW QUESTIONS

1. Relate the adjective, "linear," to the nature of the restriction and the objective function as shown in the graphical solution of linear programming.

2. Figure 2 shows the effect of the restrictions on stamping department, unit department, machine shop, and assembly department capacity in limiting the feasible solutions to the problem. What other restrictions are implicit in Figure 2?

3. What is the practical result of having an objective function that is parallel to the critical line segment of the polygon of feasible solutions in the graphical representation of linear programming?

4. Are market restrictions fundamentally different from capacity restrictions in determining the polygon of feasible solutions?

5. Outline the steps required in the algebraic solution of linear programming programs. Express the procedure in the form of a flow chart.

6. Outline the procedure for simplex solution of linear programming problems. Express the procedure in the form of a flow chart and show that the steps are equivalent to those in the algebraic procedure.

7. Contrast the effect of "requirements," "restrictions," and "equations" in the simplex procedure.

8. What is the function of slack and artificial variables in the simplex procedure?

9. What are the *primal* and the *dual* forms of the linear programming model? What are the circumstances under which we would select one format over the other?

10. Can we obtain answers to the primal problem from the solution to the dual, and vice versa? If so, how?

PROBLEMS

1. A company manufacturing television sets and radios has four major departments: chassis, cabinet, assembly, and final testing. Monthly capacities are as follows:

	Television Capacity		Radio Capacity
Chassis	1500	or	4500
Cabinet	1000	or	8000
Assembly	2000	or	4000
Testing	3000	or	9000

The marginal contribution of television is $30 each and the marginal contribution of radio is $5 each. Assuming that the company can sell any quantity of either product, determine the optimal combination of output.

2. An oil company has two additives, x and y, which they mix into their premium grade gasoline. After careful analysis the following restrictions have been determined:

    a. If more than $\frac{1}{2}$ pound of total additives are used per tank car, the additives form harmful deposits on carburetors.

    b. $2x + y$ cannot be less than one-half or the gasoline will not have its normal distinctive color (a major selling point).

    c. One pound of additive x will add 100 equivalent octane units per tank car, and one pound of additive y will add 200 equivalent octane units per tank car. The total number of equivalent units per tank car cannot be less than 60 to insure performance standards.

    d. Additive x costs $150 per pound and additive y costs $400 per pound. Graphically determine the optimum additive mixture. Algebraically check the results and compute the total cost per tank car.

3. A company makes three products, x, y, and z, out of three materials p_1, p_2, and p_3. The three products use units of the three materials according to the following table.

	p_1	p_2	p_3
x	2	0	3
y	3	2	2
z	0	5	4

The unit marginal contributions of the three products are:

Product	Marginal Contribution
x	$3
y	$5
z	$4

and the availabilities of the three materials are:

Material	Amount Available, Units
p_1	8
p_2	10
p_3	15

Determine the optimal product mix.

4. A company makes four products, v, x, y, and z, which flow through four departments, drill, mill, lathe, and assembly. The hours of department time required by each of the products per unit are:

	Drill	Mill	Lathe	Assembly
v	3	0	3	4
x	7	2	4	6
y	4	4	0	5
z	0	6	5	3

The unit marginal contributions of the four products and hours of availability in the four departments are:

Product	Marginal Contribution
v	$9
x	$18
y	$14
z	$11

Department	Hours Available
Drill	70
Mill	80
Lathe	90
Assembly	100

Determine the optimal product mix.

5. A company makes five products, u, v, x, y, and z, which flow through five departments, blanking, forming, straightening, brazing, and assembly, requiring the following processing times.

			Time Required		
Product	Blanking	Forming	Straightening	Brazing	Assemby
u	1 hr	1 hr	2 hr	0	1 hr
v	1 hr	0	$\frac{1}{2}$ hr	1 hr	2 hr
x	2 hr	3 hr	0	$\frac{1}{2}$ hr	1 hr
y	0	2 hr	2 hr	1 hr	2 hr
z	$\frac{1}{2}$ hr	1 hr	$\frac{1}{2}$ hr	2 hr	1 hr

The marginal contribution of each product is as follows:

Product	Marginal Contribution
u	$8 per unit
v	$9 per unit
x	$13 per unit
y	$15 per unit
z	$7 per unit

Time available in the various departments and the estimated incremental cost of idle time are:

Department	Time Available	Estimated Incremental Cost of Idle Time per Hour
Blanking	115 hrs	$12
Forming	100 hrs	$8
Straightening	140 hrs	$3.50
Brazing	90 hrs	$30
Assembly	110 hrs	$12

Formulate the problem in the simplex matrix.

6. A company makes five products, u, v, x, y, and z, which flow through five departments, blanking, forming, straightening, brazing, and assembly.

	Time Required					
Product	Blank-ing	Form-ing	Straight-ening	Braz-ing	Assem-bling	Marginal Contribution
u	1 hr	1 hr	2 hr		1 hr	$8 per unit
v	1 hr		$\frac{1}{2}$ hr	1 hr	2 hr	$9 per unit
x	2 hr	3 hr		$\frac{1}{2}$ hr	1 hr	$13 per unit
y		2 hr	2 hr	1 hr	2 hr	$15 per unit
z	$\frac{1}{2}$ hr	1 hr	$\frac{1}{2}$ hr	2 hr	1 hr	$7 per unit

The available amount of blanking time is 115 hours and the incremental cost of idle time is estimated to be $12 per hour. The available amount of forming time is 100 hours and the incremental cost of idle time is estimated to be $8 per hour. The available amount of straightening time is 140 hours and the incremental cost of idle time is estimated to be $3.50 per hour. The available amount of brazing time is 90 hours and the incremental cost of idle time is estimated to be $30 per hour. The available amount of assembly time is 110 hours and the incremental cost of idle time is estimated to be $12 per hour. Formulate the problem in the simplex matrix.

7. A refinery operating in Nebraska uses four crude oils: Oklahoma, West Texas, Wyoming, and Pennsylvania. These crudes have different delivered prices as indicated below. The refinery makes four basic end products: regular gasoline, high-test gasoline, diesel fuel, and fuel oil. The

catalytic cracking and reforming characteristics of the refinery dictate a limited and different product mix for the different crudes. Data is as follows:

| | Delivered Price per Gallon, cents | Optimal Throughout for Each Crude | | | |
| | | Regular Gas | High-Test Gas | Diesel Fuel | Fuel Oil |
Crude					
Oklahoma	7	30%	10%	40%	20%
West Texas	6	20%	10%	60%	10%
Wyoming	5	10%		30%	60%
Pennsylvania	9	30%	50%	20%	
Present market, gallons	—	2000	1500	2800	3300

Formulate the problem in a simplex matrix with the objective of minimizing crude costs.

8. An animal feed company makes a poultry mix out of five grains, u, v, x, y, and z. The five grains have different protein and vitamin contents and costs, and the mixture has certain minimum content requirements as summarized below:

| Grain | Cost, cents per pound | Grain Content, Units | | | | |
		Protein	Vitamin A	Vitamin B	Vitamin C	Vitamin D
u	5	40	50	100	80	30
v	$4\frac{1}{2}$	200	10	0	25	40
x	2	10	30	20	45	0
y	$2\frac{1}{2}$	45	—	60	20	35
z	$\frac{1}{2}$	5				
Required content of mixture per pound		100	90	70	40	50

Grain z is used as a filler. Formulate the problem in the simplex matrix with the objective of specifying a mixture that meets requirements at minimum cost.

9. A company makes three products, x, y, and z, out of seven materials. The material requirements and marginal contributions for each of the three products are as follows:

| Product | Unit Material Requirements | | | | | | |
	p_1	p_2	p_3	p_4	p_5	p_6	p_7
x	3		2		1		
Alternate x		3		4			1
y		2	1			2	
Alternate y	1			2	3		
z				4		2	1
Alternate z			2		6		

Product	Unit Marginal Contribution
x	$6
y	$5
z	$9

The amounts of each material that are available are:

p_1	100 units
p_2	115 units
p_3	135 units
p_4	90 units
p_5	85 units
p_6	140 units
p_7	170 units

Formulate the problem in the primal simplex matrix with the objective of maximizing marginal contribution. Convert the problem to the dual formulation.

part VI

MODELS OF INVESTMENT POLICY

13

Common Criteria for
Investment

The physical assets of an operational system present some special problems of analysis. The building and its productive equipment are quite expensive in first cost and in maintenance, and they commonly account for the largest share of the assets of an enterprise. Yet the fact that they have enduring use and value is part of the problem. Machines do not wear out in the same sense that a light bulb burns out. By maintenance and the replacement of components, the physical useful life of a machine may be extended indefinitely. This raises questions such as: when should an existing asset be replaced? How do we compare the desirability of two or more alternate machines, and are any of them justified from an economic point of view?

To see the nature of some of the analytical and practical problems involved, let us take a simple example which requires none of the refinements of analysis and technique. We have just installed a machine that performs a highly specialized operation. Because of our particular physical facilities, a custom installation was required. The result of the specialized nature of the equipment and the custom installation is that the equipment is of no value to anyone else; therefore its salvage value is zero as soon as it is installed. The installed cost of the equipment was $12,000, and, of course, this is a *sunk* cost, meaning simply that it is gone forever, regardless of what we may list as the "book value" of the equipment. Since the $12,000 is "sunk," it is completely irrelevant to any future decisions since no future decision can affect it.

The costs of owning the machine (as distinct from the costs of operating and maintaining it) are simply $12,000. We hope to spread this total over a period of time so that the *average* annual cost of ownership will not be too great. In 4 years the average cost of owning the machine will be only $12,000/4 = $3000 per year. In 10 years the average annual cost has been reduced to $1200. This decreasing average annual cost of owning the machine is diagrammed in Figure 1.

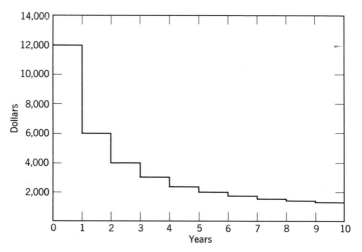

Figure 1. Decreasing annual average cost of owning a machine that cost $12.000 originally and has no salvage value at any time.

Regardless of how long we keep the equipment, this cost of owning is irrelevant because it is a past cost. The only future costs that we will incur are the costs of operating and maintaining the machine. Once the machine is installed, these are the only costs subject to managerial control by future decisions.

Let us assume that two men are required to operate the equipment at $4500 per year per man, and that the maintenance costs are expected to be $2000 the first year and increasing at the rate of $400 per year on the average. Figure 2 shows the total of these costs in relation to time. We assume that there are no other costs for us to consider. Since the original cost of the equipment is sunk and the only future costs are the operating and maintenance costs, we are in a position to see fairly clearly under what conditions we would consider the machine to be obsolete. We would want to replace it at any time that we could find a functionally equivalent setup that could offer a

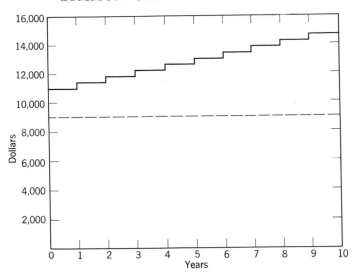

Figure 2. Operating and maintenance costs showing rising costs of maintenance.

total average annual cost of owning plus operation and maintenance that fell below the cost curve of Figure 2. Let us assume that during the fifth year of operation of our machine, a new equipment design is developed.

The new design has some important advantages over the old one which result in lower operating costs. Certain phases of the operation have been automated so that the annual labor cost to produce a comparable output is now only $3500. Maintenance charges are expected to be higher, however, being estimated at $3000 during the first year and increasing at the average rate of $500 per year. The new machine design costs $16,000 installed. Now we want to see if the average annual total of the costs of owning plus those of operating and maintaining the improved machine design is less than the $12,600 current annual expense for the present machine (from Figure 2, fifth year). First, let us note that while we ignore the original sunk cost of the present machine we cannot ignore the installed cost of the improved design, since it is still a future cost.

The decision. To see the picture clearly, let us plot on the same chart the average annual cost of owning (capital cost) and the annual operating and maintenance costs for the new design. These costs are shown in Figure 3, where we also show the total of the two costs year by year. The total cost curve is developed by simply adding the cost of owning to the operating and maintenance cost for each

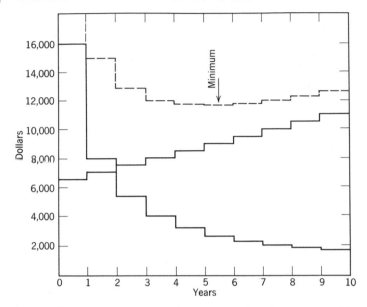

Figure 3. Year-by-year average costs for a proposed replacement machine cost-ing $16,000 initially and having no salvage value at any time.

year. Note that the total cost is very high during the first 2 years, reaches a minimum during the sixth year, and then begins to rise again. The cost is high in the early years because the annual average of the costs of owning the equipment are very high during those years. It begins to rise again after the sixth year because of the influence of the rising maintenance costs. Now let us examine the significance of the total cost curve for this simplified example. For the present machine design, the total incremental cost for this year is $12,600 as we have already noted, a sum that we expect will become larger in future years. The total average annual cost for the proposed setup, however, will be less than $12,600 after the third year. It seems clear that a decision to replace the present machine design is called for.

Opportunity costs. We have been assuming a fairly simple situation, where certain kinds of costs are ignored in order to see some of the structure of the problem. Let us introduce some additional ideas. Suppose we are discussing an asset that is used for more general purposes, such as an over-the-road semitrailer truck. Let us assume that we own such a truck and the first question is: "How much will it cost us to *own* this truck for one more year?" These costs of owning, or capital costs, cannot be derived from the ordinary accounting records of the organization. The cost of owning the truck for one more year depends on its current value. If the truck can be sold on the second-hand market for $5000, this is a measure of its economic value. Since it has value, we have two basic alternatives: we can sell it for $5000 or we can retain it. If we sell, the $5000 can earn interest or a return in an alternative investment. If we keep it, we forego the return, which then becomes an *opportunity cost* of holding the truck one more year. Similarly, if we keep the truck, it will be worth less a year from now, so there is a second opportunity cost measured by the fall in salvage value during the year.

The combined loss of opportunity to earn a return plus the loss of salvage value during the year are the costs of continued ownership. They are the opportunity costs rather than costs paid out; nevertheless, they can be of real importance in comparing alternatives that require different amounts of investment. There is one more possible component of capital cost for the next year if the truck is retained, that is, the cost of possible renewals or "capital additions" necessary to keep the truck operating. We are not thinking of ordinary maintenance here, but major overhauls, such as a new engine or an engine overhaul, that extend the physical life for some time. In summary, the capital costs, or costs of owning the truck for one more year, are as follows:

1. Opportunity costs
   (a) Interest on opening salvage value.
   (b) Loss in salvage value during the year.
2. Capital additions or renewals required to keep the truck running for at least an additional year.

By assuming a schedule of salvage values, we can compute the year-by-year capital costs for an asset. This is done in Table I for a truck that cost $10,000 initially and has the salvage schedule indicated. The final result is the projected capital cost incurred for each year. If we determine the way operating and maintenance costs increase as the truck ages, we can plot a set of curves similar to Figure 3. The combined capital plus operating and maintenance costs curve will have a minimum point as before. This minimum of the combined cost curve defines the best cost performance year in the life of the equipment. Beyond that year, the effect of rising maintenance costs more than counterbalances the declining capital costs.

TABLE I. **Year-by-Year Capital Costs for a Semitrailer Truck, Given a Salvage Schedule (interest at 10%)**

Year	Year-End Salvage Value	Fall in Salvage Value during Year	Interest on Opening Salvage Value	Capital Cost, Sum of Fall in Value and Interest
New	$10,000	—	—	—
1	8,300	$1,700	$1,000	$2,700
2	6,900	1,400	830	2,230
3	5,700	1,200	690	1,890
4	4,700	1,000	570	1,570
5	3,900	800	470	1,270
6	3,200	700	390	1,090
7	2,700	500	320	820
8	2,300	400	270	670
9	1,950	350	230	580
10	1,650	300	195	495

Obsolescence and economic life. What is the effect of obsolescence on the cost of owning and operating a machine? By definition, when a machine is obsolete there exists an alternative machine or system which is more economical to own and operate. Clearly, the existence of the new machine does not cause any increase in the cost of operating and maintaining the present machine. These costs are already determined by the design, installation, and condition of the present machine. The existence of the new machine causes the value of the present machine to fall, however, and therefore induces an increased capital cost. Thus for assets in technologically dynamic classifications, the salvage value schedule falls rapidly in anticipation of typical obsolescence rates. Economic lives are very short.

On the other hand, where the rate of innovation is relatively slow, salvage values hold up fairly well. This fact is shown in Table II, which compares year-by-year capital costs for two machines which cost $10,000 initially, but which have different salvage schedules. The value of machine 1 holds the best, machine 2 having more severe obsolescence reflected in its salvage schedule. The result is that capital costs in the initial years are greater for machine 2 than for machine 1. The average capital costs for the first five years are:

Machine 1	$1913
Machine 2	$2198

Therefore, if the schedules of operating expenses for the two machines were identical, machine 1 would seem most desirable. Since the

TABLE II. **Comparison of Capital Costs for Two Machines Costing $10,000 Initially, with Different Salvage Schedules** (interest at 10%)

	Machine 1				Machine 2		
Year-End Salvage Value	Fall in Value During Year	Interest at 10% on Opening Value	Capital Cost	Year-End Salvage Value	Fall in Value During Year	Interest at 10% on Opening Value	Capital Cost
$10,000	—	—	—	$10,000	—	—	—
8,330	$1,670	$1,000	$2,670	7,150	$2,850	$1,000	$3,850
6,940	1,390	833	2,223	5,100	2,050	715	2,765
5,780	1,160	694	1,854	3,640	1,460	510	1,970
4,820	960	578	1,538	2,600	1,040	364	1,404
4,020	800	482	1,282	1,860	740	260	1,000
3,350	670	402	1,072	1,330	530	186	716
2,790	560	335	895	950	380	133	513
2,320	470	279	749	680	270	95	365
1,930	390	232	622	485	195	68	263
1,610	320	193	513	345	140	49	189

timing of capital costs is different for the two machines, however, it would be better for comparative purposes if we could adjust all values to their equivalent present values.

Present values. Since money has a time value, future expenditures and opportunity costs will have different present or current values to us. What do we mean by the time value of money? Since money can earn interest, $1000 in hand now is equivalent to $1100 a year from now if the present sum can earn interest at 10 per cent. Similarly, if we must wait a year to receive $1000 due now, we should expect not $1000 a year hence, but $1100. When the time spans involved are extended, the appropriate interest is compounded and its effect becomes much larger. The timing of payments and receipts can make an important difference in the value of various alternatives.

Let us illustrate this point briefly and more precisely before returning to the example of the two machines. We know that if a principal sum P is invested at an interest rate i, it will yield a future total sum S in n years hence, if all of the earnings are retained and compounded. Therefore, P, in the present is entirely equivalent to S in the future by virtue of the compound amount factor:

$$S = P(1 + i)^n$$

where

$(1 + i)^n$ = the compound amount factor for interest rate i and n years

Similarly, we can solve for P to determine the present worth of a sum to be paid n years hence:

$$P = \frac{S}{(1 + i)^n} = S \times PV_{sp}$$

where

PV_{sp} = the present value of a single payment S to be made n years hence, with interest rate i

Therefore, if we were to receive a payment of $10,000 in 10 years, we should be willing to accept a smaller but equivalent sum now. If interest at 10 per cent were considered fair and adequate, that smaller but equivalent sum would be:

$$P = 10,000 \times 0.3855 = \$3855$$

since

$$\frac{1}{(1 + 0.10)^{10}} = PV_{sp} = 0.3855$$

Now let us return to the example of the two machines. The capital costs for each machine occur by different schedules, because of different salvage values. If all future values were adjusted to the present as a common base time, we could compare the totals to see which investment alternative was advantageous. This we have done in Table III, where we have assumed an operating cost schedule in column 2, determined combined operating and capital costs in columns 5 and 6, and their present values in columns 8 and 9. The present value of the entire stream of expenditures and opportunity costs is $32,398 for machine 1. The net differences in present values for the two machines are shown at the bottom of columns 8 and 9, Table III. Since the operating cost schedule was identical for both machines, the totals reflect differences in the present worth of the capital costs. Obviously the method allows for different operating cost schedules as well as revenues.

There are some difficulties in using the methods just described. First, we have assumed that the schedule of salvage values was known, and this is not often true. Second, at some point in the

TABLE III. Present Value, Capital and Operating Costs, for the Two Machines from Table II; Schedule of Operating Costs Is the Same for All Three Machines (interest at 10%)

Year (1)	Operating Cost (2)	Capital Costs (from Table II)		Combined Operating and Capital Costs		Present Worth Factor for Year Indicated (7)	Present Worth of Combined Costs for Year Indicated	
		Machine 1 (3)	Machine 2 (4)	Machine 1 (5)	Machine 2 (6)		Machine 1 (8)	Machine 2 (9)
1	$3,000	$2,670	$3,850	$5,670	$6,850	0.909	$5,154	$6,227
2	3,200	2,223	2,765	5,423	5,765	0.826	4,479	4,762
3	3,400	1,854	1,970	5,254	5,370	0.751	3,946	4,033
4	3,600	1,538	1,404	5,138	5,004	0.683	3,509	3,418
5	3,800	1,282	1,000	5,082	4,800	0.621	3,160	2,981
6	4,000	1,072	716	5,072	4,716	0.565	2,866	2,665
7	4,200	895	513	5,095	4,713	0.513	2,614	2,418
8	4,400	749	365	5,149	4,765	0.467	2,405	2,225
9	4,600	622	273	5,222	4,873	0.424	2,214	2,066
10	4,800	513	189	5,313	4,989	0.386	2,051	1,926
Totals							$32,398	$32,721

life of the machines, it becomes economical to replace them with identical models. Therefore, a chain of identical machines should be considered for comparative purposes, in which the machine is replaced during the year in which operating and capital costs are just equal to the interest on the present worth of all future costs. Most of the common criteria for comparing alternate capital investments attempt to circumvent these problems by (1) assuming an economic life, and (2) assuming some standard schedule for the decline in value of the asset. We shall now consider some of these criteria.

Common Criteria for Comparing Investment Alternatives

Some of the common criteria used for evaluating proposals for capital expenditures and for comparing alternatives involving capital assets are: (1) present values; (2) uniform equivalent annual cost;

TABLE IV. PV_{sp}, **Present Value Factors for Future Single Payments**

Years Hence	1%	2%	4%	6%	8%	10%	12%	14%	15%	16%	18%	20%
1	0.990	0.980	0.962	0.943	0.926	0.909	0.893	0.877	0.870	0.862	0.847	0.833
2	0.980	0.961	0.925	0.890	0.857	0.826	0.797	0.769	0.756	0.743	0.718	0.694
3	0.971	0.942	0.889	0.840	0.794	0.751	0.712	0.675	0.658	0.641	0.609	0.579
4	0.961	0.924	0.855	0.792	0.735	0.683	0.636	0.592	0.572	0.552	0.516	0.482
5	0.951	0.906	0.822	0.747	0.681	0.621	0.567	0.519	0.497	0.476	0.437	0.402
6	0.942	0.888	0.790	0.705	0.630	0.564	0.507	0.456	0.432	0.410	0.370	0.335
7	0.933	0.871	0.760	0.665	0.583	0.513	0.452	0.400	0.376	0.354	0.314	0.279
8	0.923	0.853	0.731	0.627	0.540	0.467	0.404	0.351	0.327	0.305	0.266	0.233
9	0.914	0.837	0.703	0.592	0.500	0.424	0.361	0.308	0.284	0.263	0.225	0.194
10	0.905	0.820	0.676	0.558	0.463	0.386	0.322	0.270	0.247	0.227	0.191	0.162
11	0.896	0.804	0.650	0.527	0.429	0.350	0.287	0.237	0.215	0.195	0.162	0.135
12	0.887	0.788	0.625	0.497	0.397	0.319	0.257	0.208	0.187	0.168	0.137	0.112
13	0.879	0.773	0.601	0.469	0.368	0.290	0.229	0.182	0.163	0.145	0.116	0.093
14	0.870	0.758	0.577	0.442	0.340	0.263	0.205	0.160	0.141	0.125	0.099	0.078
15	0.861	0.743	0.555	0.417	0.315	0.239	0.183	0.140	0.123	0.108	0.084	0.065
16	0.853	0.728	0.534	0.394	0.292	0.218	0.163	0.123	0.107	0.093	0.071	0.054
17	0.844	0.714	0.513	0.371	0.270	0.198	0.146	0.108	0.093	0.080	0.060	0.045
18	0.836	0.700	0.494	0.350	0.250	0.180	0.130	0.095	0.081	0.069	0.051	0.038
19	0.828	0.686	0.475	0.331	0.232	0.164	0.116	0.083	0.070	0.060	0.043	0.031
20	0.820	0.673	0.456	0.312	0.215	0.149	0.104	0.073	0.061	0.051	0.037	0.026
21	0.811	0.660	0.439	0.294	0.199	0.135	0.093	0.064	0.053	0.044	0.031	0.022
22	0.803	0.647	0.422	0.278	0.184	0.123	0.083	0.056	0.046	0.038	0.026	0.018
23	0.795	0.634	0.406	0.262	0.170	0.112	0.074	0.049	0.040	0.033	0.022	0.015
24	0.788	0.622	0.390	0.247	0.158	0.102	0.066	0.043	0.035	0.028	0.019	0.013
25	0.780	0.610	0.375	0.233	0.146	0.092	0.059	0.038	0.030	0.024	0.016	0.010

(3) average investment; (4) rate of return; (5) payoff period; and (6) MAPI formula.

Present value criterion. Present value methods for comparing alternatives takes the sum of present values of all future out-of-pocket expenditures and credits over the economic life of the asset. This figure is compared for each alternative. If differences in revenue are involved, their present values are also accounted for. Table IV gives the present values for single future payments or credits, and Table V gives present values for annuities for various years and

TABLE V. PV_a, **Present Value Factor for Annuities**

Years (n)	1%	2%	4%	6%	8%	10%	12%	14%	15%	16%	18%	20%
1	0.990	0.980	0.962	0.943	0.926	0.909	0.893	0.877	0.870	0.862	0.847	0.833
2	1.970	1.942	1.886	1.833	1.783	1.736	1.690	1.647	1.626	1.605	1.566	1.528
3	2.941	2.884	2.775	2.673	2.577	2.487	2.402	2.322	2.283	2.246	2.174	2.106
4	3.902	3.808	3.630	3.465	3.312	3.170	3.037	2.914	2.855	2.798	2.690	2.589
5	4.853	4.713	4.452	4.212	3.993	3.791	3.605	3.433	3.352	3.274	3.127	2.991
6	5.795	5.601	5.242	4.917	4.623	4.355	4.111	3.889	3.784	3.685	3.498	3.326
7	6.728	6.472	6.002	5.582	5.206	4.868	4.564	4.288	4.160	4.039	3.812	3.605
8	7.652	7.325	6.733	6.210	5.747	5.335	4.968	4.639	4.487	4.344	4.078	3.837
9	8.566	8.162	7.435	6.802	6.247	5.759	5.328	4.946	4.772	4.607	4.303	4.031
10	9.471	8.983	8.111	7.360	6.710	6.145	5.650	5.216	5.019	4.833	4.494	4.192
11	10.368	9.787	8.760	7.887	7.139	6.495	5.988	5.453	5.234	5.029	4.656	4.327
12	11.255	10.575	9.385	8.384	7.536	6.814	6.194	5.660	5.421	5.197	4.793	4.439
13	12.134	11.343	9.986	8.853	7.904	7.103	6.424	5.842	5.583	5.342	4.910	4.533
14	13.004	12.106	10.563	9.295	8.244	7.367	6.628	6.002	5.724	5.468	5.008	4.611
15	13.865	12.849	11.118	9.712	8.559	7.606	6.811	6.142	5.847	5.575	5.092	4.675
16	14.718	13.578	11.652	10.106	8.851	7.824	6.974	6.265	5.954	5.669	5.162	4.730
17	15.562	14.292	12.166	10.477	9.122	8.022	7.120	6.373	6.047	5.749	5.222	4.775
18	16.398	14.992	12.659	10.828	9.372	8.201	7.250	6.467	6.128	5.818	5.273	4.812
19	17.226	15.678	13.134	11.158	9.604	8.365	7.366	6.550	6.198	5.877	5.316	4.844
20	18.046	16.351	13.590	11.470	9.818	8.514	7.469	6.623	6.259	5.929	5.353	4.870
21	18.857	17.011	14.029	11.764	10.017	8.649	7.562	6.687	6.312	5.973	5.384	4.891
22	19.660	17.658	14.451	12.042	10.201	8.772	7.645	6.743	6.359	6.011	5.410	4.909
23	20.456	18.292	14.857	12.303	10.371	8.883	7.718	6.792	6.399	6.044	5.432	4.925
24	21.243	18.914	15.247	12.550	10.529	8.985	7.784	6.835	6.434	6.073	5.451	4.937
25	22.023	19.523	15.622	12.783	10.675	9.077	7.843	6.873	6.464	6.097	5.467	4.948

interest rates. An annuity is a sum that is received or paid annually. The factors in Table V convert the entire series of annual sums to a single sum in the present, for various interest rates and years. We shall use the notation PV_a for the present value factor of an annuity.

As an example, let us consider the present values of a machine which costs $12,000 installed. The economic life of the machine is estimated as 10 years, at which time the salvage value is forecasted to be $2000. The average operating and maintenance cost is estimated as $6000 per year. With interest at 8 per cent, the present value of the expenditures and credits is as follows:

Initial investment,

$$B = \$12,000 \times PV_{sp} = 12,000 \times 1.000 = 12,000$$

Annual operating and maintenance costs,

$$E = \$6000 \times PV_a = 6000 \times 6.710 = 33,500$$

Less credit of present value of salvage to be received
in 8 years,

$$S = \$2000 \times PV_{sp} = 3000 \times 0.463 = 1,390$$

Total present value $= \$44,110$

The net total of $44,110 is the present value of the expenditures and credits over the 10-year expected life of the machine. The initial investment is already at present value, that is, the present value factor is 1.000. The annual costs of operation and maintenance are a 10-year annuity so the entire stream of annual costs can be adjusted to the present value by the multiplication of PV_a from Table V. Finally, the present value of the salvage is deducted. This total could be compared with comparable figures for other alternatives over the same 10-year period. If another alternate machine was estimated to have a different economic life, perhaps 5 years, to make the present value totals comparable, two cycles of the 5-year machine would be compared with one cycle of the 10-year machine. Let us continue this example with such a comparison.

Suppose we have another alternate machine with an estimated economic life of 5 years. This machine will do the same job as the previous machine; however, its characteristics and costs are somewhat different. The installed price of the machine is $13,000 and its salvage value at the end of 5 years is expected to be $2000. This machine, however, is completely automatic, fitting into a production line in such a way that parts are fed to it automatically on a conveyor system and leave the machine automatically by way of the conveyor system to proceed to the next operation. The result is that there is no direct labor cost. The only operating costs are costs of maintenance which increase rapidly for the first five years by the following schedule:

$2000, $3200, $5000, $2600, $3000

The \$5000 estimated maintenance charge for the third year is particularly heavy because of the need for the replacement of major components. The present values of expenditures and credits for a 10-year period comparable to the life of the first machine are as follows:

First cycle,

$$B_1 = 13{,}000 \times PV_{sp} = 13{,}000$$

$$E = E_i \times PV_{sp}$$

$$
\begin{aligned}
E_1 &= 2000 \times 0.926 = & 1{,}852 \\
E_2 &= 2200 \times 0.857 = & 1{,}885 \\
E_3 &= 5000 \times 0.794 = & 3{,}970 \\
E_4 &= 2600 \times 0.735 = & 1{,}911 \\
E_5 &= 3000 \times 0.681 = & \underline{2{,}043} \\
& E_{total} & 11{,}661
\end{aligned}
$$

$$S_1 = -1000 \times PV_{sp} = -1000 \times 0.681 = -681$$

Second cycle,

$$B_2 = 13{,}000 \times PV_{sp} = 13{,}000 \times 0.681 = 8853$$

$$E = E_i \times PV_{sp}$$

$$
\begin{aligned}
E_6 &= 2000 \times 0.630 = 1260 \\
E_7 &= 2200 \times 0.583 = 1283 \\
E_8 &= 5000 \times 0.540 = 2700 \\
E_9 &= 2600 \times 0.500 = 1300 \\
E_{10} &= 3000 \times 0.463 = \underline{1389} \\
& E_{total} \quad 7932
\end{aligned}
$$

$$S_2 = -1000 \times PV_{sp} = -1000 \times 0.463 = -463$$

Total present value for 10 years = \$40,302

Note in the foregoing analysis that for 10 years of useful life it was necessary to have a net investment of \$24,000; however, the timing of the second investment reduces its present value considerably. Also note that since the expenditures for maintenance were not represented by a uniform annual cost, but by a rising cost function, the expenditure in each year must be reduced to present value separately through the factor PV_{sp}. The comparison between the basic alternatives is shown by the total present values for the equivalent span of time of 10 years, or \$44,110 for the first alternative and \$40,302 for the second. On the basis of the cost figures, the second alternative involving a purchase of two machines at 5-year intervals would be chosen. Normally, of course, there would be other intangible values which might influence the decision, especially if the economic comparison was very close.

Uniform equivalent annual cost. Instead of converting all figures to present value as we have done in the previous illustration, we can just as easily convert all figures to an equivalent annuity. Since we are commonly talking about cost figures, this annuity is usually referred to as the "uniform equivalent annual cost." The technique is a simple variant of the present value methods just described. Table V gives values for PV_a, the present value of an annuity of \$1.00 for interest rate i and n years. Knowing the amount of the annuity, we then determine the present value by

$$P = A \times PV_a$$

With the same general relationship, we could, of course, determine the equivalent annuity of a present value, thus,

$$A = \frac{P}{PV_a}$$

For example, the equivalent annuities for the two alternate machines discussed under "present value criterion" would be:

First machine:

$$P = \$44,110$$

$$PV_a = 6.710$$

$$A = 44,110/6.710 = \$6570 \text{ per year for 10 years}$$

Second group of two machines:

$$P = \$40,302$$

$$PV_a = 6.710$$

$$A = 40,302/6.710 = \$6020 \text{ per year for 10 years}$$

In other words, the equivalent average annual cost, including capital costs, operating and maintenance costs, for the first machine is \$6570 and \$6020 for the second group of two machines. As before, the second alternative is the cheaper of the two. We see that the present value criterion and the annual cost criterion are entirely equivalent. The only real difference is in the expression of the answer in terms of present values, or in terms of an equivalent annuity.

There are some instances where the uniform equivalent annual cost criterion can be expressed with slightly less computation. For example, the illustration used previously required that we consider two cycles of the second machine to compare the results to the 10-year life of the first machine. This required the separate calculation of present values for each cost item for two cycles of the machine over a 10-year period. We could have avoided this by determining the annuity from the first cycle as follows:

The present values are

$$
\begin{aligned}
B &= & \$13{,}000 \\
E &= & 11{,}661 \\
S &= 1000 \times 0.681 = & -\ 681 \\
P &= & \$23{,}980
\end{aligned}
$$

The equivalent annuity for five years is

$$ A = \frac{P}{PV_a} = \frac{\$23{,}980}{3.993} = \$6020 $$

This is, of course, the same figure we obtained by calculating the annuity based upon the 10-year period. The only difference is that one is an annuity for 5 years, the other for 10 years. Since the cost performance of the two cycles is identical, we could have used this shortcut to calculate the 10-year present value figure of $40,302 obtained under "present value criterion." We could have done so by determining the equivalent annuity for 5 years, as we have just shown. Then from Table V, we obtain for 10 years, 8 per cent, $PV_a = 6.710$. The present value for the two identical cycles over a 10-year period is then:

$$ P = 6020 \times 6.710 = \$40{,}302 $$

Whether we express answers for comparison as present values or uniform equivalent annuities is then a matter of preference. In either case, we are dealing with the *present value criterion* as a basic method for comparing economic alternatives. As we shall see later when we discuss the general model for equipment investment, expressing everything in terms of present values has an advantage in the simplicity of the mathematics involved. The businessmen, however, who are used to thinking in terms of annual costs, often prefer the uniform equivalent annual cost concept as a mode of expression.

Average investment criterion. Average investment methods estimate an average annual cost of owning plus operating and maintaining an asset, and use this total as a basis of comparison between alternatives. The average annual capital costs are approximated by average salvage loss plus interest on the average investment, assuming the decline in value of the asset is on a uniform or straight-line basis. Figure 4 shows the assumed structure for the decline in value

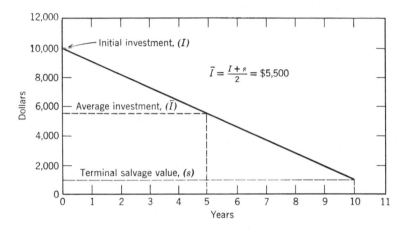

Figure 4. Relationship of initial investment, terminal salvage value, and average investment for "average investment methods."

of an asset and the calculation of average investment for a machine that costs initially $10,000 installed and is estimated to have a 10-year economic life with a salvage value at the end of that time of $1000. The capital costs are then approximated by:

1. Average annual salvage loss $= (10,000 - 1000)/10 = \$900$

2. Annual interest on average investment, at 10 per cent, $=$
$$0.10(10,000 + 1000)/2 = \$550$$

3. Average annual capital cost $= \$900 + \$550 = \$1450$

If operating and maintenance costs were estimated to average $12,500 per year over the 10-year machine life, the total average annual cost for comparison would be $1450 + 12,500 = \$13,950$. Differences in annual revenue between alternatives can be accounted for in the operating costs. We see that the average investment criterion is essentially an approximation to the uniform equivalent annual cost criterion discussed previously.

An example will serve to illustrate a decision based on this criterion. Suppose that we own a 40-year-old automatic screw machine. On investigation we find that for a total investment of $4200, a complete overhaul of that machine is possible which should extend its physical life for 10 years. At the end of that time, it is estimated that it could be salvaged for $300. Another alternative, of course, is to purchase a new automatic screw machine which is available for $16,000, has a projected life of 18 years, and has a terminal salvage value of $800.

The projected operating costs of the two alternatives favor the purchase of the new machine. Because of improvements in design, the new machine can be run at higher speeds which will result in lower direct labor cost, with a proportionate reduction in company fringe benefits. The new machine has been designed for improved maintenance so that these costs are also anticipated to be somewhat lower. Property taxes are of course higher for the new machine. These operating costs are summarized as follows:

Cost Item	Old Machine	New Machine
Direct labor	$5000	$3000
Fringe benefits	80	48
Maintenance costs	1500	1000
Property taxes	50	200
Total	$7630	$4248

A summary of the capital plus operating costs, computed on the basis of the average investment criterion, is then:

Cost Item	Old Machine	New Machine
Average annual salvage loss	$ 390	$ 843
Interest on average investment	225	840
Annual incremental operating costs	7630	4248
Total capital plus operating costs	$8245	$5931

By the average investment criterion, the purchase of the new machine is somewhat cheaper.

Rate of return criterion. One of the most common methods of evaluating new projects or comparing alternative courses of action is to calculate a per cent rate of return, which is then judged for adequacy. Usually, no attempt is made to take account of interest costs, so the resulting figure is referred to the "unadjusted" rate of return, that is, unadjusted for interest values. It is computed as follows:

Unadjusted rate of return

$$= \frac{100 \text{ (net operating advantage } - \text{ amortization)}}{\text{average investment to be recovered}}$$

The net monetary advantage reflects the algebraic sum of incremental costs of operation and maintenance plus possible differences in revenue for the new investment as compared to some existing situation. If the rate of return sought is a "before-tax" rate, then the amortization

$$\frac{\text{Incremental investment}}{\text{Economic life}}$$

is subtracted and the result is divided by average investment and multiplied by 100 to obtain a percentage return. If an "after-tax" rate is sought, the net increase in income taxes due to the project is subtracted from the net monetary advantage and the balance of the calculation is as it was before. Obviously, the adequacy of a given rate of return changes drastically if it is being judged as an after-tax return.

Let us develop an example to demonstrate the use of the rate of return criterion. A company is contemplating the installation of a large-scale conveyorized material-handling system that will interconnect a series of production operations with a unified flow system. A consideration of the new handling system is particularly appropriate, since some of the presently used trucks need replacement, and this would result in a net investment of $20,000 to continue using the present system. The new conveyorized handling system would require an investment of $150,000 for the basic system plus $80,000 for auxiliary equipment needed to implement the system. The terminal salvage value of the new system is set at zero with an economic life of 15 years. There are numerous operating advantages in the new system, including lower material-handling labor costs, lower costs due to damaged product, and considerably less handling by the direct labor operators at the individual machines and operations. Increased operating costs as a result of the new system are in maintenance, property taxes, and insurance. The pertinent operating cost figures are as follows for the new and old material-handling systems:

Cost Item	New System	Old System
Material handling labor	$ 1,000	$20,000
Cost of damaged product	500	4,000
Cost of material handling at machines	2,000	15,000
Maintenance	4,000	500
Property tax and insurance	3,000	500
Total	$10,500	$40,000

Since the net investment required to install the new system is $210,000 and the net operating advantage is $29,500, the unadjusted before-tax rate of return is:

$$\frac{29,500 - (210,000/15)}{210,000/2} \times 100 = 14.8\%$$

The after-tax rate of return requires that incremental taxes be deducted. Incremental taxable income will be the operating advantage less increased allowable tax depreciation. Assuming straight-line depreciation and an allowed depreciation term of 20 years, incremental taxable income is $29,500 less $210,000/20, or $19,000. Assuming an income tax rate of 50 per cent, the incremental tax due to the installation of a new system is $9500. Therefore, the after-tax return is:

$$\frac{29,500 - 9500 - 14,000}{105,000} \times 100 = 5.72\%$$

Whether or not either the before- or after-tax rates calculated in the example are adequate is a matter to be judged in relation to the risk involved in the particular venture and the returns possible through alternate uses of the capital.

Payoff period criterion. The payoff period is the time required for an investment to "pay for itself" through the net operating advantage or revenues which would result from its installation. It is calculated as follows:

$$\text{Payoff period, years} = \frac{\text{net investment}}{\text{net annual operating advantage after taxes}}$$

The payoff period for the conveyorized handling system we were discussing previously is:

$$\frac{\$210,000}{\$29,500 - \$9500} = 10.5 \text{ years}$$

It is the period of time for the net after-tax advantage to just equal the net total investment. Presumably, at the end of that period the after-tax advantage of $20,000 per year is all profit or return, since the invested amount has been recovered. The question might be raised: "If the economic life of the equipment is 15 years and 10 per cent is regarded as an appropriate rate of after-tax return for the project, what should the payoff period be?" Obviously, the period for both capital recovery and return is the 15-year economic life. The period of time which recovers capital only, but which also allows enough equivalent time left in the economic life to provide the return on investment, will be somewhat shorter, and will depend on the required rate of return. Let us note now that the payoff period is another interpretation that can be given to the present value factors for annuities, PV_a, given in Table V. As an example, for an economic life of 15 years and a rate of return required of 10 per cent, $PV_a =$ 7.606, from Table V. This indicates that capital recovery takes place in 7.6 years. The equivalent of 10 per cent compound interest takes place in $15.0 - 7.6 = 7.4$ years. Therefore, any of the PV_a values in Table V, for a given economic life in years and a given rate of return, indicate the shorter period in years required to return just the investment, or, more simply, they give directly the maximum payoff period that would return at least the rate of return specified for the project.

The proper procedure would be to estimate economic life and determine the applicable rate of return. From the present value tables, determine the payoff period associated with these conditions. Then compute the actual payoff period of the project in question and compare it to the standard period from the tables. If the computed payoff period is less than, or equal to, the standard period from the tables, the project meets the payoff and risk requirements imposed. If the computed value is greater than the table value, the project would earn less than the required rate.

We are now in a position to see rather easily what the *adjusted rate of return* would be for the project we have been discussing. The investment we propose to make is, of course, already at present value without further adjustment. Therefore, the actual rate of return that it will earn is determined by the rate of interest that discounts the future earnings generated over the economic life to a present value total that exactly equals the net investment. Recall the simple formula stated previously:

$$P = A \times PV_a$$

where P = a sum at present value (net investment), A = an annuity (future earnings due to operating advantage), and PV_a = the present value factor for an annuity. Therefore, when we calculate the payoff period by dividing net investment by after-tax operating advantage, we are computing the PV_a which would discount the future earnings to equal the net investment. Recall that the value was 10.5 in the previous payoff period calculation. To determine the adjusted rate of return that the project would earn, we simply search Table V for the number 10.5 in the 15-year row. By interpolating in the tables, we find that PV_a = 10.5 is associated with an interest rate of 4.88 per cent. This rate may be compared now with the value of 5.72 per cent obtained by the unadjusted rate of return methods and indicates the margin of error in that calculation.

A before-tax adjusted rate of return could also be calculated for comparative purposes. It is calculated as follows:

$$PV_a = \frac{210,000}{29,500} = 7.12$$

By interpolating in Table V for n = 15 years, we obtain an adjusted rate of return of 11.2 per cent. This rate may be compared with the unadjusted rate obtained previously of 14.8 per cent. The error in using the simpler unadjusted rate of return method is of course greater when we are dealing with longer economic lives and larger future values.

MAPI formula. The MAPI formula might be characterized as an "adjusted" after-tax rate of return criterion. In addition, the MAPI formula is different from the previously discussed rate of return methods in the following ways:

1. Instead of estimating an average rate of return over the life of the investment, the MAPI formula estimates the initial rate of return.

2. Obsolescence may be allowed for by selecting one of three standard schedules for the decline in value of the proposed investment. One schedule follows a uniform decline to terminal salvage value, the second, variant A, is a decelerated schedule, and the third, variant B, is an accelerated schedule. Figure 5 shows the form of these three schedules. Variant A has declined in value by only one-third when half of its service life has expired; however, variant B has declined two-thirds at the same point in service life.

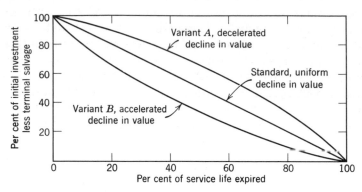

Figure 5. Three patterns for the decline in value of an asset, used by MAPI formula.

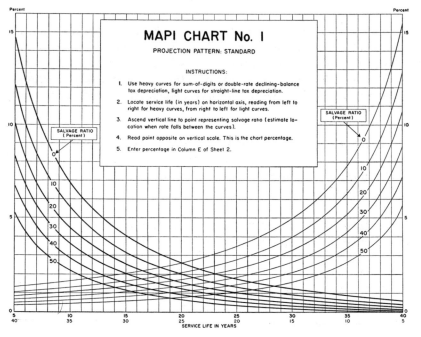

Figure 6. Reproduced by permission from G. Terborgh, *Business Investment Policy,* Machinery and Allied Products Institute, Washington, D. C., 1958.

3. In arriving at the income tax adjustment to be made, the MAPI charts account for the type of tax depreciation used, that is, whether straight line, sum-of-digits, or double declining balance.

4. A set of forms and charts help simplify the mechanics of calculation.

Basic elements in the MAPI calculation of return. The entire focus of the calculation is to determine a rate of return for the next year on net investment, relative to the conditions that would prevail if the company went on without the proposed project. Five elements enter this calculation:

1. *Net investment.* This is the acquisition plus installation cost of the project, minus any investment avoided by it.

2. *Next-year operating advantage.* This is the sum of possible increases or decreases in revenue, plus changes in operating costs resulting from the project for next year.

3. *Next-year capital consumption avoided.* This is the fall in salvage value from holding an existing asset one more year, plus the next-year allocation of possible capital additions or renewals.

4. *Next-year capital consumption incurred.* This is essentially the fall in use value of the project for next year. It is the value taken from the MAPI charts. Figures 6, 7, and 8 are reproductions of the charts used for the three patterns of obsolescence accumulation.

5. *Next-year income tax adjustment.* This is the net increase in income tax resulting from the project.

The after-tax rate of return is then calculated as follows:

$$\text{After-tax return}^* = \frac{\text{net monetary advantage of project}}{\text{net investment required by project}} \times 100$$

$$= \frac{(2) + (3) - (4) - (5)}{(1)} \times 100$$

The resulting rate of return figure is called an "urgency rating." A large number of proposed projects within a company may be ranked by this urgency rating, and if funds are limited, the most urgent projects can be taken first.

* The actual mechanics of calculation varies slightly from this form. The next-year capital consumption incurred actually includes part of the tax adjustment. Since the new project provides new tax deductions, the charts conveniently give the actual excess of capital consumption over tax saving. This is the reason that depreciation method is introduced in the charts.

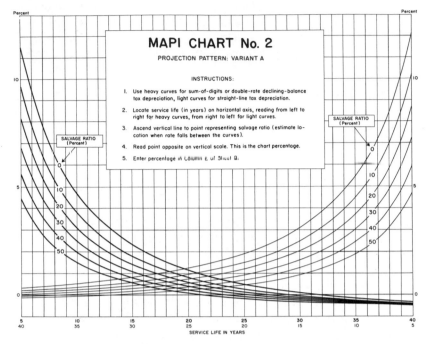

Figure 7. Reproduced by permission from G. Terborgh, *Business Investment Policy,* Machinery and Allied Products Institute, Washington, D. C., 1958.

An example using the MAPI formula. Following is an example of the analysis and a justification for a new plant. It involves both replacement of existing facilities and expansion. The example will illustrate the calculations required, and the use of the MAPI forms and charts.*

EXAMPLE OF THE ECONOMIC JUSTIFICATION FOR A NEW PLANT

The company is considering the erection of a plant for the manufacture of textile spinnings at a location where it is presently renting space and performing minimum operations. The project will cost $3500 for land, $86,500 for a building, and $40,000 for equipment. Included in this latter figure is a charge for conversion costs, duplication of services, and moving existing equipment to the new plant. It is proposed to transfer to the new plant not only the work presently performed in the rented space, but some of the work being done in another plant of the company at a different, and rather distant, location. Although these transfers will not increase the output of the

* Example reproduced from G. Terborgh, *Business Investment Policy,* Machinery and Allied Products Institute, Washington, D. C., 1958, pp. 187–190, with permission.

company itself, the new plant will have enough capacity to permit subcontract work for other manufacturers in the area.

   Analysis of operating advantage. The proposed location has a wage level considerably lower than that of the plant from which the bulk of the work will be transferred. This provides an estimated annual saving in wage costs, including fringes, of $30,000. The company assumes that these area differentials will persist over the life of the project.

   The saving of existing space rentals at the proposed location, plus the value of floor space released in the company's present plant, are placed at $13,500. The operating profit from outside work—producing spinnings for others on contract—is estimated at $10,000.

   Against the proposal are various anticipated cost increases, as follows:

Maintenance, heat, light, and janitor service	$9200
Property taxes and insurance	3000
Other:	
State income tax	1500
Telephone expense	1200
Personnel travel	1500
Traffic between main plant and new location	1300
Freight shipments from new location to customers	3500

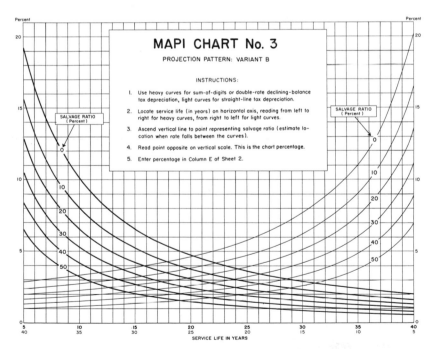

Figure 8. Reproduced by permission from G. Terborgh, *Business Investment Policy*, Machinery and Allied Products Institute, Washington, D. C., 1958.

PROJECT NO. 10 SHEET 1

SUMMARY OF ANALYSIS

(SEE ACCOMPANYING WORK SHEETS FOR DETAIL)

I. REQUIRED INVESTMENT

1	INSTALLED COST OF PROJECT	$ 130,000	1
2	DISPOSAL VALUE OF ASSETS TO BE RETIRED BY PROJECT	$	2
3	CAPITAL ADDITIONS REQUIRED IN ABSENCE OF PROJECT	$	3
4	INVESTMENT RELEASED OR AVOIDED BY PROJECT (2+3)	$	4
5	NET INVESTMENT REQUIRED (1−4)	$ 130,000	5

II. NEXT-YEAR ADVANTAGE FROM PROJECT

A. OPERATING ADVANTAGE

(USE FIRST YEAR OF PROJECT OPERATION)*

		Increase	Decrease	
6	ASSUMED OPERATING RATE OF PROJECT (HOURS PER YEAR)		2,000	6
	EFFECT OF PROJECT ON REVENUE			
7	FROM CHANGE IN QUALITY OF PRODUCTS	$	$	7
8	FROM CHANGE IN VOLUME OF OUTPUT			8
9	TOTAL	$ A	$ B	9
	EFFECT OF PROJECT ON OPERATING COSTS			
10	DIRECT LABOR	$	$ 30,000	10
11	INDIRECT LABOR			11
12	FRINGE BENEFITS			12
13	MAINTENANCE	9,200		13
14	TOOLING			14
15	SUPPLIES			15
16	SCRAP AND REWORK			16
17	DOWN TIME			17
18	POWER			18
19	FLOOR SPACE		13,500	19
20	PROPERTY TAXES AND INSURANCE	3,000		20
21	SUBCONTRACTING			21
22	INVENTORY			22
23	SAFETY			23
24	FLEXIBILITY			24
25	OTHER	9,000		25
26	TOTAL	$ 21,200 A	$ 43,500 B	26
27	NET INCREASE IN REVENUE (9A−9B)		$	27
28	NET DECREASE IN OPERATING COST (26B−26A)		$ 22,300	28
29	NEXT-YEAR OPERATING ADVANTAGE (27+28)		$ 32,300†	29

B. NON-OPERATING ADVANTAGE

(USE ONLY IF THERE IS AN ENTRY IN LINE 4)

30	NEXT-YEAR CAPITAL CONSUMPTION AVOIDED BY PROJECT:		30
	A DECLINE OF DISPOSAL VALUE DURING THE YEAR	$	A
	B NEXT-YEAR ALLOCATION OF CAPITAL ADDITIONS	$	B
	TOTAL	$	

C. TOTAL ADVANTAGE

31	TOTAL NEXT-YEAR ADVANTAGE FROM PROJECT (29+30)	$ 32,300	31

* For projects with a significant break-in period, use performance after break-in.

† Includes $10,000 estimated operating profit on subcontract work.

Figure 9. MAPI analysis of the economic justification of a new plant. Reproduced by permission from G. Terborgh, *Business Investment Policy,* Machinery and Allied Products Institute, Washington, D. C., 1958.

PROJECT NO. _____10_____   SHEET 2

III. COMPUTATION OF MAPI URGENCY RATING

32 TOTAL NEXT-YEAR ADVANTAGE AFTER INCOME TAX (31 − TAX) $ 16,150

33 MAPI CHART ALLOWANCE FOR PROJECT (TOTAL OF COLUMN F, BELOW) $ 2,287*

(ENTER DEPRECIABLE ASSETS ONLY)

Item or Group	Installed Cost of Item or Group A	Estimated Service Life (Years) B	Estimated Terminal Salvage (Percent of Cost) C	MAPI Chart Number D	Chart Percent- age E	Chart Percent- age × Cost (E × A) F
Building	$ 86,500	30	0	2	0.1	$ 87
Equipment	40,000	12	0	1	5.5	2,200
					TOTAL	$ 2,287

34 AMOUNT AVAILABLE FOR RETURN ON INVESTMENT (32 − 33) $ 13,863

35 **MAPI URGENCY RATING** (34 ÷ 5) · 100   %   11

---

* Since the chart allowance does not cover future capital additions to project assets, add an annual proration of such additions, if any, to the figure in Line 33.

Figure 9 (continued).

Stipulations:

Project operating rate	2000 hours
Projection pattern:	
Building	Variant *A*
Equipment	Standard
Service life:	
Building	30 years
Equipment	12 years
Terminal salvage ratio	0
Tax depreciation method	Declining balance
Tax rate	50 per cent

The calculations for the justification of the new plant are carried out on the standard forms shown in Figure 9. Note that in this example, the building follows the capital consumption pattern of variant *A*, therefore using MAPI chart 2, and the equipment follows the standard pattern, using MAPI chart 1. The resulting MAPI urgency rating is an adjusted first-year rate of return, after taxes, and must be judged for adequacy in relation to other uses of funds within the organization.

Summary

In this section we have attempted to analyze some of the cost factors which bear on investment decisions, such as sunk costs, opportunity costs, etc., and to describe the investment criteria most commonly used by business and industry today. These models all represent some approximation and idealization of the general equipment investment problem. For example, all require an assumption of an economic life and an assumption of some standard schedule for the decline in value of the assets being analyzed. In addition there are many other less obvious conceptual ideas for which they do not account, and we will develop this contrast in the chapter dealing with the "general model for equipment investment," and place the common criteria in context with a broader conceptual framework.

At this point, it appears that we have a "bumper crop" of investment criteria. Are they all equivalent? Are there conditions when one is preferable to the others? Are any of them valid enough for use on the operating business level? Let us attempt to answer the last question first. When properly used, the common criteria are probably good enough for general operating use. Consider for a moment the accuracy of the data used in the models. They involve forecasts of cost performance over the equipment life on salvage values, maintenance and labor costs, taxes, and many other items. At best, our estimates of these figures for the coming year could have an accuracy of plus or minus 10 per cent. When we attempt to estimate them for future years over the life of the assets, the accuracy limits widen considerably.

Are they all equivalent? No, they are not. Some of them are more approximate in nature. The present value methods (including the equivalent average annual cost method) are the most flexible and involve the least assumptions. They can be tailored to meet specific situations involving wide variations in salvage schedules, projected cost patterns, and future periodic capital additions. The average investment criterion is basically an approximation to the equivalent average annual cost criterion. It computes an average annual cost which assumes a uniform decline in salvage value of the asset and ignores the timing of expenditures by computing interest on average investment. The average investment, rate of return, and payoff period criteria all approximate future operating costs by an average period. For simple machines this may be a reasonable assumption, but for complex equipment and for buildings, future costs may have a pattern in relation to time which is not well represented by an average figure. The MAPI formula ignores the future course of operating costs and computes only a first-year rate of return.

In terms of the preference of using one criterion over another, there are some reasonable guides. If the project is one involving long projected lives with complex patterns of future expenditures, interest values may tip the balance in favor of one alternative, and the present value criteria should be used. When future operating costs are reasonably represented by an average figure, the choice between average investment, rate of return, payoff period, and the MAPI formula criteria may rest on the preference for a particular way of expressing answers, that is, in terms of return on investment, annual costs, or time to pay off. The advantage of the MAPI formula is in a procedure which may enforce a minimum level of analysis. Its disadvantage is that the system may be used blindly and, therefore, result in misuse.

REFERENCES

1. Dean, J., *Capital Budgeting*, Columbia University Press, New York. 1951.
2. Grant, E. L., *Principles of Engineering Economy*, Ronald Press Co.. New York, 3rd ed., 1950.
3. Orenstein, R. D., "Topics on the MAPI Formula," *Journal of Industrial Engineering*, 1956, pp. 282–294.
4. Terborgh, G., *Business Investment Policy*, Machinery and Allied Products Institute. Washington, D. C., 1958.

REVIEW QUESTIONS

1. Why is it that a sunk cost is irrelevant in models for investment?
2. How are book values of equipment handled in investment analysis?
3. What is an opportunity cost?
4. What are capital costs?
5. What is the structure of capital costs incurred by retaining ownership of an asset one more year?
6. What is the meaning of the term, "Economic Life"? Physical Life?
7. How is obsolescence reflected in the actual costs of owning and operating an asset?
8. What is the compound amount factor? How is it computed?
9. What is the meaning of the reciprocal of the compound amount factor?
10. What is an annuity?
11. Define the factor PV_a. What is the meaning of its reciprocal?
12. Why is it that most of the common criteria for comparing alternate capital investments assume an economic life and some standard schedule for the decline in value of the asset?
13. Outline the methodology for comparing alternate investments by the present value criterion. Compare the present value criterion with the uniform equivalent annual cost criterion and show that they are directly equivalent.
14. How are the capital costs approximated in the average investment criterion?
15. Compare the calculations required for the before- and after-tax rate of return.
16. Outline the payoff period criterion methodology. With what standard payoff period should the computed value be compared to determine if the investment is justified? How is the standard payoff period determined?
17. Outline the methodology required for the MAPI formula.
18. Compare and evaluate the five criteria for investment analysis discussed. Under what conditions might we use each of them?

PROBLEMS

1. A company is considering the purchase of a new grinder which will cost $10,000. The economic life of this machine is expected to be 6 years, at which time the salvage value will be $2000. The average operating and maintenance costs are estimated to be $5000 per year.

   a. Assuming an interest rate of 10 per cent, determine the present value of the future costs of the proposed grinder.

 b. Compare this machine to a presently owned grinder that has annual operating costs of $4000 per year and expected maintenance costs of $2000 in the next year with an annual increase of $1000 thereafter.

 c. What is the effect of using an interest rate of 6 per cent rather than 10 per cent?

 d. Express the 6 per cent and 10 per cent results as equivalent annual costs.

 2. A company owns a 5-year old turret lathe with a book value of $10,000 and a present market value of $8000. The average loss in salvage value is expected to be $1000 per year until a scrap price of $1000 is reached Maintenance costs are expected to average $700 per year. A new turret lathe would decrease direct labor and fringe benefits by $1500 per year. Such a machine costs $20,000 and could be expected to have an economic life of 12 years at which time the salvage value will be $3000. Annual maintenance is expected to average $600. Incremental property taxes will average $100 per year if the proposed machine is purchased.

 Evaluate the feasibility of acquiring the proposed machine on the basis of the average investment criterion.

 3. A large research and development company is considering the purchase of a numerically controlled jig borer. If such a machine is purchased, four jig borer operators can be eliminated at an annual savings of $28,000. In addition, two tool makers can be eliminated since complex fixtures will not be required, at a savings of $16,500 per year. The maintenance on the proposed machine is estimated to be $1000 per year. The maintenance on the five jig borers that would be replaced by the numerically controlled machine totals $2000 per year. If the proposed machine is purchased, a programmer must be hired at $9000 per year. The cost of the proposed machine is $110,000 on the floor and running. In addition, a controlled atmosphere room must be built around the machine at a cost of $10,000. It is anticipated that training costs for this equipment will be $5000. The machine is expected to have an economic life of 10 years with a salvage value of $15,000.

 a. Calculate the unadjusted before-tax rate of return.

 b. Calculate the after-tax rate of return assuming a 12-year depreciation life, $20,000 salvage value, straight-line method, and an incremental tax rate of 45 per cent.

 4. A camera manufacturer is considering the purchase of a special transfer machine which will perform seven operations at once which are presently done separately. The present method requires ten men at a total annual direct labor cost of $65,000 plus fringe benefits of $5000 annually. The factory burden rate is 150 per cent of direct labor. Two of these men will be able to run the proposed machine.

 It is estimated that utility expenses will be decreased $1200 per year since one machine would replace ten. Since all operations are to be performed simultaneously, approximately $20,000 can be cut from the average work in-process inventory. Material handling costs of approximately $2000 per year would be eliminated if the proposed investment is made. In addition, $1500 annually can be saved in expediting costs. The normal scrap expense for this operation is $5000 per year. It is estimated that the transfer machine would reduce that amount by 20 per cent. If the transfer machine is purchased, badly needed floor space can be released. The value of this space is estimated to be $5000 per year. Of the ten machines that the transfer machine would replace, seven can be sold for a total of $33,000. The remaining three (hand screw machines) are needed for other production. If they are not made available for this work, three similar machines must be purchased at a total cost of $42,000. Make an analysis that will guide the company in its decision.

5. A fishery is considering the purchase of a new boat which will cost $650,000 to have built to their specifications. Such a boat is expected to last 35 years at which time the salvage value is estimated to be $65,000. The decline in value is anticipated to be most heavy in the later years because of increasing maintenance and obsolescence. The proposed boat would have an expanded hold capacity enabling larger catches to be returned. It is expected that the increased revenue would be $85,000 per year. The proposed boat has a more efficient power plant that would decrease present fuel expenses of $40,000 a year by 15 per cent. In addition, automatic equipment would allow the boat to be operated by three less crew members at an annual savings of $18,000. Fishing net expense is expected to increase $8000 per year because of the increased volume. If the present boat is kept, the decline in salvage value next year is expected to be $15,000. The present market value of this boat is $130,000 and if kept, will require a $10,000 engine overhaul. The incremental tax rate for this fishery is 40 per cent.

    a. Compute the MAPI urgency rating if the company can use the double declining balance depreciation method.

    b. Compute the MAPI urgency rating if the company uses the straight-line method of depreciation.

6. The question is often raised, "Should you rent or buy a car?" The car in question can be purchased for $4500 or rented for $130 per month payable in advance in one-year increments for a three-year period. After consulting the automobile blue book and other sources, you estimate that a reasonable value for this type of car at the end of a three-year period is $2000. In light of bank interest charges, opportunities, etc., an interest rate of 10 per cent seems appropriate. Also the following factors may influence the decision.

    a. If you rent, the lessor requires more comprehensive insurance costing $60 more per year than you would carry if you bought.

    b. If you buy, ready cash balances will be depleted and you will have to borrow $1000 at a net cost of $50.

    c. Your present garage is not long enough to fit the proposed car; alterations will cost $1000.

    d. If you rent the car you will spend less on preventive maintenance. You anticipate that you could save $50 in the second year and $75 in the third year.

Determine the least cost alternative and the potential savings. Would your answer change if you believed a more appropriate salvage value to be $1000?

7. A job shop has been asked to bid on a one-lot manufacture of 1000 frying pans. The estimating and engineering departments have proposed three alternatives as manufacturing plans for the pans as follows:

a. Using minimal tooling. The pans could be made on existing equipment with 0.40 direct labor hour each.

b. Constructing a draw die. The pans could be made with 0.32 direct labor hour each. It has been estimated that a suitable drawing die would require 70 hours to construct.

c. A special spinning lathe can be purchased that would make the pans with 0.20 direct labor hour each. Such a lathe would cost $2500 installed, would have a useful life of 10 years, and would have no salvage value because of its specialized nature.

Material is expected to cost $0.20 per unit. The company has an average direct labor rate of $2.60 per hour, a factory burden rate of 150 per cent of direct labor, a general and administrative expense rate of 20 per cent of factory cost, and a target profit rate of 10 per cent on total cost. It has been estimated that 10 per cent of the burden items (e.g., direct supplies, power, etc.) vary in proportion to factory activity. The company uses an interest rate of 15 per cent for evaluation purposes.

Determine the least cost method of manufacture and the lowest unit price that could be accepted stating any necessary assumptions.

How would the analysis change if the company was operating at full capacity and the frying pan job could be accepted only if run entirely on overtime?

14

A General Model for
Equipment Investment

We have studied the common criteria for comparing economic alternatives, or judging the adequacy of an investment in equipment. They are all slightly different in form and some more approximate than others. Let us now generalize and develop a model which regards the common models we have discussed, as well as many other models, as special cases. We can then see the basic relationships between them.

The General Investment Problem

When we make an investment for a profit of any kind, we are expecting the discounted future net income to at least equal the investment. The rate of discount which returns the stream of future net income payments to a present value equal to the original net investment is the rate of return. Recall the relationship, $P = A \times PV_a$, where P is the present sum (net investment in this context), A is an annuity (annual net income from the investment), and PV_a is the present value factor of an annuity of $1.00 for the number of years of the expected annuity and at the interest rate which makes $A \times PV_a$ just equal the original investment P. The term of the annuity could be any number of years, including an infinite stream of income payments, and the interest rate could be any value. A direct parallel to the situation we have just stated is the investment in a $1000 bond which produces annual interest payments of $150 for 10 years. The rate of return which makes the present value of the 10-year stream of interest payments just equal to the original $1000

402

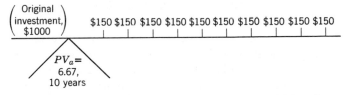

Figure 1. The rate of return is determined by the PV_a which reduces the ten annual income payments of $150 to the present value of the original investment of $1000.

investment is easily determined by the PV_a,

$$PV_a = \tfrac{1000}{150} = 6.67$$

What interest rate is associated with a 10-year PV_a of 6.67? Looking in Table V of Chapter 13, for 10 years, we see that it is approximately 8 per cent. The PV_a is in essence the fulcrum determining a balance between the original investment and the future stream of income payments (see Figure 1). Any investment problem can be reduced to the equivalent simple form given previously.

Of course, instead of determining the actual rate of return produced, we could establish a rate of return minimum based on the earning rate of other comparable investment opportunities. Then, to determine if the investment in question meets the minimum standard, we determine PV_a, given n and the minimum return r, and compute the present value of the income stream. If the present value of the income stream is equal to or greater than the investment amount, the investment earns the minimum rate of return or greater. If the present value of the income stream is less than the investment amount, the rate of return is less than the requirement. Comparing alternate investments in this way, we would select the alternative which maximizes $A(PV_a) - P$; PV_a is now the value determined by the required rate of return and the term of the investment.

Relative rates of return. The earning rates of individual pieces of equipment in a production system are often difficult to establish because their contributions to the total earning power of the system and of the enterprise as a whole are not clear. Normally then, absolute rates of return cannot be determined so that we are forced to consider relative rates of return, or a cost minimizing model. In the case of investment in equipment, the proposed new equipment is usually replacing some existing equipment or method of operation. Even though it may not be possible to assign any direct revenue to either the old or proposed systems, the equivalent of revenue may be produced by reductions in operating costs compared to present methods, if the new equipment is installed. Thus, regarding the potential operating cost reductions as the equivalent of income, we can compute a rate of return as we did with the bond, but this rate of return is relative to continuing operation with the existing equipment. Also, we can establish a minimum rate of return and compute the present value of the future operating cost advantage to see if it is larger than the required investment. Alternate equipment designs could then be compared, selecting the one which maximized the net difference between the present value of future operating advantage and net investment.

Cost minimizing models are commonly used in equipment investment policy because revenues assignable to the installation of new equipment are usually of minor significance in comparison to the outlays for initial investment and operating expenses. For each alternative, then, the sum of the present values of expenditures, less any offsetting revenues yields a positive net cost which we wish to minimize when comparing various alternatives. The general model which we shall develop uses this convention of signs.

The Equipment Investment Problem

To maximize return on investment, or minimize overall costs for the nonprofit enterprise, capital equipment must be used which provides the capacity needed in the most economical way. Since technology is continually developing new machines and systems, we must look not only at what equipment is available, but what may become available. If, for example, we had a machine in operation for some time and a new and improved design became available, part of our problem is in assessing not only the relative merits of the new machine but in deciding if even better equipment might be available in the near future. Should the present machine be replaced now, or should we wait for the future equipment which will be even better? Should replacement take place now followed by a second replacement with the even better machine at a later date? If so, at what future date? Part of the problem, then, is the consideration of a *chain* of machines rather than the isolated case of the new machine now available.

Also, because of the dynamics of technology, we find that a machine may be succeeded by a better, perhaps more automatic, machine, or that a group of machines and operations may be replaced by a new system which changes the concept of production entirely.

The General Model*

The general model which we shall develop reduces to present value all disbursements and receipts involved in the possession and operation of a succession of equipment having *varying* initial costs, life spans, salvage values, expense and revenue functions. It will be convenient to adopt the following symbols:

C = the consideration of a chain or succession of equipment in the model.

E = the present value of operating expenses or dispersements for each individual piece of equipment in the chain.

R = the present value of revenues which result from the possession or use of each individual piece of equipment in the chain.

B = the present value of the purchase price of each individual piece of equipment in the chain.

S = the present value of the salvage of each individual piece of equipment in the chain.

Thus, the investment case involving C, E, R, B, and S, ($CERBS$), is the most general situation. It considers a chain of machines, each item in the chain having its own individual purchase price and salvage value, revenue and expense functions, and individual economic life spans. The comparison for the various functionally equivalent chains of equipment would then be made on the basis of the total present value P for each chain, or,

$$P\dagger = B - S + E - R$$

The great majority of management investment decisions can be based on a comparison of cases less complicated than $CERBS$, but from this most general case all the others may be derived by simply dropping or simplifying certain terms in the general model expression. For example, if the decision rests with the alternate items of equipment which are not to be succeeded, a comparison of $ERBS$ is called

---

* Based on A. Reisman and E. S. Buffa, "A General Model for Investment Policy," *Management Science,* Vol. VIII, No. 3, April 1962.

† Note that this is for a cost minimizing model, and the signs for the terms have been assigned to produce a net positive value of P. For an investment dominated by revenue figures, such as a stock or bond, the opposite sign convention makes better sense, that is, $P = R - E - B + S$.

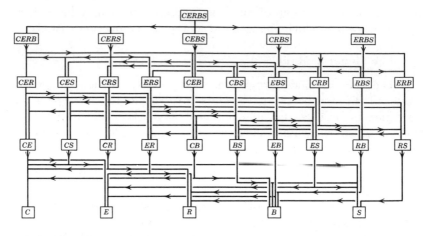

C—chain of machines
E—operating disbursements
R—operating receipts
B—capital investments
S—salvage value

Figure 2. Structure of special cases of the general model, *CERBS*.

for. If the equipment involves no revenue function, only *EBS* need be considered. Thus, the entire field of equipment investment comparisons may be covered in a systematic way. Figure 2 is a systematic symbolic representation of all cases.

Development of the Terms of the General Model

Now let us take up the development of the individual four terms in the general model. We shall begin with the implications of the purchase of a chain of machines, followed by the consideration of salvage values, expense functions, and revenue functions. Recall that for each term we will be reducing all monetary values to the present value. Perhaps the most simple device for achieving this discounting is to multiply the value by the general factor, $PV = e^{-rt}$, where e is the base of natural logarithms (**2.71828**), r is the rate of return which can be earned, and t is the elapsed time. We will use this factor in our discounting process.

Purchase price. The price of each generation of items of equipment in the chain will have its own characteristic value. We do not conceive that each generation is simply a new version of the same piece of equipment. Succeeding generations could be rather different in design, degree of automation, etc. Therefore, the first item will cost B_0, the first replacement B_1, the second replacement B_2, and, in general, the jth replacement will cost B_j. Beginning at time zero when the initial item of equipment is purchased, its present value is B_0. But the present value of the first replacement is less than its purchase price B_1, since the time T_1 equal to the economic life of the initial piece of equipment has elapsed. The present value of B_1 is, therefore, $B_1 e^{-rT_1}$, where e^{-rT_1} is the present value factor. The present value of the money required to purchase B_2 is $B_2 e^{-r(T_1+T_2)}$, where T_2 is the economic life of the first replacement. Similarly, the jth replacement will take place

$$T_1 + T_2 + T_3 + \cdots T_j = \sum_{i=0}^{j} (T_i) \tag{1}$$

time units from the present.

Hence, the present value of the money required to buy the jth replacement which will take place at the time specified by (1) is:

$$B_j e^{-r \sum_{t=0}^{j} T_i}$$

Finally, the present value of the chain of investments to be made for purchasing the initial item of equipment plus n generations of replacements is:

$$B = B_0 + B_1 e^{-rT_1} + B_2 e^{-r(T_1+T_2)} + \cdots + B_j e^{-(T_1+T_2+\cdots+T_j)}$$
$$+ \cdots + B_n e^{-r(T_1+T_2+\cdots+T_j+\cdots+T_n)}$$
$$= \sum_{j=0}^{n} B_j e^{-r \sum_{t=0}^{j} (T_i)} \tag{2}$$

This is simply a sum of the product of purchase price times the appropriate present value factor for the entire chain of investments. The present value factor for each separate generation, of course, depends on the interest rate and the elapsed time from the present. Figure 3 diagrams the time relationships of our chain of investments.

Salvage value. The value of each generation of equipment at the time of its retirement from service may, in general, vary from one to the next succeeding item in the chain. This value may be positive, negative, as when it has no market value and requires an expenditure to get rid of it, or zero. The salvage value can only be realized at the end of the life period T of the particular generation. Therefore, the present value of the salvage of the first piece of equip-

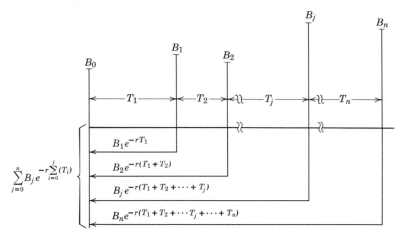

Figure 3. Timing of the purchases of a chain of machines, discounted to present values.

ment in the chain, S_{0,T_0} (read, the salvage value of the initial item, at time zero), is:

$$S_{0,T_0} = S_{0,T_1}e^{-rT_1}$$

The present value of the first replacement is:

$$S_{1,T_0} = S_{1,T_2}e^{-r(T_1+T_2)}$$

and the present value of the jth replacement is:

$$S_{j,T_0} = S_{j,T_{j+1}}e^{-r(T_1+T_2+\cdots T_j+T_{j+1})}$$

$$= S_{j,T_{j+1}}e^{-r\sum_{i=0}^{j}(T_{i+1})}$$

The total present value of the salvage of the entire chain is, therefore:

$$S = \sum_{j=0}^{n} S_{j,T_{j+1}}e^{-r\sum_{i=0}^{j}T_{i+1}} \tag{3}$$

Again, this expression is simply the sum of the product of salvage value times the appropriate present value factor, for the entire chain of investments. The notation takes account of the fact that the initial equipment is salvaged at the time of purchase of the first replacement, the first replacement salvaged at the time of purchase of the second replacement, etc. Figure 4 shows the salvage values of the equipment chain in relation to time.

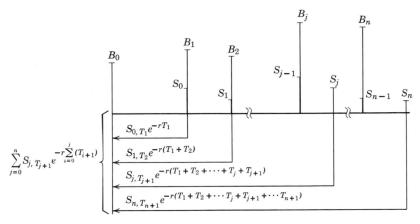

Figure 4. Timing of salvage values of a chain of machines.

Expense function. The expense function describes the total of all expenses required to operate and maintain the equipment. The expense function can take many different forms, typical cases being shown in Figure 5. With simple machines requiring little maintenance, it is possible that the average operating and maintenance expense could be constant as shown for the initial machine in Figure 5. An asset requiring no operating expense, only maintenance, may begin its life with zero maintenance cost, but increase as time passes, shown by the first replacement in Figure 5. Operating and maintenance expense may begin with some finite value and increase linearly, or increase at some increasing rate, as shown by the jth and nth replacements respectively in Figure 5. Many other forms for the expense function are, of course, possible, including decreasing curves and more complex forms.

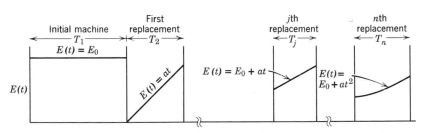

Figure 5. Typical expense functions.

We will use the notation $E(t)$, read E of t, to represent the mathematical expression for any expense function in relation to time. For example, $E(t) = E_0$, where E_0 is a constant representing the initial operating expenses, describes the expense function for the initial machine in Figure 5. For the first replacement, $E(t) = at$, describes the expense function where a is the slope of the straight line. The jth replacement in Figure 5 has an expense function described by $E(t) = E_0 + at$. Now, $E(t)$ represents the rate of expenditure for any point in time t in the life of the machine, so that the area under the curve $E(t)$ between any two lines t_1 and t_2 yields the total expenditure during that time period, as shown in Figure 6. The gross expenditure over the life of the equipment is then represented by the area under the curve $E(t)$ between the times 0 and T. This area may be determined either graphically or analytically by summing the areas of all thin rectangles such as $abcd$, shown in Figure 6. The accuracy of such a procedure varies inversely with the size of the increment Δt, that is, the smaller the increment of time, Δt, the greater the accuracy. In the limiting situation where Δt is made infinitely small, we can obtain the exact solution by means of the integral calculus.

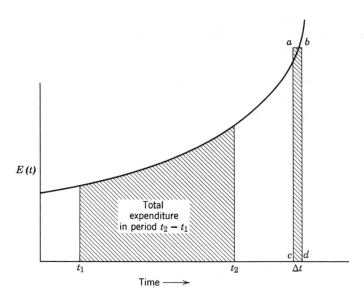

Figure 6. Total expenditure in period $t_2 - t_1$ is area under curve of $E(t)$ between t_1 and t_2. Areas under the curve may be determined graphically by summing the areas of all thin rectangles under curve of width Δt, such as $abcd$, or by the integral calculus.

Therefore, using the calculus notation, the summation of all infinitely thin rectangles may be expressed as

$$E(T) = \int_0^{T_1} E(t)\, dt$$

where $E(t)$ is some function of time describing the expected rate of expense.

Since the expenses are accumulated continuously, they must be discounted to present value continuously; therefore, the present value of $E(t)$ is

$$E - \int_0^{T_1} E(t)e^{-rt}\, dt \tag{4}$$

for the initial machine. For the replacement machines, the beginning of economic life is not at time zero, so that it is necessary to discount expenses first to the beginning of life of the machine following the form of (4), and second, to time zero. Therefore, the present value of expenses incurred by the jth machine, for example, is

$$E_j = \int_0^{T_{j+1}} E_j(t)e^{-rt}\, dt\; e^{-r(T_1+T_2+\cdots T_j)}$$

$$= \int_0^{T_{j+1}} E_j(t)e^{-rt}\, dt\; e^{-r\sum_{i=0}^{j} T_i}$$

Finally, the present value of all expenses incurred by all items in a chain of machines is

$$E = \sum_{j=0}^{n} \left[e^{-r\sum_{i=0}^{j} T_i} \int_0^{T_{j+1}} E_j(t)e^{-rt}\, dt \right] \tag{5}$$

Figure 7 shows diagrammatically the discounting procedure.

Revenue function. The meaning and derivation of the revenue function parallels exactly that of the expense function. Expected revenue functions $R(t)$ may vary with time, as with expense functions. As with expense functions, revenue functions must be discounted first to the beginning of the life of the particular machine, and second to time zero. The revenue function is then

$$R = \sum_{j=0}^{n} \left[e^{-r\sum_{i=0}^{j} T_i} \int_0^{T_{j+1}} R_j(t)e^{-rt}\, dt \right] \tag{6}$$

The general model restated. The present value of all receipts and disbursements attributable to the possession as well as operation of

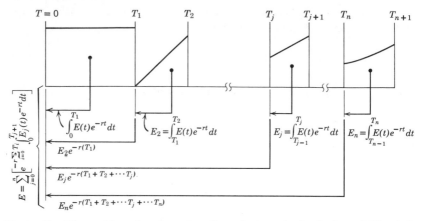

Figure 7. Discounting of expense functions, first to the beginning of life of the machine and second to time zero.

a chain of investments in equipment is

$$P = B - S + E - R$$

or

$$P = \sum_{j=0}^{n} \left[B_j e^{-r \sum_{i=0}^{j} T_i} \right] - \sum_{j=0}^{n} \left[S_j(T_{j+1})e^{-r \sum_{i=0}^{j} (T_{i+1})} \right]$$

$$+ \sum_{j=0}^{n} \left[e^{-r \sum_{i=0}^{j} T_i} \int_{0}^{T_{j+1}} E_j(t)e^{-rt} \, dt \right]$$

$$- \sum_{j=0}^{n} \left[e^{-r \sum_{i=0}^{j} T_i} \int_{0}^{T_{j+1}} R_j(t)e^{-rt} \, dt \right] \tag{7}$$

Equation 7 is solvable by the methods of the difference and differential calculus.

Note that in the development of the general model, each item in the succession of machines could have its own characteristic purchase price, salvage value, revenue and expense function, and economic life. Since any of the five elements B, S, E, R, and T may enter the model as constants, or as variables from one item in the chain of machines to the next, we may further classify subgroupings of each of the special cases of $CERBS$ shown in Figure 2. For example, in the most general case, $CERBS$, B, S, E, R, or T may be constants from item to item in the chain, or they may be variable as was true in the derivation of the general model. Therefore, one special case might be a model where a chain of machines is considered, and each machine has an expense function, a revenue function, initial purchase price and salvage value. But suppose that only the expense and revenue functions vary from item to item in the chain, the purchase price, salvage value and economic life being identical for each item in the chain. We have then the *er* subcase of *CERBS*, using lower-case letters to indicate which items appear as variables. If all five factors are identical from item to item in the chain, we have the zero subcase of *CERBS*. Figure 8 shows the 31 subgroups of *CERBS*, headed by the most general case *bsert*, where every factor is variable.

We are now in a position to classify any model in relation to the general model. First, we may classify models by Figure 2, that is, which of the elements $C, E, R, B,$ and S are accounted for. Second, we may classify models involving C, that is, a chain of machines, by determining whether or not the factors $B, S, E, R,$ and T are variable or constant in the model. Figure 8 displays the 31 subgroups of *CERBS* on this basis. Actually, any of the special cases of *CERBS* in Figure 2 which involve C, a chain of machines, could be further classified in this way. For example, we could take the special case *CEB* in Figure 2 and develop the structure of its subcases on the basis of *bet* in a way parallel to that of Figure 8.

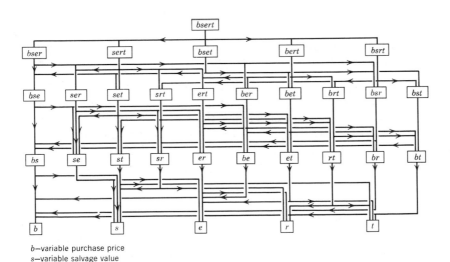

b—variable purchase price
s—variable salvage value
e—variable expense function
r—variable revenue function
t—life period

Figure 8. Structure of variables in the special cases of *CERBS*.

Classifying Models

Now that we have developed the general model, we are in a position to see how the common criteria discussed previously fit into the structure of the general model.

Present value and annual cost methods. The usual conceptual framework of these models involves the *ERBS* subcase of *CERBS*. If a chain of machines is considered (it rarely is with these methods) only nonvarying parameters are involved so we would have the zero subcase.

Average investment methods. These are merely an approximation to the annual cost approach discussed above.

Rate of return methods. These methods commonly consider E, R, B, and S, that is, the *ERBS* subcase of *CERBS*. Since a chain of machines is not considered, none of the factors are variable. In addition, expense and revenue functions are usually taken as a constant over the life of the equipment.

Payoff period methods. If it is assumed that the payoff period means the time at which all costs have been recovered, this period is obtained by determining the time in the life of the equipment when P, the present worth of all receipts and disbursements, is zero in any of the *CERBS* subcases. The usual applications of this technique, however, involve only E, R, B, and S, so that none of the factors are variable. In addition, expense and revenue functions are usually taken as constant over the life of the equipment.

MAPI formula. The MAPI formula essentially reduces to the *ERBS* subcase of *CERBS*, with some qualifications. Although Terborgh states that he considers a chain of machines, his assumption is that the successive machines are just like the first in terms of operating and maintenance costs and salvage loss. This is the same as eliminating future items in the chain from consideration and therefore the *ERBS* subcase.

Classifying Other Models

A large number of other models of equipment investment have been developed which are somewhat more sophisticated than the common criteria. The characteristics of many of these models are summarized in reference (13), and many of them have been classified in the *CERBS* framework in reference (8).

Summary

One of the important objectives of the general model presented is to place in perspective the dozens of other models, most of which are special cases of the general model. One of the real difficulties in dealing with equipment investment policy in the past has been the fact that dozens of different models have been developed to deal with special cases. Each new model had characteristics that were common with some others, with perhaps some variation in methodology or an addition to generality. The result has been considerable confusion about the applicability of the various methods. The general model presented here seems applicable to all situations, as complex as a merger of two enterprises or as simple as the evaluation of a fixed term bond. The general model has been made workable as a practical means of evaluating investment alternatives through the development of an IBM650 Computer Program (9). The computer program is only slightly restricted in generality in that it presently can handle expense and revenue functions of only certain forms; however, all those diagrammed in Figures 5 and 7 are handled by the program.

REFERENCES

1. Alchian, A., *Economic Replacement Policy*, Report R-224, Rand Corporation, Santa Monica, California, 1952.
2. Bowman, E. H., and R. Fetter, *Analysis for Production Management*, Richard D. Irwin, Homewood, Ill., revised ed., 1961.
3. Clapham, J. C. R., "Economic Life of Equipment," *Operational Research Quarterly*, Vol. 8, pp. 181–190, 1957.
4. Dean, J., "Replacement Investments," Chapter VI in *Capital Budgeting*, Columbia University Press, New York, 1951.
5. Dreyfus, S. E., "A Generalized Equipment Replacement Study," *Journal of the Society of Industrial and Applied Mathematics*, Vol. 8, Number 3, pp. 425–435, 1960.
6. Grant, E. L., *Principles of Engineering Economy*, Ronald Press Company, New York, 3rd ed., 1950.
7. Orenstein, R. D., "Topics on the MAPI Formula," *Journal of Industrial Engineering*, pp. 283–294, 1956.
8. Reisman, A., and E. S. Buffa, "A General Model for Investment Policy," *Management Science*, Vol. 8, Number 3, April 1962.
9. Reisman, A., E. S. Buffa, and E. Harris, "A General Investment Model and Computer Program," mimeographed.
10. Rifas, B. E., "Replacement Models," Chapter 17 in *Introduction to Operations Research*, Edited by C. W. Churchman, R. L. Ackoff, and E. L. Arnoff, John Wiley and Sons, New York, 1957.

11. Smith, V. L., "Economic Equipment Policies: an Evaluation," *Management Science*, Vol. 4, pp. 20–37, 1957.
12. Terborgh, G., *Business Investment Policy*, Machinery and Allied Products Institute, Washington, D. C., 1958.
13. Summaries of most of the models listed in this bibliography are also available in *Operations Research* (*Vol. 1*), Edited by R. L. Ackoff, John Wiley and Sons, New York, 1961.

REVIEW QUESTIONS

1. What future income stream for 20 years with interest at 10 per cent just equals a present value of $1000?

2. Why is it that absolute rates of return ordinarily cannot be determined for a specific equipment investment?

3. What is the meaning of a relative rate of return?

4. Why is it that cost minimizing models are most commonly used in equipment investment problems?

5. Why is it necessary, conceptually, to consider a chain of machines rather than the isolated case of the new machine now available?

6. Define each of the terms in the most general situation for an investment model, *CERBS*. Derive each of the terms in the general model.

7. What kinds of expense and revenue functions are permitted in the general model?

8. Contrast the meaning of the classification of models shown in Figure 2 as compared to the classification shown in Figure 8.

9. As normally used, how would you classify within the *CERBS* framework the five common criteria for comparing investments?

part VII

INVENTORY MODELS

15

Elementary Inventory Models

It is understandable that businessmen are concerned about the problem of inventories. It is not uncommon for a manufacturing company to have 25 per cent or more of its total invested capital tied up in inventories. On December 31, 1959, the Armstrong Cork Company had 20 per cent of its assets in inventories and the Allied Chemical Corporation had over $102,000,000, or about 13 per cent of its assets represented by inventories. The General Electric Company has had nearly $800,000,000 and the General Motors Corporation almost $2,000,000,000. Naturally, if good inventory management could change any of these totals by as much as even 10 per cent, we are talking about really big money.

The current emphasis in management science probably began with the analysis of inventory systems. In 1915, F. W. Harris (8) developed the first economic lot size equation, and this was probably the beginning of the use of mathematical models to represent management problems. In 1931, F. E. Raymond published his *Quantity and Economy in Manufacture* (12) in which he developed this idea much further, attempting to account for a wide variety of conditions. In the postwar period, the management science literature has been filled with analyses of inventory and production control systems, partly because of the great interest shown by the government and the military, as well as the interest shown by such progressive companies as the Eastman Kodak Company, the Procter and Gamble Company, Johnson and Johnson, and many others.

The Functions of Inventories

Inventories make possible rational systems for production and distribution. At each stage in the flow of goods, inventories serve the vital function of *decoupling* the various operations in the sequence beginning with raw materials, extending through all the manufacturing operations to finished goods storage, and from there to warehouse, distribution points, and finally to the ultimate consumer.

It is definitely not true that inventories should be minimized. Production-distribution systems with minimum inventories would be extremely costly. With inventories we can make operations in the sequence relatively independent so that low-cost operations can be carried out. With inventories we can keep procurement costs at reasonable levels. Furthermore, with inventories we can give good customer service and avoid costly stock shortages. With inventories we can obtain low freight and handling costs per unit if we ship in quantity. Inventories are not only desirable, they are vital. We know, of course, that the inventory question is not a one-sided one. If it were, we would have no problem. Inventories require that invested capital be tied up and, therefore, there is an appropriate opportunity cost associated with their value. In addition, they require valuable storage space and accumulate insurance and taxation charges. We are dealing with another problem which requires that good management find policies and decision rules which have the effect of balancing the various opposing costs for the system being considered.

To see the various kinds of inventories that might be appropriate for analytical purposes, let us take as an example the simple factory-warehouse system shown in Figure 1. The factory manufactures a number of products, but we will consider only one. For this particular product, there is an average demand at the warehouse of 200 units per week. Normal warehousing procedures are to prepare a procurement order to the factory when the warehouse inventory falls to a critical level called the *order point*. It takes 1 week to prepare the order, get it approved and mailed, and finally received at the factory. Similarly, once the order is received at the factory, it takes 2 weeks for loading, trucking, and unloading at the warehouse.

Transit inventories. The warehouse must, at a minimum, carry enough stock on hand to meet demand during the transit time. Figure 2 shows an idealized graph of the inventories required at the warehouse just to cover trucking time from the factory. The average transit inventory is the product of the truck time and the demand rate, or $2 \times 200 = 400$ units. At all times, then, 400 units are in motion from the factory to the warehouse, or in an equivalent sense, the warehouse must maintain an inventory which takes account of this fact. The order time delay of 1 week has the effect of a transit

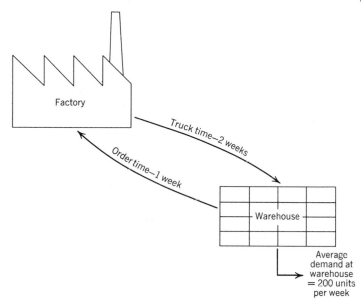

Figure 1. Simple factory-warehouse system.

time, since the warehouse must also carry inventories to cover this delay. This point is a general one. Every lag in the system generates the need for transit inventory. Inside a production system we call

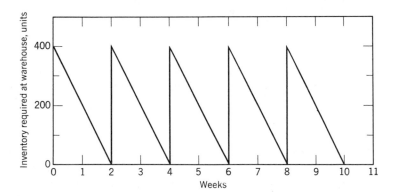

Figure 2. Idealized graph of inventories required at the warehouse to cover trucking time from the factory. The average transit inventory is the product of truck time and demand rate, or $2 \times 200 = 400$ units. Average inventory at the warehouse is $400/2 = 200$ units.

it in-process inventory, but in most instances it is not especially named, but simply called inventory.

Lot size or "cycle" inventories. Returning to our example, since the truck is to make the trip from factory to warehouse, a logical question is, "How many to truck at one time?" Most of the costs of trucking will occur anyway, and this is true of the costs of preparing the requisition and the other clerical costs involved. We will not attempt to answer the question of what the lot size should be in this instance, but the general question will be discussed at a later point. Let us assume that orders are placed for a truckload of 800 units, equivalent to 4 weeks' supply. Figure 3 shows an idealized graph of inventories required at the warehouse when orders are placed for a truckload. We see that the average inventory at the warehouse must necessarily increase.

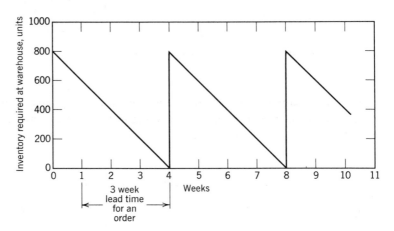

Figure 3. Idealized graph of inventories required at the warehouse when orders are placed for a truckload, 800 units. Average inventory is now $800/2 = 400$ units. Transit inventories are unchanged.

Buffer inventories. Figure 3 is, of course, completely unrealistic because it assumes that demand rate, truck time, and order time are all constant. We know, however, that these factors are not ordinarily constant so that a buffer stock is normally required to protect against unpredictable variations in demand and supply time. Figure 4 shows the contrast in inventory levels at the warehouse which might occur if the maximum demand of 300 units per week occurred during the supply time of 3 weeks. In order to not run out of stock,

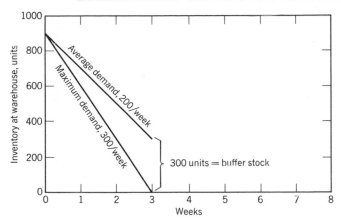

Figure 4. Contrast of idealized inventory levels required for average demand and maximum demand. The difference, 300 units, represents a minimum inventory, or "buffer stock," required to protect against the occurrence of shortages resulting from random fluctuations in demand.

a buffer inventory of 300 units would be required. As we shall see, techniques for taking account of uncertainty are of great importance in inventory models.

Decoupling inventories. Let us now look inside the factory of the simple system shown in Figure 1. We said that the factory produced several products, one of which we are using as an example. The factory has only two machines which perform the operations required on all of the products. Some products use only one of the machines, some have two operations as does our example product, and some have three operations, doubling back to the first machine for the last operation. The point is that the machinery is time shared. Figure 5 shows the flow from raw material storage through the two machines to finished goods storage for our example product. The flow diagram shows that there are six storage delays in the process. Material is stored before and after each of the two machine operations in addition to raw material and finished goods storage. These storage delays cause an increase in the in-process inventory requirements of the system. How can we eliminate them? The two storage delays that occur after operation 1 and before operation 2 could be eliminated, or drastically reduced, by a change in layout which would physically connect machine 1 to machine 2 so that the output of the first operation was directly the input of the second operation. But recall that the example product time shares the equipment. The equipment is used for other products and the sequence of operations

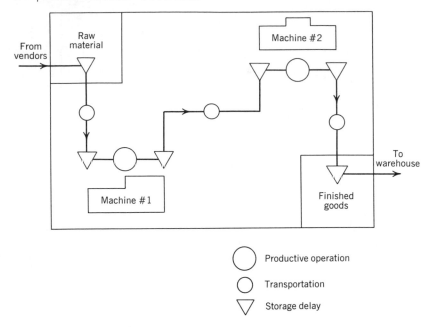

Figure 5. Schematic layout of operations and general flow of material for the inventory item discussed in text and Figures 1, 2, 3, and 4.

is not always from machine 1 to machine 2. Flexibility in flow is demanded by the particular production situation. If the demand for our example product were to increase to the point where it could more fully utilize the two machines, it might then be worthwhile to allocate the two machines solely for the use of the example product. To attempt to do this in the situation described, however, would result in very poor equipment utilization and somewhat higher equipment costs. The use of in-process inventories makes it possible to carry on the operations at machine 1 and machine 2 somewhat independent of each other. The coordination between operation 1 and operation 2 can be fairly loose. The decoupling effect of inventories in a production system is an extremely important function in many situations, if low-cost operations are to be achieved.

Seasonal inventories. Many products have a fairly predictable but seasonal pattern through the year. Where this is true, management has the choice of changing production rates over the year to absorb the fluctuation in demand or absorbing some or all the fluctuation in demand with inventories. If we attempt to follow the demand curve through the seasons by changing production rates, the capital investment for the system must provide for the peak capacity and we must absorb costs for hiring, training, and separating labor. The use of seasonal inventories can often strike a better balance of these costs. Figure 6 shows an example of a sales forecast and production plan where peak seasonal sales are met by accumulated seasonal inventories.

These five basic functions of inventories are fundamental. Without them we could not achieve smooth flow, obtain reasonable equipment utilization or reasonable material handling costs, or expect to give reasonable service to consumers. At each stage of both manufacturing and distribution, inventories serve the vital decoupling function. Between each pair of activities, inventories make the required operations independent of each other enough that low-cost operations can be carried out. Thus, when raw materials are ordered, a supply is ordered that is large enough to justify the out-of-pocket cost of putting through the order and transporting it. When production orders to manufacture parts and products are released, we try to make them big enough to justify the cost of writing the orders and setting up machines to perform the required operations. Otherwise, order writing and setup costs could easily become prohibitive. Running

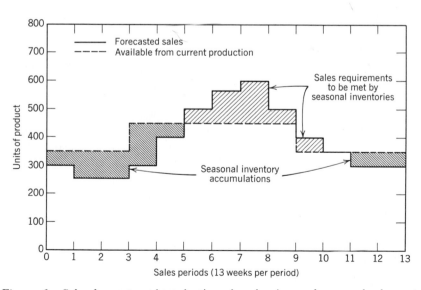

Figure 6. Sales forecasts and production plan showing peak seasonal sales met by accumulated seasonal inventories.

parts through the system in lots also tends to reduce handling costs because parts can be handled in groups. Similarly, in distributing finished products to warehouses and other stock points, freight and handling costs per unit go down if we can ship in quantity.

These advantages are partially lost when we are dealing with custom manufacture, because the lot size is dictated by the customer's order, and the order may never be repeated so we cannot risk producing to stock. Thus, order writing, material handling, and machine setup costs are just as high for the custom-sized lot as for an economically-sized lot. Similarly, when the custom order is shipped to the customer, we cannot take advantage of carload, or truckload freight rates. If the custom order were for only one part, all of these charges must be absorbed by the single part. It is easy to see why low volume special orders are exceedingly expensive.

Management Objectives and Costs

It is important that models of inventory systems reflect true incremental costs associated with alternate plans or policies. These costs represent "out-of-pocket" expenditures or foregone opportunities of profit. Cost figures derived from the normal accounting records usually do not fit the requirements. The following types of cost items are often incremental costs in inventory models: Costs depending on lot quantities, production costs, handling and storing costs, cost of shortages, and capital investment costs.

Costs depending on lot quantities. In deciding on purchased lot quantities, there are certain clerical costs of preparing purchase orders that are the same regardless of the quantity ordered. These costs are important in deriving economic purchase quantities as we shall see; however, the cost figure used must be the true incremental cost of order preparation. It is not correct to derive such a figure simply by dividing the total cost of the purchasing operation by the average number of purchase orders processed. A large segment of the total costs of the purchasing operation are fixed, regardless of the number of orders issued. There is, however, a variable component and this is the pertinent figure. Quantity discounts and shipping costs are other factors which influence the quantity of materials purchased at one time and, therefore, influence the levels of material inventories. A question parallel to the purchase quantity occurs within a production system in deciding the size of production orders, that is, the number of units to process at one time. Here, the preparation costs are the incremental costs of preparing production orders, setting up machines, and controlling the flow of orders through the shop. Intraplant material handling costs affect production lot quantities in much the same way that freight costs affect purchase lot quantities.

Production costs. Some of the components of production costs which have a bearing on inventory models such as set-up and change-over costs, and material handling costs, have been discussed in the preceding paragraph. Certain other incremental costs, however, also have a direct bearing on inventory models. For example, overtime premium and the incremental costs of production fluctuation, such as hiring, training, and separation costs need to be balanced against the cost of carrying additional inventory.

Costs of handling and storing inventory. There are certain incremental costs associated with the level of inventories. They are represented by the costs of handling material in and out of inventory, storage costs, such as insurance, taxes, rent, obsolescence, spoilage, and capital costs. These incremental costs are commonly in proportion to inventory levels.

Cost of shortages. An extremely important cost which never appears on accounting records is the cost of running out of stock. Such costs may appear in several ways. For example, within a production system a part shortage can cause idle labor on a production line or subsequent incremental labor cost to perform operations out of sequence, usually at higher than normal cost. Shortage costs can be represented by profit foregone as when impatient customers take their business elsewhere. The realization of the importance of shortage costs raises the question, "What level of service is appropriate?"

Capital costs. The opportunity cost of capital invested in inventory is an incremental cost of significance in designing inventory models. The cost figure itself is the product of inventory value per unit, the time that the unit is in inventory, and the appropriate interest rate. In general, the appropriate interest rate should reflect the opportunities for the investment of comparable funds within the organization and, of course, it should not be lower than the cost of borrowed money. Since the funds are tied up in inventories, they cannot be used for the purchase of equipment, buildings, or other profit-producing investments. There is, therefore, an opportunity cost of having funds invested in inventory and inventory models reflect this cost.

Management objectives. The overall objective of management is to design policies and decision rules which view inventories in a "systems" context so that the broadly construed set of costs we have discussed generally are minimized. In a production–distribution system, the functions of inventories and their effects on costs are distributed throughout the system from raw material intake through all intermediate stages to the final point of sale. The result is that there are interactions between basic inventory policy and production planning, labor policy, production scheduling, facilities planning, customer service, etc. Although there are some operations which may be regarded as almost purely inventory situations, the most usual structure involves an interaction between what we think of as the limited inventory problem and many of the broad policies for operating the enterprise as a whole. We shall begin our analysis of inventory systems with the more limited and simple concepts, and attempt to build a structure of concept and technique which tries to account for many of the interactions with the environment in which inventories exist.

The Classical Inventory Model

The classical inventory model assumes the highly idealized situation shown in Figure 7. Q units are ordered or manufactured at one

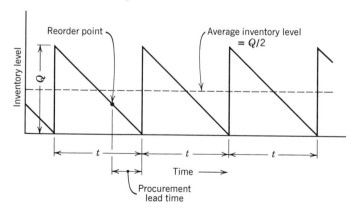

Figure 7. Graphic representation of inventory levels in the classical inventory model. Q = lot size, number purchased or manufactured at one time; t = the time between procurement orders or manufacturing runs.

time. The order is placed when the inventory level falls to a point where the normal usage would just use up the inventory within the fixed procurement lead time. The receipt of the order of lot size Q is perfectly timed so that at just the point in time when the inventory balance falls to zero, the order of size Q is received, the inventory balance is increased by Q units, and the cycle repeats. We will find this model useful in establishing the overall concepts with which we will be dealing. Let us establish the following list of symbols:

TIC = total incremental cost
TIC_0 = total incremental cost of an optimal solution
Q = lot size
Q_0 = optimal lot size
R = annual requirements in units
c_H = inventory holding cost per unit per year
c_P = preparation costs per order
c_S = shortage costs per unit per increment of time
N_0 = number of orders or manufacturing runs per year for an optimal solution
t = time between orders or manufacturing runs
t_0 = time between orders or manufacturing runs for an optimal solution

Objective. Our objective is to establish a mathematical model which expresses the relationship between Q, the variable under managerial control, and the incremental costs associated with the system. The incremental costs for the simple system we have defined are the costs associated with holding inventory and the costs associated with the procurement of an order of size Q. Therefore, the cost function we wish to minimize is:

TIC = inventory holding costs + procurement costs

We can see from Figure 7 that if Q is increased, the average inventory level, $Q/2$, will increase proportionately. If the inventory holding cost per unit per year is c_H, the annual incremental costs associated with inventory are

$$c_H \frac{Q}{2}$$

If the cost to hold a unit of inventory (interest costs, insurance, taxes, etc.) for a specific example was $c_H = \$0.10$, we could express the inventory holding cost function as $(Q/2)0.10 = 0.05Q$. We could then plot this inventory holding cost function for different values of Q as we have done in Figure 8a.

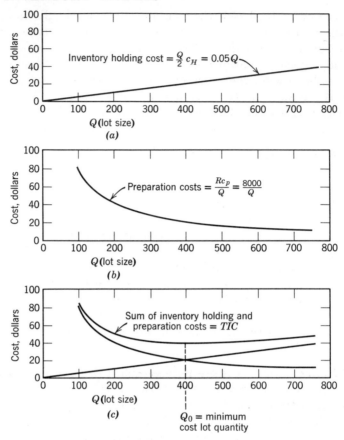

Figure 8. Graphic representation of classical inventory model. $R = 1600$ units per year, $c_P = \$5.00$, and $c_H = \$0.10$.

Similarly, the annual preparation costs depend on the number of times that orders are placed per year and the cost to place an order. The number of orders required for an annual requirement of R will vary with the lot size Q of each order, or, R/Q. If it costs c_P to place an order, the annual preparation costs may be expressed as

$$c_P \frac{R}{Q}$$

If, for a specific example, $R = 1600$ units per year, and $c_P = \$5.00$, we could express the annual preparation costs as $(1600 \times 5.00/Q) = 8000/Q$. As with inventory holding costs, we can plot the preparation costs for this example for different values of Q, as we have done in Figure 8b.

Figure 8c shows a graphic model of cost versus lot size, showing the total incremental cost curve, the calculations for which are shown in Table I. Looking at either Table I or Figure 8c, we note that the

TABLE I. Computation of Points for Cost Versus Lot Size for Curves of Figure 8. $R = 1600$ **Units per Year,** $c_P = \$5.00$, **and** $c_H = \$0.10$

(1) Lot Size, Q	(2) Inventory holding cost $= \dfrac{Q}{2} \times c_H = 0.05Q$ (See Figure 8a)	(3) Preparation costs $= \dfrac{Rc_P}{Q} = \dfrac{8000}{Q}$ (See Figure 8b)	(4) TIC = sum of columns (2) + (3) (See Figure 8c)
100	5.0	80.0	85.0
200	10.0	40.0	50.0
300	15.0	26.7	41.7
400 = Q_0	20.0	20.0	40.0
500	25.0	16.0	41.0
600	30.0	13.3	43.3
700	35.0	11.4	46.4

minimum total incremental cost, TIC_0, occurs when 400 units are ordered at one time. This is a solution for the specific data given, and we can see that the general form of the total incremental cost curve has a single minimum point.

A general solution. Regardless of the data used for specific examples, the general form of the curves are similar to those shown in Figure 8, and we can express the relationships in a completely general way,

$$TIC = \frac{c_H Q}{2} + \frac{c_P R}{Q}$$

This is an equation for the total incremental cost curve, and we wish to find a general expression for Q_0, the lot size associated with the minimum point of the total incremental cost curve. Mathematically, this may be done by finding the value of Q for which the slope of the total incremental cost curve is zero. This results in the following formula which is a general solution for the model:

$$Q_0 = \sqrt{\frac{2Rc_P}{c_H}} \tag{1}$$

The derivation of this formula is shown in Appendix A. From it, we may calculate directly the minimum cost lot quantity Q_0 if we have values for R, c_P, and c_H. Similarly, we may derive formulas for the total incremental cost of the optimal solution, TIC_0 the number of orders or manufacturing runs per year for an optimal solution N_0, and the time between orders or manufacturing runs for an optimal solution t_0. They are,

$$TIC_0 = \sqrt{2c_Pc_HR} \tag{2}$$

$$N_0 = \frac{R}{Q_0} \tag{3}$$

$$t_0 = \frac{Q_0}{R} = \frac{1}{N_0} \tag{4}$$

If we substitute the values for R, c_P, and c_H used in our example, we obtain,

$$Q_0 = \sqrt{2 \times 1600 \times \frac{5.00}{0.10}} = \sqrt{160{,}000} = 400 \text{ units}$$

$$TIC_0 = \sqrt{2 \times 5.00 \times 0.10 \times 1600} = \sqrt{1600} = \$40$$

$$N_0 = \tfrac{1600}{400} = 4 \text{ orders or manufacturing runs per year}$$

$$t_0 = \tfrac{1}{4} = 0.25 \text{ years between orders or runs}$$

An Inventory Model with Shortage Costs

When shortage costs are accounted for, the classical model becomes slightly more general—the model represented by equation 1 being a special case. The rationale for derivation parallels that given in Appendix A, but it is somewhat more complex mathematically. Derivations may be found in references (3, 7), and the resulting formulas are

$$Q_0 = \sqrt{2c_PR/c_H} \cdot \sqrt{(c_H + c_S)/c_S} \tag{5}$$

$$TIC_0 = \sqrt{2c_Hc_PR} \cdot \sqrt{c_S/(c_H + c_S)} \tag{6}$$

Note that when comparing equations 5 and 6 with the comparable formulas 1 and 2, with shortages, Q_0 is increased by the factor $\sqrt{(c_H + c_S)/c_S}$, and TIC_0 is decreased by the factor $\sqrt{c_S/(c_H + c_S)}$. The influence of shortages, then, is dependent on the relative size of c_H and c_S. If c_H is large relative to c_S, the effect of shortages on Q_0 and TIC_0 is considerable; that is, Q_0 will be increased and TIC_0 decreased compared to equations 1 and 2. If, on the other hand, c_H is small relative to c_S, minor changes in Q_0 and TIC_0 will result. The net effect of shortage costs on Q_0 and TIC_0 may at first seem to be strange. Recognize, however, that when the model permits shortages, average holding costs are reduced because of smaller average inventory balances. This will result in a larger Q_0. For the shortage case, TIC_0 is smaller than when shortages are not included because both holding costs and annual preparation costs are somewhat lower. For example, if we consider shortages in the previous example where $R = 1600$ per year, $c_P = \$5.00$ per order, $c_H = \$0.10$ per unit per year, and in addition, $c_S = \$0.50$ per unit per year, we have the following results:

$$Q_0 = \sqrt{(2 \times 5.00 \times 1600)/0.10} \ \sqrt{(0.10 + 0.50)/0.50}$$

$$= 400\sqrt{1.2} = 400 \times 1.095 = 438 \text{ units}$$

$$TIC_0 = \sqrt{2 \times 0.10 \times 5.00 \times 1600} \ \sqrt{0.50/(0.10 + 0.50)}$$

$$= 40\sqrt{0.833} = 40 \times 0.912 = \$36.50$$

The Effect of Quantity Discounts

The basic economic lot size formula assumes a fixed price. When quantity discounts enter the picture, additional simple calculations will determine if there is a net advantage. As an illustration, assume the basic data of our previous example, that is, $R = 1600$ units per year, $c_P = \$5.00$ per order, and $c_H = \$0.10$ per unit per year. Recall that the economic order quantity was computed as 400 units. In addition, however, assume that the purchase prices are quoted as $1.00 per unit in quantities below 800 and $0.98 per unit in quantities above 800. If we buy in lots of 800 we save $32 per year on the purchase price plus $10 on order costs, since only two orders need to be placed per year to satisfy annual needs. This saving of $42 per year must be greater than the additional inventory costs that would be incurred if the price discount is to be attractive. Under the 400 unit order size, average inventory is 200 units and inventory costs are $200 \times 1.0 \times 0.10 = \$20$. If orders of 800 units were placed, the inventory costs would be $400 \times 0.98 \times 0.10 = \$38$. There is a net gain of $42 - (38 - 20) = \$24$ by ordering in lots of 800 instead of in lots of 400. If the vendor had a second price break of $0.97 per unit for lots of 1600 or more, a similar analysis shows that the incremental inventory costs outweigh the incremental price and order savings, so that there is no net advantage in purchasing in lots of 1600. Table II summarizes the calculation for all three cases.

TABLE II.   Incremental Cost Analysis To Determine Net Advantage or Disadvantage when Price Discounts Are Offered

R = 1600 units per year, c_P = \$5.00 per order, c_H = \$0.10 per unit per year

	Lots of 400 Units, Price = \$1.00 per Unit	Lots of 800 Units, Price = \$0.98 per Unit	Lots of 1600 Units, Price = \$0.97 per Unit
Purchase cost of a year's supply (1600 units)	\$1600	\$1568	\$1552
Ordering cost (c_P = \$5.00 per order)	20	10	5
Inventory holding cost (avg. inv. × unit price adjustment × c_H)	20	38	74
	\$1640	\$1616	\$1631

Formal models with price breaks. We may generalize our ideas about the effect of quantity discounts by examining a formal model which takes price breaks into account. Recall that the lot size formula 1 did not need to consider price or value of the item because for every value of Q considered, the price was the same, that is, price was not an incremental cost. Let us now consider a lot size model which includes the value of the item as a factor. To reflect this idea, the total incremental cost associated with such a system may be expressed as follows:

$$TIC = \text{(annual cost of placing orders)}$$
$$+ \text{(annual purchase cost of } R \text{ items)}$$
$$+ \text{(annual holding cost for inventory)}$$
$$= c_P \frac{R}{Q} + kR + k \frac{Q}{2} F_H \tag{7}$$

where k = cost or price per unit, and F_H = *fraction* of inventory value, representing inventory holding cost on an annual basis.

Following the rationale developed previously, we seek the value of Q, Q_0, which minimizes this total incremental cost equation. This leads to the formulas:

$$Q_0 = \sqrt{2c_P R / k F_H} \tag{8}$$

$$TIC_0 = \sqrt{2c_P k F_H R} + kR \tag{9}$$

The derivations of which are shown in Appendix B.

We may now use formulas 8 and 9 in the analysis of inventory systems which involve a price break. For comparison, let us assume the data of Table II for the first price break at $b = 800$ units. Recall that in this example, the price per unit below the break point was $k_1 = \$1.00$ and that above 800 units, the price was $k_2 = \$0.98$ per unit. To fit in with the present model, we will now express the inventory holding cost factor as $F_H = 10$ per cent of inventory value. The other data remain the same, that is, $R = 1600$ units per year, and $c_P = \$5.00$ per order.

In the logic of our analysis, let us first note that the total incremental cost curve TIC_2 will fall below the curve TIC_1. This is shown in Figure 9. The logical thing to do, then, is to calculate q_{2_0} to see if it falls within the range P_2 where the price $k_2 = \$0.98$ applies. Doing this we find that $q_{2_0} = 404$ units, which is less than the break

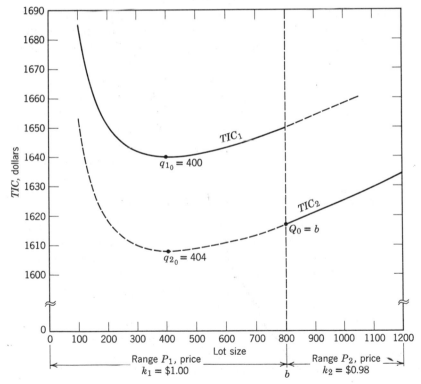

Figure 9. Total incremental cost curves for inventory model with one price break at $b = 800$ units. $R = 1600$ units per year, $c_P = \$5.00$, $F_H = 10$ per cent of inventory value.

point, $b = 800$ units. Since this is the minimum point on the TIC_2 curve, we know that the lowest possible cost of TIC_2 within the range where the price k_2 applies is at the lot size $b = 800$ units. If it had happened that q_{2_0} was in the range P_2, this would have determined immediately that the economic lot size for the system Q_0 was the value calculated q_{2_0}. Since this is not the case, however, we must continue our analysis to see if the minimum point on the curve TIC_1 is below TIC_2 at lot size $b = 800$ units. We may calculate TIC_{1_0} easily from formula 9, and its value is $1640. Also, we may calculate TIC_b using equation 7, and this we find to be $1616. The decision is now clear, $Q_0 = b = 800$, since TIC_2 at lot size b is less than TIC_{1_0}. Compare these results with those obtained by the incremental cost analysis in Table II. This of course can be seen easily from the graphs of Figure 9. Constructing the curves for each case would be laborious, however, compared to the simple computations required to come to a decision. Figure 10 shows a decision flow chart for an inventory model with one price break, indicating the flow of calculations and resulting decisions. In some instances, the final result is obtained with one calculation, as when q_{2_0} falls in the lot size range P_2 where the price k_2 is valid. Where this is not the case, simple calculations for comparative total incremental cost yield a final result.

Using the same general rationale we can develop decision processes for inventory models with two or more price breaks. Also, models could be constructed for quantity discount situations that also took account of other factors, such as shortage costs and the value added into inventory through the accumulation of preparation costs (3, 7).

Determining the Length of Production Runs

Production order quantities and runs are based on the same general concepts as purchase order quantities, as we have noted previously, but the assumption that the order is received and placed into inventory all at one time is often not true in manufacturing runs. For many manufacturing situations the production of the total order quantity Q takes place over a period of time, and the parts go into inventory, not in one large batch, but in smaller quantities as production continues. This results in an inventory pattern similar to Figure 11 when the run extends over a considerable period of time. When the run time is perhaps the 30–60 per cent of the total cycle time t shown in Figure 11, the effect on the average inventory of the system should be accounted for. Let $r =$ daily usage rate and $p =$ daily

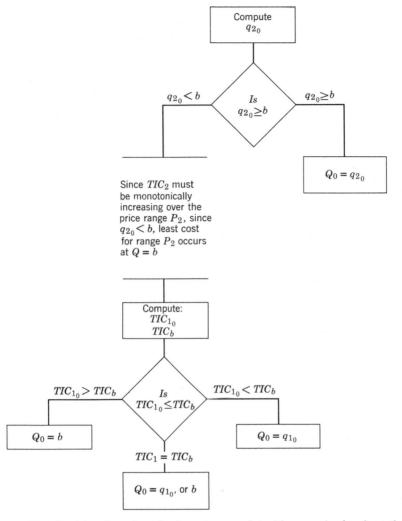

Figure 10. Decision flow chart for inventory model with one price break at the lot size b. Price k_1 applies in the lot size range P_1, price k_2 applies in the lot size range P_2.

production rate—assuming, of course, that $p > r$. Other symbols remain as previously defined. During the production period t_p, inventory is accumulating at the rate of the difference between production rate and usage rate, $p - r$. This rate of increase continues for the production period t_p, so that the peak inventory is $t_p(p - r)$, and

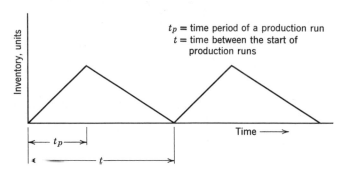

Figure 11. Diagram of inventory balance in relation to time when the lot Q is received in inventory over a period of time.

the average inventory is one-half this amount, or,

$$\frac{t_p(p-r)}{2} \tag{10}$$

Also, since Q units are produced at the rate of p per day for t_p days, $Q = pt_p$, and $t_p = Q/p$. Substituting for t_p in (10), the average inventory of the system is

$$\frac{(p-r)Q}{2p} = \left(1 - \frac{r}{p}\right)\frac{Q}{2} \tag{11}$$

Proceeding as we have previously, let us now set up an equation for the total incremental costs of the system TIC. These costs are

$$TIC = \text{annual cost of setups} + \text{annual costs of holding inventory} \tag{12}$$

The annual setup cost is as before, the product of the cost of a setup, c_P, and the number of setups per year, R/Q. The annual cost of holding inventory is the product of the cost of holding a unit of inventory per year, c_H, and the average inventory, $(1 - r/p)Q/2$. Substituting these expressions in word equation 12, we have,

$$TIC = \frac{c_P R}{Q} + \frac{c_H Q(1 - r/p)}{2} \tag{13}$$

This total incremental cost function has a minimum as with the previous cases, and we may derive the lot size Q_0, associated with that minimum cost in a way entirely parallel to the derivation of the previous lot size formulas. The results are

$$Q_0 = \sqrt{\frac{2c_P R}{c_H(1 - r/p)}} \tag{14}$$

$$TIC_0 = \sqrt{2c_P c_H R(1 - r/p)} \tag{15}$$

The optimal number of production runs of size Q_0 is, of course, $N_0 = R/Q_0$, and the optimal time between the start of production runs is $t_0 = Q/R = 1/N_0$.

Production runs for several products. When a number of products share the use of the same equipment on a cyclical basis, the overall cycle length can be established in a way similar to the single product case just described. The more general problem, however, is not to determine the economical length of a production run for each product individually, but to determine jointly the runs for the entire group of products which share the use of the same facilities. If each part or product run is set independently, it is highly likely that some conflict of equipment needs would result unless the operating level is somewhat below capacity, where considerable idle equipment time is available. Examples of this situation are a steel rolling mill that must be set up to roll different sizes and types of steel, batch chemical processes using the same mixing vats, paper-making machines that produce several grades of paper, etc.

Conceptually, the problem of determining an economical cycle is the same as for the one-product case, that is, to determine the cycle length which will minimize the total of machine setup costs plus inventory holding costs jointly for the entire set of products. The formulas applicable for the multiproduct case are as follows:

$$N_0 = \sqrt{\frac{\sum_{i=1}^{m} c_{H_i} R_i(1 - r_i/p_i)}{2\sum_{i=1}^{m} c_{P_i}}} \tag{16}$$

$$TIC_0 = \sqrt{2\sum_{i=1}^{m} c_{P_i} \sum_{i=1}^{m} c_{H_i} R_i(1 - r_i/p_i)} \tag{17}$$

where R_i = annual requirements for the individual products, r_i = equivalent requirements per production day for the individual products, p_i = daily production rates for the individual products, c_{H_i} = holding cost per unit, per year for the individual products, c_{P_i} = setup costs per run for the individual products, and m = the number of products. The derivation of these formulas is given in Appendix C.

Let us work out an example for the determination of the cycle length for the group of ten products shown in Table III, which shows

TABLE III. Sales, Production, and Cost Data for Ten Products To Be Run on the Same Equipment

(1)	(2)	(3)	(4)	(5)	(6)	(7)
		Sales per	Daily	Produc-	Annual	Setup
Prod-	Annual	Production	Produc-	tion	Inventory	Cost
uct	Sales,	Day (250 days	tion	Days	Holding	per
Num-	Units	per year)	Rate	Re-	Cost	Run
ber	R_i	r_i	p_i	quired	c_{H_i}	c_{P_i}
1	10,000	40	250	40	$0.05	$ 20
2	20,000	80	500	40	0.10	15
3	5,000	20	200	25	0.15	35
4	13,000	52	600	25	0.02	40
5	7,000	28	1000	7	0.30	25
6	8,000	32	800	10	0.40	37
7	15,000	60	500	30	0.02	42
8	17,000	68	500	35	0.05	50
9	3,000	12	200	15	0.35	16
10	1,000	4	125	8	0.10	12
				235		$292

the annual sales requirements, sales per production day, daily production rate, production days required, annual inventory holding cost, and setup costs. Table IV then shows the calculation of the number of runs per year calculated by formula 16. The minimum cost number of cycles which results is four per year, each cycle lasting approximately 59 days and producing one-fourth of the sales requirements during each run. The total incremental cost from formula 17 is $TIC_0 = \$2420$.

It is interesting to compare now the jointly determined number of runs per year with the number that would have resulted had runs been determined independently for each of the ten products. Table V summarizes these calculations. Note that products 4, 7, and 10 would have two or fewer runs per year, and products 2, 5, and 6 would have more than six runs per year. Magee (10) states a rule of thumb that if "the minimum-cost number of runs for the product alone, for any one or more products is less than half the value for all products, the product is a possible candidate for only occasional runs."

TABLE IV. Determination of the Number of Runs, Jointly, for Ten Products from Formula 16

(1)	(2)	(3)	(4)	(5)	(6)
			$c_{H_i}R_i =$		
Product Number	Ratio r_i/p_i, Col. 3/Col. 4 from Table III	$(1 - r_i/p_i)$	Col. 2 × Col. 6 from Table III	$c_{H_i}R_i$ $(1 - r_i/p_i)$ = Col. 3 × Col. 4	c_{P_i}, Col. 7 from Table III
1	0.160	0.840	500	420	$ 20
2	0.160	0.840	2000	1,680	15
3	0.100	0.900	750	675	35
4	0.087	0.913	260	237	40
5	0.028	0.972	2100	2,041	25
6	0.040	0.960	3200	3,072	37
7	0.120	0.880	300	264	42
8	0.136	0.864	850	734	50
9	0.060	0.940	1050	987	16
10	0.032	0.968	100	97	12
				10,207	$292

$$N = \sqrt{\frac{10,207}{2 \times 292}} \approx 4 \text{ cycles per year}$$

TABLE V. Calculation of Numbers of Runs, Independently for Each Product, from Formula 14

(1)	(2)	(3)	(4)	(5)	(6)
	$c_{H_i}R_i$ $(1 - r_i/p_i)$ from	c_{P_i}, from			
Product Number	Col. 5, Table IV	Col. 7, Table III	$\dfrac{\text{Col. 2}}{2 \times \text{Col. 3}}$	$N_i = \sqrt{\text{Col. 4}}$	TIC_{0_i}
1	420	$20	10.5	3.2	$ 130
2	1680	15	56.0	7.5	224
3	675	35	9.7	3.1	217
4	237	40	3.0	1.7	137
5	2041	25	40.8	6.4	101
6	3072	37	42.7	6.5	477
7	264	42	3.1	1.8	149
8	734	50	7.3	2.7	271
9	987	16	30.8	5.6	178
10	97	12	4.0	2.0	48
					$1932

Table V also summarizes the total incremental cost which would result if the number of runs for each product were determined independently. The figure of $1932 is $488 less than the total incremental cost figure of $2420 given in Table IV when the runs are determined jointly. The apparent cost saving through individual determination of production runs is, of course, illusory because it does not take account of congestion costs or possible shortage costs that might result from independent scheduling.

Summary

The models developed in this chapter are meant to build a general conceptual framework for the analysis of inventory systems. Although they may certainly be useful in some situations, they are not meant to be transplanted without modification into practical situations. Rather, they are meant to show some of the kinds of situations and factors that have been accounted for in simple inventory models. Actually, many more situations have been covered in the literature (2, 3, 5, 6, 7, 13, 15, 16). With a knowledge of the general functions of inventories, management objectives, and the nature of costs which enter inventory models, we are in a position to consider the influence of uncertainty of demand and basic systems of control which take account of uncertainty, as well as the effects on inventory planning of production planning and seasonal sales patterns.

REFERENCES

1. Arrow, K. J., T. Harris, and J. Marschak, "Optimal Inventory Policy," *Econometrica,* Vol. XIX, 1951, pp. 250–272.
2. Buchan, J., and E. Koenigsberg, *Scientific Inventory Control,* Prentice-Hall, Englewood Cliffs, N. J., 1963.
3. Churchman, C. W., R. L. Ackoff, and E. L. Arnoff, *Introduction to Operations Research,* John Wiley and Sons, New York, 1957.
4. Eilon, S., *Elements of Production Planning and Control,* Macmillan Company, New York, 1962.
5. Fetter, R. B., and W. C. Dalleck, *Decision Models for Inventory Management,* Richard D. Irwin, Homewood, Ill., 1961.
6. Hadley, G., and T. M. Whitin, *Analysis of Inventory Systems,* Prentice-Hall, Englewood Cliffs, N. J., 1963.
7. Hanssmann, F., *Operations Research in Production and Inventory Control,* John Wiley and Sons, New York, 1962.
8. Harris, F., *Operations and Cost* (Factory Management Series), A. W. Shaw Co., Chicago, 1915, pp. 48–52.
9. MacNiece, E. H., *Production Forecasting, Planning and Control,* John Wiley and Sons, New York, 2nd ed., 1957.

10. Magee, J. F., *Production Planning and Inventory Control*, McGraw-Hill Book Company, New York, 1958.
11. Moore, F. G., *Production Control*, McGraw-Hill Book Company, New York, 2nd ed., 1959.
12. Raymond, F. E., *Quantity and Economy in Manufacture*, D. Van Nostrand Company, Princeton, N. J., 1931.
13. Starr, M. K., and D. W. Miller, *Inventory Control: Theory and Practice*, Prentice-Hall, Englewood Cliffs, N. J., 1962.
14. Voris, W., *Production Control*, Richard D. Irwin, Homewood, Ill., revised edition, 1961.
15. Wagner, H. M., *Statistical Management of Inventory Systems*, John Wiley and Sons, New York, 1962.
16. Whitin, T. M., *The Theory of Inventory Management*, Princeton University Press, Princeton, N. J., 1953.

REVIEW QUESTIONS

1. What is the "decoupling" function of inventories?

2. How might we classify different kinds of inventories?

3. What functions do each of the different kinds of inventories perform?

4. By definition, what is the size of buffer stock for an individual situation?

5. What is the nature of costs affected by inventories? Outline them and discuss each.

6. What are the kinds of costs related to inventories but dependent on lot quantities? In a practical situation, how do we derive these costs?

7. What are management's objectives in designing inventory systems? In the classical inventory model, which of the variables are controllable and which are outside the control of management?

8. What is the general effect of shortage costs on lot sizes?

9. Why must the classical lot size formula be modified if we are attempting to take quantity discounts into account?

10. Outline the rationale for determining the minimum cost purchase quantity Q_0 when a price discount is involved.

11. How is the determination of a production run different from the determination of a purchase lot size?

12. How does the production run problem change when a number of products share the use of the same equipment on a cyclical basis? Is the problem the same when the operating level is somewhat below capacity?

PROBLEMS

1. Compute the optimal lot size, Q_0, when $R = 10,000$ units per year, $c_P = \$5$, and $c_H = \$10$ per unit per year.

2. What is the total incremental cost for the conditions of Problem 1?

3. How much would Q_0 change if our estimate of c_P was in error and was actually only $4 in Problem 1? What would be the difference in actual total incremental costs between the two solutions?

4. How much would Q_0 change if our estimate of c_H was in error, being only $8, in Problem 1? What would be the difference in actual total incremental costs between the two solutions?

5. What is the effect on Q_0 for Problem 1 if shortages cost $c_S = \$1$ per unit per year? What is the total incremental cost of this solution?

6. Suppose that shortages are very expensive, perhaps $100 per unit per year. What is the answer to Problem 5?

7. Suppose that for Problem 1 a price discount is offered so that orders placed in quantities below 125 cost $100 each but for orders of 125 or above this quantity the price is $95 each. Inventory holding cost is now expressed as 10 per cent of the value of the item. In what quantities should the items be purchased? Use the rationale of Figure 10.

8. Determine the number of production runs for an item if $R = 15,000$ units per year, $c_P = \$25$, $c_H = \$5$ per unit per year, and $p = 100$ units per working day. There are 250 working days per year.

9. Determine the best production cycle for the following group of products, assuming 250 working days per year.

Product Number	Annual Sales Units	Daily Production Rate	Annual Holding Cost per Unit	Setup Cost per Run
1	5,000	100	$1.00	$40
2	10,000	75	0.90	25
3	7,000	50	.30	30
4	15,000	80	.75	27
5	4,000	40	1.05	80
Total				$202

16

Uncertainty and Planning for Production-Inventory Systems

Some of the major defects in the models developed in the previous chapter, so far as practical inventory policy is concerned, are the assumptions that requirements were known exactly and that the delivery of replenishment orders was perfectly timed. Also, those models did not place the inventory system in the context of the operating environment of the broader production-distribution system. In this chapter we shall attempt to introduce the idea of uncertainty of demand and its influence on inventory policy, consider comparative systems for inventory control which take account of uncertainty, and consider the impact of planning master production programs to meet requirements on production-inventory policy.

Uncertainty of Demand

The source of our problem in dealing with uncertainty of demands or requirements is focused on the lags inherent in the system for replenishment. If we could fill requirements immediately, there would be no problem. The elements of the problems caused by lags in the system were introduced by Figure 1 in Chapter 15. In Chapter 19, we demonstrate in a more dramatic way, through the use of dynamic simulation models, the important effects of lags in the flow system (5).

As we know, the demand for an item may vary considerably owing to random causes, upward or downward trends in demand, and

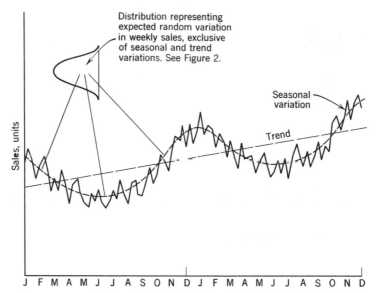

Figure 1. Three kinds of variation in demand which introduce uncertainties into inventory policy.

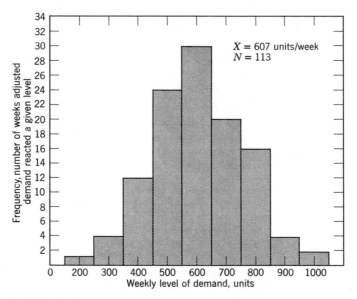

Figure 2. Distribution representing expected random variation in weekly sales, exclusive of seasonal and trend variations.

seasonal variations. Figure 1 shows a sales curve which demonstrates all three factors. Let us begin with a consideration of expected random variation and how realistic inventory policy might take it into account. Figure 2 abstracts from Figure 1 just the random variations in sales from average expected levels. Such a distribution could be abstracted from sales records from which the trend and seasonal factors have been removed, through commonly known statistical procedures. The residual variation is then simply the variation due to chance causes, comparable in every way to expected random variation in any process as discussed on pages 174–181 in connection with the concepts of statistical control.

Buffer stocks. The variations in demand are absorbed through the provision of buffer stocks which must be maintained because of our inability to forecast random variations in demand of the type shown by Figure 2. The size of these planned extra inventories depends on the stability of demand in relation to our willingness to run out of stock. If we are determined almost never to run out of stock, these planned minimum balances must be very high. If service requirements permit stock runouts and back ordering, the safety stocks can be moderate. Figure 3 shows the general structure of inventory balance with a fixed-order quantity system. The buffer stock level

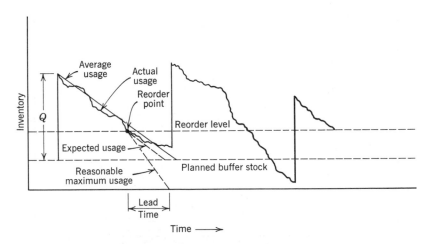

Figure 3. Structure of inventory balance for a fixed order quantity system, with safety stocks to absorb fluctuations in demand and in supply time. The buffer stock level is set so that a reasonable figure for maximum usage would draw down the inventory to zero during the lead time. Q is a fixed quantity ordered each cycle.

is set so that inventory balances would be drawn down to zero during the lead time for supply, if we should experience near-maximum demand.

The rational determination of buffer stocks, then, turns on a knowledge of the probability distribution of demand together with a decision regarding the risk of stock runout that we are willing to accept. To be most useful, the probability distribution of demand can be expressed in a form as shown by Figure 4. Figure 4 was constructed from Figure 2, first, by plotting the number of weeks that adjusted demand exceeded a given level, second, by establishing a percentage scale to represent a derived probability scale, and third, by idealizing the distribution as shown by the dashed curve of Figure 4. Since the approximate average weekly usage is 607 units, and

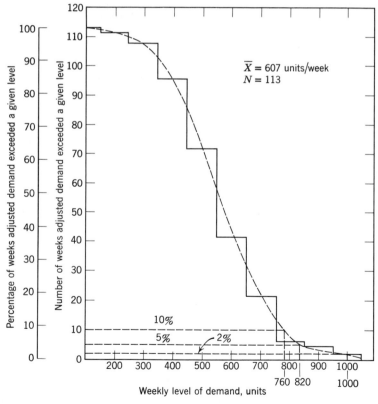

Figure 4. Distribution of per cent of weeks that demand exceeded a given level, developed from Figure 2.

assuming a normal lead time of 2 weeks, we could be 90 per cent sure of not running out of stock by having the $2 \times 760 = 1520$ units on hand when the replenishment order is placed. The safety stock is then $1520 - 1214 = 306$ units. If we wish to be 95 per cent sure of not running out of stock, the buffer stock must be $1640 - 1214 = 426$ units. Similarly, to be sure that we have only a 2 per cent risk of running out of stock, the buffer stock level must be increased to 786 units. It is easy to see from the shape of the demand curve that, for high levels of protection, the buffer stock required goes up rapidly, and, therefore, the cost of providing this assurance goes up. This is shown by the calculations in Table I where we have assumed the

TABLE I. Cost of Providing the Three Levels of Service Shown in Figure 4, when the Item Is Valued at $50 Each and Inventory Holding Costs Are 20 Per Cent

	Service Level		
	90%	95%	98%
Expected maximum usage for 2-week replenishment time	1520	1640	2000
Buffer stock required	306	426	786
Average inventory required for service level during replenishment period = $(I_{max} - \text{Buffer})/2 + \text{Buffer}$	913	1033	1393
Value of average inventory at $50 per unit	$45,650	$51,650	$69,650
Inventory cost at 20%	$ 9,130	$10,330	$13,930

demand curve of Figure 4, assigning a value of $50 to the item and inventory holding costs of 20 per cent of value. The average inventory required to cover expected maximum usage rates during the lead time of 2 weeks are calculated for the three service levels shown. To offer service at the 95 per cent level instead of the 90 per cent level requires an incremental $1200 per year, but to move to the 98 per cent level of service from the 95 per cent level requires an additional $3600 in inventory cost.

The demand curve, then, provides a rational basis for the determination of buffer stock levels by helping to establish a reasonable maximum usage rate during the lead time. To establish this rate, however, management must decide what risk of stock runout is acceptable. In some instances this must be a judgment, but where a cost of shortages can be realistically assigned, a simple incremental cost analysis can determine whether additional protection is worthwhile.

For example, for the data shown in Table I, there would be an incremental saving of $1580 in moving from the 90 per cent to the 95 per cent level of service if the cost of a shortage was $1 each (607 × 52 × 0.05 × 1.00). This incremental gain exceeds the incremental cost of $1200 shown in Table I. On the other hand, to move from the 95 per cent to the 98 per cent level the incremental gain is only $950 whereas the incremental cost is $3600 as shown in Table I. The 98 per cent level of service is obviously too expensive in this instance.

In summary, we have a fairly general procedure. To determine buffer stocks, we must determine reasonable maximum usage rates during the lead time, and this requires the derivation of a demand distribution which reflects only the variation due to random fluctuations. Here, however, management must decide on a risk level for running out of stock, or if realistic shortage costs can be assigned, an incremental cost study can be made to determine the best risk level. If demand for the item is subject to seasonal variation or an upward or downward trend, the average of the distribution shifts, and it is necessary to reassess buffer stock level periodically. In such an instance, it would be better to express the demand distribution curve shown in Figure 4 in terms of deviations from expected mean values.

Basic Inventory Control Systems and Uncertainty

In attempting to develop automatic control systems for inventories, it is necessary to take account of random fluctuations in demand as just discussed and actual shifts in average demand of either a seasonal or long-term nature. The variables of the system which can be manipulated by management to develop a control system are the size of the replenishment order, the frequency of replenishment orders, the frequency of review and forecast of usage levels, and the method of information feedback on which the reviews are based. Alternate inventory control systems blend these factors in somewhat different ways.

The fixed-order quantity system. This system is diagrammed in Figure 3. This system has a reorder level set which allows the inventory level to be drawn down to the buffer stock level within the lead time if average usage rates are experienced. Replenishment orders are placed in a fixed predetermined amount (not necessarily the minimum cost quantity, Q_0) timed to be received at the end of the lead time. The maximum inventory level averages the order quantity Q plus the buffer stock I_{min}. The average inventory expected is, then,

$I_{min} + Q/2$. Usage rates are reviewed periodically in an attempt to react to seasonal or long-term trends of the type shown in Figure 1. At the time of the periodic reviews, the order quantity and buffer stock levels may be changed to reflect the new conditions. Demand for an item is ordinarily taken from the subsequent operation. Assume that we are considering the can of the capacitor in Figure 5. The

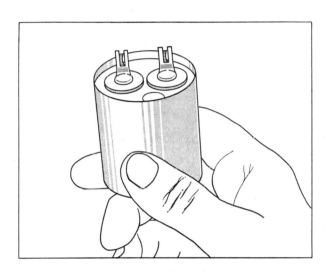

Figure 5. A capacitor, showing its several parts.

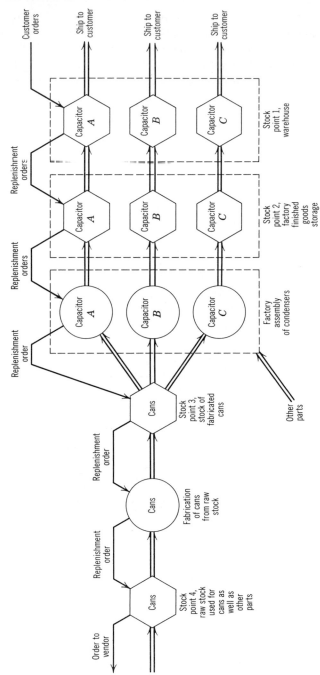

Figure 6. Chain of demand for the capacitor can shown in Figure 5.

capacitor is made in three sizes of electrical capacity. The can which houses the capacitor, however, is identical for all three sizes. (Recall that this is the capacitor for which the operation process chart was constructed as Figure 3 in Chapter 3.)

Figure 6 shows the chain of demand for the can as reflected back through the series of stock points and manufacturing operations. Customer orders are placed at the warehouse which maintains an inventory with controls as described by Figure 3. When the warehouse inventory level falls to the reorder point, a replenishment order is sent to the factory, and the factory ships from its finished goods stock. When the finished goods inventory falls to a reorder point, however, a requisition is sent to the manufacturing department and more condensers are assembled. To assemble the condensers, however, cans and other parts are requisitioned from stock point 3, a stock of fabricated cans. When the stock of fabricated cans falls to a reorder level, a shop order is written for a run of cans to be fabricated. The shop order requires raw stock which is drawn from stock point 4, raw material storage. When the inventory for the raw material falls to the reorder level, a purchase requisition is issued to vendors for replacement. Thus the demand for the capacitor can is reflected back in a chain involving 4 stock points and 2 factory operations. Figure 6 represents the structure of the information feedback system.

Fixed-reorder quantity systems are common where a perpetual inventory record is kept and with low-valued items such as nuts and bolts, where the inventory level is under rather continuous surveillance so that notice can be given when the reorder level is reached. One of the simplest methods for maintaining this close watch on inventory level is the use of the "two bin" system. In this system, the inventory is physically separated into two bins, one of which contains an amount equal to the reorder level. The balance of the stock is placed in the other bin and day-to-day needs are drawn from it until it is empty. At that point it is obvious that the reorder level has been reached and a stock requisition is issued. From that point on, stock is drawn from the second bin, which contains an amount equal to average usage over the lead time plus a buffer stock. When the stock is replenished by the receipt of the order, the physical segregation into two bins is made again and the cycle is repeated.

Fixed-reorder cycle systems. These systems focus control on a periodic basis, so that orders are placed weekly, monthly, or by some other cycle. The size of the order, however, is varied for each

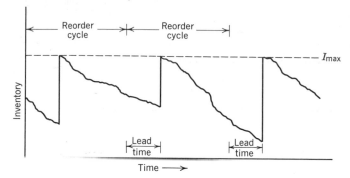

Figure 7. Fixed reorder cycle system of control. An order is placed at regular intervals which replenishes stock, based on the inventory balance on hand and on order plus the amount needed for one cycle.

cycle to absorb the fluctuations in usage from period to period, as shown by Figure 7. The amount ordered covers normal usage during the procurement lead time plus the quantity necessary to replenish inventories to the level required for one cycle's usage plus buffer stock. This is, of course, the I_{max} level shown on Figure 7. As with the fixed-quantity system, periodic reviews of usage rates are required to react to changes in the average usage rates of the type shown in Figure 1. Fixed-reorder cycle systems are prominent with higher valued items and where a large number of items are regularly ordered from the same vendor. With fixed-cycle ordering, freight cost advantages can often be gained by grouping these orders together for shipment. The common information feedback system for fixed-cycle systems is diagrammed in Figure 6, based on a chain of demand.

The main operating difficulties with the fixed reorder systems described lie in the time lags in the information chain, and the apparently irresistible temptation to outguess shifts in requirement rates. The shifts in usage rates are most often simply random shifts, and the buffer stock has been designed to absorb these variations. If we respond to these random shifts in requirements we will surely drive ourselves insane. Suppose we are ordering on a monthly cycle the fabrication of cans for stock point 3 of Figure 6. Average requirements have been 500 cans monthly, but last month's requirements jumped to 600 units. If we assume that this will be a continuing requirement, we might decide to place an order for the current month which not only replenishes the 600 units drawn, but adds another 100 units to build up inventory to meet the expected continuation of 600 units per month. This makes a total order of 700 units. Suppose, however, that last months increase was simply a random fluctuation, and in a true expression of the capriciousness of random processes, requirements for this period turn out to be only 300 units. We now have a 400-unit excess inventory, and we need place an order for only 100 units for the coming period to meet average requirements. The result is that the random variations in demand from 600 units to 300 units have been translated into variations in shop orders for cans ranging from 700 units to 100 units. Demand variability has been amplified, leading to severe problems on the production floor in attempting to accommodate these wide variations.

The question of amplification of demand variability is of extreme importance in designing stable inventory-production control systems, and we shall consider it more carefully at a later point. The immediate question is, however, "How can we tell if a change in demand is merely a random fluctuation or a true shift in average requirements?" We have an obvious application of the principles of statistical control. Appropriate control limits could be established and requirements plotted in relation to the control limits. Variations in requirements that fall within the control limits may be ignored, since buffer stocks were designed to absorb them. When points fall outside the control limits the question may be raised whether planning figures for average requirements should be revised. Even then, adjustments in planning figures for requirements should be relatively modest, taking a wait and see attitude, in order to avoid the costly results of fluctuations as in the situation described in this paragraph.

Control theory applied to inventory systems. Engineers have been interested in the design of automatic control systems, and the result has been the development of concepts and systems of control which have been applied largely in automation and other physical systems. These self-correcting systems establish automatic control over some variable (a dimension, temperature, pressure, etc.) through a feedback loop. Conceptually, the feedback loop is comprised of some *sensing unit* which measures the output of the variable being controlled, a *comparator* which compares the actual output with the desired level, and a *decision maker* which interprets the error information and finally commands the *effector* to make a correction in the proper magnitude and direction so that output will meet standards. Figure 8 shows a schematic representation of the maintenance of the temperature of flowing water under automatic control.

Many management control problems can be viewed in the same conceptual framework. For example, Figure 9 shows a diagram for

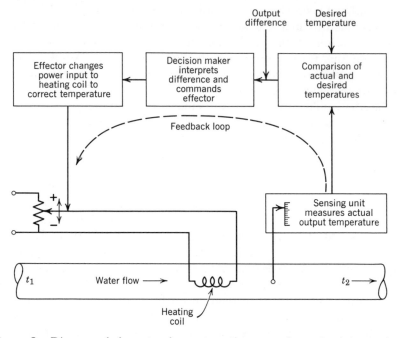

Figure 8. Diagram of elements of an automatic system for maintaining a given output temperature of water flow. The basic components of the feedback loop are common to automatic control systems.

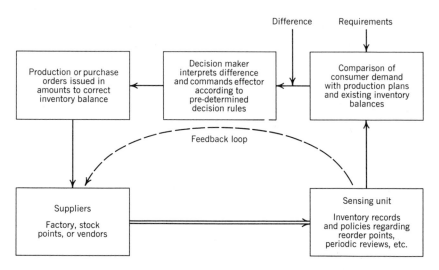

Figure 9. Information feedback loop for an inventory control system.

information feedback for the control of inventories and production levels. The parallels between the physical system and the inventory system are direct. From the principles of process control, we can learn some basic control concepts of considerable value in controlling inventories. These concepts are related to time lags and their effect on the stability of the system. Let us see what actual dynamic effects we might expect from an inventory system which was originally stable and now is stimulated by a 10 per cent step increase in retail sales, the new sales level remaining stable.

Forrester (5), using a simulation model of the production-distribution system shown in Figure 10, demonstrates the dynamic effects dramatically. Figure 10 shows three levels of inventories, factory, distributor, and retailer. The circled lines show the flow of orders for goods from customers to retailers, retailers to distributors, distributors to factory warehouse, and finally from the warehouse as orders for the factory to produce. The solid lines show the flow of the physical

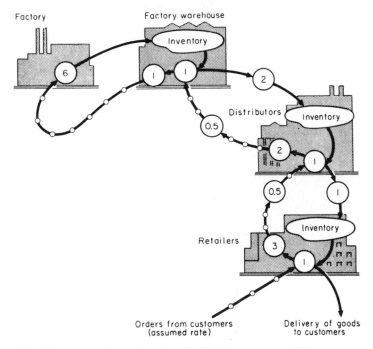

Figure 10. Structure of a production-distribution system. Solid lines represent physical flow, lines with dots represent information flow, and circled numbers represent time delays in weeks. From J. Forrester, *Industrial Dynamics*, John Wiley and Sons, New York, 1961.

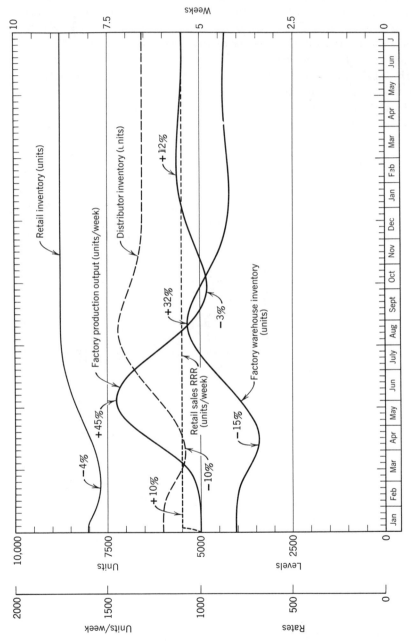

Figure 11. Response of inventories at three levels and factory output to a step increase in retail sales of 10 per cent. Adapted from J. Forrester, *Industrial Dynamics*, John Wiley and Sons, New York, 1961.

goods between each of the levels of the structure in response to the orders. The circled numbers represent the time delays in weeks for each of the activities to take place. Figure 11 shows the effect of the 10 per cent step increase in retail sales on inventories at the three levels, as well as on factory production output. The surprise is, of course, that whereas the sales increase was simple and orderly, the response of the inventory and production system shows wild oscillations which increase in magnitude as we go up stream in the system from the retail level to the distributor, factory warehouse, and to the actual factory output. We will not demonstrate it at this point; however, reducing the time lags in the system, for example, by eliminating the distributor level, or reducing the time for clerical delays will reduce considerably the magnitude of the fluctuations.

More direct information feedback to the various stock points instead of through the chain of demand shown in Figure 5 will have important effects in stabilizing the entire system. We will consider these dynamic effects more carefully and in greater detail in our discussion of large-scale system simulation. At this point, however, a conclusion we might draw is that a more direct information feedback system similar to that shown in Figure 12 for the capacitor can production-inventory system will have a stabilizing effect so that no amplification of demand *variability* will take place at stock points up stream from the consumer inventory level. At each stock point in the system, then, we are working against actual consumer demand rather than against the secondary and tertiary effects of demand as reflected back through the chain. Reducing the lag in information flow has a stabilizing effect, regardless of the inventory system used.

Base stock system. The base stock system (10) is a blend of the fixed quantity and fixed cycle systems which uses an information feedback system to that diagrammed in Figure 12. In this system, stock levels are reviewed on a periodic basis, but orders are placed only when inventories have fallen to a predetermined "reorder level." At this point an order is placed to replenish inventories to the "base stock" level, which is sufficient for buffer stock plus a fixed quantity calculated to cover current usage needs. Periodic reviews of current usage rates can result in upward or downward revisions in the base stock levels. The base stock system has the advantages of close control associated with the fixed cycle system which makes it possible to carry minimum buffer stocks. On the other hand, since replenishment orders are placed only when the reorder point has been reached,

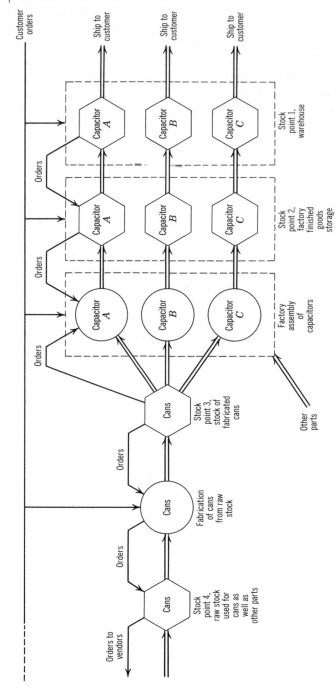

Figure 12. Current demand from customers fed back directly to stock points and operations so that all links in the production-inventory chain work against current demand.

fewer orders, on the average, are placed so that order costs are comparable to those associated with the fixed quantity systems. Since all stock points are working against consumer demand, we do not have the amplification of demand variability at points up stream. Therefore, buffer stocks can be reduced even further since the extreme levels of maximum demand are not experienced. Another result is a reduction in the cost of production fluctuations (hiring, separation, and training), since the magnitude of production fluctuations is also associated with the type of information feedback system used.

Planning Master Production-Inventory Programs

Master production programs are plans that indicate how production capacity, outside capacity, and inventories will be used in meeting expected requirements. When demand takes on seasonal aspects, the construction of master plans becomes somewhat more complex, and the problem becomes one of minimizing the combined incremental costs of seasonal inventories, the costs of changing production levels, overtime premium and extra shift costs, and subcontracting costs. The master production program serves as a framework for more detailed plans of labor, equipment and procurement schedules, and for inventory controls.

Forecasts. The subject of forecasting and forecasting methods is an important and complex one. Our objective is not to cover this subject, but to state the forecasting needs of inventory and production control. The demand forecasting function is usually directly connected with sales. These demand forecasts need to be in a form that can be translated into demands for time in certain equipment classifications, demands for certain labor skills, and demands for certain materials. Thus, forecasts of gross dollar demand, of gross demand by customer class, or forecasts by broad product classes may have value in planning sales programs, but are distinctly limited for planning production-inventory programs.

To be useful as a basis for planning master programs, demand must be translated into hours or days of time needed for men and equipment, and into pounds, bales, pieces, etc., of materials needed. Finally, forecast data for inventory and production planning need to reflect the uncertainty of the data. Forecasts are never accurate and are not expected to be. If the probable margin of error were included, however, attention would be immediately focused on the fact that whatever production plans are made need to be flexible enough to shift up or down to accommodate normal forecasting errors. One way to do this is to state forecasts as a range representing the reasonably expected maximum and minimum values.

Production Plans for Seasonal Sales

The use of seasonal inventories can help to reduce other important production costs such as overtime premium payments, the costs of production fluctuation associated particularly with labor turnover outside subcontracting costs, and the capital costs of providing for peak capacity. Level production, of course, uses seasonal inventories to the maximum possible as a means of reducing these other costs to a minimum. Whether or not this represents a minimum cost solution to a particular enterprise problem depends on the relationship of the various cost factors involved. Let us illustrate with an example.

TABLE II. Forecast of Production Requirements and Buffer Stocks

Month	Expected Production Requirements	Cumulative Production Requirements	Required Buffer Stocks	Production Days	Cumulative Production Days
January	4,000	4,000	2,500	22	22
February	3,000	7,000	2,200	18	40
March	3,000	10,000	2,200	22	62
April	4,000	14,000	2,500	21	83
May	7,000	21,000	3,200	22	105
June	9,000	30,000	3,500	21	126
July	11,000	41,000	4,000	21	147
August	9,000	50,000	3,500	13	160
September	6,500	56,500	3,200	20	180
October	6,000	62,500	2,800	23	203
November	5,500	68,000	2,700	21	224
December	4,000	72,000	2,500	20	244
			34,800		

$$\text{Average buffer stock} = \frac{34,800}{12} = 2900 \text{ units}$$

Table II shows a forecast of production requirements and buffer stocks for a year hence. The expected production requirements for each month take account of the fact that production must lead the time of expected sale. We see that there is a pronounced seasonal in the requirements, apparently equal to $11,000/3000 = 3.67$ (peak in

July, 11,000; low point in February and March, 3000). Actually, however, the magnitude of the seasonal swing is much greater from the point of view of the production plan because of the variation of working days available in each month, emphasized by the fact that the plant shuts down for two weeks in August for vacations. The resulting seasonal swing in requirements per production day is from 136 units per day in March to 682 units per day in August,

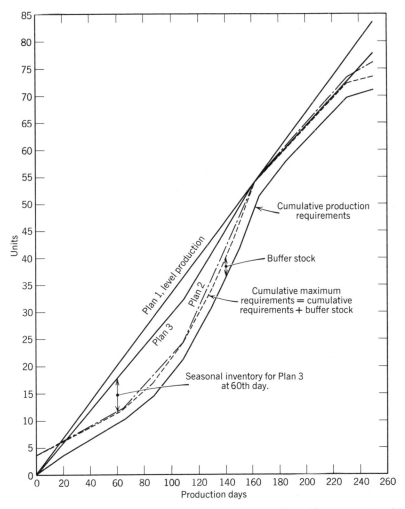

Figure 13. Cumulative requirements with three alternate programs which meet maximum requirements.

or a ratio $682/136 = 5.02$. Table II also shows the required buffer stocks for each month which average 2900 units.

Figure 13 shows a graph of the cumulative production requirements calculated in Table II. By adding, for each month, the buffer stock requirements to the cumulative requirements curve, we can obtain a curve of cumulative maximum requirements. The importance of this cumulative requirements curve in preparing alternate production plans is that *any line representing the way requirements are to be produced must fall entirely above the cumulative maximum requirements line to provide the stock needed for sale and still provide the desired protection against stock runout.* Three such plans are shown in Figure 13, and we shall discuss them in greater detail. For any plan, the seasonal inventory (inventory over and above buffer stock) for a given point in time is represented by the distance between the curve for the production plan in question and the cumulative maximum requirements curve. An example of the seasonal inventory at the eightieth day for plan 3 is shown in Figure 13. Although a chart similar to Figure 13 is of the greatest value for comparing alternate feasible plans, a chart similar to Figure 14 may be more meaningful in visualizing the differences between the alternate plans in relation to the projected requirements. Figure 14 shows the production rates in units per day for the three plans.

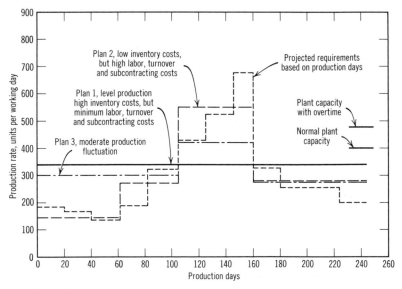

Figure 14. Comparison of three production programs that meet requirements.

Plan 1 calls for level production which will result in high seasonal inventory costs, but will minimize labor, turnover, and subcontracting costs. Plan 2 follows the requirements curve quite closely, and this, of course, results in very low inventory costs. The costs associated with changing production levels, however, are bound to be high. Plan 3 is a compromise between the extremes of plans 1 and 2. To come to a decision on which of the three plans might be best, we must have additional data about the plant and its costs.

Normal production capacity is 400 units per day and we can obtain up to 480 units per day by using overtime capacity. The use of overtime capacity, however, adds $10 per unit to the cost of the product. Also, we may exceed the 480 unit per day limit through the use of subcontracting, but at an extra cost of $15 per unit, compared to in-plant normal time production. Inventory carrying cost is $60 per year per unit, and to change production rate by 20 units per day requires the employment or separation of 40 men at a cost of hiring and training of $200 per employee. With this basic data, we may now compute the incremental costs of seasonal stock, labor turnover, overtime premium, and subcontracting for each of the three alternate plans. Table III shows the calculation of seasonal stock for production plan 3. The seasonal stocks for plans 1 and 2 may

TABLE III. Calculation of Seasonal Stock for Production Plan 3

(1) Month	(2) Production Days	(3) Production Rate, units per day	(4) Production in Month	(5) Cumulative Production	(6) Cumulative Maximum Requirements	(7) Seasonal Stock = Col. 5 − Col. 6	(8) Seasonal Stock × Prod. Days = Col. 2 × Col. 7
January	22	300	6600	6,600	6,500	100	2,200
February	18	300	5400	12,000	9,200	2800	50,400
March	22	300	6600	18,600	12,200	6400	140,800
April	21	300	6300	24,900	16,500	8400	176,300
May	22	300	6600	31,500	24,200	7300	160,500
June	21	420	8820	40,320	33,500	6820	143,300
July	21	420	8820	49,140	45,000	4140	87,000
August	13	420	5460	54,600	53,500	1100	14,300
September	20	280	5600	60,200	59,700	500	10,000
October	23	280	6440	66,640	63,300	3340	76,800
November	21	280	5880	72,520	70,700	1820	38,250
December	20	280	5600	78,120	74,500	3620	72,300
	244						972,150

$$\text{Average seasonal stock} - \frac{972{,}150}{244} = 3985 \text{ units.}$$

TABLE IV. **Comparative Incremental Costs for
Three Production Programs**

	Plan 1 Level Production	Plan 2	Plan 3
Average seasonal stock, units	5100	791	3985
Average buffer stock, units	2900	2900	2900
Total average inventory, units	8000	3691	6885
Peak capacity required:			
(Plan 1 = 100)	100	165	126
Incremental costs:			
Seasonal stock cost[1]	$318,000	$ 47,300	$239,000
Labor turnover cost[2]	0	104,000	48,000
Overtime premium[3]	0	44,000	11,000
Subcontracting cost[4]	0	57,750	0
	$318,000	$253,050	$298,000

[1] Inventory carrying cost computed at $60 per unit per year.

[2] A change in production rate of 20 units per day requires the employment or separation of forty men, at a cost of hiring and training an employee of $200.

[3] Units produced at overtime labor rates cost $10 per unit extra.

[4] Units produced by subcontractors cost $15 per unit extra.

be computed in a comparable way. Table IV summarizes the comparative incremental costs for the three production programs. Note that plan 2 has the lowest total incremental cost of $253,050. Recall that plan 2 resulted in relatively low inventory costs achieved by varying production rate, using overtime and subcontracting to absorb the peak requirements. Plan 2 is not necessarily the plan with minimum possible costs; however, other plans could be analyzed in a comparable way. Plan 2 has some important disadvantages which are not easy to measure in a quantitative way. It involves a large labor force fluctuation which could have an effect on employee morale and on community relationships. Also, if these employees are of relatively high skills and scarce, it would be important to minimize turnover. The quantitative difference in monetary values resulting from the analysis may be balanced by the manager against the intangible values.

Planning for several products. The preceding example lends itself quite well to the graphical type of analysis we have used, because of its relative simplicity. Obviously, when many different products which time share the same facilities are involved, the graphical technique becomes difficult. Nevertheless, management often seeks additional products as a means of leveling labor force requirements and, at the same time, increasing the utilization of existing plant and equipment. The incremental costs of adding a product to a company's line that complements existing seasonal patterns would be fairly modest, compared to the setup of a special plant and organization to make only the new product, because of the existence of idle capacity. Therefore, incremental costs for the new product are mainly the variable costs of material, labor, power and supplies. The decision problem is parallel to that of making an item presently bought, when idle capacity exists in the plant.

Linear programming methods. A production program is, of course, an allocation of available capacity to demand, and it can be placed in the framework of a formal linear programming model. In general terms, we are attempting to allocate available production capacity to various periods in a way which meets requirements while minimizing some function of incremental inventory and production costs. The incremental production costs may include overtime premium, turnover costs, extra subcontracting costs, etc., as we have discussed in the previous one-product example. The value of the quantitative techniques over the graphical methods comes in the more complex multiproduct situations, where it is difficult to see intuitively what effect shifts in a particular program will have.

An example—the Camtor Company

Ferguson and Sargent (6) describe the Camtor Company case (fictitious name), a manufacturer of a quality line of cameras and projectors, as an application of linear programming to determine a least cost production program which satisfies fluctuating sales demand from a given plant capacity, maintaining a relatively fixed level of employment. The program was constructed to minimize inventory and outside purchase costs. The requirements for cameras and projectors follow a seasonal pattern with maximum sales in October, November, and early December, reflecting the Christmas trade. Relatively low sales occur during January and February, with gradual increases beginning in late March, continuing through April and May to meet the vacation demand. Within the manufacturing division of the company, production releases are issued quarterly, each release authorizing approximately 3 months supply.

Table V summarizes the basic data for thirty parts, for which a linear programming solution was developed (the problem has been scaled down for presentation). In Table V we are given machine hour requirements by quarters for each of the thirty parts, as well as cost data on the comparative advan-

TABLE V.   Camtor Company Basic Data for Linear Programming Model to Smooth Production for Seasonal Requirements*

		Requirements, Machine Hours Quarter					Incremental Cost to Purchase instead of Manufacture. M Signifies Always Manufactured	Inventory Carrying Cost per Quarter per Hour of Production, dollars
		1	2	3	4	Total		
Part	1	500	700	900	1,000	3,100	20.00	1.25
	2	300	375	400	500	1,575	15.00	1.46
	3	100	140	180	200	620	10.00	0.833
	4	480	600	640	800	2,520	7.75	3.12
	5	120	150	160	200	630	6.50	0.417
	6	400	560	720	800	2,480	6.50	0.104
	7	75	105	135	150	465	6.00	0.417
	8	$\begin{cases} 250 \\ 180 \end{cases}$	350 225	450 240	$\begin{cases} 500 \\ 300 \end{cases}$	2,495	6.00	0.146
	9	60	75	80	100	315	5.75	0.104
	10	75	105	135	150	465	5.00	0.125
	11	150	210	270	300	930	4.50	0.083
	12	60	75	80	100	315	4.25	0.833
	13	$\begin{cases} 100 \\ 120 \end{cases}$	140 150	180 160	$\begin{cases} 200 \\ 200 \end{cases}$	1,250	3.75	0.017
	14	120	150	160	200	630	3.50	0.073
	15	100	140	180	200	620	2.00	0.625
	16	50	70	90	100	310	1.75	0.417
	17	60	75	80	100	315	0.75	0.250
	18	120	150	160	200	630	0.00	0.042
	19	60	75	80	100	315	−0.75	0.104
	20	$\begin{cases} 100 \\ 60 \end{cases}$	140 75	180 80	$\begin{cases} 200 \\ 100 \end{cases}$	935	−1.00	0.012
	21	60	75	80	100	315	−3.00	0.059
	22	200	280	360	400	1,240	−3.25	0.417
	23	100	140	180	200	620	M	0.625
	24	350	490	630	700	2,170	M	6.25
	25	240	300	320	400	1,260	M	0.625
	26	350	490	630	700	2,170	M	0.833
	27	300	375	400	500	1,575	M	2.08
	28	$\begin{cases} 50 \\ 30 \end{cases}$	70 38	90 40	$\begin{cases} 100 \\ 50 \end{cases}$	468	M	0.208
	29	84	105	112	140	441	M	0.083
	30	100	140	180	200	620	M	0.083
Total requirements		5,504	7,338	8,762	10,190	31,794		
Capacity†		5,600	5,800	6,000	6,400	23,800		
Overload		−96	1,538	2,762	3,790	7,994		

* Adapted from R. O. Ferguson and L. F. Sargent, *Linear Programming*, McGraw-Hill Book Company, New York, 1958.

† Capacity is the effective available capacity allowing for downtime, setup, and expected production efficiency. Braces indicate parts used in both cameras and projectors.

Part number	Quarter	Allocated hours					Requirements (hours)	
		Manufacture				Purchase (Slack)	By quarters	Total
		First quarter	Second quarter	Third quarter	Fourth quarter			
23	1	0	+M	+M	+M	+M	100	620
	2	+0.63	0	+M	+M	+M	140	
	3	+1.25	+0.63	0	+M	+M	180	
	4	+1.88	+1.25	+0.63	0	+M	200	

Cost of carrying inventory. (Zero if produced in quarter needed.) (If produced before needed, cost is value from Table V, x number of quarters in advance of need.)

Incremental cost if part purchased instead of being manufactured. M means overwhelming cost and therefore, not admissible in solution. Values from Table V.

	Quarter	First quarter	Second quarter	Third quarter	Fourth quarter	Purchase (Slack)	By quarters	Total
1	1	0	+M	+M	+M	+20	500	3100
	2	+1.25	0	+M	+M	+20	700	
	3	+2.50	+1.25	0	+M	+20	900	
	4	+3.75	+2.50	+1.25	0	+20	1000	

	Quarter	First quarter	Second quarter	Third quarter	Fourth quarter	Purchase (Slack)	By quarters	Total
19	1	0	+M	+M	+M	−0.75	60	315
	2	+0.10	0	+M	+M	−0.75	75	
	3	+0.21	+0.10	0	+M	−0.75	80	
	4	+0.31	+0.21	+0.10	0	−0.75	100	

Machine hours available	5600	5800	6000	6400	7994 (Slack)	31,794

Figure 15. Basic form of distribution matrix for allocating requirements for various parts to four manufacturing quarters and parts to be purchased so that incremental costs of carrying inventories and purchasing are minimized. Employment levels are held relatively steady. Adapted from R. O. Ferguson and L. F. Sargent, *Linear Programming,* McGraw-Hill Book Company, New York, 1958.

TABLE VI. Four Quarter Program Showing Allocation of 31,794 Solution by Distribution Methods of Linear Program- *Linear Programming*, McGraw-Hill

Part Num-ber	First Quarter Program								Second Quarter Program							
	Make Hours for Quarter				Buy Hours for Quarter				Make Hours for Quarter				Buy Hours for Quarter			
	1	2	3	4	1	2	3	4	1	2	3	4	1	2	3	4
1	500								700							
2	300								375							
3	100								140							
4	480								600							
5	120								150							
6	400	560		19							720	172				
7	75								105							
8	430								575							
9	60									75	80	100				
10	75								105							
11					150									210		
12					60									75		
13					220									290		
14					120									150		
15					100									140		
16					50									70		
17					60									75		
18					120									150		
19					60									75		
20					160									215		
21					60									75		
22					200									280		
23	100									140						
24	350									490						
25	240									300						
26	350									490						
27	300									375						
28	80									108						
29	84	105	112	140												
30	100	140	180	200												
Total Hours	5600				1360				5800				1805			

tage of purchasing and inventory holding cost. We see from the total requirements by quarters that the seasonal swing is in the ratio $10,190/5504 = 1.85$. Also, the planned capacity figures in hours indicate an increasing overload as the year progresses, totaling 7994 hours. The inventory carrying cost has been expressed in dollars per quarter for one hour's production.

To construct a distribution matrix, we note that we have requirements in each of four quarters for each of thirty different parts. These requirements form the 120 rows of the distribution matrix, and total 31,794 hours. Similarly, we have total capacity available in four quarters totaling 23,800 hours and we have presumably unlimited capacity to purchase outside. Purchasing then takes up the slack between requirements and manufacturing

**Requirements Hours to "Make" or "Buy" for Thirty Parts.
ming. Adapted from R. O. Ferguson and L. F. Sargent,
Book Company, New York, 1958**

Third Quarter Program								Fourth Quarter Program							
Make Hours for Quarter				Buy Hours for Quarter				Make Hours for Quarter				Buy Hours for Quarter			
1	2	3	4	1	2	3	4	1	2	3	4	1	2	3	4
		900									1000				
		400									500				
		180									200				
		640									800				
		160									200				
			509								100				
			135								150				
			690								800				
			96			39									150
						270									300
						80									100
						340									400
						160									200
						180									200
						90									100
						80									100
						160									200
						80									100
						260									300
						80									100
						360									400
			180								200				
			630								700				
			320								400				
			630								700				
			400								500				
			130								150				
6000				2179				6400				2650			

capacity and becomes a fifth source of capacity. We have then a distribution matrix of 120 rows and 5 columns, the cost elements of which are inventory carrying cost for the 4 columns representing manufacture, and incremental cost to purchase (over and above in-plant manufacturing cost) representing the cost element in the purchase column. Figure 15 shows the elements of the matrix for three typical parts. Part 23 is typical of the parts that are never purchased outside. Part 1 is typical of parts that can be either manufactured or purchased, but which represent those parts where there is a marked cost disadvantage in purchasing. Part 19 is representative of the parts that could be either manufactured or purchased, but which represent those parts having a cost advantage in purchasing.

Each of the cost elements under the 4 columns for manufacturing are computed as follows. If the item is to be manufactured in the first quarter, for example, we assume that there is no incremental cost to carry inventory, since it cannot be manufactured later and still meet requirements. In the first quarter, however, we can manufacture parts in advance which may be required for the second, third, or fourth quarters. Therefore, an incremental carrying cost is justified. If the part were to be made one quarter in advance, one quarter's incremental carrying cost would be justified. If the part is to be made two quarters in advance of requirements, two quarters' incremental carrying cost is justified, etc. For example, for part 23 under the column, "First quarter," the costs are zero if the part is made in the first quarter, 0.63 if made for second-quarter requirements = value from Table V $\times$ 1, 1.25 if made for third-quarter requirements = 0.625 $\times$ 2, etc. Looking across the row for part 23, quarter one, we find a cost of 0 under the first quarter, but the letter M (indicating an overwhelming cost so that the allocation is not admissible in a solution) under each of the other three columns. This merely indicates that a requirement in the first quarter cannot be manufactured in a subsequent quarter and still meet the requirements of solution.

Results. Table VI shows the final results of the allocation made by the distribution model. For each quarter it shows the hours allocation for each part to be made for that quarter and for future quarters, as well as, the parts to be purchased outside to meet requirements in the quarter. The solution represents a minimum inventory carrying cost–incremental purchase cost solution. Ferguson and Sargent discuss a number of alternate programs which represent variations of the basic program just presented. Specifically they are as follows:

1. Scheduling an exactly constant load of 5800 machine hours per quarter.

2. Increasing the forecast by 10 per cent as a hedge.

3. Revising the program for the last quarter to correct for earlier unplanned variations.

4. Determining the profitability of including additional machine capacity.

5. Correcting for decreases in the forecast.

6. Determining the economy of overtime operation during the peak requirements period.

Summary

In this chapter we have tried to develop the importance of the factor of uncertainty and its impact on inventory planning. In doing this, we have developed the rational determination of buffer stocks and discussed systems of inventory control which take account of uncertainty. In connection with these systems of inventory control, the concepts of process control and information feedback were introduced and the important effects of time lags shown. Finally, we have attempted to develop some important concepts of planning production programs and in this context the important function of seasonal inventories in minimizing other costs was shown.

REFERENCES

1. Biegel, J. E., *Production Control,* Prentice-Hall, Englewood Cliffs, N. J., 1963.
2. Bowman, E. H., "Production Scheduling by the Transportation Method of Linear Programming," *Journal of the Operations Research Society of America,* Vol. 4, No. 1, 1956, pp. 100–103.
3. Eilon, S., *Elements of Production Planning and Control,* The Macmillan Company, New York, 1962.
4. Fetter, R. B., and W. C. Dalleck, *Decision Models for Inventory Management,* Richard D. Irwin, Homewood, Ill., 1961.
5. Forrester, J. W., *Industrial Dynamics,* John Wiley and Sons, New York, 1961.
6. Ferguson, R. O., and L. F. Sargent, *Linear Programming,* McGraw-Hill Book Company, New York, 1958.
7. Hadley, G., and T. M. Whitin, *Analysis of Inventory Systems,* Prentice-Hall, Englewood Cliffs, N. J., 1963.
8. Holt, C. C., F. Modigliani, J. F. Muth, and H. A. Simon, *Planning Production, Inventories, and Work Force,* Prentice-Hall, Englewood Cliffs, N. J., 1960.
9. MacNiece, E. H., *Production, Forecasting, Planning, and Control,* John Wiley and Sons, New York, 1957.
10. Magee, J. F., *Production Planning and Inventory Control,* McGraw-Hill Book Company, New York, 1958.
11. Metzger, R. W., *Elementary Mathematical Programming,* John Wiley and Sons, New York, 1958.
12. Moore, F. G., *Production Control,* McGraw-Hill Book Company, New York, 2nd ed., 1959.
13. Starr, M. K., and D. W. Miller, *Inventory Control: Theory and Practice,* Prentice-Hall, Englewood Cliffs, N. J., 1962.
14. Vassian, H. J., "Application of Discrete Variable Servo Theory to Inventory Control," *Journal of the Operations Research Society of America,* Vol. 3, No. 3, August 1955, pp. 272–282.
15. Voris, W., *Production Control,* Richard D. Irwin, Incorporated, Homewood, Illinois, 1961.
16. Wagner, H. M., *Statistical Inventory Management,* John Wiley and Sons, New York, 1962.

REVIEW QUESTIONS

1. What are the three kinds of variations which we might expect in sales curves, which result in uncertainty of demand?

2. Why is it that we wish to abstract just the random variations due solely to chance causes from the total variation in demand curves from all causes, for use in determining buffer stocks?

3. How can we determine what stock runout level to use for a specific situation?

4. Describe each of the three inventory control systems which take account of uncertainty of demand which are described in this chapter.

5. What are the variables in inventory control systems that are subject to managerial control?

6. Which system has closer control over inventory levels, the fixed reorder quantity system or the fixed reorder cycle system?

7. What techniques may be applied to determine if an apparent change in demand is merely a random fluctuation or a true shift in average requirements?

8. Relate the general principles of process control to inventory control systems.

9. Describe the effects on retail inventories, distributor inventories, factory warehouse inventories, and on factory production levels when consumer demand changes, assuming the structure of a production distribution system as shown in Figure 10.

10. What are the requirements of demand forecast data for planning master production-inventory programs?

11. Referring to the cumulative requirements curves of Figure 13, what is the difference at any point in time between the cumulative production requirements curve and the cumulative maximum requirements curve?

12. What kinds of incremental costs must be accounted for in comparing alternate production-inventory programs?

13. What are the conditions under which linear programming might be used as a technique for determining a minimum cost production-inventory program?

PROBLEMS

1. Weekly demand for a product exclusive of seasonal and trend variations is represented by the empirical distribution given below. What buffer stock would be required for the item to insure that one would not run out of stock more than 15 per cent of the time? Five per cent of the time? One per cent of the time?

Weekly Demand, units	Frequency, Number of Weeks Demand Reached, Level Given
0	0
20	2
30	5
40	10
50	9
60	20
70	30
80	25
90	18
100	17
110	10
120	8
130	6
140	3
150	2
Total	165

2. If the item for which data is given in Problem 1 has a unit value of $100, shortages costs of $10 each, and has an annual inventory carrying cost 25 per cent of the average inventory value, which of the three levels of service would be most appropriate?

3. The following data show expected production requirements for an item together with buffer stock requirements and available production days in each month. Develop a chart for cumulative requirements and cumulative maximum requirements similar to Figure 13.

Month	Production Requirements	Required Buffer Stocks	Production Days
January	10,000	2,000	22
February	8,000	1,600	18
March	4,000	800	22
April	3,000	600	21
May	3,000	600	22
June	2,500	500	21
July	4,000	800	21
August	6,000	1,200	13
September	8,000	1,600	20
October	12,000	2,400	23
November	15,000	3,000	21
December	12,000	2,400	20
	87,500	17,500	244

4. Using the data of Problem 3, compare the total incremental costs involved in level production, a plan which follows maximum requirements

quite closely and some intermediate plan. Normal plant capacity is 400 units per working day. An additional 20 per cent can be obtained through overtime but at an additional cost of $15 per unit. Inventory carrying cost is $40 per unit per year. Changes in production level cost $6000 per 10 units in production rate. Extra capacity may be obtained from subcontracting at an extra cost of $20 per unit.

17

Operating Production-
Inventory Systems

In Chapter 16 we tried to show the influence of uncertainty of demand on inventory models, and in connection with planning of master production-inventory programs, the influence on inventories of labor force stabilization, use of overtime and second shifts, and subcontracting was shown. The important concept to carry over into this chapter is that inventory models must take account of the environment in which they are operated and cannot be considered as an isolated problem. This suggests that the basic concepts introduced with the classical inventory models are idealizations beyond reasonable levels of workability, and we shall attempt to show that this is true. We will focus on some of the major problems of operating a production-inventory system. This in turn breaks down into two areas of interest, controlling production-inventory levels and dispatching and controlling operations. As we shall see, inventories play a major role.

Controlling Production Levels

When a basic production-inventory program has been developed, the result is a schedule of planned production levels and inventory balances based on forecasts of requirements similar to that shown in Table III of Chapter 16. This table shows the production planned in each period (column 4) and the seasonal stock required (column 7) in order to meet requirements. As sales proceed, however, we must have some system for compensating for the differences between

477

planned and actual requirements in order to maintain inventories at proper levels. If actual requirements exceed plans, we run the risk of running out of stock, with resulting poor customer service and possible additional costs related to shortages. If actual requirements are below expectations, inventories will build up with resulting high carrying costs. Therefore, a control plan is needed which adjusts production and inventory levels in keeping with sales experience. Such a control plan might be accomplished by constructing periodically a new production program that takes into account existing inventories by adjustments in the short-run levels of production. Our objective in this control plan is *to increase or decrease production levels in the period ahead, proportional to differences between actual and forecast sales, by an amount that minimizes the incremental costs of inventories and fluctuations of production levels.* If the planning period is fairly short, this adjustment of levels would continuously correct inventory levels to be in keeping with present demand, thus preventing stock-outs or the buildup of excessive inventories because of changes in demand. The basic elements of this control plan are comparable to those described in Chapter 16 and illustrated by Figure 9 in that chapter. We wish to construct a feedback control system where information on desired levels of inventories (indicated by current requirements) is compared with actual inventories to determine an error function which is fed back and compared with information on planned production levels for the coming period. By some predetermined rule, the production level is then adjusted to compensate for the demand fluctuation and bring inventories into line.

Decision rules for controlling production levels. Let us first state an obvious kind of rule for controlling production levels as actual requirements vary from forecasted requirements. The rule we will use for introductory purposes is that when actual requirements deviate from forecasts, we will add or subtract the difference as soon as possible to the amount produced in order to compensate for the variation from planned inventory levels. Let us illustrate with the forecast of requirements for 10 weeks shown in column 2 of Table I. Column 3 shows the planned production program for the product, and the planned inventories are easily calculated in column 4. But as we would expect, actual requirements vary from forecast as shown in column 5 and the difference between actual and forecast requirements in column 6. The production lead time is 2 weeks, so that when a deviation from forecasted requirements occurs we can change production rate for the production period two weeks hence. Therefore, no change occurs from production plans in the first 2

TABLE I. Calculation of Production Levels and Inventories when the Difference between Forecasted and Actual Requirements is Absorbed Entirely by Changes in Production Level 2 Weeks Hence. Beginning Inventory is 500 Units

(1) Week	(2) Forecasted Requirements	(3) Planned Production	(4) Planned Inventories = Beginning Inventories + Col. 3 − Col. 2	(5) Actual Requirements	(6) Difference between Actual and Forecasted Requirements, Col. 5 − Col. 2	(7) Actual Production Level = Planned Production + Difference between Actual and Forecasted Requirements, 2 Weeks Ago; Col. 3 + Col. 6 for 2 Weeks Ago	(8) Actual Inventory Level = Beginning Inventory + Actual Production − Actual Requirements = Beginning Inventory + Col. 7 − Col. 5
0			500				500
1	590	600	510	595	5	600	505
2	590	600	520	430	−160	600	675
3	590	600	530	590	0	605	690
4	590	600	540	1000	410	440	130
5	600	600	540	50	−550	600	680
6	600	600	540	625	25	1010	1065
7	600	600	540	570	−30	50	545
8	600	600	540	575	−25	625	595
9	610	600	530	680	70	570	485
10	610	600	530	705	95	575	355
	5980	6000		5820		5675	

Actual average production rate = 567.5 units per week.
Actual average inventory level = 573 units.

weeks shown in column 7, but the third weeks' production reflects the shortage in planned requirements of five units. Similarly, the fourth week reflects the overage of 160 units which occurred in the second week, and so on. Actual inventory levels shown in column 8 are simply, beginning inventory plus the amount produced during the week (column 7) less the actual requirements (column 5).

We see that this rule does indeed compensate for the variations, with a 2-week time lag, but at what cost? Actual production levels vary from 50 units to 1000 units per week in the short space of 10 weeks. But, notice that over the 10 weeks, actual total requirements were quite close to forecasted total requirements. Variation from forecast was largely week-to-week variation. As a matter of fact, the week-to-week variation reflects the random variations described in the distribution of Figure 4 in Chapter 16. In other words, it was variation that we should have expected to occur. Perhaps there is a better way to absorb this variation than by changing production level.

Let us test the idea just stated. Why not damp the effects of variation in actual requirements from forecast by changing production level by only 50 per cent of the difference instead of 100 per cent as we did previously. This is shown in Table II under, "50% Reaction." The original forecast of requirements and production and inventory plans are identical to those of Table I, but notice that violent swings in both production and inventory levels have been damped out considerably. Why not carry this idea farther? What happens with a 10 or 5 per cent reaction rate? This is also shown in Table II with additional stabilizing factors. With the 10 per cent reaction we have included the additional restriction that we will not respond to the variation from forecast at all unless 10 per cent of the difference exceeds 10 units. In addition, with the 5 per cent reaction we have included the 10-unit minimum and the restriction that larger changes in production level are made only in increments of 10 units. Therefore, if 5 per cent of the difference is 27.5 units as it is in the fifth week, a change in production level of 30 units is made in the seventh week. Notice the results of progressively decreasing reaction rates in Table II. The results are more stable production and inventory levels. Also note, however, that average inventory levels have increased as reaction rate was decreased.

The effect of reducing reaction rate could have been forecast. By using a relatively low reaction rate we are assuming that most deviations in actual requirements from forecasts are simply random deviations, so why become excited about them? If the deviation looks

TABLE II. Actual Production and Inventory Levels when only 50 Per Cent, 10 Per Cent, or 5 Per Cent of the Difference between Forecasted and Actual Requirements is Absorbed by Changes in Production Level from Plan, 2 Weeks Hence. Buffer Stocks Absorb the Balance of the Variation. Data for Forecasted and Actual Requirements and Planned Production and Inventory Levels Are Shown in Table I

Week	50% Reaction		10% Reaction 10-Unit Minimum		5% Reaction 10-Unit Minimum, Increments 10 Units	
	Actual Production Level	Actual Inventory Level	Actual Production Level	Actual Inventory Level	Actual Production Level	Actual Inventory Level
0	—	500	—	500	—	500
1	600	505	600	505	600	505
2	600	675	600	675	600	675
3	603	688	600	685	600	685
4	520	208	584	269	590	275
5	600	758	600	819	600	825
6	805	938	641	835	620	820
7	375	743	545	810	570	820
8	613	781	600	835	600	845
9	585	686	600	755	600	765
10	587	568	600	650	600	660
Average for 10 Weeks	589	655	597	684	598	688

large, perhaps we should increase or decrease production rate *a little*, just in case it really marks the beginning of a trend. The question is, then, what should be the reaction rate for optimal cost performance? It is a good question, but it is slightly premature. Let us first discuss the general aspects of the decision rule and develop the ideas of reaction rates, review periods, and their interrelations.

Our decision rule really operates in the following context:

1. A longer-term forecast of requirements on which is based a broad production program of the type discussed on pages 461–472.

2. A shorter-term forecast or "review" to refine the forecast of requirements for the immediate periods ahead.

3. Based on this short-term review and forecast of requirements we can:

    a. Determine a production plan for these periods.

    b. Set planned inventory levels for these periods.

4. In the shortest-term planning period which is equal to the production lead time (the shortest notice used to change production

levels in the period ahead), we can make a final adjustment in production level which takes account of the latest information we have regarding the comparison of actual and forecasted requirements.

5. The decision rule used is that production level in the immediate period ahead will be adjusted by some fraction k of the difference between actual and forecasted requirements for the current period.

In this context, we see that there are really two parameters we can manipulate to develop a model for the control of production levels. They are the value of k—the reaction rate—and the length of the review period mentioned in number 2 and 3 in the preceding outline. The importance of the reaction rate has already been discussed and demonstrated in the text material related to Tables I and II. In summary, k may take on values between the number 0 and 1.00, representing no reaction to deviations from forecasted requirements when $k = 0$, to 100 per cent reaction and compensation when $k = 1.00$. In general terms, low values of k lead to stable production levels and relatively high buffer stock requirements, since variations from the plan must be absorbed by inventories. Conversely, high values of k lead to large production fluctuations and relatively low buffer stocks because variations from plan are absorbed by changing production levels.

The frequency of review also has a direct effect on both the magnitude of production fluctuations and the size of needed buffer stocks. The reason is easy to see in relation to the general principal of process control which we discussed on pages 455–459. The longer the period between reviews, P, the greater the chance that forecasts of requirements may not reflect the most current trends. Therefore, it is more likely that relatively large differences between actual and forecasted requirements would accumulate. For a given value of k, longer review periods lead to both relatively large production fluctuations and buffer stocks in order to provide the needed compensation. Short periods between reviews, then, lead to closer control and relatively small production fluctuations and buffer stocks, whereas longer periods between reviews lead to looser control and larger production fluctuations and buffer stock requirements.

Determining k and P. Magee (8) derives two approximate formulas useful in solving the problem of determining the reaction rate k and the review period P for specific situations. He shows that the expected magnitude of production fluctuations is approximately proportional to

$$\sqrt{kP/(2 - k)} \qquad (1)$$

and that the required factory buffers stock will be approximately proportional to

$$\sqrt{[T(2k - k^2) + P]/(2k - k^2)} \qquad (2)$$

where T = production lead time, P = length of review period, and k = reaction rate in decimals.

The cost of production fluctuation, then, is proportional to (1) and the cost of buffer stocks are proportional to (2). Figure 1 shows

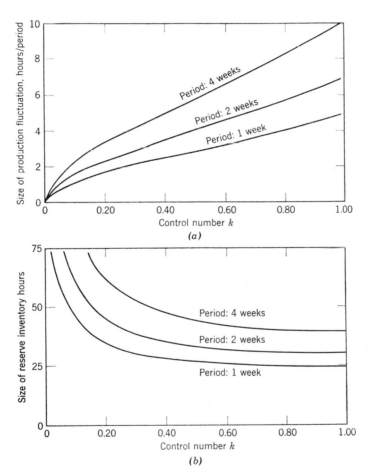

Figure 1. (*a*) Magnitude of production fluctuations versus control number and length of review period. (*b*) Reserve inventory required versus control number and length of review period. By permission from *Production Planning and Inventory Control*, by J. F. Magee, McGraw-Hill Book Company, New York, copyright, 1958.

the relationship of reaction rates and review period to the size of production fluctuations and reserve inventory requirements, expressed in equivalent hours. For a specific case, then, suppose that at $k = 1.00$ we experience a production fluctuation cost of \$5000 and a buffer stock cost of \$500, when the review period and production lead times are each 1 week. Using (1) and (2), we can compute points for the curves shown in Figure 2 to find a value of k approximating 0.075 for minimum total incremental cost. Further similar calculations with different review periods would yield a combination of k and P which would minimize incremental costs for the entire system. Obviously, the right combination for a specific case like that shown in Figure 2 depends on the relative magnitudes of inventory carrying cost and the cost of production changes.

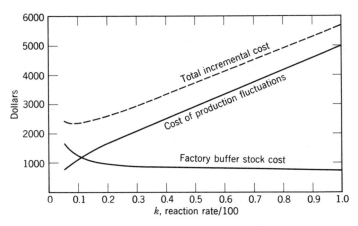

Figure 2. Relationship between incremental costs and k, when the cost of production fluctuations and factory buffer stocks are \$5000 and \$500 respectively at $k = 1$. Review period and lead time are 1 week.

Let us summarize at this point some of the aspects of the control of inventories under uncertainty in a production-inventory system. In Chapter 16 we discuss systems for controlling inventories that involved fixing the quantity ordered at one time, letting the frequency of ordering vary, fixing the frequency of ordering, letting the quantity ordered vary, and the base stock system which was a combination of the elements of the two different systems. Also, differences in the information feedback pattern and their effects were noted. In the operation of a production-inventory system we have noted that the cost of production fluctuations is also an important factor to take into account. By way of summary, let us now consider the overall comparison of systems of control.

A COMPARATIVE EXAMPLE

Magee (8) relates a hypothetical case called the Hibernian Co. which compares operation and costs for different basic systems of production and inventory control. The example considers a company that manufactures and sells about 5000 small machines per year for $100 each. The factory supplies four warehouses located in strategic areas around the country, which in turn supply the customer. We shall show the calculated results for four alternate systems of control: an economical order quantity system, a two-week fixed reorder cycle system, a base stock system with a review period of 1 week and reaction rate of 100 per cent, and a base stock system with a 1-week review period but involving a production reaction rate of 5 per cent.

Each of the four branches sold an average of 25 units per week, or 1300 units per year. This average rate was, of course, subject to considerable variation, and Table III shows distributions of demand at each of the four

TABLE III. Distribution of Demand at Each of Four Branches by Eight Different Time-Period Groupings

Per Cent of Periods Exceeding Levels Given	Units of Sales Period, weeks							
	1	2	3	4	5	6	7	8
90	19	41	64	87	111	134	158	182
60	24	46	71	95	124	144	168	193
50	25	50	75	100	125	150	175	200
20	29	56	82	108	134	160	186	212
10	31.4	60	86	113	139	166	192	218
1	37	67	95	123	151	179	206	233

branches for 1-week periods, 2-week periods, etc. For example, at any given branch, sales would be expected to exceed 37 units per week only 1 per cent of the time, 67 units per 2-week period 1 per cent of the time, and so on. Requirements aggregated at the factory warehouse, reflecting demand from all four of the branches, are also shown in Table IV for eight different time groupings. Figure 3 shows the structure of the production-distribution system.

1. *Economical fixed reorder quantity system.* Using an economical fixed reorder quantity system, we must analyze the requirements for buffer stocks, cycle stocks, transit stocks, and reordering costs for the branches, as well as, buffer stocks, cycle stocks, in-process inventory, ordering costs, and the cost of production fluctuations at the factory and warehouse.

TABLE IV. Distribution of Demand on Factory Warehouse from Branches by Eight Different Time-Period Groupings

Per Cent of Periods Exceeding Levels Given	Units of Requirements in Period, weeks							
	1	2	3	4	5	6	7	8
90	87	182	278	374	471	569	666	764
60	95	193	291	389	488	587	686	785
50	100	200	300	400	500	600	700	800
20	108	212	314	417	519	621	722	824
10	113	218	322	426	529	631	734	836
1	123	233	341	447	553	658	762	866

Branches. At each branch, the economical quantity to be ordered at one time may be calculated if we know that $c_P = \$19$ ($6 clerical cost, \$13 cost of packing, shipping, receiving, and stocking), $R = 1300$, and $c_H = \$5$. Q_0 is then,

$$\sqrt{(2 \times 19 \times 1300)/5} = 100 \text{ units}$$

Therefore, each branch would place an order for 100 units each, 4 weeks on the average. The average *cycle stock* in each branch would therefore be $\frac{100}{2} = 50$ units. The branch *buffer stock* is based on a 1 per cent risk of running out of stock. Since the total lead time was 2 weeks, we can determine the reasonable maximum demand during that period from Table III as 67 units. Since normal demand during the 2-week lead time would be 50 units, the buffer stock is then the difference, or 17 units. Finally, the average

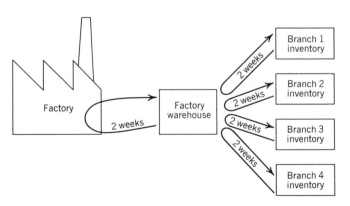

Figure 3. Structure of production-distribution system for Hibernian Bay Co.

transit stock is equal to the delivery time multiplied by the average demand rate, or 50 units. Average branch inventory is then as follows:

$$\begin{array}{lll} \text{Buffer stock,} & 4 \times 17 = & 68 \text{ units} \\ \text{Cycle stock,} & 4 \times 50 = & 200 \\ \text{Transit stock,} & 4 \times 50 = & \underline{200} \\ & & 468 \text{ units} \end{array}$$

Since $c_H = \$5$ per unit per year, this average inventory of 468 units has an annual cost of \$2340. Since each branch places an order once every 4 weeks, on the average, there are 52 orders per year from the four branches which cost \$19 each or a total annual reordering cost of \$990.

Factory warehouse and factory. The factory warehouse is, of course, reflecting the aggregate of demand from the four branches so that its economical order quantity reflects annual requirements, $R = 5200$ units, and its own inventory holding and preparation costs of $c_H = \$3.50$, and $c_P = \$13.50$. Calculating Q_0, as before, we obtain $Q_0 = 200$ units. Maximum 2-week demand from the branches (using a 1 per cent run-out risk criterion) under the economical reorder quantity system is 500 units, so that *factory warehouse buffer stocks* are set at $500 - 200 = 300$ units. *Cycle stocks are* $\frac{200}{2} = 100$ units, and *in-process inventories* in the factory average one-half the order quantity or 100 units. Total average inventory at the factory warehouse is therefore 500 units. On the average, 26 factory production orders per year must be issued at a cost of \$13.50 or \$350 per year. Table V summarizes the inventory and ordering costs for the economical

TABLE V. Summary of Incremental Costs of Economical Order Quantity System for Hibernian Co.   From Magee (8)

Inventory costs	
Four branches	\$ 2,340
Factory	1,750
Reorder costs	
Four branches	990
Factory	350
Production fluctuations	8,500
	\$13,930

order quantity system. To this total we must add the *cost of production fluctuations* which occur with the economical order quantity system. Figure 4a shows a typical pattern of orders on the factory and the resulting factory production levels set. Note that very large fluctuations in production levels result and these fluctuations cost \$8500 per year.

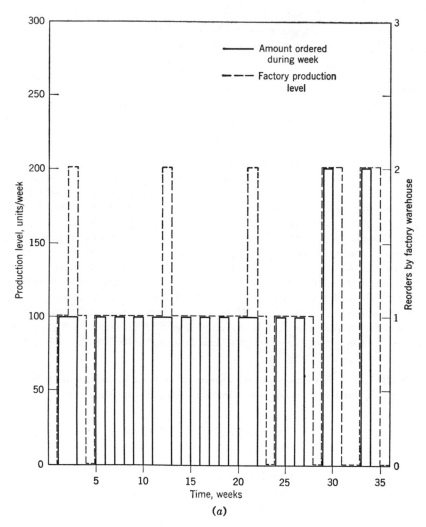

Figure 4. (a) Factory orders and production level, economic reorder quantity system. (b) Production level, fixed reorder cycle system. (c) Production level, base-stock system; reaction rate = 5 per cent. Adapted by permission from *Production Planning and Inventory Control,* by J. F. Magee, McGraw-Hill Book Company, New York, copyright, 1958.

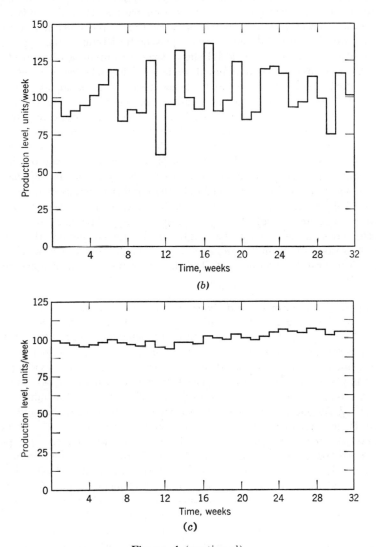

Figure 4 (continued).

2. *Fixed Reorder Cycle System.*

Branches. Under the fixed reorder cycle system, each branch warehouse maintains its inventory sufficient to fill reasonable maximum demands during the review period plus the 2-week delivery time. We must first compare system costs for several different review periods to determine the appropriate length of review period. Table III shows the distribution of demand at each branch warehouse for eight different periods. Therefore, we can determine *buffer stock* requirements for each review period considered, at the 1 per cent risk level, by looking at the numbers on the row for the per cent of period sales exceeding the 1 per cent level. The buffer stock requirements for a 1-week review period plus the 2-week lead time are $95 - 75 = 20$. Buffer stock requirements computed in the same way are shown for the various review periods in Table VI. *Cycle stock* would average one-half of the normal shipment. A shipment is made once each period so that the average amount shipped would be $25 \times$ (the number of weeks in the period). Table VI shows the appropriate cycle stocks for each review period. *Transit stock* remains at 50 units for each review period. The number of orders placed varies inversely with the length of the review period, therefore, a 1-week period results in 52 orders per year at $19 per order or $990 per year. The branch ordering costs for the other periods are summarized in Table VI.

Factory warehouse and factory. Factory warehouse *buffer stocks* are set at the 1 per cent risk level, and Table IV shows the distribution of demand on the factory warehouse from branches by eight different time-period groupings. Since the factory lead time is 2 weeks, reasonable maximum demand must be calculated over the lead time plus one review period, for example, for a 1-week review period, maximum demand is 341 units and average usage is 300 units. The resulting buffer stock is the difference or 41 units. The factory buffer stocks shown in Table VI are computed from Table IV in a parallel way. Factory warehouse *cycle stocks* and factory *in-process inventories* are equal to one-half the average requirements per period and are computed as shown in Table VI. The factory warehouse *ordering cost* are inversely proportional to the length of the review period, and are calculated at $13.50 each. The cost of production changes is computed at $1600 annually for the close control resulting from a 1-week review period, and Magee (8) shows that the cost of production changes for the other review periods is proportional to $\sqrt{n}$. Figure 4b shows production levels for a 2-week period reorder system, which we see is the least cost of the six review periods analyzed in Table VI.

3. *Base Stock System, k = 100 Per Cent.* A third system for comparison is the general base stock system which we discussed in Chapter 16. Here the four branches report sales periodically and the factory consolidates demand from these sources and puts an equivalent amount into production. The branch stocks are then replenished when sales have exceeded a minimum

TABLE VI. * **Comparison of System Costs for Different Lengths of Review Periods**

	Length of Review Period, weeks					
	1	2	3	4	5	6
Branch warehouses, each branch						
Inventory						
Buffer stock	20	23	26	29	31	33
Cycle stock	12.5	25	37.5	50	62.5	75
Transit stock	50	50	50	50	50	50
Total	82.5	98	113.5	129	143.5	158
Annual inventory cost at $5	$ 412.5	$ 490	$ 567.5	$ 645	$ 717.5	$ 790
Ordering cost	990	495	330	250	195	165
Total	$1402.5	$ 985	$ 897.5	$ 895	$ 912.5	$ 955
Total, four branches	$5610	$3940	$3590	$3580	$3650	$ 3,820
Factory warehouse						
Buffer stock	41	47	53	58	62	67
Cycle stock	50	100	150	200	250	300
In-process stock	50	100	150	200	250	300
Total	141	247	353	458	562	667
Annual inventory cost at $3.50	$ 493	$ 865	$1235	$1630	$1967	$ 2,335
Ordering cost	700	350	235	175	140	120
Total factory warehouse cost	$1193	$1195	$1470	$1805	$2107	$ 2,455
Cost of changing production levels	$1600	$2250	$2760	$3180	$3560	$ 3,900
Total system costs	$8403	$7385	$7820	$8565	$9317	$10,175

* Modified from J. F. Magee, *Production Planning and Inventory Control*, McGraw-Hill Book Company, New York, 1958.

shipment quantity. The two main questions to be tied down then, are, "How often should the branches report sales?", and "How big should the minimum replenishment shipment be?" The possible advantages of the base stock system compared to the fixed cycle system just discussed are:

1. If the branches can justify weekly sales reporting, production fluctuations and buffer stocks might be reduced even more.

2. It might be possible to make less frequent shipments from the factory to branches, thereby making further cost reductions.

Looking at Table VI, we see that if we go to weekly review periods instead of the 2-week period decided on, branch safety stocks can be reduced from 23 to 20 per branch resulting in an inventory cost reduction of $60.

Similarly, factory warehouse buffer stocks would be reduced from 47 to 41, resulting in a modest reduction of $21. From the closer control of the 1-week review period, the cost of production changes goes down from $2250 to $1600 resulting in a net reduction of $650.

Recall that the value of $c_P = \$19$ was made up of $6 for clerical costs and $13 for shipping and related costs. Therefore, we can compute an economical shipping quantity as follows:

$$\sqrt{(2 \times 13 \times 1300)/5} = 82 \text{ units}$$

This means an average of 16 shipments annually to each branch, or a total cost of $16 \times 4 \times 13 = \$828$. This compares with 26 shipments required for the two week reorder period which totaled $1352, resulting in a net shipping cost reduction of $524.

These cost reductions are partially offset by increases in the cost of branch reports and cycle stock costs. A branch report costs $6 each and there would be 52 of them required for each branch per year instead of 26, which results in a net increase in cost of $625. Finally, the cycle stock at the branches is increased from 25 units per branch to one-half the new average shipping quantity, or 41 units. This results in a net increase in cycle stock cost of $320. The net result is that the base stock system with $k = 100$ per cent decreases net system costs by a modest $290.

4. *Base Stock System, $k = 5$ Per Cent.* If we now decrease the reaction rate at the factory to 5 per cent, the cost of production changes is reduced and Figure 4c shows the startling stabilizing effect of the 5 per cent reaction rate on production levels. From Table VI, for a review period of 1 week, we see that the cost of production changes is $1600. Recall that we stated earlier that the cost of production changes was proportional to formula 1. Thus we may compute the cost of production changes when the reaction rate is 5 per cent by $1600 \times \sqrt{0.05/1.95} = \$256$. Similarly, using formula 2 and noting from Table VI that the factory buffer of 41 units costs $144 per year, when $k = 100$ per cent, we can calculate the cost of buffer stock when $k = 5$ per cent as $299.

Table VII shows the final summary of incremental costs for the four systems. The base stock system with 1-week review and a reaction rate of 5 per cent has the lowest total of $6345. This compares with $13,930 for the "so-called" economical order quantity system, more than twice the cost of the former. Thus we see demonstrated what is perhaps the most important factor in the design of a production-inventory system. The lesson is that it must reflect the "systems" point of view, that is, consider not only inventory models in isolation, but take account of the interaction of inventory costs with other costs in the overall production system. The result is that the economical order quantity view is not valid, even when uncertainty of demand is accounted for, except in the few situations which we may regard as almost purely inventory systems. In the following sections we shall see this basic point carried even further, for the particular way in which we assign

TABLE VII. Comparative Incremental Costs for Four Systems

	Economical Order Quantity System	2-Week Fixed Cycle Reorder System	Base Stock, 1-Week Review, $k = 100\%$	Base Stock, 1-Week Review, $k = 5\%$
Inventory costs				
Four branches	$ 2,360	$1960	$2240	$2240
Factory warehouse	1,750	865	844	1143
Reorder costs				
Four branches	990	1980	1456	1456
Factory warehouse	350	350	350	350
Branch reports	—	625	1250	1250
Cost of production fluctuations	8,500	2250	1600	256
Total incremental costs	$13,930	$8030	$7740	$6345

orders within a production system will affect the in-process inventory levels of the system.

Dispatching and Control of Operations

We have shown that the construction of a master production-inventory program normally represents an allocation of available capacity to demand. We have also shown, that the best plan may often involve the use of planned seasonal inventories to reduce certain other costs, such as overtime premium, subcontracting, and most importantly, the cost of production fluctuations. The minimum cost plan represents a compromise of these costs and usually no single one of these costs so dominates the model that the best solution results from minimizing that particular cost item. Such a master program represents a medium-range plan for the best use of production and inventory resources. We know, however, that the forecasts of the amounts and timing of demand will vary from plan, simply because of random variations in demand, as well as the development of trends not anticipated when the master production-inventory plan was constructed.

The result is that we need a system for controlling production and inventory levels to take account of shorter-run forecasts of requirements and the most up-to-date reports on the *actual* progress of sales. Therefore, in the preceding section, models for controlling production and inventory levels were developed that had the objective of minimizing the costs of carrying inventory, ordering costs, and the costs of production fluctuation in the short run. Finally, in the shortest possible range of planning, someone must decide for each process in the chain of production operations the sequence in which orders or jobs will be processed. This function is called dispatching, and as we shall see the decision rules used can have an important bearing on in-process inventories and other measures of effectiveness, such as machine and labor utilization and meeting schedules. We can visualize a production facility as a network of waiting lines in which the machines are the various service facilities, and the orders being processed are the arrivals. The sequence in which orders are to be processed from each waiting line represents the queue discipline, and we refer to these queue disciplines as priority dispatch decision rules in a production system. We shall divide our discussion into two main classifications, job shop dispatching and flow shop dispatching. This classification follows the intermittent-continuous production system classification made in the discussion of general systems of production.

Job shop dispatching decision rules. Of course, the simplest decision rule to use in the dispatching function is to take orders in the sequence in which they arrive at the machine or machine center. This first come–first served decision rule is probably the most common, and because of its simplicity and pervasive use, represents a kind of standard to which alternate decision rules are invariably compared. Obviously we can assign priorities to jobs or orders on many different bases; for example, we could take orders in the sequence of the due dates, taking those with the earliest due dates first. As new orders arrive at the machine center for processing, an order which might have been next in line could be pre-empted by the receipt of an order with an earlier due date. Is such a priority system better, on balance, than first come–first served? We can rationalize advantages and disadvantages, but nothing substitutes for a test in practice, measuring the comparative performance results. Because such tests would be so disruptive to shop operations, they are not normally carried out in practice. Also, since job shop systems are so complex, mathematical models of an equivalent network of waiting lines are impractical. The result is that research workers have turned to large-scale system simulation as the laboratory technique of value in the testing of priority decision rules.

The simulation technique is flexible, does not disrupt operations, and can collapse to a few minutes or hours of computer time several years of operation with a given decision rule. Recent work by Jackson (5, 6) and Rowe (9) has opened an intensive inquiry into priority dispatching by simulation methods. Rowe, using a simulation model of one of the machine shops of the General Electric Company tested six different priority decision rules and determined the effects on three measures of plant performance. These yardsticks were the time of job completions in relation to schedule, labor utilization, and in-process inventory carrying cost. The six decision rules were as follows:

Decision Rule 1. *First come–first served.*
Decision Rule 2. *First come–first served, within priority class.*
The dollar value of jobs was the basis of priority. Three value classes

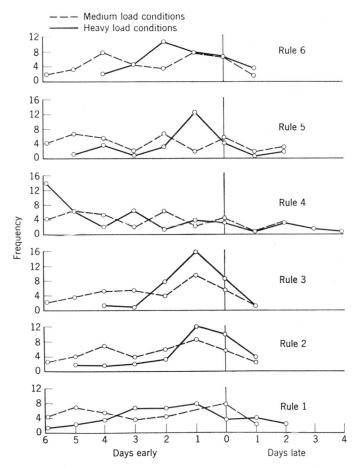

Figure 5. Distribution of job completions. From A. J. Rowe, "Application of Computer Simulation to Sequential Decision Rules in Production Scheduling," *Proceedings, Eleventh Annual Industrial Engineering Institute,* University of California, Berkeley-Los Angeles, 1959, pp. 33–43.

were used: high, medium, and low. All high-value jobs were taken first in the order of their arrival, then all of the medium-value jobs, etc.

Decision Rule 3. *Sequential rule.* This rule was a complex mathematical function which took into account a flow allowance, remaining processing to be completed, and, in an indirect way, inventory.

Decision Rule 4. *Minimum imminent processing time.* This rule allowed the jobs requiring a short total time to be processed first, since they did not affect the waiting time of other jobs very much.

Decision Rule 5. *Maximum imminent processing time;* that is, completing the jobs first that had the longest processing time.

Decision Rule 6. *Earliest start date.* Jobs were dispatched in the order of their start dates, the earliest dates coming first.

The simulation model was designed to cover the equivalent of 4 months of factory operation in 15 minutes of computer time. Two load conditions were used, characterized as a medium-shop load and a heavy-shop load. Typical results are shown by Figure 5 and Table VIII. Rules 2, 3, and 6 tend to minimize "days late." Rule 4,

TABLE VIII. Comparison of Labor Utilization and Inventory Carrying Cost Ratios for Six Dispatching Decision Rules by Computer Simulation

Dispatching Decision Rule	Labor Utilization	Inventory Carrying Cost Ratio
Rule 1 First come–first served	85.6%	70.1%
Rule 2 First come–first served within priority class	85.6	41.9
Rule 3 Sequential rule	88.2	42.4
Rule 4 Minimum imminent processing time	88.6	72.4
Rule 5 Maximum imminent processing time	76.9	53.6
Rule 6 Earliest start date	85.6	51.1

minimum imminent processing time, apparently induces both more late and early orders, especially for the heavier load condition. Table VIII shows the labor utilization and inventory carrying cost ratios for one of the trial runs. Rules 3 and 4 have the highest labor utilization, but Rule 3 shows a significantly better carrying cost ratio than Rule 4. The effect of the variability of early and late orders in the distribution of completion times for Rule 4 is seen in the high-inventory carrying cost of that rule. This brings home an idea fundamental to the operation of a production system. Our interest is not merely one of minimizing late orders. We are also concerned that orders not be completed too early, because inventory carrying cost will be increased under these conditions.

Generalizing for the rules tested and for the shop conditions at the General Electric Company, several of the rules yield almost equivalent labor utilization, but only Rules 2 and 3 minimize inventory costs. Other conditions of machine load, product mix, and other variations in shop conditions could be tested in the same general fashion. We are, of course, dealing with a situation where multiple criteria are of importance. In the usual production system, we cannot minimize any one of the criteria at the expense of the others; rather, we are again faced with a problem of attempting to achieve the best balance of the various criteria, some of which may be conflicting.

Rowe's exploratory work in comparing the effectiveness of various dispatch decision rules has opened the door for more intensive investigations. The fact that Rowe used a simulation model of an existing plant facility also helped gain acceptance from operating personnel that the ideas involved were no mere research playthings. Further exploratory work has been done by Conway, Johnson, and Maxwell (2) and LeGrand (7), and a more complete discussion of LeGrand's work at the Hughes Aircraft Company is included in Chapter 19, dealing with large-scale system simulation. The most recent work has been concentrated on two types of decision rules, the "shortest operation" rule examined by Conway and Maxwell (3), and "dynamic priorities" being examined by Jackson (6) and Grindley (4). A dynamic priority is one in which as time passes, the probability decreases that orders with higher priorities will arrive. Priorities related to due dates are of this type, and they tend to minimize late orders.

Shortest operation rule. It can be proved for a single-stage production system (one machine) that the priority decision rule that processes jobs in the sequence of priority numbers proportional to the processing time required is optimal according to a number of different criteria (11). This decision rule is called the shortest operation rule, and the convention used assigns the lowest numbers the highest priority. Specifically, mathematical analysis and proof has shown that for single-stage systems using the shortest operation rule, the following statements are true (3):

1. The total completion time is minimized.
2. The average completion time is minimized.

3. The average number of jobs in process is minimized.

4. The average waiting time is minimized.

5. If lateness is defined for a given job as the difference between completion time and due date, the average lateness is minimized.

Any rule that accomplishes these objectives is of considerable practical, as well as, theoretical interest. The one big disadvantage of the shortest operation rule is that there may be very long waiting times for individual orders or jobs even though average waiting time has been minimized. The theorctical analysis also leaves several other questions open. Among them are: Do conclusions with regard to the optimality of the rule extend to the more realistic multimachine case, comparable to real job shops? How accurately must processing times be known, that is, is the performance of the rule sensitive to errors in the estimated processing times? Is the rule sensitive to shop size, that is, does it work well with a one machine, or small shop, but break down in the more complex situation representative of medium to large job shops? A study by Conway and Maxwell (3) addresses itself to these questions.

To consider more complex systems, Conway and Maxwell used a computer simulation of waiting line networks in which comparisons were made between the shortest operation rule and others. In some of the simulated experiments, shop size was varied, and other runs were made to determine if the effectiveness of the rule would break down if the estimates of processing time were progressively poorer. The results showed rather conclusively that the superiority of the shortest operation rule does transfer to the more complex multimachine case, and that the rule is not sensitive to shop size, shop loading, or to errors in estimating the process times. Finally, the question of the disadvantage of the rule which results in very long waiting time for a few jobs was dealt with by considering modified shortest operation rules. For example, a truncated shortest operation rule places an upper limit on the amount of waiting time for any job. If the job remains in the waiting line as long as this time limit, it then moves to the head of the line and is processed. Of course, some of the advantage of the shortest operation rule is lost by the modified rule. For example, when the waiting time limit was set at 2.5 times the mean waiting time for a first come–first served rule, about two-thirds of the advantage in idle time of the shortest operation rule over the first come–first served rule was lost.

The great advantages of the shortest operation rule are its simplicity in application and its relative effectiveness. Conway and

Maxwell state that a rule, superior to the shortest operation rule, could probably be constructed that takes account of other factors in the information horizon, such as the current status of the shop, the characteristics of other jobs in the waiting line, subsequent operations, etc., but such a rule may be a very complex one. We may expect continuing research and progress in the field of priority dispatching decision rules.

Flow shop dispatching. It is unnecessary to control individual orders in a flow shop, characterized by our continuous model of production, because each group or lot of products is just like the preceding group. Indeed, any attempt to control product flow, operation by operation, is unrealistic because the standardized products may flow through a fixed sequence of operations over mechanical routes. We may liken such a system to a single giant machine, and all we need to do to schedule each of the operations within the machine is to schedule the giant machine itself. All operations within are automatically coordinated with that schedule by the mechanical design of the system. Production scheduling is then practically complete when the production level is set by the master program. Control is achieved by merely adjusting product on levels in accordance with sales experience, as discussed previously. This adjustment of production level is an adjustment of the rate of flow, and, therefore, the term *flow control* is commonly used.

In true flow control situations, even incoming raw materials are set up on this basis. Rates of flow of materials, parts, and subassemblies are set up to match those of the final product. Suppliers must then maintain these flow rates. Contracts for supply often contain volume flexibility within certain limits, so that the plant can adjust supply rates to maintain control over raw material inventories. Here, the costs of placing repeat orders for materials are replaced by a single contract to supply over a period of time. Concepts of economical order quantities give way to parallel concepts of economical shipping quantities. In many very high-volume plants, such as automobile assembly, deliveries of some items are made daily, and they are taken directly to the point of use in the plant rather than to an intermediate stock point.

These comments are not intended to infer that scheduling and control are simple problems in continuous industries. Actually, control must be more precise because the high-volume rates can quickly run a minor error into a costly one. Delays because of material and part shortages can hold up an entire sequence of operations, so that down-time costs are heavy. Even though the final product is handled on a flow-control basis, many parts and subassemblies may be handled on a job shop basis because time requirements do not justify their continuous manufacture. Therefore, even though overall flow rates for these parts can be set, they will be fabricated in lots, using facilities that are time shared with other products, so we experience the problems of intermittent manufacture anyway.

Summary

In considering the problems posed by inventories, we are forced to consider several levels of planning covering different time spans. These are as follows:

1. *Long-range plans for plant capacity.* Since plant capacity is affected by seasonal peaks, and there are capital costs associated with this capacity. What combination of in-plant capacity, use of seasonal inventories, overtime, and subcontracting will minimize the combined capital costs, seasonal inventory costs, labor costs, production fluctuation costs, and extra costs of subcontracting? Is new capacity justified?

2. *Intermediate-range plans for a few months to a year* in advance which attempt to determine for the expectations of sales what will be the best allocation of the resources of existing capacity. We are asking what combination of production within periods, and seasonal inventories will minimize the combined costs of production fluctuation, seasonal inventory cost, labor costs, and extra subcontracting costs.

3. *Short-range plans for the immediate period ahead.* Since actual requirements will change from forecasts, we must take a last look within the lead time to change production level, but neither can we change production levels capriciously because large costs can be involved, nor can we ignore what might develop into a huge inventory buildup. The result is that we need a control system that minimizes in the short range the costs of inventories and production fluctuations.

4. *In the shortest range of planning,* we need automatic decision rules that dispatch work to each and every workplace and machine. There is no time to ponder the question at this point. We must develop an automatic rule which operates quickly and accurately, indicating the best sequence in which to process orders at a given machine or machine center. Here we are looking for a model of flow which will minimize inventory and idle labor costs while providing a high level of service to customers by completing their work on time.

Inventories have an important impact at all stages of planning and execution. The result is that we must view inventories in their multifunction role in the broad system from raw material input, flow through the production-distribution system, and to the consumer. They cannot be examined in isolation with realism.

REFERENCES

1. Biegel, J. E., *Production Control,* Prentice-Hall, Englewood Cliffs, N. J., 1963.
2. Conway, R. W., B. M. Johnson, and W. L. Maxwell, "An Experimental Investigation of Priority Dispatching," *Journal of Industrial Engineering,* Vol. XI, No. 3, May–June 1960, pp. 221–229.
3. Conway, R. W., and W. L. Maxwell, "Network Dispatching by the Shortest Operation Discipline," *Operations Research,* Vol. 10, No. 1, February 1962, pp. 51–73.
4. Grindley, A., "Tandem Queues with Dynamic Priorities," *Doctoral Dissertation,* UCLA, 1962.
5. Jackson, J. R., "Networks of Waiting Lines," *Operations Research,* August 1957.
6. Jackson, J. R., "Queues with Dynamic Priority Discipline," *Management Science,* Vol. 8, No. 1, October 1961, pp. 18–35.
7. LeGrande, E., *Development of a Factory Simulation System Using Actual Operating Data,* Hughes Aircraft Co., March 1962.
8. Magee, J. S., *Production Planning and Inventory Control,* McGraw-Hill Book Company, New York, 1958.
9. Rowe, A. J., "Application of Computer Simulation to Sequential Decision Rules in Production Scheduling," *Proceedings, Eleventh Annual Industrial Engineering Institute,* University of California, Berkeley-Los Angeles, 1959, pp. 33–43.
10. Rowe, A. J., "Sequential Decision Rules in Production Scheduling," *Doctoral Dissertation,* UCLA, 1959.
11. Smith, W. E., "Various Optimizers for Single-Stage Production," *Naval Research Logistics Quarterly,* No. 3, pp. 59–66, 1956.

REVIEW QUESTIONS

1. What is the nature of our objective in controlling production levels?

2. Compare the expected results when a production control rule is used with reaction rates of 100, 50, 10, and 5 per cent.

3. In controlling production levels, what are the two main variables that are under our control?

4. What is the general relationship between reaction rates and the frequency of adjustment of production levels? Which combinations produce high costs of production fluctuation? High costs of reserve inventories?

5. How can the mathematical statements 1 and 2 on pages 482 and 483 help to determine the best reaction rate to use in a specific situation?

6. Make a complete analysis of the four systems of control used in the Hibernian Co. case, checking all calculations, to show exactly where the different systems have relative advantages and disadvantages.

7. What is a dispatching decision rule? In the simulation of decision rules discussed in this chapter, which rules yielded the best results in terms of early versus late orders, labor utilization, and inventory carrying cost?

8. What is the nature of the "shortest operation rule"? What are its advantages and disadvantages?

9. Compare the dispatching function in a job shop and in a flow shop.

10. Compare the kinds of plans which must be made at the four levels indicated, that is, long-range plans, intermediate-range plans, short-range plans for the immediate period ahead, and automatic dispatching decision rules. What is the role of inventories at each stage?

11. Discuss the validity of the economic lot size concept.

part VIII

SIMULATION MODELS

18

Simulation Models

Simulation models of operations systems have been growing rapidly and promise to become a dominant technique for assisting management in the decision-making process for day-to-day problems, as well as for comparing basic alternatives of operating policy. With simulation models, we can determine the effects of dozens of alternate policies without tampering with the actual physical system. The result is that we do not risk upsetting the existing system without prior assurance that the changes contemplated will be beneficial. In a very real sense then, the common reference to simulation as management's laboratory is true.

Business and industry have already made important applications of the simulation technique, ranging from models of relatively simple waiting line situations, to models of integrated systems of production. For example, Warren Alberts of United Air Lines reports a model of an air line maintenance facility in which 100 days of operation are simulated in less than 12 minutes of computer time (17). Brown discusses a general purpose inventory controls simulator (17). The simulator makes it possible to evaluate customer service, the number of orders placed, the production workload, and the total investment for the comparison of alternate systems of control. Feorene of Eastman Kodak Company has published reports of a machine maintenance simulation which makes it possible to determine the optimum number of maintenance mechanics for various conditions (7). When Rowe was with the General Electric Company, he developed a job shop simulator and used it for evaluating alternate dispatch decision rules (19). Sprowls has developed a model of a simulated firm (22). Forrester has developed dynamic simulation models of production-distribution systems which show time-varying effects of changing market conditions and various alternate policies (8). Another important branch of applications of simulation has been in the development of management games. In management simulation games, the characteristics of a business, or some subsystem of a business are simulated. Individuals or teams then give the model inputs in the form of key decisions, and they determine the effects of these decisions through the simulation model. Through this gaming technique, years of decision-making experience can be collapsed into a few hours.

In general, simulation is useful in situations where mathematical analysis is either too complex or too costly. If a particular type of problem can be shown to be well represented by a mathematical model, the analytical approach will ordinarily be somewhat cheaper to follow. Quite often, however, we find situations where the problem faced is incredibly complex, because of a maze of interacting variables, or where the problem itself may be relatively simple in structure, but involves a projection of mathematical analysis into unknown areas. An example of the latter would be a simple waiting line model where the nature of the distributions of arrivals for service times do not fit the standard ones for which analytical solutions have been worked out. In such situations, we might spend a great deal of time attempting to work out a mathematical analysis for the specific empirical distribution, or may fail in this attempt. To simulate the unique problem, however, would be relatively simple. A simulation model may be constructed which represents the essential features of the system under study. Then, by "driving" the simulation model with input data, we may observe the reactions of the system components and of the system output. As with any model, the ultimate value of the simulation model is determined by how well it predicts behavior of the system under study. One of the advantages of simulation models, however, is their relative flexibility in adaptation to the requirements of the real system. Simulation, then, often provides a bypass for difficult or impossible mathematical analysis. For the complex problems to which we have referred, simulation is by no means a cheap mode of analysis. It does, however, provide an approach to many problems which could not be attacked by other known techniques.

In our discussion we first introduce Monte Carlo methods that make it possible to introduce statistical variation into simulation models. This also serves to introduce the general concepts of simulation modeling. A number of applications are discussed in this chapter to illustrate Monte Carlo methods as well as the general simulation technique. In Chapter 19 we consider large-scale system simulation for both static and dynamic situations. These larger-scale models may or may not require Monte Carlo techniques. They are simply larger in scale, more complex, and in the case of dynamic models, they have some special features of considerable interest for operations management. In Chapter 20, we discuss operational gaming. Here, we develop two hand-computed games which can be played in the classroom, and discuss the nature of some games which are more complex and require the services of a computer.

SIMULATED SAMPLING

Simulated sampling, known generally as Monte Carlo, makes it possible to introduce data into a system which have the statistical properties of some empirical or other distribution. If the model involves the flow of orders according to the actual demand distribution experienced, we can simulate the "arrival" of an order by Monte Carlo sampling from the actual distribution, so that the timing and flow of orders in the simulated system parallels the actual experience. If we are studying the breakdown of a certain machine due to bearing failure, we can simulate typical breakdown times through simulated sampling from the distribution of bearing lives. Let us take an example to illustrate how simulated sampling is achieved.

Suppose we are dealing with the maintenance of a bank of thirty machines, and, initially, we wish to estimate what level of service can be maintained by one mechanic. We can see that we have the elements of a waiting-line situation, with machine breakdowns representing arrivals, the mechanic being the service facility, and repair time representing service or processing time. Of course, if the distributions of breakdown and service times followed the negative exponential, the simplest procedure would be to use the formulas and calculate the average time that a machine waits, the mechanic's idle time, etc. We can see by inspection of Figures 1 and 2 that the distributions are not similar to the negative exponential, so that we decide to simulate. Our procedure is as follows:

1. *Determine the distributions of time between breakdowns and service time.* If they were not available directly, we would have to make a study to determine these distributions, or, hopefully, records of the breakdown and repair of machines may be available from which the distributions may be constructed. Figures 1 and 2 show

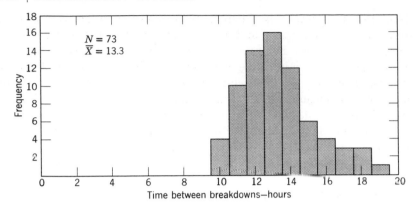

Figure 1. Frequency distribution of the time between breakdowns for 30 machines.

the distributions of breakdowns and repair time for 73 breakdowns, and will be the basis for our simulation.

2. *Convert the frequency distributions to cumulative probability distributions (see Figures 3 and 4).* This conversion is accomplished by summing the frequencies that are less than or equal to each breakdown or repair time and plotting them. The cumulative frequencies are then converted to per cents by assigning the number 100 to the maximum value. As an example, let us take Figure 1 and convert it to the cumulative distribution of Figure 3. Beginning at the lowest value for breakdown time, 10 hours, there are four occurrences. Four

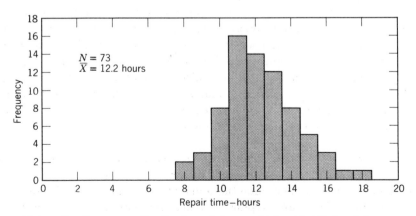

Figure 2. Frequency distribution of the repair time for 73 breakdowns.

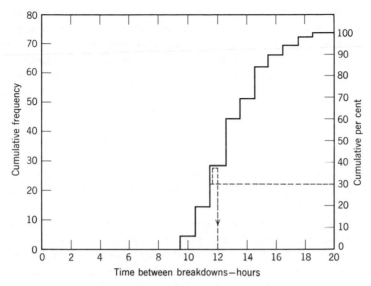

Figure 3. Cumulative distribution of breakdown times.

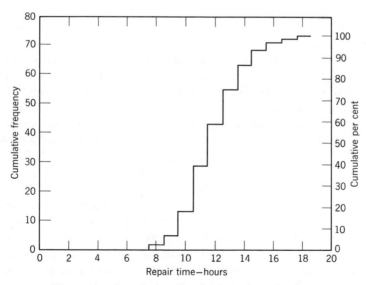

Figure 4. Cumulative distribution of repair times.

is plotted on the cumulative chart for the breakdown time, 10 hours. For the breakdown time, 11 hours, there were 10 occurrences, but there were 14 occurrences of 11 hours or less, so the value 14 is plotted for 11 hours. For the breakdown time, 12 hours, there were 14 occurrences recorded, but there were 28 occurrences of breakdowns for 12 hours or less. Figure 3 was constructed from Figure 1 by proceeding in this way. When the cumulative frequency distribution was completed, a cumulative per cent scale was constructed on the right of Figure 3 by assigning the number 100 to the maximum value, 73, and dividing the resulting scale into 10 equal parts. This results in a cumulative probability distribution. From Figure 3 we can say that 100 per cent of the breakdown time values were 19 hours or less; 99 per cent were 18 hours or less, etc. Figure 4 was constructed from Figure 2 in a comparable way.

3. *Sample at random from the cumulative distributions to determine specific breakdown times and repair times to use in simulating the repair operation.* We do this by selecting numbers between 0 and 100 at random (representing probabilities or per cents). The random numbers could be selected by any random process, such as drawing numbered chips from a box. The easiest way is to use a table of random numbers, such as those included in Table IV of Appendix *D*.

The random numbers are used to enter the cumulative distributions to obtain time values. An example is shown in Figure 3. The random number 30 is shown to select for us a breakdown time of 12 hours. We can now see the purpose behind the conversion of the original distribution to a cumulative distribution. Only one breakdown time can now be associated with a given random number. In the original distribution, two values would result because of the bell shape of the curve. By using random numbers to obtain breakdown time values in this fashion from Figure 3, we will obtain breakdown time values in proportion to the probability of occurrence indicated by the original frequency distribution. As a matter of fact, at this point we can construct a table of random numbers that select certain breakdown times. For example, reading from Figure 3, the random numbers 6 through 19 give us a breakdown time of 11 hours, etc. This is the same as saying that 5 per cent of the time we would obtain a value of 10 hours, 14 per cent of the time we would obtain a breakdown time of 11 hours, etc. Table I shows the random number equivalents for Figures 3 and 4.

Sampling from either the cumulative distributions of Figures 3 and 4 or from Table I will now give breakdown times and repair

TABLE I. **Random Numbers Used To Draw Breakdown Times and Repair Times in Proportion to the Occurrence Probabilities of the Original Distributions**

Breakdown Times		Repair Times	
These Random Numbers →	Select These Breakdown Times	These Random Numbers →	Select These Repair Times
↓	↓	↓	↓
1–5	10 hours	1–3	8 hours
6–19	11	4–7	9
20–38	12	8–18	10
39–60	13	19–40	11
61–77	14	41–59	12
78–85	15	60–75	13
86–90	16	76–86	14
91–95	17	87–93	15
96–99	18	94–97	16
100	19	98–99	17
		100	18

times in proportion to the original distributions, just as if actual breakdowns and repairs were happening. Table II gives a sample of 20 breakdown and repair times determined in this way.

4. *Simulate the actual operation of breakdowns and repairs.* The structure of what we wish to do in simulating the repair operation is shown by the flow chart of Figure 5. This operation involves the selection of a breakdown time, and determining whether or not the mechanic is available. If the mechanic is not available, the machine must wait until he is, and we may compute that wait time easily. If the mechanic is available, the question is, did the mechanic have to wait? If he did, we compute the mechanic's idle time. If the mechanic did not have to wait, we select a repair time and proceed according to the flow chart, repeating the overall process as many times as desired, providing a mechanism for stopping the procedure when the desired number of cycles has been completed.

The simulation of the repair operation is shown in Table III. Here we have used the breakdown times and repair times selected by random numbers in Table II. We assume that time begins when the first machine breaks down and cumulate breakdown time from that point. The repair time required for the first breakdown was 15 hours, and since this is the first occurrence in our record, neither the machine nor the mechanic had to wait. The second breakdown

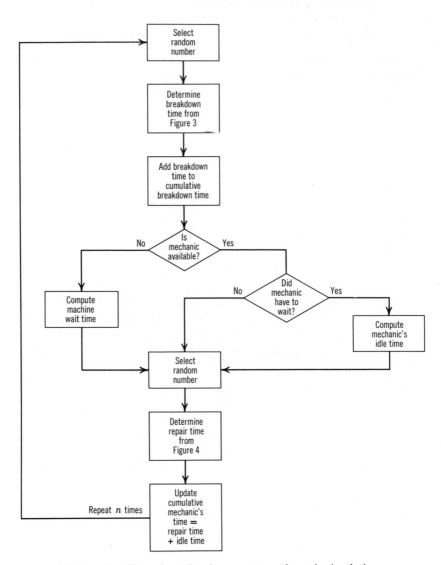

Figure 5. Flow chart showing structure of repair simulation.

**TABLE II. Simulated Sample of Twenty Breakdown
and Repair Times**

Breakdown Times		Repair Times	
Random Number	Breakdown Time from Figure 3	Random Number	Repair Time from Figure 4
83	15	91	15
97	18	4	9
88	16	72	13
12	11	12	10
22	12	30	11
16	11	32	11
24	12	91	15
64	14	29	11
37	12	33	11
62	14	8	10
52	13	25	11
9	11	74	13
64	14	97	16
74	14	70	13
15	11	15	10
47	13	43	12
86	16	42	12
79	15	25	11
43	13	71	13
35	12	14	10

occurred at 18 hours, but the mechanic was available at the end of 15 hours, so he waited 3 hours for the next breakdown to occur. We proceed in this fashion, adding and subtracting, according to the requirements of the simulation model to obtain the record of Table III. The summary at the bottom of Table III shows that for the sample of twenty breakdowns, total machine waiting time was 11 hours, and total mechanic's idle time was 26 hours. To obtain a realistic picture we would have to use a much larger sample. Using the same data on breakdown time and repair time distributions, 1000 runs using an IBM 7090 Computer yielded 15.9 per cent machine wait time and 7.6 per cent mechanic's idle time.

If a computer were programmed to simulate the repair operation, we would place the two cumulative distributions in the memory unit of the computer. Through the program, the computer would generate a random number and thereby select a breakdown time. By compar-

**TABLE III. Simulated Breakdown and Repair
for Twenty Breakdowns**

Time of Breakdown	Time Repair Begins	Time Repair Ends	Machine Wait Time	Repair Mechanics Idle Time
0	0	15	0	0
18	18	27	0	3
34	34	47	0	7
45	47	57	2	0
5/	57	68	0	0
68	68	70	0	0
80	80	95	0	1
94	95	106	1	0
106	106	117	0	0
120	120	130	0	3
133	133	144	0	3
144	144	157	0	0
158	158	174	0	1
172	174	187	2	0
183	187	197	4	0
196	197	209	1	0
212	212	224	0	3
227	227	238	0	3
240	240	253	0	2
252	253	263	1	—

Total machine wait time = 11 hours
Total mechanic's idle time = 26 hours

ing cumulative breakdown time with cumulative mechanic's time, the computer could determine whether or not the mechanic was available, and if he was available, whether or not he had to wait. The computations of machine wait time, or mechanic's idle time, would be routinely made, and the computer would be directed to select another random number, thereby determining a repair time. The other necessary computations could then be made, the computer holding in memory the resulting values. The cycle would then repeat as many times as directed, so that a large run could be made easily and with no more effort than a small run. When a computer is used the simulation model can become very realistic, reflecting all sorts of contingency situations which may be representative of the real problem. The following example of the simulation of optimal repair crew sizes is meant to show an application in a realistic situation.

EXAMPLES OF SIMULATION

Simulation of Optimal Repair Crew Size

Feorene (7) reports a study made of the Eastman Kodak Company of the size of repair crews. A group of twenty automatic machines were being maintained by a crew of six mechanics. Production forecasts indicated the need for two more machines to meet capacity needs, and this raised the question of whether or not the size of the repair crew should be enlarged. The basic structure of the simulation is parallel to the simple one presented previously; however, a new variable has been added, the number of mechanics. We will note that the specific conditions in effect are reflected in the data used and in the structure of the simulation model.

After careful study, the following data were gathered from the maintenance and down-time records available in the production department:

1. A breakdown-time distribution which showed the length of time that the machines would run before requiring service. Of course, this distribution determines the "arrivals" to the maintenance system. Figure 6 shows the breakdown-time distribution, and in this instance, the distribution happens to follow the negative exponential quite closely.

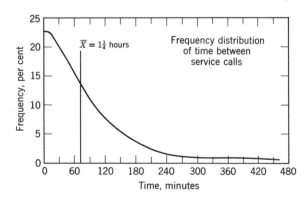

Figure 6. Breakdown time distribution for a bank of automatic machines. Adapted from O. J. Feorene, "The Gentle Art of Simulation," *Proceedings, Twelfth Annual Industrial Engineering Institute,* University of California, Berkeley-Los Angeles, 1960.

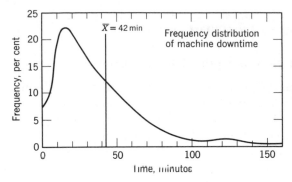

Figure 7. Service-time distribution for downtime calls. Adapted from O. J. Feorene, "The Gentle Art of Simulation," *Proceedings, Twelfth Annual Industrial Engineering Institute,* University of California, Berkeley-Los Angeles, 1960.

2. An analysis of records showed that two-thirds of the time, the machines could be serviced while they were operating and continuing to produce. The other third of the time, the machine had to be shut down while the repairs and adjustments were made. In this latter instance, the mechanic remained at the machine after it was functioning again in order to make final adjustments.

3. A distribution of the service time required when the machine was down, being serviced by the mechanic. This distribution is shown in Figure 7.

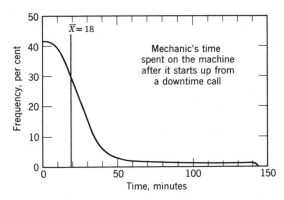

Figure 8. Run-in time distribution, the time spent by the mechanic after the machine starts up from a downtime call. Adapted from O. J. Feorene, "The Gentle Art of Simulation," *Proceedings, Twelfth Annual Industrial Engineering Institute,* University of California, Berkeley-Los Angeles, 1960.

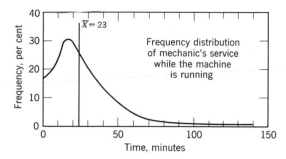

Figure 9. Service-time distribution for run calls. Adapted from O. J. Feorene, "The Gentle Art of Simulation," *Proceedings, Twelfth Annual Industrial Engineering Institute,* University of California, Berkeley-Los Angeles, 1960.

4. A distribution of the time spent by the mechanic with the machine after it had been started again, in order to make final adjustments and insure that it was ready for service. This is the mechanic's "run-in" time and is shown in Figure 8.

5. A distribution of the mechanic's service time in those instances in which the machine could be serviced while it was still operating (Figure 9). This is the mechanic's service time for the run-calls which represent 67 per cent of the cases.

The simulation. Figure 10 shows the structure of the simulation model used. Note the five places in the model where Monte Carlo methods of sampling from the empirical distributions have been used.

The simulation model was programmed for an IBM 705 Computer and simulation runs were made for different levels of production (that is, number of machines in operation), each time computing costs for different numbers of mechanics servicing the system. The incremental costs were those associated with machine down-time and maintenance labor cost. One of the curves for twenty-two machines available is shown in Figure 11, and we note that even with the two additional machines, the minimum cost is achieved with only four mechanics instead of the six used prior to the study. Feorene estimates that the total cost of the project for analysis and programming was less than $2000. The IBM 705 Computer required only 15 minutes to simulate all of the alternatives. The recommendations indicated by simulation were installed and the results vindicated the model. Obviously, the study represented an immediate net gain for the company, and in addition provided a model which could be used again to evaluate future projected loads.

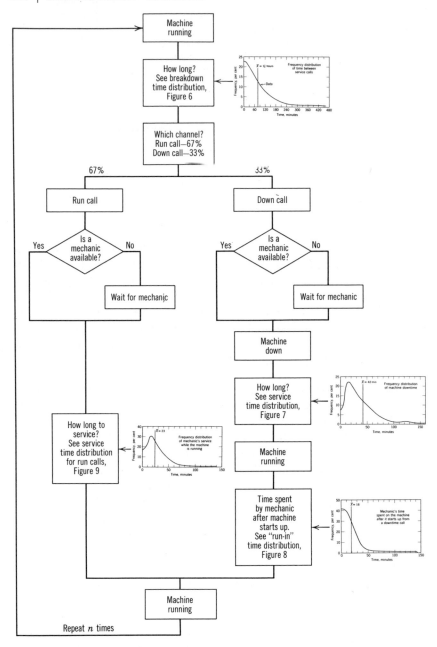

Figure 10. Structure of simulation model for the determination of optimal repair crew size. Adapted from O. J. Feorene, "The Gentle Art of Simulation," *Proceedings, Twelfth Annual Industrial Engineering Institute,* University of California, Berkeley-Los Angeles, 1960.

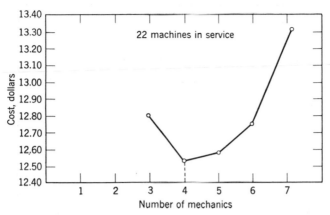

Figure 11. Curve of cost versus number of mechanics in repair crew for 22 machines in service. Adapted from O. J. Feorene, "The Gentle Art of Simulation," *Proceedings, Twelfth Annual Industrial Engineering Institute,* University of California, Berkeley-Los Angeles, 1960.

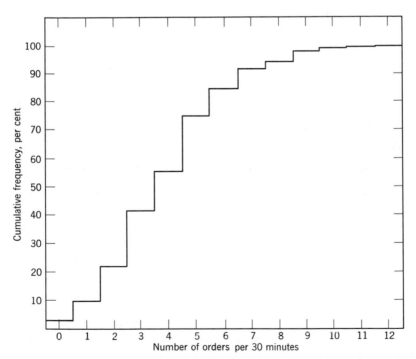

Figure 12. Cumulative order distribution for mixed chemicals. Adapted from O. J. Feorene, "The Gentle Art of Simulation," *Proceedings, Twelfth Annual Industrial Engineering Institute,* University of California, Berkeley-Los Angeles, 1960.

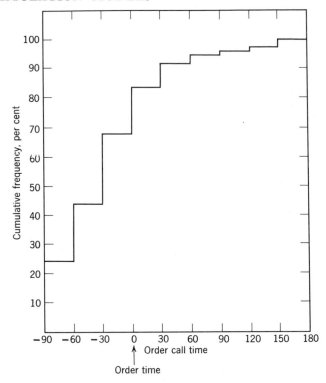

Figure 13. Cumulative call-time distribution. Adapted from O. J. Feorene, "The Gentle Art of Simulation," *Proceedings, Twelfth Annual Industrial Engineering Institute,* University of California, Berkeley-Los Angeles, 1960.

Simulation of a Mixed Chemicals Distribution System

Another application carried out at Eastman Kodak Company (7) involved a department that mixed chemicals for use in two general locations in nearby buildings. The general pattern was that orders were placed with the mixed chemicals department by the using departments, ordinarily to be delivered within 1 hour because of close scheduling of a series of operations in the using departments. A marshaling area was set aside in the mixed chemicals department for hand trucks loaded with filled orders waiting for call from the using departments. Although the using department had placed an order for a specific time, there was considerable variation from the order time in the actual call time, as we shall see. After being called for, the order was delivered to the using department by means of the hand truck, so that the truck was unavailable for an additional period of time before it was returned to the mixed chemicals department for reuse. This trucking time also had considerable variation and was different for the two using departments. At any given moment, there were as many as thirty-three hand trucks in the system.

The problem. A projected increase in production requirements seemed to indicate the need for additional trucks as well as an increase in the size of the marshaling area. Considerable congestion had already developed with the existing system. The real question which evolved was, how many trucks are necessary to operate the system?

The simulation. To simulate the system, the following data were gathered:

1. A distribution of the order rates. Figure 12 shows a cumulative distribution of the number of orders placed per 30-minute interval.
2. The distribution of order-call time. Figure 13 shows a cumulative distribution of call times, indicating that orders might be called

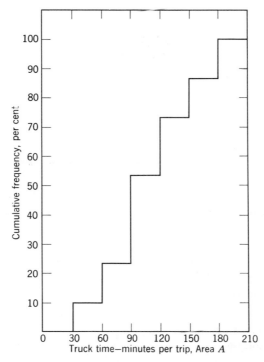

Figure 14. Cumulative truck-time distribution for Area *A*. Adapted from O. J. Feorene, "The Gentle Art of Simulation," *Proceedings, Twelfth Annual Industrial Engineering Institute,* University of California, Berkeley-Los Angeles, 1960.

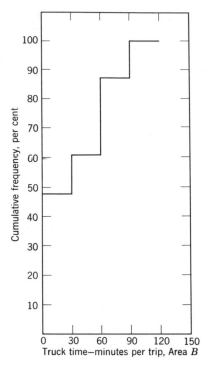

Figure 15. Cumulative truck-time distribution for Area B. Adapted from O. J. Feorene, "The Gentle Art of Simulation," *Proceedings, Twelfth Annual Industrial Engineering Institute,* University of California, Berkeley-Los Angeles, 1960.

for as much as $1\frac{1}{2}$ hours before the order time, or as much as 3 hours after the order time.

3. The truck destinations. An analysis of truck destinations revealed that **58** per cent of the orders were for area A and **42** per cent for area B.

4. A distribution of the time spent for a round trip by trucks with orders going to each of the two using departments. Figures **14** and **15** show cumulative distributions of truck time for areas A and B respectively.

The system was then simulated for various numbers of trucks available. Figure **16** shows the simple structure of the simulation. Simulated sampling takes place at five points in the system: the determination of orders from Figure **12**, the determination of the destination of orders, the determination of call time from Figure

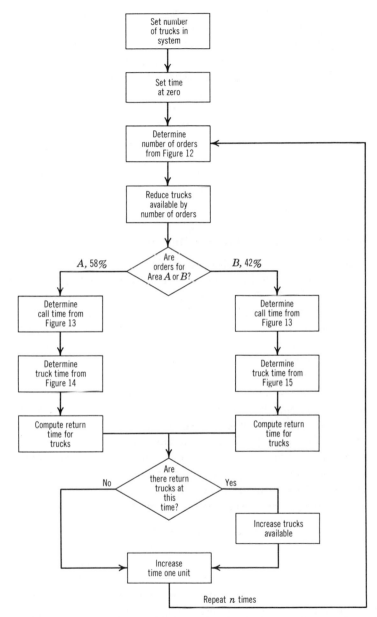

Figure 16. Structure of mixed chemicals simulation. Adapted from O. J. Feorene, "The Gentle Art of Simulation," *Proceedings, Twelfth Annual Industrial Engineering Institute,* University of California, Berkeley-Los Angeles, 1960.

13, and the determination of truck times from either Figure 14 or 15, depending on destination. In simulating the operation of the system, it is necessary to work trucks through the system, depending on order rates, destinations, call times, and truck times, so that we may keep track of the number of trucks being used and the number of trucks available for use. The simulation indicated that the existing production level could be met with twenty-four trucks in the system, nine less than the original figure. This reduction in the number of trucks eliminated the congestion in the aisles and marshaling area, and eliminated the need for an expansion of the marshaling area which was originally thought to be necessary. Also, the model could be used to estimate needs for other production levels if conditions were to change.

Simulation of Steel-Making Operations

A somewhat more complex model is illustrated by the simulation of six open-hearth furnaces and related operations by the steel company of Wales Limited, as reported by Neate and Dacey (16). The simulation study was initiated following a trial carried out on one open-hearth furnace using the new technique of enriching preheated combustion air with oxygen during the charging period. The analysis for the trial period had shown that the use of oxygen enrichment had caused an increase of about 20 per cent in the production rate of the furnace. The possibility of increasing overall production by using oxygen enrichment prompted the desire for an estimate of the production capability when using the technique on all furnaces. It was unlikely that a proportionate increase could be obtained because of the limitations imposed by ancillary equipment and by congestion delays. As we shall see, there is considerable interaction between the operation of the six furnaces because of limited crane facilities, teeming (ingot pouring) facilities, and the number of unpredictable delays.

Layout and process. Figure 17 shows the general layout of the area covered by the study. The six open-hearth furnaces are charged with solid materials and hot metal from the furnace bay and are tapped, and ingots poured at one of the four platforms on the casting bay side. Figure 18 shows a simplified flow process chart for the operation of one furnace. When a furnace is ready to tap, the first procedure is to obtain a crane to position the ladle and remove the molten steel when tapping is complete. At this point, there may be a delay if the available cranes are already in use in connection with other furnaces or with the pouring of ingot molds, or

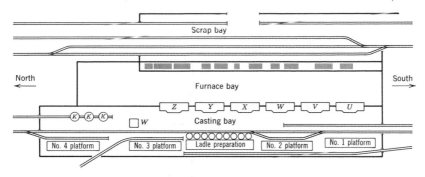

Figure 17. Layout of furnace and casting bays. From R. Neate and W. J. Dacey, "A Simulation of Melting Shop Operations by Means of a Computer," *Process Control and Automation,* July, 1958, pp. 264–272.

other activities. The occurrence of this delay is random, of course, and depends on the interaction of many factors in the overall operation of the shop.

After the furnace is tapped, it must be prepared for a new charge. This process is called "fettling," and the time required varies according to a distribution. Once the furnace is prepared, a charging machine must be obtained and here again, a delay can occur if the chargers are in use. Once the charger is obtained, however, a second delay called a "scrap delay" may occur if there is not an ample supply of full-scrap boxes in position. If scrap material is available, however, the charging process begins. If after a period of charging and before the solids charge is complete, the melter considers it undesirable to add any more scrap to the furnace, there is an "assimilation delay" during which the furnace digests the scrap already charged into it. Following the assimilation delay, it may be that a charger is again unavailable, in which case a second charger delay may occur. The charge of solid material is then completed. A delay dictated by the process now occurs before hot metal can be added. When the time arrives for the addition of hot metal, a crane must be obtained, and a second crane delay may occur. The hot metal is then added to the furnace, and the steel-making process continues through a melt time and a refining time, both of which are variable. At the end of the refining time, the furnace is again ready to tap.

During the operations of the furnace just described, the casting bay and its associated equipment are used at two different times. First, the furnace is tapped into a large ladle, and this ladle is moved

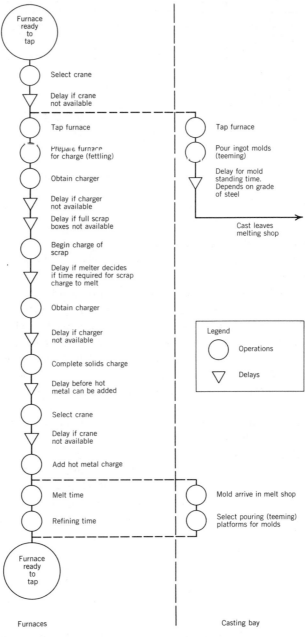

Figure 18. Basic flow process chart for melting shop operations. Based on R. Neate and W. J. Dacey, "A Simulation of Melting Shop Operations by Means of a Computer," *Process Control and Automation*, July 1958, pp. 264–272.

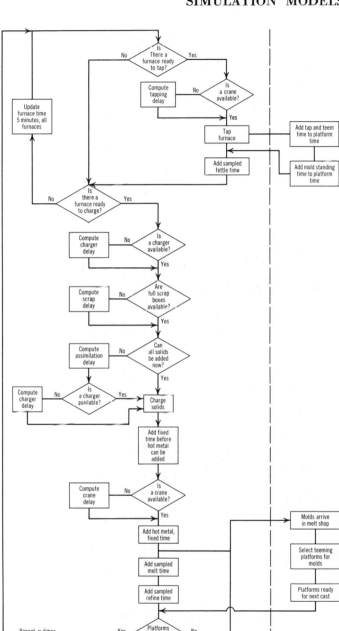

Figure 19. Structure of simulation for melting shop operations. Based on R. Neate and W. J. Dacey, "A Simulation of Melting Shop Operations by Means of a Computer," *Process Control and Automation,* July 1958, pp. 264–272.

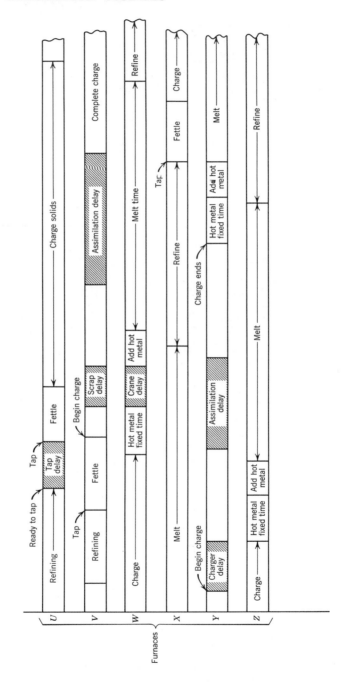

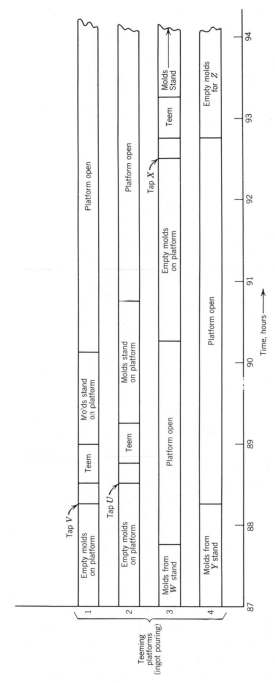

Figure 20. Simulation chart for 7 hours of operation. Based on R. Neate and W. J. Dacey, "A Simulation of Melting Shop Operations by Means of a Computer," *Process Control and Automation*, July 1958, pp. **264–272**.

to one of the teeming platforms to pour ingot molds. These molds stand on the platform for a period of time, depending on the grade of steel, and finally the entire cast is moved out of the melting shop. Second, prior to the time of tapping, empty molds are brought into the shop and placed in one of the four platform positions.

Simulation. To simulate the operation of the melting shop, it is necessary to take account of all of the furnace times which are variable through the Monte Carlo sampling process. Looking at the simulation flow chart of Figure 19, these Monte Carlo samplings occur when determining fettle times, melt times, and refine times. The delays in the system are computed internally within the simulation model. A 5-minute time unit was adopted for the model, and the basic simulation flow chart revolves around two questions which are asked in sequence at each 5-minute interval. The first question is, "Is there a furnace ready to tap?" If there is, the sequence of simulated operations of crane selection, furnace tapping, and fettling must be accounted for. If there is no furnace ready to tap, the second question is, "Is there a furnace ready to charge?" If there is a furnace ready to charge, the entire sequence of simulated operations following must be accounted for, computing the delays if they are appropriate, adding in the fixed and simulated sampled times as required to update furnace time for the particular furnace which is being charged. If the answer to the second question is no, the system updates all six furnace times by the next 5-minute interval and asks the two questions again. The procedure is repeated the desired number of times through the computer program and stopped automatically when completed.

Figure 20 shows a graphical simulation chart for 7 hours of simulated operation. In essence, a time record is being kept for each of the six furnaces and the four teeming platforms. When the model detects that a furnace is ready to tap, or ready to be charged, appropriate times are added to the time record for that furnace. Some of these times are based on Monte Carlo sampling, such as the melt time; some are fixed times for each occurrence, such as the time for addition of hot metal; and some of the times are computed, such as the delays waiting for equipment. The output of the simulation system yields information indicating the simulated output of the shop for the period of simulation—found by adding the number of casts— and the values of the various delays in the system. With the model, proposed changes in operating procedures can be evaluated prior to installation. For example, what would be the effect on output of

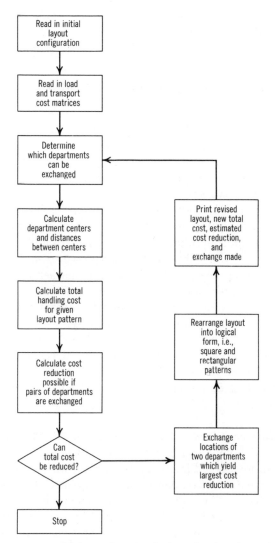

Figure 21. Basic flow diagram for simulating the location of facilities and selecting only alternate layouts which represent improved material handling costs. Based on G. C. Armour and E. S. Buffa, "A Heuristic Algorithm and Simulation Approach to Relative Location of Facilities," *Management Science,* Vol. 9, No. 2, January 1963.

increasing the number of cranes, chargers, or other limiting ancillary equipment? The effects of such changes are not immediately obvious because of the complex interaction of so many factors in the operating system. The simulation model, however, could be used to evaluate their effect.

Simulation Solution to the Determination of Relative Location of Facilities

Recall that on pp. 44–51 we discussed a graphical approach to the determination of the relative location of physical facilities. A review of that material at this time will provide an orientation to the basic nature of the relative location problem. Recall that the graphical solution worked reasonably well for problems where the number of departments was relatively small and the flow patterns between departments not too complex. When the problem becomes complex, the graphical solution breaks down rapidly because of the difficulty of seeing which changes in location will result in net improvement. In addition, the graphical solution neither accounts for differences in material-handling cost between different departments because of different handling systems, nor of different area requirements for the different departments in the best way.

A computer program has been developed which simulates the cost of alternate layouts and progressively selects only layouts that represent improved total material-handling cost. Figure 21 shows a vastly simplified flow diagram which describes the basic structure of the program.

Input data required. The program requires three types of input data: an initial layout configuration, a load matrix, and a material-handling cost matrix. Figure 22 represents an initial layout for a plant with twenty departments, with physical dimensions of 200 feet by 300 feet. The initial solution is completely arbitrary. It is arranged so that each line is represented by one IBM punched card. The card is punched with the sequence of letters, for example, line 1 would be punched, *AAAAAABBBLLLLLLL*, etc. When this sequence of IBM cards is printed, it takes on the configuration of a block layout as shown in Figure 22. The lines separating the various groupings of letters in Figure 22 have been added to show more clearly the relative sizes and shapes of departmental areas. Each character represents 100 square feet for the particular problem of Figure 22.

Location Pattern   Iteration 0

```
     1  2  3  4  5  6  7  8  9  10 11 12 13 14 15 16 17 18 19 20 21 22 23 24 25 26 27 28 29 30
 1 | A  A  A  A  A  A | B  B  B | L  L  L  L  L  L  L | S  S  S  S  S  S  S  S | W  W  W  W  W  W
 2 | A  A  A  A  A  A | B  B  B | L  L  L  L  L  L  L | S  S  S  S  S  S  S  S | W  W  W  W  W  W
 3 | A  A  A  A  A [ B  B  B  B | L  L  L  L  L  L  L | S  S  S  S  S  S  S  S | W  W  W  W  W  W
 4 | A  A  A  A  A  A| B  B  B  B | L  L  L  L  L  L  L | S  S  S  S  S  S  S  S | W  W  W  W  W  W
 5 | A  A  A  A  A  A| B  B  B  B | L  L  L  L  L  L  L | S  S  S  S  S  S  S  S | W  W  W  W  W  W
 6 | C  C  C  C  C  C | D  D  D | L  L  L  L  L  L  L | S  S  S  S  S  S  S  S | W  W  W  W  W  W
 7 | C  C  C  C  C  C | D  D  D | L  L  L  L  L  L | G  G  G | S  S  S  S  S  S  S | W  W  W  W  W  W
 8 | C  C  C  C  C  D  D  D  D | L  L  L  L  L  L | G  G  G | S  S  S  S  S  S  S | W  W  W  W  W  W
 9 | C  C  C  C  C  D  D  D  D | L  L  L  L  L  L | G  G  G | S  S  S  S  S  S  S | W  W  W  W  W  W
10 | C  C  C  C  C  D  D  D  D | N  N  N  N  N  N | H  H  H | T  T  T  T  T  T  T  T  T  T  T  T
11 | E  E  E  E  E  E | F  F  F | N  N  N  N  N  N | H  H  H | T  T  T  T  T  T  T  T  T  T  T  T
12 | E  E  E  E  E  E | F  F  F | N  N  N  N  N  N | H  H  H | T  T  T  T  T  T  T  T  T  T  T  T
13 | E  E  E  E  E  E | F  F  F | P  P  P  P  P  P  P | J  J  J | T  T  T  T  T  T  T  T  T  T  T  T
14 | K  K  K  K  K  K | F  F  F | P  P  P  P  P  P  P | J  J  J | T  T  T  T  T  T  T  T  T  T  T  T
15 | K  K  K  K  K  K | F  F  F | P  P  P  P  P  P  P | J  J  J | U  U  U  U  U  U | T  T  T  T | V  V
16 | K  K  K  K  K  K | F  F  F | P  P  P  P  P  P  P | R  R  R | U  U  U  U  U  U | V  V  V  V  V
17 | K  K  K  K  K  K | M  M  M  M  M  M | R  R  R  R  R  R | U  U  U  U  U  U | V  V  V  V  V
18 | M  M  M  M  M  M | M  M  M  M  M  M | R  R  R  R  R  R | U  U  U  U  U  U | V  V  V  V  V
19 | M  M  M  M  M  M | M  M  M  M  M  M | R  R  R  R  R  R | U  U  U  U  U  U | V  V  V  V  V
20 | M  M  M  M  M  M | M  M  M  M  M  M | R  R  R  R  R  R | U  U  U  U  U  U | V  V  V  V  V
```

Total cost $10,164.34   Estimated cost reduction 0   MOVEA   MOVEB

Figure 22. Initial relative location pattern, iteration 0. Scale: one matrix element equals 100 square feet. Each row and column equals 10 feet. From G. C. Armour and E. S. Buffa, "A Heuristic Algorithm and Simulation Approach to Relative Location of Facilities," *Management Science*, Vol. 9, No. 2, January 1963.

Figure 23 shows the load matrix. This is simply a tabulation of the number of loads which flow between all combinations of departments. The matrix is symmetrical on its main diagonal; for example, the flow from A to B is shown as 120.0 and this is also shown as the flow from B to A. This information could be summarized from records of past orders, and for very large plants it would probably represent a random sample of orders.

Figure 24 shows the interdepartmental material-handling cost per unit load per each 100 feet moved. For this particular example, three methods of material handling were used: manual truck, fork-life truck, and low-bed lift truck, with respective costs of $0.026, $0.015, and $0.012 per unit load per 100 feet. In some instances, figures other than these appear in Figure 24, and these are weighted averages of the base figures and indicate that more than one method of material handling is in use between the departments concerned.

	A	B	C	D	E	F	G	H	J	K	L	M	N	P	R	S	T	U	V	W
A	0.	120.0	80.0	0.	0.	0.	0.	0.	0.	40.0	80.0	0.	0.	80.0	0.	0.	0.	0.	0.	0.
B	120.0	0.	80.0	1630.0	30.0	0.	930.0	0.	80.0	90.0	0.	0.	0.	0.	0.	0.	0.	0.	460.0	0.
C	80.0	80.0	0.	0.	0.	130.0	0.	0.	210.0	260.0	0.	0.	0.	870.0	0.	0.	0.	0.	910.0	0.
D	0.	1630.0	0.	0.	60.0	380.0	500.0	0.	130.0	0.	0.	70.0	0.	0.	0.	0.	0.	100.0	1050.0	0.
E	0.	30.0	0.	60.0	0.	0.	150.0	90.0	0.	60.0	0.	0.	0.	0.	90.0	0.	0.	0.	0.	0.
F	0.	0.	130.0	380.0	0.	0.	410.0	0.	0.	0.	0.	30.0	0.	0.	0.	0.	0.	70.0	0.	0.
G	0.	930.0	0.	500.0	150.0	410.0	0.	1600.0	0.	110.0	0.	0.	0.	60.0	0.	0.	0.	0.	0.	250.0
H	0.	0.	0.	0.	90.0	0.	1600.0	0.	0.	0.	0.	0.	40.0	0.	0.	0.	0.	0.	0.	2230.0
J	0.	80.0	210.0	130.0	0.	0.	0.	0.	0.	0.	0.	0.	500.0	0.	0.	0.	500.0	0.	500.0	0.
K	40.0	90.0	260.0	0.	60.0	0.	110.0	0.	0.	0.	30.0	800.0	0.	1240.0	160.0	0.	350.0	90.0	0.	0.
L	80.0	0.	0.	0.	0.	0.	0.	0.	0.	30.0	0.	150.0	0.	200.0	80.0	0.	1500.0	0.	350.0	0.
M	0.	0.	0.	70.0	0.	30.0	0.	0.	0.	800.0	150.0	0.	0.	0.	110.0	0.	1000.0	0.	560.0	0.
N	0.	0.	0.	0.	0.	0.	0.	40.0	500.0	0.	0.	0.	0.	500.0	40.0	500.0	0.	60.0	0.	0.
P	80.0	0.	870.0	0.	0.	0.	60.0	0.	0.	1240.0	200.0	0.	500.0	0.	650.0	0.	0.	60.0	0.	0.
R	0.	0.	0.	0.	90.0	0.	0.	0.	0.	160.0	80.0	110.0	40.0	650.0	0.	0.	350.0	0.	0.	0.
S	0.	0.	0.	0.	0.	0.	0.	0.	0.	0.	0.	0.	500.0	0.	0.	0.	1000.0	0.	0.	0.
T	0.	0.	0.	0.	0.	0.	0.	0.	500.0	350.0	1500.0	1000.0	0.	0.	350.0	1000.0	0.	0.	0.	0.
U	0.	0.	0.	100.0	0.	70.0	0.	0.	0.	90.0	0.	0.	60.0	60.0	0.	0.	0.	0.	310.0	0.
V	0.	460.0	910.0	1050.0	0.	0.	0.	0.	500.0	0.	350.0	560.0	0.	0.	0.	0.	0.	310.0	0.	0.
W	0.	0.	0.	0.	0.	0.	250.0	2230.0	0.	0.	0.	0.	0.	0.	0.	0.	0.	0.	0.	0.

Figure 23. Interdepartment product flow in tens of unit loads per annum. From G. C. Armour and E. S. Buffa, "A Heuristic Algorithm and Simulation Approach to the Relative Location of Facilities," *Management Science*, Vol. 9, No. 2, January 1963.

	A	B	C	D	E	F	G	H	J	K	L	M	N	P	R	S	T	U	V	W
A	0.	0.015	0.015	0.	0.	0.	0.	0.	0.	0.026	0.014	0.	0.	0.015	0.	0.	0.	0.	0.	0.
B	0.015	0.	0.012	0.015	0.026	0.	0.015	0.015	0.015	0.015	0.	0.	0.	0.	0.	0.	0.	0.	0.015	0.
C	0.015	0.012	0.	0.	0.	0.017	0.	0.015	0.015	0.015	0.	0.	0.	0.015	0.	0.	0.	0.	0.015	0.
D	0.	0.015	0.	0.	0.018	0.015	0.015	0.018	0.	0.	0.	0.020	0.	0.	0.	0.	0.	0.015	0.015	0.
E	0.	0.026	0.	0.018	0.	0.	0.015	0.015	0.018	0.026	0.	0.	0.	0.	0.015	0.	0.	0.	0.	0.
F	0.	0.	0.017	0.015	0.	0.	0.015	0.	0.	0.	0.	0.015	0.	0.	0.	0.	0.	0.015	0.	0.
G	0.	0.015	0.	0.015	0.015	0.015	0.	0.015	0.	0.017	0.	0.	0.	0.016	0.	0.	0.	0.015	0.	0.015
H	0.	0.015	0.015	0.018	0.015	0.	0.015	0.	0.	0.	0.	0.	0.015	0.	0.	0.	0.	0.	0.015	0.015
J	0.	0.015	0.015	0.	0.018	0.	0.	0.	0.	0.	0.	0.	0.	0.	0.	0.015	0.015	0.	0.	0.
K	0.026	0.015	0.015	0.	0.026	0.	0.017	0.	0.	0.	0.012	0.015	0.	0.	0.	0.	0.	0.	0.015	0.
L	0.014	0.	0.	0.	0.	0.	0.	0.	0.	0.012	0.	0.015	0.	0.	0.	0.	0.	0.	0.015	0.
M	0.	0.	0.	0.020	0.	0.015	0.	0.	0.	0.015	0.015	0.	0.	0.	0.	0.	0.015	0.	0.015	0.
N	0.	0.	0.	0.	0.	0.	0.	0.015	0.	0.	0.	0.	0.	0.016	0.026	0.012	0.	0.	0.	0.
P	0.015	0.	0.015	0.	0.	0.	0.016	0.	0.	0.	0.	0.	0.016	0.	0.015	0.	0.	0.	0.	0.
R	0.	0.	0.	0.	0.015	0.	0.	0.	0.	0.	0.	0.	0.026	0.015	0.	0.012	0.	0.	0.	0.
S	0.	0.	0.	0.	0.	0.	0.	0.	0.015	0.	0.	0.	0.012	0.	0.012	0.	0.012	0.	0.	0.
T	0.	0.	0.	0.	0.	0.	0.	0.	0.015	0.	0.	0.015	0.	0.	0.	0.012	0.	0.	0.015	0.
U	0.	0.	0.	0.015	0.	0.015	0.015	0.	0.	0.	0.	0.	0.	0.	0.	0.	0.	0.	0.015	0.
V	0.	0.015	0.015	0.015	0.	0.	0.	0.015	0.	0.015	0.015	0.015	0.	0.	0.	0.	0.015	0.015	0.	0.
W	0.	0.	0.	0.	0.	0.	0.015	0.015	0.	0.	0.	0.	0.	0.	0.	0.	0.	0.	0.	0.

Figure 24. Interdepartment material handling cost per unit load per 100 feet moved in dollars. From G. C. Armour and E. S. Buffa, "A Heuristic Algorithm and Simulation Approach to the Relative Location of Facilities," *Management Science*, Vol. 9, No. 2, January 1963.

The simulation. With the three items of basic data available, the program uses the following rationale (see the flow diagram of Figure 21):

1. The program determines which of the departments can be exchanged. A limitation in the program specifies that the only candidates for exchange are departments of equal size, or departments adjacent to each other even though they may not be equal in size. Although it appears that this may limit the exchanges which can be made, actually it does not, because through a sequence of exchanges of departments any pair of departments may finally be exchanged.

2. The program calculates the physical centers of the various departments and then determines the distances between all combinations of departments.

3. Data is now available to calculate the total handling cost for a given layout pattern. This is computed from the input data on loads and unit transport costs between departments and the matrix of distances calculated in 2 above. Of course the first layout pattern for which total material-handling costs are calculated will be the initial pattern.

4. The program now evaluates what changes in total cost would occur if each department was exchanged with all other departments in location. It does this by exchanging temporarily the two departments in question and recalculating total material-handling cost. This requires $(n^2 - n)/2 = 190$ evaluations for the example problem.

5. If any of the changes in location produce a reduction in material-handling cost, the program proceeds. If not, the program stops, for the best possible solution is the one for which computations have just been made.

6. If there are exchanges that produce cost reduction, the program selects the exchange of the two departments that yield the largest cost reduction and affects their exchange in the layout pattern.

7. Since some of the exchanges will be for departments of unequal size, program subroutines are required to rearrange the layout into a logical form, that is, square or rectangular patterns.

8. The program now calls for the printing of the revised layout, the new total cost, the estimated cost reduction, and the record of the exchanges just made. Figure 25 shows the print-out for the first iteration of the example problem. It shows that by exchanging the locations of departments A and V, a net improvement in material-handling cost of almost 12 per cent has been obtained.

Location Pattern   Iteration 1

	1	2	3	4	5	6	7	8	9	10	11	12	13	14	15	16	17	18	19	20	21	22	23	24	25	26	27	28	29	30
1	V	V	V	V	V	V	B	B	B	L	L	L	L	L	L	L	S	S	S	S	S	S	S	S	S	W	W	W	W	W
2	V	V	V	V	V	V	B	B	B	L	L	L	L	L	L	L	S	S	S	S	S	S	S	S	S	W	W	W	W	W
3	V	V	V	V	V	B	B	B	B	L	L	L	L	L	L	L	S	S	S	S	S	S	S	S	S	W	W	W	W	W
4	V	V	V	V	V	B	B	B	B	L	L	L	L	L	L	L	S	S	S	S	S	S	S	S	S	W	W	W	W	W
5	V	V	V	V	V	B	B	B	B	L	L	L	L	L	L	L	S	S	S	S	S	S	S	S	S	W	W	W	W	W
6	C	C	C	C	C	C	D	D	D	L	L	L	L	L	L	L	S	S	S	S	S	S	S	S	S	W	W	W	W	W
7	C	C	C	C	C	C	D	D	D	L	L	L	L	L	L	L	G	G	G	S	S	S	S	S	S	W	W	W	W	W
8	C	C	C	C	C	D	D	D	D	L	L	L	L	L	L	L	G	G	G	S	S	S	S	S	S	W	W	W	W	W
9	C	C	C	C	C	D	D	D	D	L	L	L	L	L	L	L	G	G	G	S	S	S	S	S	S	W	W	W	W	W
10	C	C	C	C	C	D	D	D	D	N	N	N	N	N	H	H	H	T	T	T	T	T	T	T	T	T	T	T	T	T
11	E	E	E	E	E	E	F	F	F	N	N	N	N	N	N	H	H	H	T	T	T	T	T	T	T	T	T	T	T	T
12	E	E	E	E	E	E	F	F	F	N	N	N	N	N	N	H	H	H	T	T	T	T	T	T	T	T	T	T	T	T
13	E	E	E	E	E	E	F	F	F	P	P	P	P	P	P	J	J	J	T	T	T	T	T	T	T	T	T	T	T	T
14	K	K	K	K	K	K	F	F	F	P	P	P	P	P	P	J	J	J	T	T	T	T	T	T	T	T	T	T	T	T
15	K	K	K	K	K	K	F	F	F	P	P	P	P	P	P	J	J	J	U	U	U	U	U	U	T	T	T	T	A	A
16	K	K	K	K	K	K	F	F	F	F	F	P	P	P	P	R	R	R	U	U	U	U	U	U	U	A	A	A	A	A
17	K	K	K	K	K	K	M	M	M	M	M	M	R	R	R	R	R	R	U	U	U	U	U	U	U	A	A	A	A	A
18	M	M	M	M	M	M	M	M	M	M	M	M	R	R	R	R	R	R	U	U	U	U	U	U	U	A	A	A	A	A
19	M	M	M	M	M	M	M	M	M	M	M	M	R	R	R	R	R	R	U	U	U	U	U	U	U	A	A	A	A	A
20	M	M	M	M	M	M	M	M	M	M	M	M	R	R	R	R	R	R	U	U	U	U	U	U	U	A	A	A	A	A

Total cost $8,979.26   Estimated cost reduction $1,185.08   MOVEA A   MOVEB V

Figure 25. First improved relative location pattern. From G. C. Armour and E. S. Buffa, "A Heuristic Algorithm and Simulation Approach to the Relative Location of Facilities," *Management Science*, Vol. 9, No. 2, January 1963.

9. The program now repeats the basic steps until no further cost reduction can be achieved, the last iteration representing the best possible solution. Figure 26 shows the seventh and final iteration for the sample problem. The final solution shows a 23 per cent reduction in material-handling cost, as compared to the initial layout configuration, and the entire solution required 0.62 minute to execute on an IBM 7090 computer. The final block diagram of Figure 26 would be used as a basis for the development of a more detailed templet layout.

The most recent version of the computer program (at the time of the publication of this book) allows for a maximum of forty departments and makes it possible to fix the location of any number of the departments. This latter feature is often important as a practical matter since it is sometimes true that not all departments can be changed in location. For example, the existing location of a railroad spur or road may determine the desirable location for receiving and

Location Pattern   Iteration 7

```
    1  2  3  4  5  6  7  8  9 10 11 12 13 14 15 16 17 18 19 20 21 22 23 24 25 26 27 28 29 30
 1  E  E  E  E  E  E  F  F  F  L  L  L  L  L  L  L  L  S  S  S  S  S  S  S  S  S  U  U  U  U  U
 2  E  E  E  E  E  E  F  F  F  L  L  L  L  L  L  L  L  S  S  S  S  S  S  S  S  S  U  U  U  U  U
 3  E  E  E  E  E  F  F  F  F  L  L  L  L  L  L  L  L  S  S  S  S  S  S  S  S  S  U  U  U  U  U
 4  E  C  C  C  C  C  F  F  F  F  L  L  L  L  L  L  L  L  S  S  S  S  S  S  S  S  U  U  U  U  U
 5  C  C  C  C  C  C  F  F  F  F  L  L  L  L  L  L  L  L  S  S  S  S  S  S  S  S  U  U  U  U  U
 6  C  C  C  C  C  C  D  D  D  L  L  L  L  L  L  L  L  S  S  S  S  S  S  S  S  S  U  U  U  U  U
 7  C  C  C  C  C  C  D  D  D  L  L  L  L  L  L  L  L  G  G  G  S  S  S  S  S  S  U  U  U  U  U
 8  C  C  C  C  C  D  D  D  D  L  L  L  L  L  L  L  G  G  G  S  S  S  S  S  S  S  W  W  W  W  U
 9  C  V  V  V  V  D  D  D  D  L  L  L  L  L  L  L  G  G  G  S  S  S  S  S  S  W  W  W  W  W  U
10  V  V  V  V  V  D  D  D  D  N  N  N  N  N  N  H  H  H  T  T  T  T  W  W  W  W  W  W  W  W  W
11  V  V  V  V  V  V  B  B  B  N  N  N  N  N  N  H  H  H  T  T  T  T  W  W  W  W  W  W  W  W  W
12  V  V  V  V  V  V  B  B  B  N  N  N  N  N  N  H  H  H  T  T  T  T  W  W  W  W  W  W  W  W  W
13  V  V  V  V  V  V  B  B  B  P  P  P  P  P  P  J  J  J  T  T  T  T  W  W  W  W  W  W  W  W  W
14  K  K  K  K  K  K  B  B  B  P  P  P  P  P  P  J  J  J  T  T  T  T  W  W  W  W  W  W  W  W  W
15  K  K  K  K  K  K  B  B  B  P  P  P  P  P  P  J  J  J  T  T  T  T  T  W  W  W  W  A  A
16  K  K  K  K  K  K  B  B  B  P  P  P  P  P  P  R  R  R  T  T  T  T  T  T  A  A  A  A  A
17  K  K  K  K  K  K  M  M  M  M  M  M  R  R  R  R  R  R  T  T  T  T  T  T  A  A  A  A  A
18  M  M  M  M  M  M  M  M  M  M  M  M  R  R  R  R  R  R  T  T  T  T  T  T  A  A  A  A  A
19  M  M  M  M  M  M  M  M  M  M  M  M  R  R  R  R  R  R  T  T  T  T  T  T  A  A  A  A  A
20  M  M  M  M  M  M  M  M  M  M  M  M  R  R  R  R  R  R  T  T  T  T  T  T  A  A  A  A  A
```

Total cost $7,862.09   Estimated cost reduction $213.54   MOVEA E   MOVEB C

Figure 26. Suboptimum relative location pattern. Exchanging any two departments from their locations above here would increase the objective function, annual material handling expense. From G. C. Armour and E. S. Buffa, "A Heuristic Algorithm and Computer Simulation Approach to the Relative Location of Facilities," *Management Science,* Vol. 9, No. 2, January 1963.

shipping facilities. In such an instance, we wish to determine the best location of the other departments, given the location of the receiving and shipping departments.

General Purpose System Simulator (9)

Geoffrey Gordon of the Advanced Systems Development Division, IBM, has developed a computer processor that makes possible the simulation of many kinds of systems when they can be described adequately by a block diagram developed in a manner consistent with the computer processor. Whereas this seems at first to be a limitation, a study of the simulator indicates that the clever conception of a wide variety of blocks of different characteristics, taken in various combinations, makes possible the representation of a multitude of actual systems.

The simulation allows the user to follow the flow through the system and observe the effects of blocking caused either by the need to time-share facilities or caused by limited capacity of parts of the system. Outputs of the program give information on:

1. The amount of traffic flowing through system, or parts of the system.
2. The average time and the time distribution for traffic to pass through the system, or between selective points in the system.
3. The extent to which elements of the system are loaded.
4. Queues in the system.

Simscript (14)

Markowitz, Hausner, and Karr of the RAND Corp. have developed a simulation programming language called SIMSCRIPT. This computer language is similar in general concept to FORTRAN, but is specifically designed to accommodate simulation programs. It is felt by those familiar with both the General Purpose System Simulator and with SIMSCRIPT that the latter is the more flexible and has the most general application.

The implications of the existence of the General Purpose System Simulator and SIMSCRIPT are tremendous, for once they are learned, programming time is considerably reduced.

Summary

The examples were chosen to illustrate applications of different kinds of activities and various levels of complexity. For example, the Eastman Kodak studies of mechanics and of mixed chemicals are largely illustrative of the Monte Carlo technique in practical situations. The simulation of steel making was meant to show how a more complex system with many interdependent variables can be handled. The layout example shows how a simulation model can be coupled with an algorithm which can produce an essentially optimal solution.

REFERENCES

1. Armour, G. C., and E. S. Buffa, "A Heuristic Algorithm and Simulation Approach to the Relative Location of Facilities," *Management Science,* Vol. 9, No. 2, January 1963.

2. Banbury, J., and R. J. Taylor, "A Study of Congestion in the Melting Shop of a Steelworks," *Operations Research Quarterly,* Vol. IX, No. 2.

3. Bowman, E. H., and R. B. Fetter, *Analysis for Production Management,* Richard D. Irwin, Homewood, Ill., 2nd ed., 1961.

4. Carrabino, J. D., "Determination of Optimum Sizes and Economic Feasibility of Shipping Containers Using Operations Analysis Techniques," *Journal of Industrial Engineering,* November–December 1958.

5. Cohen, K. J., "Determining the Best Possible Inventory Levels," *Industrial Quality Control,* Vol. XV, October 1958.

6. Colman, H., and C. P. Smallwood, *Computer Language: An Autoinstructional Introduction to Fortran,* McGraw-Hill Book Company, New York, 1962.

7. Feorene, O. J., "The Gentle Art of Simulation," *Proceedings, Twelfth Annual Industrial Engineering Institute,* University of California, Berkeley-Los Angeles, 1960.

8. Forrester, J., *Industrial Dynamics,* John Wiley and Sons, New York, 1961.

9. Gordon, G., *A General Purpose System Simulator,* IBM Advanced Systems Development Division, October 1961.

10. Hillier, F. S., "Quantitative Tools for Plant Layout Analysis," *Journal of Industrial Engineering,* Vol. XIV, No. 1, January–February 1963.

11. Jones, H. G., and A. M. Lee, "Monte Carlo Methods in Heavy Industry," *Operations Research Quarterly,* Vol. VI, No. 3.

12. Malcolm, D. G., "New Method Pre-test Ideas," *Nation's Business,* Vol. XLVI, No. 2, February 1958.

13. Malcolm, D. G., "System Simulation—A Fundamental Tool for Industrial Engineering," *Journal of Industrial Engineering,* Vol. IX, No. 3, May–June 1958.

14. Markowitz, H. M., B. Hausner, and H. W. Karr, *SIMSCRIPT: A Simulation Programming Language,* Memorandum RM-3310-PR, The RAND Corp., Santa Monica, Calif., November 1962.

15. Mitchner, M., and R. P. Peterson, "An Operations Research Study of the Collection of Defaulted Loans," *Operations Research,* Vol. V, No. 4, August 1957.

16. Neate, R., and W. J. Dacey, "A Simulation of Melting Shop Operation by Means of a Computer," *Process Control and Automation,* Vol. V, No. 7, July 1958.

17. *Report of System Simulation Symposium,* Cosponsored by AIIE, ORSA, and TIMS, New York, May 1957.

18. *Report of System Simulation Symposium No. 2,* Cosponsored by AIIE, ORSA, and TIMS, New York, February 1959.

19. Rowe, A. J., "Application of Computer Simulation to Sequential Decision Rules in Production Scheduling," *Proceedings, Eleventh Industrial Engineering Institute,* University of California, Berkeley-Los Angeles, 1959, pp. 33–43.

20. Sasieni, M., A. Yaspan, and L. Friedman, *Operations Research,* John Wiley and Sons, New York, 1959.

21. Schiller, D. H., and M. M. Lavin, "Determining Required Warehouse Dock Facilities," *Operations Research,* Vol. IV, No. 2, April 1956.

22. Sprowls, R. C., and M. Asimow, "A Computer Simulated Business Firm," in *Management Control Systems,* edited by D. G. Malcolm and A. J. Rowe, John Wiley and Sons, New York, 1959.

REVIEW QUESTIONS

1. Discuss the general situation in which simulation is preferable to mathematical analysis.

2. What are Monte Carlo methods and what is their place in simulation?

3. In simulated sampling, why do we normally convert frequency distributions to cumulative probability distributions?

4. In the example of simulated sampling (machine breakdown and repair) used in this chapter, how can we be sure that the occurrence of machine breakdowns and the repair times are representative of the true situation?

5. Discuss the example of the determination of repair crew size at the Eastman Kodak Company. Given the existence of the simulation model, how could it be of continuing usefulness to the company in evaluating current practices and policies?

6. Discuss the simulation of the mixed chemicals distribution system at Eastman Kodak Company. How could this simulation model be of continuing usefulness to the organization?

7. The objective of the simulation of steel making operations given as an example in this chapter was to determine the capacity of operations. How else might such a model be used?

8. Discuss the simulation of the relative location of facilities. Outline the major steps involved in the operation of the simulator. Is this simply a simulation model?

PROBLEMS

1. A sample of 100 arrivals of customers at a checkout station of a small store are according to the following distribution:

Time between Arrivals, min.	Frequency
0.5	2
1.0	6
1.5	10
2.0	25
2.5	20
3.0	14
3.5	10
4.0	7
4.5	4
5.0	2
	100

A study of the time required to service the customers by adding up the bill, receiving payment, making change, placing packages in bags, etc., yields the following distribution:

Service Time, minutes	Frequency
0.5	12
1.0	21
1.5	36
2.0	19
2.5	7
3.0	5
	100

a. Convert the distributions to cumulative probability distributions.
b. Using a simulated sample of 20, estimate the average per cent customer waiting time and the average per cent idle time of the server.

2. The manager of a drive-in restaurant is attempting to determine how many "car hops" he needs during his peak load period. As a policy he wishes to offer service such that average customer waiting time does not exceed 2 minutes. How many car hops does he need if the arrival and service distributions are as follows, and any car hop can service any customer? Simulate for various alternate numbers of car hops with a sample of twenty arrivals in each case.

Time between Successive Arrivals, minutes	Frequency	Service Time, minutes	Frequency
0	10	0	0
1.0	35	1.0	5
2.0	25	2.0	20
3.0	15	3.0	40
4.0	10	4.0	35
5.0	5		100
	100		

3. A company maintains a bank of machines which are exposed to severe service, causing bearing failure to be a common maintenance problem. There were three bearings in the machine that caused trouble. The general practice had been to replace bearings when they failed. However, excessive downtime costs raised the question whether or not a preventive policy was worthwhile. The company wished to evaluate three alternate policies:
a. The current practice of replacing bearings that fail.
b. When a bearing fails, replace all three.
c. When a bearing fails, replace that bearing plus other bearings that have been in use 1700 hours or more.

Time and cost data are as follows:

Maintenance mechanics time:

Replace 1 bearing	5 hours
Replace 2 bearings	6 hours
Replace 3 bearings	7 hours
Maintenance mechanic's wage rate	$3 per hour
Bearing cost	$5 each
Down-time costs	$2 per hour

A record of the actual working lives of 200 bearings results in the following distribution:

Bearing Life, hours	Frequency
1100	3
1200	10
1300	12
1400	20
1500	27
1600	35
1700	30
1800	25
1900	18
2000	15
2100	4
2200	1
	200

Simulate approximately 20,000 hours of service for each of the three alternate policies.

4. Following the structure of the flow chart of Figure 16, and the cumulative distributions of Figures 12, 13, 14, and 15, simulate the mixed chemicals operation for 20 cycles.

19

Large-Scale System Simulation

The distinction between the material in the preceding section and the material here is one of scale. The same general methods are applied in both the large- and small-scale simulations. A possible exception is that a high-speed computer is a necessity with large-scale simulations, whereas, in some instances, hand computation is feasible with simple problems. In addition, we will treat dynamic output simulation models which represent a fairly recent innovation of considerable interest to operations management.

The tremendous interest in large-scale system simulation represents a recognition of the need for a "systems" approach to the broad problems of the management of operations, indeed, the management of the entire enterprise. Past progress in operations management has of necessity focused on problems of limited dimensions, and these efforts have certainly produced rewards, both in terms of understanding the nature of the problems with which we deal, and in terms of the improvement of actual practice. But throughout these developments of models of work performance and measurement, allocation, waiting lines, facility design, inventories, and investment policy, the frontier thinkers have known that each compartmentalized problem that had been apparently solved had interactions with other compartmentalized problems. They were aware that the need was for a gigantic model where each area of past endeavor might represent a subsystem. Only with such a model could the complex interactions between subsystems be accounted for. Here, of course, mathematical analysis has not been effective. The answer to this call had to wait for the development first, of the large-scale high-speed electronic computer, and second, for the development of skill in simulation. Some of the outstanding work done in the large-scale simulations for business has been due to Richard Conway (3), Jay Forrester (4), Alan Rowe (9), and R. Clay Sprowls (10). In the material that follows we shall discuss the TASK Manufacturing Corporation (a simulated firm), the IBM job shop simulator and some of the applications which have been made with it, and dynamic output models developed at the Massachusetts Institute of Technology.

TASK Manufacturing Corporation*

The TASK Manufacturing Corporation is a small simulated business firm employing about 400 people, 200 of whom are engaged in direct labor and 200 in indirect labor. It has five related products of the general building hardware type which sell for about $1 each, and has a total annual sales between $3 and $3.5 million. The sales pattern is influenced by the seasonal nature of the building industry, and in addition, each item has a life cycle, which implies a research and development function for its replacement in the product line.

The five items in the product line are manufactured in some combination of seven different manufacturing departments. Four of these departments are in a machine shop (drill press, punch press, screw machine, and spot welding) and the other three are finishing, assembly, and packaging. Only the packaging department treats all five products and no one product uses all seven of the manufacturing operations. The products flow continuously through the departments with the outputs from some stages being the inputs to others. Production is in anticipation of sales so that items are stocked in inventory from which sales orders are filled.

Sales are made from the home office in Los Angeles, California, to customers scattered geographically over the United States. At any one time, between 100 and 150 customers are in the market for the product of the firm.

The raw materials from which these products are made are castings, steel strip, and steel bars. Foundries in the local area are the vendors of the castings. Local steel mills and distributors are the primary vendors for the steel strip and bars, as are Midwestern steel mills.

Subsystems of the TASK simulation. The simulation of the operations of a complete business firm impose the development of idealized representations or models of a number of component sub-

---

* Summarized from R. Clay Sprowls and Morris Asimow, "A Computer Simulated Business Firm," in *Management Control Systems* (D. G. Malcolm and A. J. Rowe, editors), John Wiley and Sons, New York, 1960.

systems. These subsystems include a work force, production facilities, customers, products, raw materials, inventories, accounting systems, credit sources, and so on. The subsystems which comprise TASK Manufacturing Corporation are shown in Figure 1. Each subsystem is sufficiently general, self-contained, and complete so that it can be dealt with as an entity. In a sense, each model of a subsystem is analogous to a "black box," and if certain inputs are specified, outputs will be generated.

Of course, a collection of subsystems does not comprise a business firm; therefore, the subsystems must be coupled together to permit inputs and outputs to come from and exit to both the external world and other subsystems. Formal policies, managerial decisions, and informal policies which have developed from customs and traditions determine the ways in which these couplings are allowed to occur. The set of human and material subsystems and the couplings conditioned by formal and informal policies comprise the business firm. Correspondingly the set of separately programmable models, or of subsystems, coupled by interconnecting programs comprises a representation of a business firm; that is, a simulated firm which can be manipulated on a computer. Some, but by no means all, of these interconnections are shown in Figure 1.

There are two definite phases in the operation of the simulated system. The first corresponds to the function of *planning* and the second to *operation*. The forecasting model supplies a plan of operation, and the production model supplies the counterpart of actual operations. The forecasting model prepares a suggested plan of operation for each of the 13 weeks of the ensuing quarter. The plan is prepared on the computer and is subject to the physical constraints of such things as the number of available employees, number of machines, cash, and to policy constraints, such as hiring, new equipment purchases, and borrowing. The forecasting model may suggest a different plan of operation for a department than its current state. Putting this plan of operation into effect may involve a change in the machine-product assignment, a change in scheduled overtime, the hiring of new employees and their assignments, etc.

The production model consists only of employees and the machines at each stage in its development. Employees and machines are in each department, with an employee assigned to operate a specific machine, which is assigned to work on one of the five specified products. As of the end of a given operating period, for example, 1 week, each department has a given state with respect to employee-machine-product-operating hours assignments. If none of these is

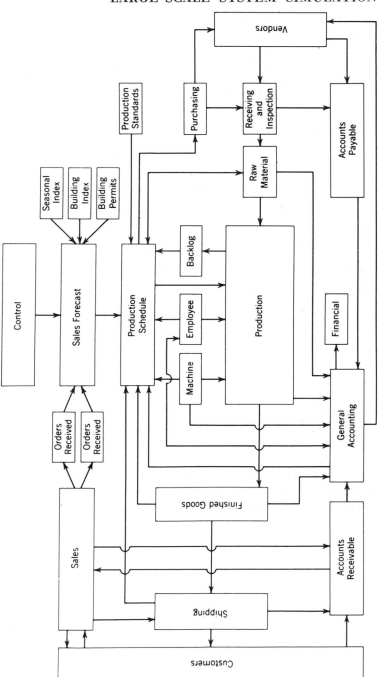

Figure 1. Subsystems of TASK Manufacturing Corp. From R. C. Sprowls and M. Asimow, "A Computer Simulated Firm," in *Management Control Systems*, D. G. Malcolm and A. J. Rowe, editors, John Wiley and Sons, New York, 1960, Figure VI-D-5.

changed, the department operates with the same assignments during the next operating period.

Example of a subsystem model. The machine model is taken as an example of one of the subsystems within the TASK Manufacturing Corporation. It is described here in general terms. The term "machine" is used loosely to mean the physical production process in any one of the seven operating departments. In the drill press department, the machine is obviously meant to be a drill press. In the finishing, assembling, and packaging departments, "machine" means only a production process. A machine is in one of two operating states as of any given time period: broken down, or in operating order. If the machine is in operating order, its productive capability is an exponential function, decreasing with time, the parameters of which reflect the following characteristics:

1. Age since purchase.
2. Capabilities when new.
3. Recency of overhaul.
4. Level of production.
5. Immediate mechanical state, which includes:
   a. How recently overhauled.
   b. Breakdown record.
   c. Level of maintenance service.

An overhaul policy governs when a machine which is in operating order is pulled off the production line for an overhaul. The probability that the machine is not in operating order, but is broken down, is a function of: (1) The number of overhauls, (2) the time since the last overhaul, and (3) its breakdown history. The latter is included on the assumption that if a machine initially exhibits frequent breakdowns, this implies some inherent fault in its design or construction which predisposes it to more frequent failures. All the machines in the seven operating departments have the same general characteristics. Each is described by a different set of parameter values to distinguish it from other machines with respect to the characteristics listed previously. The ease with which these parameters can be changed gives great flexibility in changing production model characteristics for experimental and educational purposes.

Future use of the TASK simulator. The authors of TASK envision the development of many models of component subsystems. Eventually there would be a library of such models available to serve as the building blocks from which a particular system, simulating a particular firm, may be synthesized. Some of these models may reflect in great detail a theory about the behavior of their real life counterparts and be useful for testing hypotheses about this behavior. Others may be merely the sampling from distribution functions which appear to reflect real life data and behavior without any attempt at modeling a theory behind the phenomenon being simulated.

Job Shop Simulation

For some time there has been a great deal of interest in the simulation of intermittent production systems, the most complex of which is commonly termed the job shop. The job shop probably represents the most complex of production systems, because in the most extreme situation the same product is never made twice so that the flow of parts and products through the system may follow any one of an extremely large number of possible paths. As we have noted previously, the characteristics of such a system demand a high degree of flexibility. We might state the overall problem of the operation of a job shop as one of balancing the costs of carrying in-process inventory, labor, the capital costs of capacity and the costs associated with meeting specified order completion dates. To have a high degree of labor and machine utilization it would be necessary to have a large number of orders waiting so that labor and equipment are very seldom idle. The result is relatively high inventory carrying costs and poor schedule performance.

If we strive to meet order completion dates without fail, however, we need a very large equipment and labor capacity so that ordinarily, orders would not have to wait. This would result in relatively low in-process inventory costs but poor machine and labor utilization. The problem of balancing these costs in a complex system is at best a difficult one. Thus there has been a focus on system simulation as a technique for testing alternate decision rules. Early work in the simulation of job shop systems was done by Jackson (6) and Rowe (8). In conjunction with Rowe's work at the General Electric Company, which is summarized on pp. 494–497, the I.B.M. Corporation developed a generalized simulation program which they called, "The job shop simulator." This program is flexible in terms of the input and characteristics of the system to be simulated and has been used effectively by the General Electric Company, Hughes Aircraft Company, Westinghouse Electric Corporation, and others. The general characteristics of the job shop simulator are shown in Figure 2.

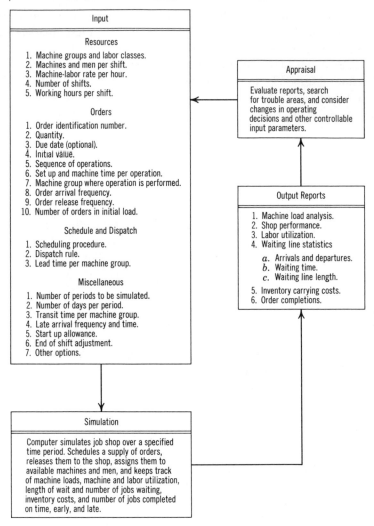

Input
Resources
1. Machine groups and labor classes.
2. Machines and men per shift.
3. Machine-labor rate per hour.
4. Number of shifts.
5. Working hours per shift.
Orders
1. Order identification number.
2. Quantity.
3. Due date (optional).
4. Initial value.
5. Sequence of operations.
6. Set up and machine time per operation.
7. Machine group where operation is performed.
8. Order arrival frequency.
9. Order release frequency.
10. Number of orders in initial load.
Schedule and Dispatch
1. Scheduling procedure.
2. Dispatch rule.
3. Lead time per machine group.
Miscellaneous
1. Number of periods to be simulated.
2. Number of days per period.
3. Transit time per machine group.
4. Late arrival frequency and time.
5. Start up allowance.
6. End of shift adjustment.
7. Other options.

Appraisal
Evaluate reports, search for trouble areas, and consider changes in operating decisions and other controllable input parameters.

Output Reports
1. Machine load analysis.
2. Shop performance.
3. Labor utilization.
4. Waiting line statistics
a. Arrivals and departures.
b. Waiting time.
c. Waiting line length.
5. Inventory carrying costs.
6. Order completions.

Simulation
Computer simulates job shop over a specified time period. Schedules a supply of orders, releases them to the shop, assigns them to available machines and men, and keeps track of machine loads, machine and labor utilization, length of wait and number of jobs waiting, inventory costs, and number of jobs completed on time, early, and late.

Figure 2. Overall characteristics of the job-shop simulator. From E. LeGrande, *Development of a Factory Simulation System Using Actual Operating Data,* Hughes Aircraft Co., El Segundo Division, March 1962, Figure IV–1.

Hughes Aircraft Company's application of the I.B.M. job shop simulator represents an adaptation of the program to the company's El Segundo plant operations. The adaptation made it possible to take order input data directly from RAMAC files, transposed to the form required for simulation, and supplied with other input data to the simulator. Figure **3** shows the overall flow characteristics of the adapted job shop simulator. Earl LeGrande (5) made an initial study testing various dispatch decision rules with the El Segundo job shop simulation process similar to the study Rowe reported in Chapter **17**. Recall that a dispatch decision rule is a rule for determining which order will be processed next by a given machine center. By operating the simulated shop according to each of the six decision rules used and measuring results by certain criteria which we shall discuss, it was possible to compare the effectiveness of the six different rules. The rules used in the study were as follows:

1. *Minimum Processing Time Per Operation:* Of the jobs waiting in line at a machine group, this rule assigns the next job to be worked on by choosing the one with the shortest processing time (set up plus machining time).

2. *Minimum Slack Time Per Operation:* The next order to be worked on is determined by subtracting the remaining processing time for the order from the total time remaining (due date minus present time), and dividing the result by the number of remaining operations. The order for which this amount is smallest will be assigned to be processed next.

3. *First Come–First Served:* This rule places orders in line as they arrive at a machine group, choosing the next order to be processed from the front of the line.

4. *Minimum Planned Start Date Per Operation:* In this rule the order assigned next is the order with the earliest planned start date for the current operation. This is the theoretical operations start date which has been calculated previously by the scheduling procedure.

5. *Minimum Due Date Per Order:* This rule is based on the due dates for orders waiting in line. The order that has the earliest planned due date will be assigned first.

6. *Random Selection:* This rule has no special priorities. The order to be assigned next is selected at random from all of the orders waiting in line at the machine group.

The criteria by which the various simulation runs were evaluated are as follows:

1. Number of orders completed.
2. Per cent of orders completed late.
3. Mean of the distribution of completions.
4. Standard deviation of the distribution of completions.
5. Average number of orders waiting in the shop.

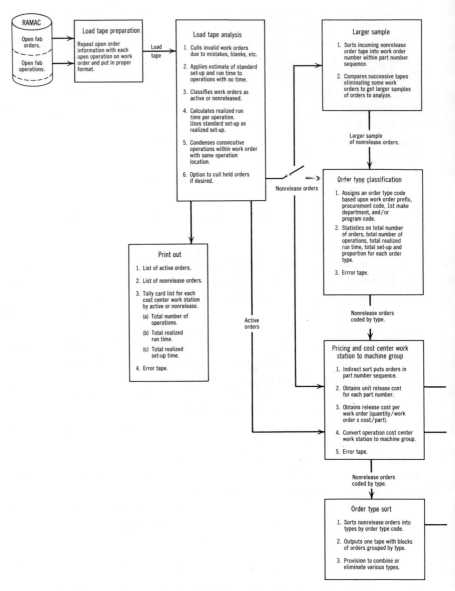

Figure 3. Characteristics of the El Segundo job-shop simulation process. From E. LeGrande, *Development of a Factory Simulation System Using Actual Operating Data,* Hughes Aircraft Co., El Segundo Division, March 1962, Figure V–1.

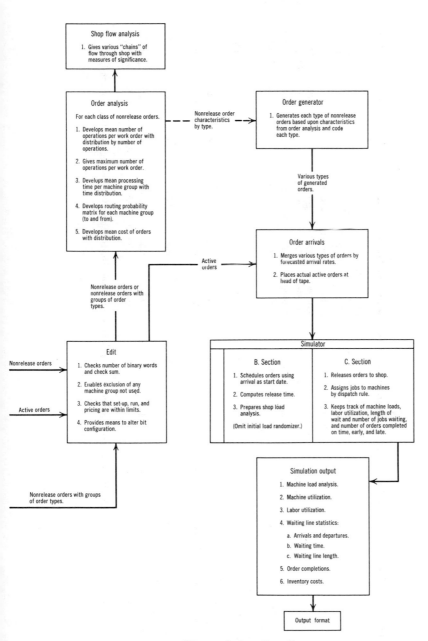

Figure 3 (continued).

TABLE 1. Results of Hughes Aircraft Company El Segundo Job Shop Simulation of Dispatch Decision Rules*

Criteria, Rank

Decision Rule	(1) Number of Orders Completed	(2) Per Cent of Orders Completed Late	(3) Mean of Distribution of Completions	(4) Standard Deviation of Distribution of Completions	(5) Average Number of Orders Waiting in Shop	(6) Average Wait Time of Orders	(7) Yearly Cost of Carrying Orders in Queue	(8) Ratio of Inventory Carrying Cost	(9) Per Cent of Labor Utilized	(10) Per Cent of Machine Capacity Utilized	Total Relative Rank
Minimum processing time per operation	1.00	0.83	1.00	0.20	1.00	1.00	0.76	0.51	1.00	1.00	8.70
Minimum slack time per operation	0.87	1.00	0.63	1.00	0.73	0.52	0.96	0.99	0.92	0.92	8.54
First come-first served	0.86	0.54	0.54	0.20	0.73	0.38	0.84	0.98	0.93	0.93	6.93
Minimum planned start date per operation	0.84	0.48	0.46	0.22	0.68	0.36	0.91	1.00	0.91	0.91	6.77
Minimum due date per order	0.94	0.62	0.64	0.24	0.84	0.51	1.00	0.99	0.87	0.87	7.52
Random selection	0.84	0.68	0.79	0.20	0.67	0.66	0.80	0.93	0.92	0.91	7.40

* Earl LeGrande, *Development of a Factory Simulation System Using Actual Operating Data*, Hughes Aircraft Co., El Segundo, Calif., March 1962.

6. Average wait time of orders.

7. Yearly cost of carrying orders in queue.

8. Ratio of inventory carrying cost while waiting to inventory cost while on the machine.

9. Per cent of labor utilized.

10. Per cent of machine capacity utilized.

Table I shows a summary of the results for each of the six decision rules by each of the ten criteria. For each criterion relative ranks were assigned on the basis of the 1.00 maximum, the lower rankings being representative of relative effectiveness. The total relative rank is based on an equal weighting of the ten criteria. Figure 4 shows the distributions of order completions for the six decision rules. On the basis of an equal weighting of the criteria, the minimum processing time per operation rule gives the best results. As LeGrande points out, a different weighting with perhaps emphasis on getting orders out on time would tend to favor minimum slack time per operation as a decision rule.

The probable future uses of the El Segundo job shop simulator are summarized by the following list of ways in which the company feels that the simulator can assist management:

1. To establish more realistic scheduling lead times.

2. To establish more realistic order of schedules.

3. To evaluate the effects of various dispatch rules.

4. To forecast shop load.

5. To plan equipment layout.

6. To test various sets of operating decisions.

General Electric manufacturing simulator (GEMS). Although the General Electric Company has at this writing released very little information on the GEMS program, it appears that it is an extremely powerful job shop simulator. It has been designed as a series of computer subroutines, instead of one large all-inclusive computer program. Thus many different versions of GEMS can be created simply by selecting and piecing together the appropriate subroutines from the GEMS library. A partial list of the GEMS capabilities includes (2):

1. Alternate routing.

2. Overtime.

3. Assembly of any numbers of levels of subassemblies and parts.

4. Use of outside vendors.

5. Lot splitting.

Dispatch Rule	MINSD	FCFS	MINDD	MINSOP	RANDOM	MINPRT
Per cent orders early	54	57	63	68	65	71
Per cent orders on due date	6	5	5	12	5	5
Per cent orders late	44	38	32	20	30	24
Mean of completions (days)	E3.0	E3.6	E4.2	E4.2	E5.2	E6.6
Standard deviation (days)	9.2	10	8.2	8.2	10.4	9.9
Total number of orders completed	3118	3190	3484	3217	3117	3708

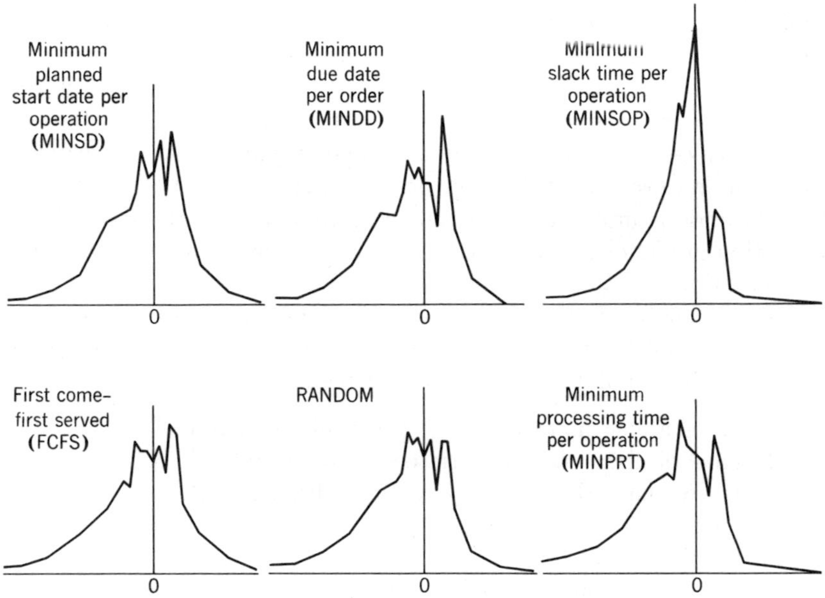

Figure 4. Distributions for the time of order completions. From E. LeGrande, *Development of a Factory Simulation System Using Actual Operating Data,* Hughes Aircraft Co., El Segundo Division, March 1962, Figure VI–11.

6. Expediting.
7. Rescheduling.
8. Random machine breakdowns.
9. Floating manpower.
10. Labor stealing.
11. Job groupings to save setups.

A "Flow" Shop Simulator

In contrast to the job shop simulator just discussed, the General Electric Company has developed a simulator applicable to a continuous type production system (2). The model was developed specifically for defining the capabilities of the company's distribution transformer plant at Hickory, North Carolina. The model may be used to simulate the flow characteristics for any manufacturing production line type situation which falls within the limits of the model which are specified as follows:

1. Up to twenty-five machines (in series).
2. Up to twenty-five inventories.
3. Up to twenty different product variations per run.
4. Up to ten product physical characteristics (that is, for set-ups).
5. Up to 250 jobs can be processed at one time.
6. Up to 300 jobs can be in inventory at one time.

With regard to the application at the Hickory Tank Shop (2), simulated runs were made with various schedules, different arrangements and additions of equipment, and with other conditions changed. For example, simulation runs were made which compared the effect of scheduling all tank types (10–100 Kva transformers) once each week, three times per week, and daily. The results indicated, much to the surprise of plant personnel, that the effect of setup time was not nearly as important a factor as had been originally thought. Other simulation runs varied the quantities and varieties of shop equipment. One such series indicated that the tank shop could achieve more output from two fin welders and an overhead storage conveyor, permitting constant use of the two welders, than from four or more fin welders used intermittently. These and other runs indicated that the simulator would be an extremely valuable device for plant administration.

MODELS WITH DYNAMIC OUTPUT

It is often revealing in the simulation of something as complex as a business firm to show dynamically the impact of changes in environmental factors, such as market demand, and changes in alternate policies. By dynamic we mean simply in relation to time. Although other simulation models could obtain such data by printing out intermediate results and plotting them on a time scale, Jay Forrester (4) has developed simulation models which do this in a unique way, so that much of the computer output is in the form of graphs of important measures of effectiveness in relation to time. The particular advantages of this type of output is in its usefulness in the demonstration and analysis of the effects of lags in the information system. As we shall see, average results of comparative policies often mask important dynamic effects. Forrester's approach provides insight into the inner workings of complex systems, particularly in the application of control theory to the business system.

Example of a Production-Distribution System

Figure 5 shows the gross structure of a production-distribution system in a typical hard goods industry like household appliances, for which Forrester has developed a dynamic simulation model. This is the same model shown as Figure 10 of Chapter 16. Note that three levels of inventory exist—factory, distributor, and retailer. The circled lines show the flow of orders for goods from customers to retailers, retailers to distributors, distributors to the factory warehouse, and finally from the warehouse as orders for the factory to produce. The solid lines show the flow of the physical goods between each level of the structure in response to the orders. The circled

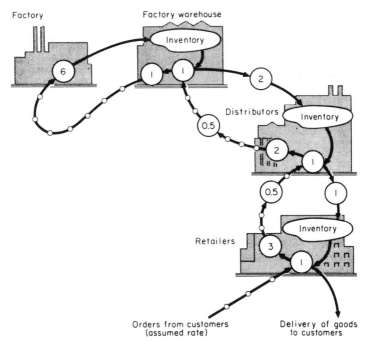

Figure 5. Organization of production-distribution system. From J. Forrester, *Industrial Dynamics,* John Wiley and Sons–MIT Press, 1961, Figure 2–1.

numbers represent the time delays in weeks for each of the activities to take place. "Delivery of goods to the customer averages a week after the customer places an order. At the retail level, the accounting and purchasing delays average 3 weeks between time of sale and the time when the sale is reflected in an order sent out to obtain a replacement. Mailing delay for the order is half a week. The distributor takes a week to process the order, and shipment of goods to the retailer takes another week. Similar delays exist between the distributor and the factory warehouse. The factory lead time averages 6 weeks between the decision to change production rate and the time that factory output approaches the new level.

"Policy on orders and inventories. To complete the initial description of the example, we need to know the policies that govern the placing of orders and the maintaining of inventory at each distribution level. We shall consider three principal components of orders: (1) Orders to replace goods sold, (2) orders to adjust inventories upwards or downwards as the level of business activity changes, and (3) orders to fill the supply pipelines with in-process orders and shipments. Orders are treated in the following ways:

"1. After a sales analysis and purchasing delay (3, 2, and 1 weeks for the three levels), orders to the next higher level of the system include replacement for the actual sales made by the ordering level.

"2. After sufficient time for averaging out short term sales fluctuations (8 weeks), a gradual upward or downward adjustment is made in inventories as the rate of sales increases or decreases.

"3. One component of orders in process (orders in the mail, unfilled orders at the supplier, and goods in transit) is necessarily proportional to the average level of business activity and to the length of time required to fill an order. Both an increased sales volume and an increased delivery lead time necessarily result in increased total orders in the supply pipeline. These 'pipeline' orders are unavoidable. They are a part of the 'basic physics' of the system structure. If not ordered explicitly for the purpose of pipeline filling (and often they will not be), the pipeline demand will come from a depletion of inventories, and the pipeline orders will be placed unknowingly in the name of inventory adjustments.

"The ordering rate will also depend on some assumption about future sales. Prediction methods that amount to extending forward (extrapolating) the present sales trend will in general produce a more unstable and fluctuating system. For our example, however, we shall use the usually conservative practice of basing the ordering rate on the assumption that sales are most likely to continue at their present level." (4)

Effect of 10 per cent increase in retail sales. What happens when the system has previously been stable with retail orders flowing in at a constant rate followed by a simple 10 per cent increase in retail sales, retail sales remaining constant at the new level? Figure 6 shows the effects of this simple change on distributor orders from retailers, inventories at the retail, distributor, and factory warehouse levels, and on factory production output. Figure 6 is almost identical to Figure 11 of Chapter 16. Instead of a smooth and orderly adjustment to the new level of retail sales demand, we see that there are wild fluctuations in some of these measures. The reasons are related to the lags in the system and to the inventory and ordering procedures used.

Because of delays in accounting, purchasing, and mailing, the increase in distributors' orders from retailers lags about a month in reaching the new 10 per cent level. The surprise is, of course, that it does not stop at 10 per cent, but reaches a peak of 18 per cent at the eleventh week because of new orders added at the retail level (1) to increase inventories somewhat and (2) to raise the level of orders and goods in transit in the supply pipeline by 10 per cent to correspond to the increase in the sales rate. "These inventory and pipeline increments occur as 'transient' or nonrepeating additions to the order rate, and when they have been satisfied, the retailers' orders to the distributors drop back to the enduring 10 per cent increase."

The fluctuation in factory warehouse orders from distributors (not shown) is amplified beyond the 18 per cent increase in distributor orders from retailers to a peak of 34 per cent above the previous December. This occurs because the incoming order level at the distributors remains above retail sales for more than 4 months and is mistaken for a continuing increase in retail sales demand. Distributors' orders to the factory, therefore, include not only the 18 per cent increase in orders which they have received but also a corresponding increase for the distributor inventories and for orders and goods in transit between distributors and the factory.

Finally, manufacturing orders to the factory are amplified even more because they are placed on the basis of the increasing factory warehouse orders and the falling warehouse inventories which we note is reduced to 15 per cent below the previous December level. The result is that manufacturing orders to the factory increase to

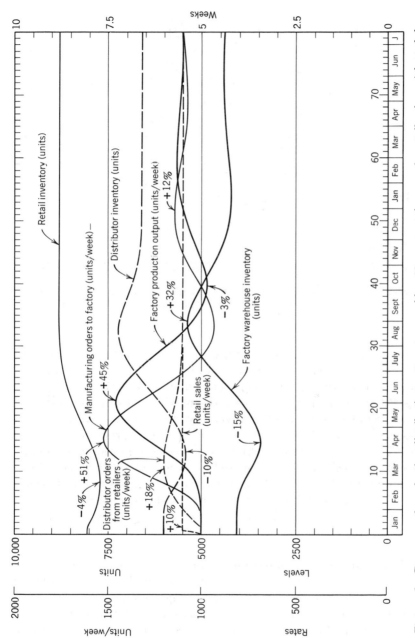

Figure 6. Response of production-distribution system to a sudden 10 per cent increase in retail sales. Adapted from J. Forrester, *Industrial Dynamics*, John Wiley and Sons–MIT Press, 1961, Figure 2-2.

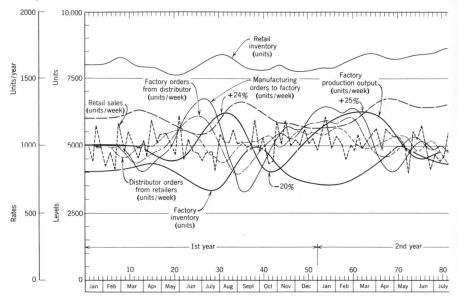

Figure 7. Effect of random deviation at retail sales. Adapted from J. Forrester, *Industrial Dynamics,* John Wiley and Sons–MIT Press, 1961, Figure 2–4.

a maximum of 51 per cent during the fifteenth week. Factory output which is delayed by a factory lead time of 6 weeks reaches a maximum of 45 per cent during the twenty-first week. Meanwhile retail sales remain at 10 per cent above the previous December level.

As retailers satisfy their inventory requirements with the increased shipments they receive, they reduce their orders to distributors. The distributors then find that their inventories and supply rates exceed their needs and so reduce orders to the factory. Factory output finally drops to 3 per cent below the initial rate in December. The great fluctuations in factory production output have, of course, occurred at considerable expense, as well as both heartache and headache.

Effects of random fluctuations in sales. A logical question at this point is, if a simple 10 per cent increase produces oscillations of the type we have noted, what happens when retail sales vary in a random pattern as we might expect? Figure 7 shows the output record for just such a situation, where retail sales are fluctuating from week to week over a range having a normal deviation of 10 per cent of average sales. Note that factory production fluctuates over periods

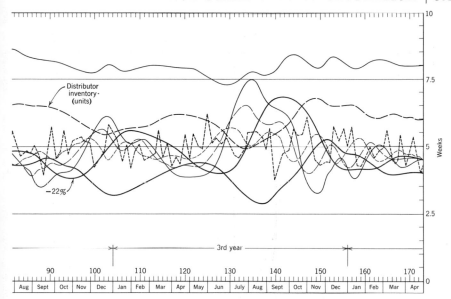

Figure 7 (continued).

of several months with peak levels of 25 per cent or more from the average. Also, there seems to be a periodic oscillation in factory output even though sales demand follows a random pattern.

Effect of eliminating distributor level. Let us consider the effects of changing the basic structure of the production distribution system. If the distributor level is eliminated and retailers' orders placed directly with the factory warehouse, some of the normal delays in the system are removed. This results in a dramatic reduction in the production fluctuations which result when a simple 10 per cent step input is introduced as is shown in Figure 8. The comparable curve from Figure 6 based on the original production-distribution system structure is included for comparison. We are not, of course, suggesting that middlemen should automatically be eliminated, because the total arguments on that point are somewhat more complex than we have presented. Nevertheless, the dynamic model has shown an important advantage of simple, more direct distribution systems.

Effects of changing inventory policy. The inventory policies described in the original model are of considerable importance in determining the behavior of the system. As we have noted previ-

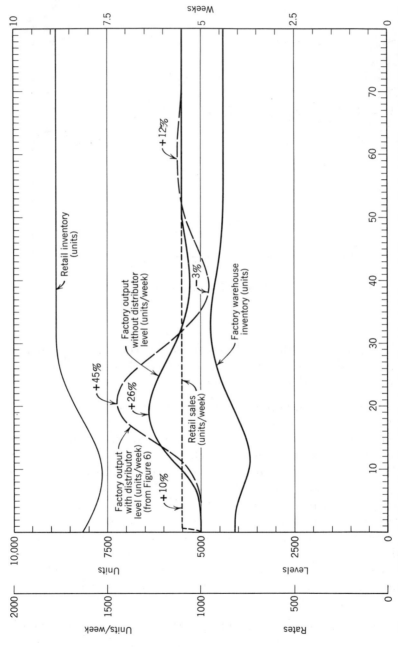

Figure 8. Effect of eliminating the distributor level. Adapted from J. Forrester, *Industrial Dynamics*, John Wiley and Sons–MIT Press, 1961, Figure 2–7.

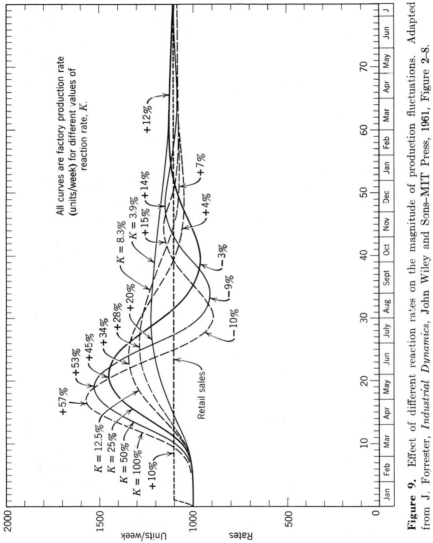

Figure 9. Effect of different reaction rates on the magnitude of production fluctuations. Adapted from J. Forrester, *Industrial Dynamics*, John Wiley and Sons–MIT Press, 1961, Figure 2–8.

ously in Chapter 17, pp. 480–484, the reaction rate of adjustment and the length of review periods are both of considerable importance in determining the magnitude of production fluctuations and reserve inventory requirements. To illustrate this, Figure 9 is based on the same production-distribution system as before but shows the effect on factory production rate for different reaction rates of adjustment (length of review period remaining constant). For example, a curve marked with a reaction rate $K = 100$ indicates a policy in which a discrepancy between inventory and orders are reflected in increases or decreases in production orders equal to the full difference. When $K = 50$, only half the difference between inventory and orders is reflected in changes in production order levels, and so on. The heavy black line, where $K = 25$, represents the policy described for the original model on which the curves for Figures 6, 7, and 8 were based. Note that the smaller the value of K, the smaller the magnitude of production fluctuations which result. This corroborates the result shown earlier by Magee, using a static model.* Recall that we discussed Magee's work in Chapter 17, "Operating Production-Inventory Systems."

It seems obvious that the potential of dynamic output models is very great in analyzing the interacting effects of many different conditions and management policies.

Summary

The power of the large-scale systems simulation technique is actually only beginning to show itself. We should expect to learn a great deal about the interaction of the many variables in large-scale systems, and test out management policies and decision rules similar to the testing of dispatch decision rules at Hughes Aircraft Company and the General Electric Company. Dynamic output simulation models promise to teach us a great deal about the effect of time lags in the information system of large scale enterprises. Finally, large-scale detailed simulations of an entire firm similar to the TASK Manufacturing Company offer something comparable to a laboratory for learning and training people in the operation of an enterprise.

* John F. Magee, "Guides to Inventory Policy, II Problems of Uncertainty," *Harvard Business Review*, March–April 1956.

REFERENCES

1. Baker, C. T., and B. P. Dzielinski, "Simulation of a Simplified Job Shop," *Management Science,* Vol. 6, No. 3, pp. 311–323, 1960.
2. Clement, R. S., "Computer Simulation of Manufacturing Operations in The General Electric Company," *Proceedings, Thirteenth Annual Industrial Engineering Institute,* University of California, Berkeley, Los Angeles, February 1961.
3. Conway, R. W., B. M. Johnson, and W. L. Maxwell, "Some Problems of Digital Systems Simulation," *Management Science,* Vol. 6, No. 1, October 1961.
4. Forrester, J., *Industrial Dynamics,* John Wiley and Sons, New York, 1961.
5. LeGrande, E., *Development of a Factory Simulation System Using Actual Operating Data,* Hughes Aircraft Company, El Segundo Division, March 1962.
6. Jackson, J. R., "Simulation Research on Job-Shop Production," *Naval Research Logistics Quarterly,* Vol. 4, No. 4, December 1957.
7. Malcolm, D. G., "System Simulation—a Fundamental Tool for Industrial Engineering," *Journal of Industrial Engineering,* Vol. 9, No. 3, May–June 1958.
8. Markowitz, H. M., B. Hausner, and H. W. Karr, *SIMCRIPT: A Simulation Programming Language,* Memorandum RM-3310-PR, The RAND Corp., Santa Monica, Calif., November 1962.
9. Rowe, A. J., "Toward a Theory of Scheduling," *The Journal of Industrial Engineering,* Vol. XI, No. 2, March–April 1960.
10. Sprowls, R. C., and M. Asimow, "A Computer Simulated Business Firm," in *Management Controls Systems,* Editors B. G. Malcolm, A. J. Rowe, and L. F. McConnell, John Wiley and Sons, New York, 1959.
11. Sprowls, R. C., and M. Asimow, "A Model of Customer Behavior for the TASK Manufacturing Corporation," *Management Science,* Vol. 8, No. 3, April 1962.
12. *The Job Shop Simulator,* International Business Machines Corp., Data Systems Division, New York, revised, 1960.

REVIEW QUESTIONS

1. Discuss the advantages and possible applications of large-scale system simulation in business and industry.

2. What are some of the possible uses for a model of a simulated firm, such as TASK Manufacturing Corporation?

3. Discuss the subsystems of the TASK Manufacturing Corporation as diagrammed in Figure 1. Are there other interconnections between the subsystems not shown on the diagram?

4. Describe the general characteristics of the "Job Shop Simulator."

5. Discuss the characteristics of the "El Segundo Job Shop Process."

6. Using the Hughes Aircraft Company simulation as a basis for your answer, is there any reason to use any dispatch decision rule other than random selection of orders?

7. What are the general characteristics and limitations of the "Flow Shop Simulator" developed by the General Electric Company?

8. What are the general characteristics of the dynamic output models developed by Jay Forrester?

9. Describe the general effects of a 10 per cent increase in retail sales as shown by Forrester's dynamic output models. What are the basic characteristics of the production-distribution model which cause the kinds of effects noted?

10. Do random fluctuations in sales produce basically different results than a simple 10 per cent step increase in sales?

11. What are the effects of eliminating the distributor level from the production-distribution model? Of tightening time lags due to clerical delays?

12. What are the effects of changing the reaction rate of factory production?

13. Discuss some of the probable future applications of dynamic output models similar to those developed by Jay Forrester.

20

Operational Gaming

Operational games are an application of the general simulation technique which offer considerable promise for education in the business field. To develop a game, we must build a simulation model of the behavior of the system which is the subject of the game in a fashion similar to the methods discussed in the previous section. The data used to drive the model, however, are the decisions of the individuals or teams playing the game. Output from the model shows the effect of the decisions made and represents a feedback of the information which may influence future decisions by the players. Through a sequence of decisions, the equivalent of many months or years of experience with the simulated system can be collapsed into a few hours of play. These games may range from models of fairly limited, rather specific situations, such as the operation of an inventory system, to the broad operation of an enterprise, where the key decisions of the management of a firm are required. In the latter case, the simulated situation may include all major phases of operation and planning, such as organization, financing, market strategy, labor negotiations, as well as the detailed operational decisions of production and inventory planning, scheduling, labor utilization, etc. In some games, teams or players are pitted against a simulated environment, such as in the Univac "Manufacturing Simulation Game," and in others, the game stresses competition between teams, such as in the AMA Management Game, the Carnegie Institute of Technology Management Game, and the two UCLA Management Games.

Uses of Games

In general, games are meant to be a substitute for experience. Whereas previous material, such as graphic and schematic models, programming models, statistical models, and waiting-line models tend to focus on specific kinds of problems in operations systems, games tend to focus on the tasks of operation so that the student must face something comparable to both "jobs" in business and industry, as well as typical problems which occur. One of the beneficial results is that he develops a "feel" for the real decision-making situations. Games can make it possible to apply many of the quantitative techniques and concepts to see their value and limitations in operating situations. Some of the applications of the UCLA games 2 and 3 which have been reported are as follows (10):

1. With undergraduate majors in business and management science at UCLA, to teach basic skills of decision making, to teach concepts in statistics and operations research, and to stimulate students' interest in other business courses.

2. With seniors in management science at Case Institute of Technology, to show that mathematical and statistical techniques in themselves are not sufficient to solve all the problems that a manager faces.

3. With graduate students at Stanford University, to teach how to interpret accounting reports and to pose the problem of defining policies and decisions rules in a way that others can follow effectively.

4. With foreign students at Stanford University, as an "icebreaker" to break down social and cultural barriers among them from different countries.

5. With executives at several schools, to demonstrate what "model" and "simulation" mean and to show their values as managerial tools.

6. With freshmen at Michigan State University, to illustrate what the job of a manager is like and to attract good men toward majors in business administration.

7. With graduate students in an organization theory course at Pennsylvania State College, to let them observe, analyze, and record the structure and behavior of undergraduate teams of players.

8. With industrial engineering students at the University of Michigan, to show the importance of subunits within a firm and to teach the design of reporting and control systems.

9. With students at Case Institute of Technology and the Pennsylvania State College, to get experience in making plans and decisions under conditions of low- and high-time pressure.

10. With graduate students at Harvard University, to show how the functions within a business interact, to show how today's decisions

create tomorrow's environment, and to show the dependence of goal attainment on the planning and execution of a series of decisions.

TWO HAND-COMPUTED GAMES

The two games which follow are illustrative of relatively simple situations where the players are pitted against a simulated environment. Their simplicity makes it possible to play them without the use of a computer. The first deals with the decision of setting production levels for 26 two-week periods in a year in such a way that the total incremental costs are minimized. This game is played for two basic conditions of the environment: (1) when orders average 100,000 cases per period, but vary randomly from this mean rate, and (2) when the average order pattern follows a seasonal curve, with random variation from the average seasonal curve. The second game deals with the operation of a maintenance facility to minimize the combined costs of repair kit inventories and ordering, inventory shortages, labor, labor turnover, outside processing, and machine downtime. It requires decisions to be made for hiring and separation of labor, use of outside processing and overtime, and the ordering and maintenance of inventories.

Production Control Game

Condition 1. You are the production control manager of a company making a single product. Your plant has unlimited capacity within the potential sales range. Orders for your product vary from period to period, and it is your job to devise a production plan that will fill shipping orders each period from available inventory. The goal of the plan should be to minimize the total annual costs for holding inventories, failing to meet orders on time, and changing the current production rate.

Since it takes time to change the production rate, there is a one period interval between the time that you make a decision and the time that the change goes into effect. Thus a decision made at the end of the first period goes into effect during the second period. Any change in the output level must be in thousand-case lots and may not be less than five-thousand cases nor more than ten-thousand cases. Excess production is stored in plant warehouses up to a total capacity of 240,000 cases. Inventory above this amount may be stored in outside facilities at extra cost.

At the beginning of the year, the following rules and conditions apply:

1. Opening inventory—to be furnished by game referee.

2. Current shipments average 100,000 cases per period with the following approximate distribution:
    a. 76 per cent of the time shipments will be between 70,000 and 130,000 cases per period.
    b. 96 per cent of the time shipments will be between 50,000 and 150,000 cases per period.

3. To change the production rate costs $5000 per change, regardless of the magnitude of the change.

4. There is an inventory holding charge of $200 per year for each 1000 cases of average inventory. In addition, each 1000 cases stored in outside facilities costs $500 per year.

5. There is a charge of $750 per period for each 1000 cases ordered which cannot be shipped because of insufficient inventory. (100 per cent back-order rate.)

6. The plant shuts down for vacation during the thirteenth period. Orders continue to be shipped, although production is zero.

Procedure. Figure 1 shows the work sheet to be used. Beginning inventory at the time play starts in period one will be furnished by the game referee.

1. Enter the figure for beginning inventory furnished by the game referee on line 1 under column 2.

2. Set the initial production level for period zero and period one and enter in column 3.

3. Calculate "available" (column 4), the sum of beginning inventory (column 2) for the period plus "production" (column 3) for the previous period.

4. Decide on production levels for the next period by entering the amount in column 3 for period two.

5. Record "orders" for period one in column 5. This figure will be read by the game referee and represents a Monte Carlo sampling from the order distribution. As an example, the orders for period one are shown as 70 in Figure 1.

6. Calculate "ending inventory" (column 6) by subtracting orders for the period from the total available for the period.

7. Calculate "excess inventory" (column 7) by subtracting 240 from the ending inventory for the period. For the example shown in

(1)	(2)	(3)	(4)	(5)	(6)	(7)
Two–Week Period Number	Beginning Inventory, 1000's	Production Level Set, 1000's	Available = Beginning Inventory in Period + Previous Period's Production, 1000's	Orders in Period, Sampled from Order Distribution, 1000's	Ending Inventory = Available − Orders, 1000's	Excess Inventory Over 240, 1000's
0		90				
1	300	90	390	70	320	80
2						
3						
4						
5						
6						
7						
8						
9						
10						
11						
12						
13		Vacation				
14						
15						
16						
17						
18						
19						
20						
21						
22						
23						
24						
25						
26						

Figure 1. Work sheet–production and inventory control game.

Figure 1, the excess inventory which must be stored at extra cost in outside facilities is 80.

8. Transfer the figure for ending inventory to column 2, beginning inventory, for the next period.

9. Repeat for twenty-six periods, making sure to account for the vacation in the thirteenth period during which time no production

will occur, but during which orders will be delivered. If during any period orders exceed the amounts available, simply record negative ending inventory and beginning inventory for the next period. This takes account of the 100 per cent back-order rule.

10. Compute incremental costs. Using the form shown in Figure 2, calculate costs for production changes, inventory costs, excess inventory costs, and stock shortage costs. The total of these four costs represents a measure of the effectiveness of the sequence of decisions made.

Condition 2. In the second condition of the game, all rules for play remain the same. The only thing which has changed is that the order pattern exhibits a seasonality, as shown by Figure 3. Shipments are seasonal, but still average 100,000 cases per period over the entire year. The variability of the order distribution is still expressed by the deviation from mean values as indicated previously. Thus, while the average order level for the fifth period is 60,000 cases,

Cost Calculations	Condition 1	Condition 2
1. Production changes. Multiply the number of changes made in the year by $5000 per change.	_____	_____
2. Inventory holding cost. Total ending inventories for each 2-week period, divide by 26 and multiply the number of 1000 cases resulting by $200. (Do not deduct shortages.)	_____	_____
3. Outside storage facilities. Total excess inventory (over 240,000 for each 2-week period), divide by 26 and multiply by $500.	_____	_____
4. Stock shortage cost. Determine the number of 1000 case shortages and multiply by $750.	_____	_____
5. Total yearly cost.	$_____	$_____

Figure 2. Form for calculating costs.

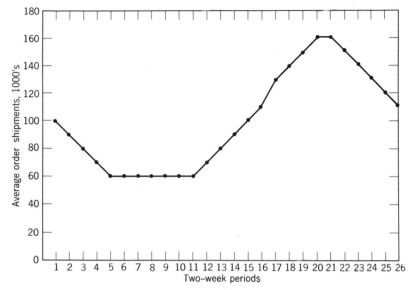

Figure 3. Seasonal pattern of shipments.

as indicated by Figure 3, in any given fifth period, random variation could result in a minimum of no orders, or a maximum of orders for 120,000 cases.

Maintenance Facility Game

You are the manager of a maintenance facility which maintains and overhauls machines. The maintenance facility has capacity within the potential demand. When breakdowns occur, the machines are sent to the facility for either repair or overhaul, and in general, 10 per cent of the breakdowns require overhaul. All repairs must be handled within the repair facility; however, you have the option of sending overhauls to an outside repair facility at a cost of $800 per overhaul, including all labor and materials. You have within your control the number of maintenance mechanics available. You may hire or separate a mechanic for a cost of $300, and you may use overtime up to a limit of 20 per cent of the regular time available. You are also responsible for maintaining inventories of repair kits and overhaul kits required in the repair or overhaul of a machine. If inventory is not available, the machines affected are held over to the following period, or in the case of overhauls, you may decide

1	2	3	4	5	6	7	8	9	10	11	12	13	14	15	16
2–Week Period Number	Work Load						Kit Inventories								
	Repairs			Overhauls			Repair Kits						Overhaul Kits		
	New This Period	Held Over	Total This Period	New This Period	Held Over	Total This Period	Begin-ning Inventory	Orders 2–Period Delivery Enter on Line for Period of Delivery	Orders 1–Period Delivery Enter on Line for Period of Delivery	Used from Column 27	Ending Inventory 8 + 9 + 10−11	Begin-ning Inventory	Orders 2–Period Delivery Enter on Line for Period of Delivery	Orders 1–Period Delivery Enter on Line for Period of Delivery	Used from Column 29
1															
2															
3															
4															
5															
6															
7															
8															
9															
10															
11															
12															
13															
14															
15															
16															
17															
18															
19															
20															
21															
22															
23															
24															
25															
26															
Totals															

Figure 4. Player's work sheet.

to send the machine to the outside processor. Also, if there is not enough mechanic's time available in a given period, repairs and overhauls may be held over to the following period. When repairs or overhauls are held over because of inventory shortages or lack of mechanic's time available, however, machine downtime is extended at a cost of $10 per hour.

Repair breakdowns average twenty per 2-week period, and vary from a minimum of ten to a maximum of thirty. Overhaul breakdowns average two per 2-week period, and vary from zero to four. The service time for a repair averages 10 hours, and varies from 6 to 14 hours, whereas the service time for an in-plant overhaul averages 80 hours, varying from 70 to 90 hours.

Your objective is to operate the maintenance facility in such a way that the incremental costs of downtime, materials, material

17	18	19	20	21	22	23	24	25	26	27	28	29	30	31	32	33
		Mechanic's Time Available			Time Demands					Allocations					Hours Used	
			Hours Available		Repairs		Overhauls		Total	Repairs		Overhauls				
Ending Inventory 13 + 14 + 15 − 16	Number Hired or Separated — Enter on Line for One Period hence with + or − Sign	Number Mechanics Available This Period — Add or Subtract from Column 18	Regular Number Available from Column 19 x 80	Over-time 20% of Column 20	Average Repair Time This Period Given by Game Referee	Repair Hours Required This Period Column 4 x Column 22	Average Overhaul Time This Period Given by Game Referee	Overhaul Hours Required This Period Column 7 x Column 24	Hours Required Column 23 + Column 25	To Be Done in Plant	Carried Over Enter in Column 3 for Next Period	To Be Done in Plant	To Be Done Outside	Carried Over Enter in Column 6 for Next Period	Regular Cannot Exceed Column 20 for This Period	Over-time Cannot Exceed Column 21 for This Period

Figure 4 (continued).

ordering, inventory holding, labor, turnover, and outside processing are at a minimum.

Procedure.

1. Write the number of repairs in column 2 of the player's work sheet (see Figure 4), and the number of overhauls in column 5 for the current period. These figures will be read to players by the game referee.

2. Add columns 2 + 3, and place the total in column 4. Add columns 5 + 6, and place the total in column 7.

3. Determine if kit inventories are adequate for this period's needs. Check column 8 for repair kits and column 13 for overhaul kits. If adequate, enter the tentative carryovers in column 28 and 31 to the next period of those that cannot be processed because of

inventory shortages. These carry-over figures may be altered by subsequent decisions.

4. Calculate the mechanic's time available for the period.

    a. From column 18, determine if mechanics were hired or separated for this period.

    b. Determine mechanics available during this period in column 19.

    c. Determine "regular" time available in column 20. There are 80 hours available per period per mechanic; therefore, multiply the number of mechanics (column 19) by 80.

5. Make the required decisions:

    a. Are workers to be hired or separated for the coming period? If so, enter the number in column 18, for one period hence. Hiring or separating a mechanic costs $300.

    b. Place orders for repair and overhaul kits.

        (1) Normal delivery (two periods). Enter number of kits to be delivered in columns 9 and 14, on the line two periods hence. The cost of placing each order is $10.

        (2) Expedited delivery (one period). Enter number of kits to be delivered in columns 10 and 15. Expedited orders cost $20 each.

    c. Determine the number of overhauls to be done by outside processors. Enter the number in column 30. Outside overhaul costs $800 per overhaul, but this includes the overhaul kit, valued at $200, and results in a reduced machine downtime from 40 hours to 20 hours.

6. Write the average hours to repair and overhaul in columns 22 and 24 respectively. These figures will be read to players by the game referee.

7. Compute time demands:

    a. Repair hours required: multiply the tentative number of repairs to be done this period, column 4 less tentative carryovers in column 28, by the average repair hours in column 22.

    b. Overhaul hours required: multiply the tentative number of overhauls to be done in-plant, column 7 less columns 30 and 31, by the average overhaul hours in column 24.

    c. Total hours required: enter the sum of columns 23 and 24 in column 26.

8. Make final allocations: compare the time demands of column 26 with the mechanic's hours available, columns 20 and 21, to determine if a restriction exists. Note the tentative carryovers due to

kit shortages, column **28** and **31**, and previous decision on outside overhauls, column **30**. Now make final allocations within the restrictions of time available, kit shortages, and outside overhauls; that is, enter the final disposition of this period's breakdown in columns **27, 28, 29, 30** and **31**.

9. Enter carryovers from columns **28** and **31** in columns **3** and **6** respectively for the next period.

10. Compute the time used:

    a. Repair time = column **27** × column **22**.

    b. Overhaul time = column **29** × column **24**.

    c. Total time = sum of *a* and *b*.

    d. If *c* is less than regular time available, enter *c* in column **32**.

    e. If *c* is greater than regular time available, enter regular time available in column **32**, and the excess as overtime in column **33**. Note again the restriction on overtime available in column **21**.

11. Compute ending inventories:

    a. Repair kits:

        (1) Enter kits used in column **11** from column **27**.

        (2) Ending inventory (column **12**) = beginning inventory plus orders received during period, less kits used in period, **(8)** + **(9)** + **(10)** − **(11)**.

        (3) Beginning inventory for the next period (column **8**) = ending inventory for present period.

    b. Overhaul kits:

        (1) Enter kits used in column **16** from column **29**.

        (2) Ending inventory (column **17**) = beginning inventory plus orders received during period, less kits used during period, **(13)** + **(14)** + **(15)** − **(16)**.

        (3) Beginning inventory for next period **(13)** = ending inventory for present period.

12. Repeat procedure for **26** periods.

13. Calculate costs using the form of Figure 5.

Summary

The two hand-computed games just described are representative of simple games with fairly restricted objectives. The number of games that have been designed and are available for play is tremendous. When computing facilities are available, naturally the scope and complexity of possible games which may be used increases tremendously.

1. Downtime cost   = Downtime hours $\times$ 10.00
   Downtime hours = hours for normal in-plant repair or overhaul
                  + hours for outside overhaul
                  + hours for repairs or overhauls carried over
                  = (40) $\times$ (total of cols. 27 + 29)
                  + (20) $\times$ (total of col. 30)
                  + (80 $\times$ (total of cols. 3 + 6)
                  = _____
   Downtime cost   = downtime hours $\times$ 10.00
                  = _____ $\times$ 10.00 = _____

2. Material cost = total kits used $\times$ value/kit
   a. Repair kits ($50.00 each)
        (total of col. 27) $\times$ 50.00
        _____ $\times$ 50.00 = _____
   b. Overhaul kits ($200.00 each)
        (total of col. 29) $\times$ 200.00
        _____ $\times$ 200.00 = _____
   c. Total material cost = $a + b$ = _____

3. Ordering cost = (No. regular orders) $\times$ 10.00
                + (No. expedited orders) $\times$ 20.00
                = _____ $\times$ 10.00 + _____ $\times$ 20.00 _____

4. Inventory holding cost = (average inventory) $\times$ holding cost/unit
   a. Repair kits
        (total col. $\frac{12}{26}$) $\times$ 10.00
        $\dfrac{}{26}$ $\times$ 10.00 = _____
   b. Overhaul kits
        (total col. $\frac{17}{26}$) $\times$ 40.00
        _____ $\times$ 40.00 = _____
        Total inventory holding cost, $a + b$ = _____

5. Labor cost
   a. Regular time = (regular hours available) $\times$ 5.00
                 = (total col. 20) $\times$ 5.00
                 = _____ $\times$ 5.00 = _____
   b. Overtime   = (overtime hours used) $\times$ 7.50
                 = (total col. 33) $\times$ 7.50
                 = _____ $\times$ 7.50 = _____
        Total labor cost, $a + b$ = _____

6. Turnover cost = (No. mechanics hired or separated) $\times$ 300.00
                 = (total col. 18) $\times$ 300.00
                 = _____ $\times$ 300.00 = _____

7. Outside processing cost = (No. overhauls done outside) $\times$ 800.00
                         = (total col. 30) $\times$ 800.00
                         = _____ $\times$ 800.00 = _____
   Total incremental cost, sum of items 1–7 = _____

Figure 5. Form for calculating costs.

REFERENCES

1. Andlinger, G. R., "Business Games—Play One!", *Harvard Business Review,* Vol. XXXVI, No. 2, pp. 115–125, March–April 1958.
2. Andlinger, G. R., "What Can Business Games Do?", *Harvard Business Review,* Vol. XXXVI, No. 4, pp. 148–160, July–August 1958.
3. Cohen, K. J., and E. Rhenman, "The Role of Management Games in Education and Research," *Management Science,* Vol. VII, 1961, pp. 131–161.
4. Craft, C. J., et al., *Management Games,* Reinhold Publishing Company, New York, 1961.
5. Dill, W. R., W. Hoffman, H. J. Leavitt, and T. O'Mara, "Experiences with a Complex Management Game," *California Management Review,* Vol. III, No. 3, pp. 38–51, Spring, 1961.
6. Dill, W. R., "What Management Games Do Best," *Business Horizons,* Fall, 1961.
7. Greenlaw, P. S., et al., *Business Simulation,* Prentice-Hall, Englewood Cliffs, N. J., 1962.
8. Jackson, J. R., "Learning from Experience in Business Decision Games," *California Management Review,* Vol. I, No. 2, 1959, pp. 92–107.
9. *Proceedings of the National Symposium on Management Games,* Center for Research in Business, The University of Kansas, Lawrence, Kansas, May 1959.
10. *Proceedings of the Conference on Business Games,* Edited by W. R. Dill, J. R. Jackson, and J. W. Sweeney, Tulane University, New Orleans, 1961.
11. Shubik, M., "Bibliography on Simulation, Gaming, Artificial Intelligence, and Other Topics," *Journal of the American Statistical Association,* Vol. LV, 1960, pp. 736–751.
12. Vance, S., *Management-Decision Simulation,* McGraw-Hill Book Company, New York, 1960, 50 pp.

part IX
SYNTHESIS

21

Summary and Conclusion

We have studied the major kinds of graphic, mathematical, and simulation models which have been applied to the operational system. What have we learned? How do the materials tie together and relate to other areas of knowledge of formal organizations? Are these models significant in the study of production and operations management?

What we have learned may seem at first to be some detailed knowledge about models of flow and man-machine systems, statistical methods, waiting-line models, programming models, models of investment, and inventory and simulation models. But it should have been more than that. Formal models should also teach us something about the basic structure of certain kinds of important problems. For example, in studying linear programming we learn not only the structure and application of this important model, but we learn something fundamental about allocation problems in general. We learn to handle the effects of interacting and competing demands for limited resources and, perhaps more important, we learn the general nature of optimum solutions. This is important, for these general concepts should carry over into situations where the formal model is not applied. In the practical operating situation, allocations of limited resources must often be made on an intuitive basis either because there is not time for formal analysis, or because the most important variables are not quantifiable. I believe that you can do this best if you understand the basic nature of the formal problem and the probable nature of good solutions. Another excellent example is the general waiting-line model. The individual who understands formal waiting-line models should be able to make a good snap judgment about the level of service to provide in a practical situation, because he real-

585

izes the great value of idle time of the server. The value of idle time, of course, is a concept which runs contrary to our fundamental training to conserve time, yet in the design of many systems provision of apparent overcapacity is the key to success.

Another important concept that the study of formal models fosters is the broader view of any problem, the "system's" view. This was perhaps best demonstrated by our study of inventory models where we discovered progressively that apparent advantages in inventory costs might be counterbalanced by large costs of production fluctuations. In general, we should learn that there is a substitution rate for everything. Sometimes it is better to substitute high labor rates for low time requirements, setup time for run time, scrap costs for direct labor, indirect labor for direct labor, delivery time for labor cost, and so on. The result is that in a production-distribution system we should produce some scrap, some late orders, incur some stock shortages, and have some idle labor. If we have none of these "wastes" we are undoubtedly overcontrolling some factors at extremely high cost to obtain advantages of little relative value. In short, we are suboptimizing.

The newer analytical techniques also involve a *philosophy* worth considering. These new methods are broadly applicable to operational systems, not just the manufacturing case. We need to broaden our thinking and develop the most general cases of the problems with which we deal. Then, a systematic analysis of the special cases puts both the broad problem and the special cases in context. The general model for investment analysis, *CERBS*, is a good example of this. We need to develop generalized models of production-distribution systems which apply to any special situation when the characteristics of that special case are inserted.

There are many things, however, which qualify as models of production or operations systems which we have not studied in this book. Many of these are important areas of specific interest which we should pursue. For example, considerable knowledge exists about labor measurement. We assumed that labor standards existed in many of the specific models which were studied. Yet, the work measurement situation itself represents an analytical model. Plant location analysis has been studied carefully and today is represented by well-developed analytical models. Game theory represents a fascinating analysis of competitive models. The principles of automation and process control are also important to production systems and the general theory of managerial control. Time availability has been our master in eliminating these important and interesting subjects.

It was felt that the models selected for study were the ones of central interest and importance for a basic course.

We should state further that even for the subjects studied we have only scratched the surface. For example, in our study of programming, we considered only linear programming, yet there is considerable literature in the subjects of dynamic, quadratic, and integer programming. It would not be difficult to spend an entire semester on linear programming itself. Our coverage of waiting-line theory dealt with only the most basic models and considered only the steady-state conditions. There is also considerable literature that deals with transient conditions and with other assumptions for arrival and service distributions as well as other queue disciplines. Statistical analysis is a vast field, especially for the research worker. The new field of system simulation is moving so rapidly that it is difficult to say what will have been accomplished and what its position will be among the tools of production and operations analysis only a year hence.

Relationship to Other Fields

Production and operations analysis by the formal models we have discussed is a part of the broader study of formal organizations. Formal organizations do, of course, occur in a wide variety of situations including business, industry, government, religion, and so on. We have discussed the occurrence of production and operations systems in a similar context. The development of the study of formal organizations has at least two main branches:

1. *Decision theory,* which focuses on how decisions should be made. Decision theory develops formal models of rational behavior.
2. *Organizational behavior,* which studies how decisions are actually made. This branch is more empirical and observational in nature and studies individuals, and small and large groups, focusing on actual human behavior in many of the decision-making situations. It has its roots in individual and social psychology, and sociology.

As might be expected, representatives of the two lines of thought are often critical of each other. Since the material that we have studied is more closely allied with decision theory, we will attempt to deal with some of the main criticisms leveled against it and to place the ideas of "how decisions are actually made" in context with formal decision-making models as an approach. Critics imply that the formal decision-making models are irrelevant, or nearly so, because people and their psychosociological characteristics are ignored in these models.

Recent observations in the human relations area often show that a work group, when left to their own devices to plan and organize their efforts, will develop methods of operation which are superior to those specified by some technically oriented person. The picture usually developed is one of the technically oriented person, usually an engineer (who apparently understands things but not people), who has designed a work system. It is assumed that the work system is ideal from the engineer's point of view. The behavioral science researcher enters the picture at this point to experiment with different organizational structures of the group, which ordinarily involve relaxing controls, giving workers greater flexibility in designing and organizing their own work situation. When left to their own devices, the workers reorganize activities to suit themselves, and productivity as well as other measures of effectiveness improve, often considerably. The implied conclusion is, then, that expertise is ineffective since workers can organize a superior system anyway; the important things are the psychological and sociological aspects of the situation, and structure, or formal analysis, are of secondary importance. There are several things wrong with these kinds of observations which make it difficult to draw firm conclusions of any kind.

1. The experimental design of the situation is loose so that we cannot appraise the independent effects of the real variables of the system. Indeed the variables are seldom defined. For example, in such experimental situations, what is the "Hawthorne effect"? Recall that the Hawthorne studies, discussed briefly in Chapter 4, indicated that an experimental group of employees tended to produce spurious experimental results.

2. Was the engineer's solution necessarily an optimal one to be used for comparison? If it was not, all we can say is that an existing design can often be improved. It might have been possible to improve it even more than was accomplished by the work group through careful analysis.

3. Who left the work group as a result of the reorganizations? If productivity went up, the size of the work group was probably reduced. Were the individuals who left the work group the high producers or the low producers? The selections were probably made by the work group itself, and the ones who did not fit into the group's standards may have been the poor producers. The result is that the combination of the Hawthorne effect plus the selection of workers could easily mask the effects of what could actually be poorer basic work methods.

The feeling of the behavioral scientist is apparently that the system designer is at home with rigidity, with everything neatly in its place, whereas work groups perform best when they have flexibility. This is pointed up by the "case of the speeding assembly line" reported by Bavelas* and quoted by Clark.† The setting is a paced line conveyor in a toy factory. "There, a group of girls were allowed to control the speed of the conveyor on which they were working. They sped it up when they felt like working, and they slowed it down when they didn't. Productivity and earnings soared, and soared higher by far than that which the engineers had believed to be normal output. Consequently, the engineers took the control of the lines' speed away from the workers, and restored it to a steadily predictable pace. The girls, apparently, had established an equilibrium of their own, for they all quit in protest."

The interesting thing about this case is that based on research knowledge about the effective design of production lines, neither the engineer's solution nor the work group's solution represents ideal design. Here, formal analysis using a waiting-line model‡ and experimental research§ indicates that rigid pacing at any speed represents a relatively poor solution to serialized operations.

The best design would eliminate rigid conveyor pacing completely, replacing it with a system where the conveyor provided only transportation between the several operations, but allowing queues of material to build up between each of the operations in the sequence. The rationale is simply that the greater flexibility allowed when queues can build up makes it possible for operators to average their slow cycles against their fast cycles in their work-time distribution pattern. The result is more effective utilization of labor on the line. Here is a situation where formal analysis demands flexibility in the design, even more flexibility than the workers themselves had thought desirable. Solutions specified by formal analysis are not

---

* William F. Whyte, et al., *Money and Motivation,* Harper and Brothers, New York, 1955, Chapter X.

† James V. Clark, "A Healthy Organization," *California Management Review,* Vol. IV, No. 4, 1962.

‡ G. C. Hunt, "Sequential Arrays of Waiting Lines," *Operations Research,* Vol. IV, p. 674, 1956.

§ R. Conrad, *Setting the Pace,* Medical Research Council, APU232-55, Applied Psychology Research Units, London, 1955; R. Conrad and B. A. Hille, "Comparison of Paced and Unpaced Performance at a Packing Task," *Occupational Psychology,* Vol. XXIX, No. 1, 1955, pp. 15–28; E. S. Buffa, "Pacing Effects in Production Lines," *Journal of Industrial Engineering,* Vol. XII, No. 6, 1961.

necessarily rigid ones. We should recognize that the thing which work groups constructing their own methods and procedures contribute is not the most effective systems and procedures possible, but a high level of morale and this is certainly not to be minimized.

At the level of local methods and procedures, it may well be that psychosociological factors may be the most important. The evidence to date indicates that this is a sound hypothesis which should be tested by a really well-designed experimental research program. If the conclusion is that letting work groups design their own methods and procedures is the most effective approach, on balance, this means that business and industry should include as a part of worker training an attempt to transmit some of the principles of effective work design. This has been done to an extent in work simplification training programs offered to workers by a few forward-looking companies.

But what about the broader problems of programming, facilities design, and inventory systems which cut across work group lines? Here we are dealing with problems of incredible complexity which transcend the knowledge and capability of the work group. Does the work group understand linear programming, investment policy and theory, statistical theory, and waiting-line theory? Can they do as well as a computer simulation program in evaluating the best dispatch decision rule, or in generating alternate production programs? The point is that there seems to be a realm where the work group might operate effectively, but it is generally at the local level. We soon outrun their capability to make rational decisions when we are talking about problems on a broader level. Here even the local supervisor or a technically oriented person with a local point of view is likely to be inadequate.

Can Formal Models Account for Human Factors?

If we mean that the model directly accounts for human values, the answer is no; however, in many instances we can account for restrictions imposed by management which are intended to reflect the needs of people and work groups. For example, let us consider the nature of the solutions to the problem of relative location of physical facilities described in Chapter 18. For a problem involving twenty departments there are many excellent solutions and perhaps hundreds of good solutions; that is, where the total annual material-handling cost is not more than 5 per cent different from the best solution. If there is good reason for keeping two departments adjacent because of factors related to the social structures of the work groups involved, let this be stated as a requirement. The computer program can accept such a restriction. Also, it can evaluate the economic effect of such a restriction in 0.5 minute of computer time. Although such flexibility in optimal solutions is not always present, it is true for a surprising number of cases. Recall the nature of linear programming solutions where alternate optima exist. We can generate an infinite number of optimal solutions, and there are always solutions which are not optimum, but which are near the optimum, as in the case of the relative location program just discussed. The dish-shaped total incremental cost curve is usually relatively flat near the minimum point. The practical effect of this is that we are not confronted with rigidity in problem solutions, but with great flexibility. As a practical matter, we should always recognize this fact. It can often be used to satisfy other nonquantifiable needs such as those imposed by psychosociological values. One of the great traps of formal models is preoccupation with optimal solutions.

Is It Significant?

Is the material we have studied significant? The production and operations phases of any organization ordinarily account for the largest expenditures for capital, materials, and labor, and represent the vital function of the creation of goods and services in our economy. From a sociological point of view, such systems are of tremendous importance, for they employ the bulk of our labor force, and these people spend a large fraction of their lives working in such systems. Whether or not production systems are effectively designed and operated determines in an important way the real wages and salaries of these people. From an academic point of view, the formal models we have discussed represent the development of a theory of operational systems where none existed only a few years ago. We are witnessing the healthy growth of an applied science. From a practical point of view, the models we have discussed provide insight into the nature of many kinds of operational problems. The manager who has a basic understanding of the models and, therefore, the problems, can be expected to make better and more effective decisions. It is significant!

APPENDIXES

A

Derivation of the Classical Economic Lot Size Model

The total incremental cost equation from page 431 is:

$$TIC = c_H \frac{Q}{2} + c_P \frac{R}{Q} \tag{1}$$

Using the calculus, the first differential of (1) with respect to Q is:

$$\frac{d(TIC)}{dQ} = \frac{1}{2} c_H - \frac{c_P R}{Q^2} \tag{2}$$

recalling that the rule for differentiation of a simple variable $x = ay^n$ is $dx/dy = nay^{n-1}$. For the first term of (1) the equivalent form which must be differentiated is $c_H Q^1/2$, where $c_H/2$ is equivalent to the constant, a. Therefore $dc/dQ = (1)(c_H/2)Q^{1-1}$, since $Q^{1-1} = Q^0 = 1$, and $dc/dQ = c_H/2$.

Similarly, the equivalent form for the second term of (1) is

$$c_P R Q^{-1}$$

where $c_P R$ is equivalent to the constant, a. Therefore,

$$\frac{dc}{dQ} = (-1)(c_P R)Q^{-1-1} = -c_P R Q^{-2} = -\frac{c_P R}{Q^2}$$

The value of equation (2) is, in fact, the slope of the line tangent to the total incremental cost curve. We wish to know the value of Q when this slope is zero; therefore, we set (2) equal to zero, and solve for Q:

$$\frac{c_H}{2} - \frac{c_P R}{Q_0{}^2} = 0$$

$$Q_0{}^2 = \frac{2c_P R}{c_H}$$

and

$$Q_0 = \sqrt{2c_P R / c_H}$$

The cost of an optimal solution may be derived by substituting the value, Q_0, in equation 1.

$$TIC_0 = \frac{c_H Q_0}{2} + c_P \frac{R}{Q_0}$$

$$= c_H \sqrt{\frac{2c_P R / c_H}{2}} + \frac{c_P R}{\sqrt{2c_P R / c_H}}$$

Combining the two terms with the common denominator

$$2\sqrt{2c_P R / c_H}$$

we have

$$TIC_0 = \frac{c_H \times \dfrac{2c_P R}{c_H} + 2c_P R}{2\sqrt{2c_P R / c_H}} = \frac{2c_P R}{\sqrt{2c_P R / c_H}}$$

and

$$TIC_0 = \frac{\sqrt{(2c_P R)^2}}{\sqrt{2c_P R}} \cdot \sqrt{c_H} = \sqrt{2c_P c_H R} \qquad (3)$$

B

Derivation of Lot Size Model Which Accounts for the Price or Value of the Item

The total incremental cost equation from page 434 is:

$$TIC = c_P \frac{R}{Q} + kR + k\frac{Q}{2}F_H \qquad (1)$$

The first differential of (1) with respect to Q is:

$$\frac{d(TIC)}{dQ} = -\frac{c_P R}{Q^2} + \frac{1}{2}kF_H \qquad (2)$$

Setting (2) to zero, we have

$$0 = \frac{-c_P R}{Q_0^2} + \frac{kF_H}{2}$$

$$Q_0^2 = \frac{2c_P R}{kF_H}$$

and

$$Q_0 = \sqrt{\frac{2c_P R}{kF_H}}$$

The cost of an optimal solution may be derived by substituting the value of Q_0 in equation 1.

$$TIC_0 = \frac{c_P R}{\sqrt{2c_P R/kF_H}} + kR + \frac{kF_H}{2} \cdot \sqrt{2c_P R/kF_H}$$

$$= \frac{2c_P R + kF_H \left(\dfrac{2c_P R}{kF_H}\right)}{2\sqrt{2c_P R/kF_H}} + kR$$

$$= \frac{2c_P R}{\sqrt{2c_P R/kF_H}} + kR$$

$$= \sqrt{2c_P kF_H R} + kR$$

C

Derivation of the Number of Production Runs for the Multiproduct Case

Refer to pp. 436–439 for the general setting of the problem and for notation.

Inventory Costs

The maximum inventory for a given product is $(p_i - r_i)t_p$, and the average inventory is $(p_i - r_i)t_p/2$. However, $Q_i = p_i t_p = R_i/n$. Therefore, average inventory can be expressed as

$$\frac{(p_i - r_i)t_p}{2} = (p_i - r_i)\frac{R_i}{2p_i n} = \frac{1 - r_i}{p_i}\frac{R_i}{2n} \tag{1}$$

The annual inventory cost for a given product is then the product of the average inventory, given by (1), and the cost to hold a unit in inventory per year, c_{H_i}, or

$$\frac{c_{H_i}R_i}{2n}\frac{1 - r_i}{p_i} \tag{2}$$

The annual inventory cost for the entire set of m products is, then, the sum of m expressions of the form of (2), or

$$\frac{1}{2n}\sum_{i=1}^{m} c_{H_i}R_i\frac{1 - r_i}{p_i} \tag{3}$$

Setup Costs

The setup costs for a given product are given by c_{p_i}, in dollars per run. Therefore, the total setup cost per year for that product is nc_{p_i}, where n is the number of production runs per year. Finally, the total annual setup cost is the sum of nc_{p_i} for the entire set of m products, or

$$\sum_{i=1}^{m} nc_{p_i}$$

and since n is the same for all products, the total annual setup cost is,

$$n \sum_{i=1}^{m} c_{p_i} \qquad (4)$$

Total Incremental Cost

The total incremental cost associated with the entire set of m products is then

$$TIC = \text{annual setup cost} + \text{annual inventory holding cost}$$

$$= n \sum_{i=1}^{m} c_{p_i} + \frac{1}{2n} \sum_{i=1}^{m} c_{H_i} R_i \frac{1 - r_i}{p_i} \qquad (5)$$

Our objective is to determine the minimum of the TIC curve with respect to n, the number of production runs. Therefore, following the basic procedure outlined in Appendix A for the derivation of the classical lot size model, the first derivative of TIC with respect to n is

$$\frac{d(TIC)}{dn} = \sum_{i=1}^{m} c_{p_i} - \frac{1}{2n^2} \sum_{i=1}^{m} c_{H_i} R_i \frac{1 - r_i}{p_i} = 0$$

solving for n, we have

$$n_0 = \sqrt{\frac{\sum_{i=1}^{m} c_{H_i} R_i (1 - r_i/p_i)}{2 \sum_{i=1}^{m} c_{p_i}}} \qquad (6)$$

The Total Cost of an Optimal Solution, TIC_0

The total cost of an optimal solution is found by substituting n_0 for n in (5), or

$$TIC_0 = n_0 \sum_{i=1}^{m} c_{p_i} + \frac{1}{2n_0} \sum_{i=1}^{m} c_{H_i} R_i \frac{1 - r_i}{p_i}$$

Substituting the expression for n_0 shown in (6) and simplifying leads to

$$TIC_0 = \sqrt{2 \sum_{i=1}^{m} c_{p_i} \sum_{i=1}^{m} c_{H_i} R_i \frac{1 - r_i}{p_i}} \tag{7}$$

D

Tables

TABLE I. Areas Under the Normal Curve

Areas under the normal curve to the left of x for decimal units of σ' from the mean, $\bar{x}'$.

x	Area	x	Area	x	Area	x	Area
$\bar{x}' - 3.0\sigma'$	.0013	$\bar{x}' - 1.5\sigma'$	.0668	$\bar{x}' + .1\sigma'$	.5398	$\bar{x}' + 1.6\sigma'$	.9452
$\bar{x}' - 2.9\sigma'$	.0019	$\bar{x}' - 1.4\sigma'$	.0808	$\bar{x}' + .2\sigma'$	.5793	$\bar{x}' + 1.7\sigma'$	.9554
$\bar{x}' - 2.8\sigma'$	.0026	$\bar{x}' - 1.3\sigma'$	.0968	$\bar{x}' + .3\sigma'$	.6179	$\bar{x}' + 1.8\sigma'$	.9641
$\bar{x}' - 2.7\sigma'$	.0035	$\bar{x}' - 1.2\sigma'$	.1151	$\bar{x}' + .4\sigma'$	.6554	$\bar{x}' + 1.9\sigma'$	.9713
$\bar{x}' - 2.6\sigma'$	.0047	$\bar{x}' - 1.1\sigma'$	.1357	$\bar{x}' + .5\sigma'$	.6915	$\bar{x}' + 2.0\sigma'$	.9772
$\bar{x}' - 2.5\sigma'$	.0062	$\bar{x}' - 1.0\sigma'$	.1587	$\bar{x}' + .6\sigma'$	.7257	$\bar{x}' + 2.1\sigma'$	.9821
$\bar{x}' - 2.4\sigma'$	.0082	$\bar{x}' - .9\sigma'$	.1841	$\bar{x}' + .7\sigma'$	.7580	$\bar{x}' + 2.2\sigma'$	.9861
$\bar{x}' - 2.3\sigma'$	.0107	$\bar{x}' - .8\sigma'$	.2119	$\bar{x}' + .8\sigma'$	.7881	$\bar{x}' + 2.3\sigma'$	.9893
$\bar{x}' - 2.2\sigma'$	.0139	$\bar{x}' - .7\sigma'$	.2420	$\bar{x}' + .9\sigma'$	.8159	$\bar{x}' + 2.4\sigma'$	.9918
$\bar{x}' - 2.1\sigma'$	.0179	$\bar{x}' - .6\sigma'$	.2741	$\bar{x}' + 1.0\sigma'$	.8413	$\bar{x}' + 2.5\sigma'$	.9938
$\bar{x}' - 2.0\sigma'$	.0228	$\bar{x}' - .5\sigma'$	.3085	$\bar{x}' + 1.1\sigma'$	.8643	$\bar{x}' + 2.6\sigma'$	.9953
$\bar{x}' - 1.9\sigma'$	.0287	$\bar{x}' - .4\sigma'$	.3446	$\bar{x}' + 1.2\sigma'$	.8849	$\bar{x}' + 2.7\sigma'$	.9965
$\bar{x}' - 1.8\sigma'$	.0359	$\bar{x}' - .3\sigma'$	.3821	$\bar{x}' + 1.3\sigma'$	.9032	$\bar{x}' + 2.8\sigma'$	.9974
$\bar{x}' - 1.7\sigma'$	.0446	$\bar{x}' - .2\sigma'$	.4207	$\bar{x}' + 1.4\sigma'$	.9192	$\bar{x}' + 2.9\sigma'$	.9981
$\bar{x}' - 1.6\sigma'$	.0548	$\bar{x}' - .1\sigma'$	.4602	$\bar{x}' + 1.5\sigma'$	.9332	$\bar{x}' + 3.0\sigma'$	.9987
		$\bar{x}'$	.5000				

σ' units from the mean, $\bar{x}'$, associated with given values of the area under the normal curve to the left of x.

x	Area	x	Area
$\bar{x}' - 3.090\sigma'$	.001	$\bar{x}' + 3.090\sigma'$	.999
$\bar{x}' - 2.576\sigma'$	.005	$\bar{x}' + 2.576\sigma'$	.995
$\bar{x}' - 2.326\sigma'$	.010	$\bar{x}' + 2.326\sigma'$	.990
$\bar{x}' - 1.960\sigma'$	.025	$\bar{x}' + 1.960\sigma'$	.975
$\bar{x}' - 1.645\sigma'$	.050	$\bar{x}' + 1.645\sigma'$	.950
$\bar{x}' - 1.282\sigma'$	.100	$\bar{x}' + 1.282\sigma'$	.900
$\bar{x}' - 1.036\sigma'$	.150	$\bar{x}' + 1.036\sigma'$	.850
$\bar{x}' - .842\sigma'$	.200	$\bar{x}' + .842\sigma'$	.800
$\bar{x}' - .674\sigma'$	.250	$\bar{x}' + .674\sigma'$	.750
$\bar{x}' - .524\sigma'$	.300	$\bar{x}' + .524\sigma'$	.700
$\bar{x}' - .385\sigma'$	.350	$\bar{x}' + .385\sigma'$	.650
$\bar{x}' - .253\sigma'$	.400	$\bar{x}' + .253\sigma'$	.600
$\bar{x}' - .126\sigma'$	.450	$\bar{x}' + .126\sigma'$	.550
$\bar{x}'$	.500		

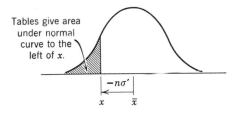

Tables give area under normal curve to the left of x.

$-n\sigma'$

$x \qquad \bar{x}$

TABLE II. Factors Useful in the Construction of Control Charts*

| Number of Observations in Sample, N | Chart for Averages | | | Chart for Standard Deviations | | | | | | Chart for Ranges | | | | | | |
| | Factors for Control Limits | | | Factors for Central Line | | Factors for Control Limits | | | | Factors for Central Line | | Factors for Control Limits | | | | |
	A	A_1	A_2	c_2	$1/c_2$	B_1	B_2	B_3	B_4	d_2	$1/d_2$	d_2	D_1	D_2	D_3	D_4
2	2.121	3.760	1.880	0.5642	1.7725	0	1.843	0	3.267	1.128	0.8865	0.853	0	3.686	0	3.267
3	1.732	2.394	1.023	0.7236	1.3820	0	1.858	0	2.568	1.693	0.5907	0.888	0	4.358	0	2.575
4	1.500	1.880	0.729	0.7979	1.2533	0	1.808	0	2.266	2.059	0.4857	0.880	0	4.698	0	2.282
5	1.342	1.596	0.577	0.8407	1.1894	0	1.756	0	2.089	2.326	0.4299	0.864	0	4.918	0	2.115
6	1.225	1.410	0.483	0.8686	1.1512	0.026	1.711	0.030	1.970	2.534	0.3946	0.848	0	5.078	0	2.004
7	1.134	1.277	0.419	0.8882	1.1259	0.105	1.672	0.118	1.882	2.704	0.3698	0.833	0.205	5.203	0.076	1.924
8	1.061	1.175	0.373	0.9027	1.1078	0.167	1.638	0.185	1.815	2.847	0.3512	0.820	0.387	5.307	0.136	1.864
9	1.000	1.094	0.337	0.9139	1.0942	0.219	1.609	0.239	1.701	2.970	0.3367	0.808	0.546	5.394	0.184	1.816
10	0.949	1.028	0.308	0.9227	1.0837	0.262	1.584	0.284	1.716	3.078	0.3249	0.797	0.687	5.469	0.223	1.777
11	0.905	0.973	0.285	0.9300	1.0753	0.299	1.561	0.321	1.679	3.173	0.3152	0.787	0.812	5.534	0.256	1.744
12	0.866	0.925	0.266	0.9359	1.0684	0.331	1.541	0.354	1.646	3.258	0.3069	0.778	0.924	5.592	0.284	1.716
13	0.832	0.884	0.249	0.9410	1.0627	0.359	1.523	0.382	1.618	3.336	0.2998	0.770	1.026	5.646	0.308	1.692
14	0.802	0.848	0.235	0.9453	1.0579	0.384	1.507	0.406	1.594	3.407	0.2935	0.762	1.121	5.693	0.329	1.671
15	0.775	0.816	0.223	0.9490	1.0537	0.406	1.492	0.428	1.572	3.472	0.2880	0.755	1.207	5.737	0.348	1.652
16	0.750	0.788	0.212	0.9523	1.0501	0.427	1.478	0.448	1.552	3.532	0.2831	0.749	1.285	5.779	0.364	1.636
17	0.728	0.762	0.203	0.9551	1.0470	0.445	1.465	0.466	1.534	3.588	0.2787	0.743	1.359	5.817	0.379	1.621
18	0.707	0.738	0.194	0.9576	1.0442	0.461	1.454	0.482	1.518	3.640	0.2747	0.738	1.426	5.854	0.392	1.608
19	0.688	0.717	0.187	0.9599	1.0418	0.477	1.443	0.497	1.503	3.689	0.2711	0.733	1.490	5.888	0.404	1.596
20	0.671	0.697	0.180	0.9619	1.0396	0.491	1.433	0.510	1.490	3.735	0.2677	0.729	1.548	5.922	0.414	1.586
21	0.655	0.679	0.173	0.9638	1.0376	0.504	1.424	0.523	1.477	3.778	0.2647	0.724	1.606	5.950	0.425	1.575
22	0.640	0.662	0.167	0.9655	1.0358	0.516	1.415	0.534	1.466	3.819	0.2618	0.720	1.659	5.979	0.434	1.566
23	0.626	0.647	0.162	0.9670	1.0342	0.527	1.407	0.545	1.455	3.858	0.2592	0.716	1.710	6.006	0.443	1.557
24	0.612	0.632	0.157	0.9684	1.0327	0.538	1.399	0.555	1.445	3.895	0.2567	0.712	1.759	6.031	0.452	1.548
25	0.600	0.619	0.153	0.9696	1.0313	0.548	1.392	0.565	1.435	3.931	0.2544	0.709	1.804	6.058	0.459	1.541
Over 25	$\dfrac{3}{\sqrt{n}}$	$\dfrac{3}{\sqrt{n}}$	—	—	—	†	‡	†	‡	—	—	—	—	—	—	—

$$\dagger\; 1 - \frac{3}{\sqrt{2n}} \qquad\qquad \ddagger\; 1 + \frac{3}{\sqrt{2n}}$$

Chart	Central Line	3σ Control Limits
$\bar{X}$	$\bar{X}$	$\bar{X} \pm A_1 s_x$ or
		$\bar{X} \pm A_2 \bar{R}$
	μ_x	$\mu_x \pm A\sigma_x$
R	$\bar{R}$	$D_3 \bar{R}$ and $D_4 \bar{R}$
	$d_2 \sigma_x$	$D_1 \sigma_x$ and $D_2 \sigma_x$
σ_x	s_x	$B_3 s_x$ and $B_4 s_x$
	σ_x	$B_1 \sigma_x$ and $B_2 \sigma_x$

Definitions: $A = 3/\sqrt{n}$, $A_1 = \dfrac{3}{c_2\sqrt{n}}$, $A_2 = \dfrac{3}{d_2\sqrt{n}}$, $B_1 = c_2 - K$,

$B_2 = c_2 + K$, $B_3 = 1 - \dfrac{K}{c_2}$, $B_4 = 1 + \dfrac{K}{c_2}$, $D_1 = d_2 - 3d_3$, $D_2 = d_2 + 3d_3$,

$D_3 = 1 - 3\dfrac{d_3}{d_2}$, and $D_4 = 1 + 3\dfrac{d_3}{d_2}$, where $K = 3\sqrt{\dfrac{(n-1)}{n}} - c_2{}^2$.

Warning: The fourth significant figures for D_1, D_2, D_3, and D_4 are in doubt for N greater than 5.

* Reproduced with permission from Table B2 of the *A.S.T.M. Manual on Quality Control of Materials*, p. 115. The c_2 factor is also given in Table 29 of W. A. Shewhart, *Economic Control of Quality of Manufactured Product*, D. Van Nostrand, Princeton, N. J., 1931, p. 185.

TABLE III. Finite Queuing Tables*
POPULATION 5

X	M	D	F	X	M	D	F	X	M	D	F
POPULATION			5	.100	1	.386	.950	.200	2	.194	.976
				.105	2	.059	.997		1	.689	.801
.012	1	.048	.999		1	.404	.945	.210	3	.032	.998
.019	1	.076	.998	.110	2	.065	.996		2	.211	.973
.025	1	.100	.997		1	.421	.939		1	.713	.783
.030	1	.120	.996	.115	2	.071	.995	.220	3	.036	.997
.034	1	.135	.995		1	.439	.933		2	.229	.969
.036	1	.143	.994	.120	2	.076	.995		1	.735	.765
.040	1	.159	.993		1	.456	.927	.230	3	.041	.997
.042	1	.167	.992	.125	2	.082	.994		2	.247	.965
.044	1	.175	.991		1	.473	.920		1	.756	.747
.046	1	.183	.990	.130	2	.089	.993	.240	3	.046	.996
.050	1	.198	.989		1	.489	.914		2	.265	.960
.052	1	.206	.988	.135	2	.095	.993		1	.775	.730
.054	1	.214	.987		1	.505	.907	.250	3	.052	.995
.056	2	.018	.999	.140	2	.102	.992		2	.284	.955
	1	.222	.985		1	.521	.900		1	.794	.712
.058	2	.019	.999	.145	3	.011	.999	.260	3	.058	.994
	1	.229	.984		2	.109	.991		2	.303	.950
.060	2	.020	.999		1	.537	.892		1	.811	.695
	1	.237	.983	.150	3	.012	.999	.270	3	.064	.994
.062	2	.022	.999		2	.115	.990		2	.323	.944
	1	.245	.982		1	.553	.885		1	.827	.677
.064	2	.023	.999	.155	3	.013	.999	.280	3	.071	.993
	1	.253	.981		2	.123	.989		2	.342	.938
.066	2	.024	.999		1	.568	.877		1	.842	.661
	1	.260	.979	.160	3	.015	.999	.290	4	.007	.999
.068	2	.026	.999		2	.130	.988		3	.079	.992
	1	.268	.978		1	.582	.869		2	.362	.932
.070	2	.027	.999	.165	3	.016	.999		1	.856	.644
	1	.275	.977		2	.137	.987	.300	4	.008	.999
.075	2	.031	.999		1	.597	.861		3	.086	.990
	1	.294	.973	.170	3	.017	.999		2	.382	.926
.080	2	.035	.998		2	.145	.985		1	.869	.628
	1	.313	.969		1	.611	.853	.310	4	.009	.999
.085	2	.040	.998	.180	3	.021	.999		3	.094	.989
	1	.332	.965		2	.161	.983		2	.402	.919
.090	2	.044	.998		1	.638	.836		1	.881	.613
	1	.350	.960	.190	3	.024	.998	.320	4	.010	.999
.095	2	.049	.997		2	.177	.980		3	.103	.988
	1	.368	.955		1	.665	.819		2	.422	.912
.100	2	.054	.997	.200	3	.028	.998		1	.892	.597

* From L. G. Peck and R. N. Hazelwood, *Finite Queuing Tables*, John Wiley and Sons, New York, 1958.

TABLE III (Continued). Finite Queuing Tables

POPULATION 5–10

X	M	D	F	X	M	D	F	X	M	D	F
.330	4	.012	.999	.520	2	.779	.728	POPULATION			10
	3	.112	.986		1	.988	.384				
	2	.442	.904	.540	4	.085	.989	.016	1	.144	.997
	1	.902	.583		3	.392	.917	.019	1	.170	.996
.340	4	.013	.999		2	.806	.708	.021	1	.188	.995
	3	.121	.985		1	.991	.370	.023	1	.206	.994
	2	.462	.896	.560	4	.098	.986	.025	1	.224	.993
	1	.911	.569		3	.426	.906	.026	1	.232	.992
.360	4	.017	.998		2	.831	.689	.028	1	.250	.991
	3	.141	.981		1	.993	.357	.030	1	.268	.990
	2	.501	.880	.580	4	.113	.984	.032	2	.033	.999
	1	.927	.542		3	.461	.895		1	.285	.988
.380	4	.021	.998		2	.854	.670	.034	2	.037	.999
	3	.163	.976		1	.994	.345		1	.302	.986
	2	.540	.863	.600	4	.130	.981	.036	2	.041	.999
	1	.941	.516		3	.497	.883		1	.320	.984
.400	4	.026	.997		2	.875	.652	.038	2	.046	.999
	3	.186	.972		1	.996	.333		1	.337	.982
	2	.579	.845	.650	4	.179	.972	.040	2	.050	.999
	1	.952	.493		3	.588	.850		1	.354	.980
.420	4	.031	.997		2	.918	.608	.042	2	.055	.999
.420	3	.211	.966		1	.998	.308		1	.371	.978
	2	.616	.826	.700	4	.240	.960	.044	2	.060	.998
	1	.961	.471		3	.678	.815		1	.388	.975
.440	4	.037	.996		2	.950	.568	.046	2	.065	.998
	3	.238	.960		1	.999	.286		1	.404	.973
	2	.652	.807	.750	4	.316	.944	.048	2	.071	.998
	1	.969	.451		3	.763	.777		1	.421	.970
.460	4	.045	.995		2	.972	.532	.050	2	.076	.998
	3	.266	.953	.800	4	.410	.924		1	.437	.967
	2	.686	.787		3	.841	.739	.052	2	.082	.997
	1	.975	.432		2	.987	.500		1	.454	.963
.480	4	.053	.994	.850	4	.522	.900	.054	2	.088	.997
	3	.296	.945		3	.907	.702		1	.470	.960
	2	.719	.767		2	.995	.470	.056	2	.094	.997
	1	.980	.415	.900	4	.656	.871		1	.486	.956
.500	4	.063	.992		3	.957	.666	.058	2	.100	.996
	3	.327	.936		2	.998	.444		1	.501	.953
	2	.750	.748	.950	4	.815	.838	.060	2	.106	.996
	1	.985	.399		3	.989	.631		1	.517	.949
.520	4	.073	.991					.062	2	.113	.996
	3	.359	.927						1	.532	.945

TABLE III (Continued)

POPULATION 10

X	M	D	F	X	M	D	F	X	M	D	F
.064	2	.119	.995	.125	3	.100	.994	.180	2	.614	.890
	1	.547	.940		2	.369	.962		1	.975	.549
.066	2	.126	.995		1	.878	.737	.190	5	.016	.999
	1	.562	.936	.130	4	.022	.999		4	.078	.995
.068	3	.020	.999		3	.110	.994		3	.269	.973
	2	.133	.994		2	.392	.958		2	.654	.873
	1	.577	.931		1	.893	.718		1	.982	.522
.070	3	.022	.999	.135	4	.025	.999	.200	5	.020	.999
	2	.140	.994		3	.121	.993		4	.092	.994
	1	.591	.926		2	.415	.952		3	.300	.968
.075	3	.026	.999		1	.907	.699		2	.692	.854
	2	.158	.992	.140	4	.028	.999		1	.987	.497
	1	.627	.913		3	.132	.991	.210	5	.025	.999
.080	3	.031	.999		2	.437	.947		4	.108	.992
	2	.177	.990		1	.919	.680		3	.333	.961
	1	.660	.899	.145	4	.032	.999		2	.728	.835
.085	3	.037	.999		3	.144	.990		1	.990	.474
	2	.196	.988		2	.460	.941	.220	5	.030	.998
	1	.692	.883		1	.929	.662		4	.124	.990
.090	3	.043	.998	.150	4	.036	.998		3	.366	.954
	2	.216	.986		3	.156	.989		2	.761	.815
.090	1	.722	.867		2	.483	.935		1	.993	.453
.095	3	.049	.998		1	.939	.644	.230	5	.037	.998
	2	.237	.984	.155	4	.040	.998		4	.142	.988
	1	.750	.850		3	.169	.987		3	.400	.947
.100	3	.056	.998		2	.505	.928		2	.791	.794
	2	.258	.981		1	.947	.627		1	.995	.434
	1	.776	.832	.160	4	.044	.998	.240	5	.044	.997
.105	3	.064	.997		3	.182	.986		4	.162	.986
	2	.279	.978		2	.528	.921		3	.434	.938
	1	.800	.814		1	.954	.610		2	.819	.774
.110	3	.072	.997	.165	4	.049	.997		1	.996	.416
	2	.301	.974		3	.195	.984	.250	6	.010	.999
	1	.822	.795		2	.550	.914		5	.052	.997
.115	3	.081	.996		1	.961	.594		4	.183	.983
	2	.324	.971	.170	4	.054	.997		3	.469	.929
	1	.843	.776		3	.209	.982		2	.844	.753
.120	4	.016	.999		2	.571	.906		1	.997	.400
	3	.090	.995		1	.966	.579	.260	6	.013	.999
	2	.346	.967	.180	5	.013	.999		5	.060	.996
	1	.861	.756		4	.066	.996		4	.205	.980
.125	4	.019	.999		3	.238	.978		3	.503	.919

TABLE III (Continued). Finite Queuing Tables

POPULATION 10

X	M	D	F	X	M	D	F	X	M	D	F
.260	2	.866	.732	.340	6	.049	.997	.480	8	.015	.999
	1	.998	.384		5	.168	.983		7	.074	.994
.270	6	.015	.999		4	.416	.938		6	.230	.973
	5	.070	.995		3	.750	.816		5	.499	.916
	4	.228	.976		2	.968	.584		4	.791	.799
	3	.537	.908	.360	7	.014	.999		3	.961	.621
	2	.886	.712		6	.064	.995		2	.998	.417
	1	.999	.370		5	.205	.978	.500	8	.020	.999
.280	6	.018	.999		4	.474	.923		7	.093	.992
	5	.081	.994		3	.798	.787		6	.271	.966
	4	.252	.972		2	.978	.553		5	.553	.901
	3	.571	.896	.380	7	.019	.999		4	.830	.775
	2	.903	.692		6	.083	.993		3	.972	.598
	1	.999	.357		5	.247	.971		2	.999	.400
.290	6	.022	.999		4	.533	.906	.520	8	.026	.998
	5	.093	.993		3	.840	.758		7	.115	.989
	4	.278	.968		2	.986	.525		6	.316	.958
	3	.603	.884	.400	7	.026	.998		5	.606	.884
	2	.918	.672		6	.105	.991		4	.864	.752
	1	.999	.345		5	.292	.963		3	.980	.575
.300	6	.026	.998		4	.591	.887		2	.999	.385
.300	5	.106	.991		3	.875	.728	.540	8	.034	.997
	4	.304	.963		2	.991	.499		7	.141	.986
	3	.635	.872	.420	7	.034	.993		6	.363	.949
	2	.932	.653		6	.130	.987		5	.658	.867
	1	.999	.333		5	.341	.954		4	.893	.729
.310	6	.031	.998		4	.646	.866		3	.986	.555
	5	.120	.990		3	.905	.700	.560	8	.044	.996
	4	.331	.957		2	.994	.476		7	.171	.982
	3	.666	.858	.440	7	.045	.997		6	.413	.939
	2	.943	.635		6	.160	.984		5	.707	.848
.320	6	.036	.998		5	.392	.943		4	.917	.706
	5	.135	.988		4	.698	.845		3	.991	.535
	4	.359	.952		3	.928	.672	.580	8	.057	.995
	3	.695	.845		2	.996	.454		7	.204	.977
	2	.952	.617	.460	8	.011	.999		6	.465	.927
.330	6	.042	.997		7	.058	.995		5	.753	.829
	5	.151	.986		6	.193	.979		4	.937	.684
	4	.387	.945		5	.445	.930		3	.994	.517
	3	.723	.831		4	.747	.822	.600	9	.010	.999
	2	.961	.600		3	.947	.646		8	.072	.994
.340	7	.010	.999		2	.998	.435		7	.242	.972

TABLE III (Continued)

POPULATION 10–20

X	M	D	F	X	M	D	F	X	M	D	F
.600	6	.518	.915	POPULATION			20	.040	2	.202	.994
	5	.795	.809						1	.712	.929
	4	.953	.663	.005	1	.095	.999	.042	3	.047	.999
	3	.996	.500	.009	1	.171	.998		2	.219	.993
.650	9	.021	.999	.011	1	.208	.997		1	.740	.918
	8	.123	.988	.013	1	.246	.996	.044	3	.053	.999
	7	.353	.954	.014	1	.265	.995		2	.237	.992
	6	.651	.878	.015	1	.283	.994		1	.767	.906
	5	.882	.759	.016	1	.302	.993	.046	3	.059	.999
	4	.980	.614	.017	1	.321	.992		2	.255	.991
	3	.999	.461	.018	2	.048	.999		1	.792	.894
.700	9	.040	.997		1	.339	.991	.048	3	.066	.999
	8	.200	.979	.019	2	.053	.999		2	.274	.989
	7	.484	.929		1	.358	.990		1	.815	.881
	6	.772	.836	.020	2	.058	.999	.050	3	.073	.998
	5	.940	.711		1	.376	.989		2	.293	.988
	4	.992	.571	.021	2	.064	.999		1	.837	.866
.750	9	.075	.994		1	.394	.987	.052	3	.080	.998
	8	.307	.965	.022	2	.070	.999		2	.312	.986
	7	.626	.897		1	.412	.986		1	.858	.851
	6	.870	.792	.023	2	.075	.999	.054	3	.088	.998
.750	5	.975	.666		1	.431	.984		2	.332	.984
	4	.998	.533	.024	2	.082	.999		1	.876	.835
.800	9	.134	.988		1	.449	.982	.056	3	.097	.997
	8	.446	.944	.025	2	.088	.999		2	.352	.982
	7	.763	.859		1	.466	.980		1	.893	.819
	6	.939	.747	.026	2	.094	.998	.058	3	.105	.997
	5	.991	.625		1	.484	.978		2	.372	.980
	4	.999	.500	.028	2	.108	.998		1	.908	.802
.850	9	.232	.979		1	.519	.973	.060	4	.026	.999
	8	.611	.916	.030	2	.122	.998		3	.115	.997
	7	.879	.818		1	.553	.968		2	.392	.978
	6	.978	.705	.032	2	.137	.997		1	.922	.785
	5	.998	.588		1	.587	.962	.062	4	.029	.999
.900	9	.387	.963	.034	2	.152	.996		3	.124	.996
	8	.785	.881		1	.620	.955		2	.413	.975
	7	.957	.777	.036	2	.168	.996		1	.934	.768
	6	.995	.667		1	.651	.947	.064	4	.032	.999
.950	9	.630	.938	.038	3	.036	.999		3	.134	.996
	8	.934	.841		2	.185	.995		2	.433	.972
	7	.994	.737		1	.682	.938		1	.944	.751
				.040	3	.041	.999	.066	4	.036	.999

TABLE III (Continued). Finite Queuing Tables

POPULATION 20

X	M	D	F	X	M	D	F	X	M	D	F
.066	3	.144	.995	.105	1	.999	.476	.150	4	.388	.968
	2	.454	.969	.110	5	.055	.998		3	.728	.887
	1	.953	.733		4	.172	.992		2	.976	.661
.068	4	.039	.999		3	.438	.964	.155	7	.021	.999
	3	.155	.995		2	.842	.837		6	.068	.997
	2	.474	.966	.115	5	.065	.998		5	.185	.990
	1	.061	.716		4	.195	.990		4	.419	.963
.070	4	.043	.999		3	.476	.958		3	.758	.874
	3	.165	.994		2	.870	.816		2	.982	.641
	2	.495	.962	.120	6	.022	.999	.160	7	.024	.999
	1	.967	.699		5	.076	.997		6	.077	.997
.075	4	.054	.999		4	.219	.988		5	.205	.988
	3	.194	.992		3	.514	.950		4	.450	.957
	2	.545	.953		2	.895	.793		3	.787	.860
	1	.980	.659	.125	6	.026	.999		2	.987	.622
.080	4	.066	.998		5	.088	.997	.165	7	.029	.999
	3	.225	.990		4	.245	.986		6	.088	.996
.080	2	.595	.941		3	.552	.942		5	.226	.986
	1	.988	.621		2	.916	.770		4	.482	.951
.085	4	.080	.997	.130	6	.031	.999		3	.813	.845
	3	.257	.987		5	.101	.996		2	.990	.604
	2	.643	.928		4	.271	.983	.170	7	.033	.999
	1	.993	.586		3	.589	.933		6	.099	.995
.090	5	.025	.999		2	.934	.748		5	.248	.983
	4	.095	.997	.135	6	.037	.999		4	.513	.945
	3	.291	.984		5	.116	.995		3	.838	.830
	2	.689	.913		4	.299	.980		2	.993	.587
	1	.996	.554		3	.626	.923	.180	7	.044	.998
.095	5	.031	.999		2	.948	.725		6	.125	.994
	4	.112	.996	.140	6	.043	.998		5	.295	.978
	3	.326	.980		5	.131	.994		4	.575	.930
	2	.733	.896		4	.328	.976		3	.879	.799
	1	.998	.526		3	.661	.912		2	.996	.555
.100	5	.038	.999		2	.960	.703	.190	8	.018	.999
	4	.131	.995	.145	6	.051	.998		7	.058	.998
	3	.363	.975		5	.148	.993		6	.154	.991
	2	.773	.878		4	.358	.972		5	.345	.971
	1	.999	.500		3	.695	.900		4	.636	.914
.105	5	.046	.999		2	.969	.682		3	.913	.768
	4	.151	.993	.150	7	.017	.999		2	.998	.526
	3	.400	.970		6	.059	.998	.200	8	.025	.999
	2	.809	.858		5	.166	.991		7	.074	.997

TABLE III (Continued)

POPULATION 20

X	M	D	F	X	M	D	F	X	M	D	F
.200	6	.187	.988	.260	6	.446	.953	.310	5	.892	.788
	5	.397	.963		5	.712	.884		4	.985	.643
	4	.693	.895		4	.924	.755	.320	11	.018	.999
	3	.938	.736		3	.995	.576		10	.053	.997
	2	.999	.500	.270	10	.016	.999		9	.130	.992
.210	8	.033	.999		9	.049	.998		8	.272	.977
	7	.093	.995		8	.125	.992		7	.483	.944
	6	.223	.985		7	.270	.978		6	.727	.878
	5	.451	.954		6	.495	.943		5	.915	.768
	4	.745	.874		5	.757	.867		4	.989	.624
	3	.958	.706		4	.943	.731	.330	11	.023	.999
	2	.999	.476		3	.997	.555		10	.065	.997
.220	8	.043	.998	.280	10	.021	.999		9	.154	.990
	7	.115	.994		9	.061	.997		8	.309	.973
	6	.263	.980		8	.149	.990		7	.529	.935
	5	.505	.943		7	.309	.973		6	.766	.862
	4	.793	.852		6	.544	.932		5	.933	.748
	3	.971	.677		5	.797	.848		4	.993	.605
.230	9	.018	.999		4	.958	.708	.340	11	.029	.999
	8	.054	.998		3	.998	.536		10	.079	.996
	7	.140	.992	.290	10	.027	.999		9	.179	.987
.230	6	.306	.975		9	.075	.996		8	.347	.967
	5	.560	.931		8	.176	.988		7	.573	.924
	4	.834	.828		7	.351	.967		6	.802	.846
	3	.981	.649		6	.592	.920		5	.949	.729
.240	9	.024	.999		5	.833	.828		4	.995	.588
	8	.068	.997		4	.970	.685	.360	12	.015	.999
	7	.168	.989		3	.999	.517		11	.045	.998
	6	.351	.969	.300	10	.034	.998		10	.112	.993
	5	.613	.917		9	.091	.995		9	.237	.981
	4	.870	.804		8	.205	.985		8	.429	.954
	3	.988	.623		7	.394	.961		7	.660	.901
.250	9	.031	.999		6	.639	.907		6	.863	.812
	8	.085	.996		5	.865	.808		5	.971	.691
	7	.199	.986		4	.978	.664		4	.998	.555
	6	.398	.961		3	.999	.500	.380	12	.024	.999
	5	.664	.901	.310	11	.014	.999		11	.067	.996
	4	.900	.780		10	.043	.998		10	.154	.989
	3	.992	.599		9	.110	.993		9	.305	.973
.260	9	.039	.998		8	.237	.981		8	.513	.938
	8	.104	.994		7	.438	.953		7	.739	.874
	7	.233	.983		6	.684	.893		6	.909	.777

TABLE III (Continued). Finite Queuing Tables
POPULATION 20

X	M	D	F	X	M	D	F	X	M	D	F
.380	5	.984	.656	.480	11	.289	.974	.560	8	.976	.713
	4	.999	.526		10	.484	.944		7	.996	.625
.400	13	.012	.999		9	.695	.893	.580	16	.015	.999
	12	.037	.998		8	.867	.819		15	.051	.997
	11	.095	.994		7	.962	.726		14	.129	.991
	10	.205	.984		6	.994	.625		13	.266	.978
	9	.370	.962	.500	14	.033	.998		12	.455	.952
	8	.598	.918		13	.088	.995		11	.662	.908
	7	.807	.845		12	.194	.985		10	.835	.847
	6	.942	.744		11	.358	.965		9	.941	.772
	5	.992	.624		10	.563	.929		8	.986	.689
.420	13	.019	.999		9	.764	.870		7	.998	.603
	12	.055	.997		8	.908	.791	.600	16	.023	.999
	11	.131	.991		7	.977	.698		15	.072	.996
	10	.265	.977		6	.997	.600		14	.171	.988
	9	.458	.949	.520	15	.015	.999		13	.331	.970
	8	.678	.896		14	.048	.997		12	.532	.938
	7	.863	.815		13	.120	.992		11	.732	.889
	6	.965	.711		12	.248	.979		10	.882	.824
	5	.996	.595		11	.432	.954		9	.962	.748
.440	13	.029	.999		10	.641	.911		8	.992	.666
.440	12	.078	.995		9	.824	.846		7	.999	.583
	11	.175	.987		8	.939	.764	.650	17	.017	.999
	10	.333	.969		7	.987	.672		16	.061	.997
	9	.540	.933		6	.998	.577		15	.156	.989
	8	.751	.872	.540	15	.023	.999		14	.314	.973
	7	.907	.785		14	.069	.996		13	.518	.943
	6	.980	.680		13	.161	.988		12	.720	.898
	5	.998	.568		12	.311	.972		11	.872	.837
.460	14	.014	.999		11	.509	.941		10	.957	.767
	13	.043	.998		10	.713	.891		9	.990	.692
	12	.109	.993		9	.873	.821		8	.998	.615
	11	.228	.982		8	.961	.738	.700	17	.047	.998
	10	.407	.958		7	.993	.648		16	.137	.991
	9	.620	.914		6	.999	.556		15	.295	.976
	8	.815	.846	.560	15	.035	.998		14	.503	.948
	7	.939	.755		14	.095	.994		13	.710	.905
	6	.989	.651		13	.209	.984		12	.866	.849
	5	.999	.543		12	.381	.963		11	.953	.783
.480	14	.022	.999		11	.586	.926		10	.988	.714
	13	.063	.996		10	.778	.869		9	.998	.643
	12	.147	.990		9	.912	.796	.750	18	.031	.999

TABLE III (Continued)

POPULATION 20–30

X	M	D	F
.750	17	.113	.993
	16	.272	.980
	15	.487	.954
	14	.703	.913
	13	.864	.859
	12	.952	.798
	11	.988	.733
	10	.998	.667
.800	19	.014	.999
	18	.084	.996
	17	.242	.984
	16	.470	.959
	15	.700	.920
	14	.867	.869
	13	.955	.811
	12	.989	.750
	11	.998	.687
.850	19	.046	.998
	18	.201	.988
	17	.451	.965
	16	.703	.927
.850	15	.877	.878
	14	.962	.823
	13	.991	.765
	12	.998	.706
.900	19	.135	.994
	18	.425	.972
	17	.717	.935
	16	.898	.886
	15	.973	.833
	14	.995	.778
	13	.999	.722
.950	19	.377	.981
	18	.760	.943
	17	.939	.894
	16	.989	.842
	15	.999	.789

POPULATION 30

X	M	D	F
.004	1	.116	.999
.007	1	.203	.998
.009	1	.260	.997
.010	1	.289	.996
.011	1	.317	.995
.012	1	.346	.994
.013	1	.374	.993
.014	2	.067	.999
	1	.403	.991
.015	2	.076	.999
	1	.431	.989
.016	2	.085	.999
	1	.458	.987
.017	2	.095	.999
	1	.486	.985
.018	2	.105	.999
	1	.513	.983
.019	2	.116	.999
	1	.541	.980
.020	2	.127	.998
	1	.567	.976
.021	2	.139	.998
	1	.594	.973
.022	2	.151	.998
	1	.620	.969
.023	2	.163	.997
.023	1	.645	.965
.024	2	.175	.997
	1	.670	.960
.025	2	.188	.996
	1	.694	.954
.026	2	.201	.996
	1	.718	.948
.028	3	.051	.999
	2	.229	.995
	1	.763	.935
.030	3	.060	.999
	2	.257	.994
	1	.805	.918
.032	3	.071	.999

X	M	D	F
.032	2	.286	.992
	1	.843	.899
.034	3	.083	.999
	2	.316	.990
	1	.876	.877
.036	3	.095	.998
	2	.347	.988
	1	.905	.853
.038	3	.109	.998
	-2	.378	.986
	1	.929	.827
.040	3	.123	.997
	2	.410	.983
	1	.948	.800
.042	3	.138	.997
	2	.442	.980
	1	.963	.772
.044	4	.040	.999
	3	.154	.996
	2	.474	.977
	1	.974	.744
.046	4	.046	.999
	3	.171	.996
	2	.506	.972
	1	.982	.716
.048	4	.053	.999
	3	.189	.995
	2	.539	.968
	1	.988	.689
.050	4	.060	.999
	3	.208	.994
	2	.571	.963
	1	.992	.663
.052	4	.068	.999
	3	.227	.993
	2	.603	.957
	1	.995	.639
.054	4	.077	.998
	3	.247	.992
	2	.634	.951
	1	.997	.616
.056	4	.086	.998

TABLE III (Continued). Finite Queuing Tables

POPULATION 30

X	M	D	F	X	M	D	F	X	M	D	F
.056	3	.267	.991	.085	5	.108	.997	.120	2	.999	.555
	2	.665	.944		4	.282	.987	.125	8	.024	.999
	1	.998	.595		3	.607	.948		7	.069	.998
.058	4	.096	.998		2	.955	.768		6	.171	.993
	3	.288	.989	.090	6	.046	.999		5	.367	.977
	2	.695	.936		5	.132	.996		4	.666	.927
	1	.009	.574		4	.326	.984		3	.940	.783
.060	5	.030	.999		3	.665	.934	.130	8	.030	.999
	4	.106	.997		2	.972	.732		7	.083	.997
	3	.310	.987	.095	6	.057	.999		6	.197	.991
	2	.723	.927		5	.158	.994		5	.409	.972
	1	.999	.555		4	.372	.979		4	.712	.914
.062	5	.034	.999		3	.720	.918		3	.957	.758
	4	.117	.997		2	.984	.697	.135	8	.037	.999
	3	.332	.986	.100	6	.071	.998		7	.098	.997
	2	.751	.918		5	.187	.993		6	.226	.989
.064	5	.038	.999		4	.421	.973		5	.451	.966
	4	.128	.997		3	.771	.899		4	.754	.899
	3	.355	.984		2	.991	.664		3	.970	.734
	2	.777	.908	.105	7	.030	.999	.140	8	.045	.999
.066	5	.043	.999		6	.087	.997		7	.115	.996
	4	.140	.996		5	.219	.991		6	.256	.987
	3	.378	.982		4	.470	.967		5	.494	.960
	2	.802	.897		3	.816	.879		4	.793	.884
.068	5	.048	.999		2	.995	.634		3	.979	.710
	4	.153	.995	.110	7	.038	.999	.145	8	.055	.998
	3	.402	.979		6	.105	.997		7	.134	.995
	2	.825	.885		5	.253	.988		6	.288	.984
.070	5	.054	.999	.110	4	.520	.959		5	.537	.952
	4	.166	.995		3	.856	.857		4	.828	.867
	3	.426	.976		2	.997	.605		3	.986	.687
	2	.847	.873	.115	7	.047	.999	.150	9	.024	.999
.075	5	.069	.998		6	.125	.996		8	.065	.998
	4	.201	.993		5	.289	.985		7	.155	.993
	3	.486	.969		4	.570	.950		6	.322	.980
	2	.893	.840		3	.890	.833		5	.580	.944
.080	6	.027	.999		2	.998	.579		4	.860	.849
	5	.088	.998	.120	7	.057	.998		3	.991	.665
	4	.240	.990		6	.147	.994	.155	9	.029	.999
	3	.547	.959		5	.327	.981		8	.077	.997
	2	.929	.805		4	.619	.939		7	.177	.992
.085	6	.036	.999		3	.918	.808		6	.357	.976

TABLE III (Continued)

POPULATION 30

X	M	D	F	X	M	D	F	X	M	D	F
.155	5	.622	.935	.200	9	.123	.995	.250	11	.095	.996
	4	.887	.830		8	.249	.985		10	.192	.989
	3	.994	.644		7	.446	.963		9	.345	.975
.160	9	.036	.999		6	.693	.913		8	.552	.944
	8	.090	.997		5	.905	.814		7	.773	.885
	7	.201	.990		4	.991	.665		6	.932	.789
	6	.394	.972	.210	11	.030	.999		5	.992	.666
.160	5	.663	.924		10	.073	.997	.260	13	.023	.999
	4	.910	.811		9	.157	.992		12	.056	.998
	3	.996	.624		8	.303	.980		11	.121	.994
.165	9	.043	.999		7	.515	.952		10	.233	.986
	8	.105	.996		6	.758	.892		9	.402	.967
	7	.227	.988		5	.938	.782		8	.616	.930
	6	.431	.967		4	.995	.634		7	.823	.864
	5	.702	.913	.220	11	.041	.999		6	.954	.763
	4	.930	.792		10	.095	.996		5	.995	.641
	3	.997	.606		9	.197	.989	.270	13	.032	.999
.170	10	.019	.999		8	.361	.974		12	.073	.997
	9	.051	.998		7	.585	.938		11	.151	.992
	8	.121	.995		6	.816	.868		10	.279	.981
	7	.254	.986		5	.961	.751		9	.462	.959
	6	.469	.961		4	.998	.606		8	.676	.915
	5	.739	.901	.230	12	.023	.999		7	.866	.841
	4	.946	.773		11	.056	.998		6	.970	.737
	3	.998	.588		10	.123	.994		5	.997	.617
.180	10	.028	.999		9	.242	.985	.280	14	.017	.999
	9	.070	.997		8	.423	.965		13	.042	.998
	8	.158	.993		7	.652	.923		12	.093	.996
	7	.313	.980	.230	6	.864	.842		11	.185	.989
	6	.546	.948		5	.976	.721		10	.329	.976
	5	.806	.874		4	.999	.580		9	.522	.949
	4	.969	.735	.240	12	.031	.999		8	.733	.898
	3	.999	.555		11	.074	.997		7	.901	.818
.190	10	.039	.999		10	.155	.992		6	.981	.712
	9	.094	.996		9	.291	.981		5	.999	.595
	8	.200	.990		8	.487	.955	.290	14	.023	.999
	7	.378	.973		7	.715	.905		13	.055	.998
	6	.621	.932		6	.902	.816		12	.117	.994
	5	.862	.845		5	.986	.693		11	.223	.986
	4	.983	.699		4	.999	.556		10	.382	.969
.200	11	.021	.999	.250	13	.017	.999		9	.582	.937
	10	.054	.998		12	.042	.998		8	.785	.880

TABLE III (Continued). Finite Queuing Tables

POPULATION 30

X	M	D	F	X	M	D	F	X	M	D	F
.290	7	.929	.795	.340	16	.016	.999	.420	18	.024	.999
	6	.988	.688		15	.040	.998		17	.056	.997
	5	.999	.575		14	.086	.996		16	.116	.994
.300	14	.031	.999		13	.169	.990		15	.212	.986
	13	.071	.997		12	.296	.979		14	.350	.972
	12	.145	.992		11	.468	.957		13	.521	.948
	11	.266	.982		10	.663	.918		12	.700	.910
.300	10	.437	.962		9	.836	.858		11	.850	.856
	9	.641	.924		8	.947	.778		10	.945	.789
	8	.830	.861		7	.990	.685		9	.986	.713
	7	.950	.771		6	.999	.588		8	.998	.635
	6	.993	.666	.360	16	.029	.999	.440	19	.017	.999
.310	15	.017	.999		15	.065	.997		18	.041	.998
	14	.041	.998		14	.132	.993		17	.087	.996
	13	.090	.996		13	.240	.984		16	.167	.990
	12	.177	.990		12	.392	.967		15	.288	.979
	11	.312	.977		11	.578	.937		14	.446	.960
	10	.494	.953		10	.762	.889		13	.623	.929
	9	.697	.909		9	.902	.821		12	.787	.883
	8	.869	.840		8	.974	.738		11	.906	.824
	7	.966	.749		7	.996	.648		10	.970	.755
	6	.996	.645	.380	17	.020	.999		9	.994	.681
.320	15	.023	.999		16	.048	.998		8	.999	.606
	14	.054	.998		15	.101	.995	.460	19	.028	.999
	13	.113	.994		14	.191	.988		18	.064	.997
	12	.213	.987		13	.324	.975		17	.129	.993
	11	.362	.971		12	.496	.952		16	.232	.985
	10	.552	.943		11	.682	.914		15	.375	.970
	9	.748	.893	.380	10	.843	.857		14	.545	.944
	8	.901	.820		9	.945	.784		13	.717	.906
	7	.977	.727		8	.988	.701		12	.857	.855
	6	.997	.625		7	.999	.614		11	.945	.793
.330	15	.030	.999	.400	17	.035	.999		10	.985	.724
	14	.068	.997		16	.076	.996		9	.997	.652
	13	.139	.993		15	.150	.992	.480	20	.019	.999
	12	.253	.983		14	.264	.982		19	.046	.998
	11	.414	.965		13	.420	.964		18	.098	.995
	10	.608	.931		12	.601	.933		17	.184	.989
	9	.795	.876		11	.775	.886		16	.310	.977
	8	.927	.799		10	.903	.823		15	.470	.957
	7	.985	.706		9	.972	.748		14	.643	.926
	6	.999	.606		8	.995	.666		13	.799	.881

TABLE III (Continued)
POPULATION 30

X	M	D	F	X	M	D	F	X	M	D	F
.480	12	.910	.826	.560	19	.215	.986	.650	16	.949	.818
	11	.970	.762		18	.352	.973		15	.983	.769
	10	.993	.694		17	.516	.952		14	.996	.718
	9	.999	.625		16	.683	.920		13	.999	.667
.500	20	.032	.999		15	.824	.878	.700	25	.039	.998
	19	.072	.997		14	.920	.828		24	.096	.995
	18	.143	.992		13	.972	.772		23	.196	.989
.500	17	.252	.983		12	.993	.714		22	.339	.977
	16	.398	.967		11	.999	.655		21	.511	.958
	15	.568	.941	.580	23	.014	.999		20	.681	.930
	14	.733	.904		22	.038	.998		19	.821	.894
	13	.865	.854		21	.085	.996		18	.916	.853
	12	.947	.796		20	.167	.990		17	.967	.808
	11	.985	.732		19	.288	.980		16	.990	.762
	10	.997	.667		18	.443	.963		15	.997	.714
.520	21	.021	.999		17	.612	.936	.750	26	.046	.998
	20	.051	.998		16	.766	.899		25	.118	.994
	19	.108	.994		15	.883	.854		24	.240	.986
	18	.200	.988		14	.953	.802		23	.405	.972
	17	.331	.975		13	.985	.746		22	.587	.950
	16	.493	.954		12	.997	.690		21	.752	.920
	15	.663	.923		11	.999	.632		20	.873	.883
	14	.811	.880	.600	23	.024	.999		19	.946	.842
	13	.915	.827		22	.059	.997		18	.981	.799
	12	.971	.767		21	.125	.993		17	.995	.755
	11	.993	.705		20	.230	.986		16	.999	.711
	10	.999	.641		19	.372	.972	.800	27	.053	.998
.540	21	.035	.999		18	.538	.949		26	.143	.993
	20	.079	.996	.600	17	.702	.918		25	.292	.984
	19	.155	.991		16	.837	.877		24	.481	.966
	18	.270	.981		15	.927	.829		23	.670	.941
	17	.421	.965		14	.974	.776		22	.822	.909
	16	.590	.938		13	.993	.722		21	.919	.872
	15	.750	.901		12	.999	.667		20	.970	.832
	14	.874	.854	.650	24	.031	.999		19	.991	.791
	13	.949	.799		23	.076	.996		18	.998	.750
	12	.985	.740		22	.158	.991	.850	28	.055	.998
	11	.997	.679		21	.281	.982		27	.171	.993
	10	.999	.617		20	.439	.965		26	.356	.981
.560	22	.023	.999		19	.610	.940		25	.571	.960
	21	.056	.997		18	.764	.906		24	.760	.932
	20	.117	.994		17	.879	.865		23	.888	.899

TABLE III (Continued)   Finite Queuing Tables
POPULATION 30

X	M	D	F	X	M	D	F	X	M	D	F
.850	22	.957	.862	.900	26	.683	.953	.950	28	.574	.973
	21	.987	.823		25	.856	.923		27	.831	.945
	20	.997	.784		24	.947	.888		26	.951	.912
	19	.999	.745		23	.985	.852		25	.989	.877
.900	29	.047	.999		22	.996	.815		24	.998	.842
	28	.200	.992		21	.999	.778				
	27	.441	.977	.950	29	.226	.993				

TABLE IV. Table of Random Digits*

78466	83326	96589	88727	72655	49682	82338	28583	01522	11248
78722	47603	03477	29528	63956	01255	29840	32370	18032	82051
06401	87397	72898	32441	88861	71803	55626	77847	29925	76106
04754	14489	39420	94211	58042	43184	60977	74801	05931	73822
97118	06774	87743	60156	38037	16201	35137	54513	68023	34380
71923	49313	59713	95710	05975	64982	79253	93876	33707	84956
78870	77328	09637	67080	49168	75290	50175	34312	82593	76606
61208	17172	33187	92523	69895	28284	77956	45877	08044	58292
05033	24214	74232	33769	06304	54676	70026	41957	40112	66451
95983	13391	30369	51035	17042	11729	88647	70541	36026	23113
19946	55448	75049	24541	43007	11975	31797	05373	45893	25665
03580	67206	09635	84612	62611	86724	77411	99415	58901	86160
56823	49819	20283	22272	00114	92007	24369	00543	05417	92251
87633	31761	99865	31488	49947	06060	32083	47944	00449	06550
95152	10133	52693	22480	50336	49502	06296	76414	18358	05313
05639	24175	79438	92151	57602	03590	25465	54780	79098	73594
65927	55525	67270	22907	55097	63177	34119	94216	84861	10457
59005	29000	38395	80367	34112	41866	30170	84658	84441	03926
06626	42682	91522	45955	23263	09764	26824	82936	16813	13878
11306	02732	34189	04228	58541	72573	89071	58066	67159	29633
45143	56545	94617	42752	31209	14380	81477	36952	44934	97435
97612	87175	22613	84175	96413	83336	12408	89318	41713	90669
97035	62442	06940	45719	39918	60274	54353	54497	29789	82928
62498	00257	19179	06313	07900	46733	21413	63627	48734	92174
80306	19257	18690	54653	07263	19894	89909	76415	57246	02621
84114	84884	50129	68942	93264	72344	98794	16791	83861	32007
58437	88807	92141	88677	02864	02052	62843	21692	21373	29408
15702	53457	54258	47485	23399	71692	56806	70801	41548	94809
59966	41287	87001	26462	94000	28457	09469	80416	05897	87970
43641	05920	81346	02507	25349	93370	02064	62719	45740	62080
25501	50113	44600	87433	00683	79107	22315	42162	25516	98434
98294	08491	25251	26737	00071	45090	68628	64390	42684	94956
52582	89985	37863	60788	27412	47502	71577	13542	31077	13353
26510	83622	12546	00489	89304	15550	09482	07504	64588	92562
24755	71543	31667	83624	27085	65905	32386	30775	19689	41437
38399	88796	58856	18220	51016	04976	54062	49109	95563	48244
18889	87814	52232	58244	95206	05947	26622	01381	28744	38374
51774	89694	02654	63161	54622	31113	51160	29015	64730	07750
88375	37710	61619	69820	13131	90406	45206	06386	06398	68652
10416	70345	93307	87360	53452	61179	46845	91521	32430	74795
99258	03778	54674	51499	13659	36434	84760	76446	64026	97534
58923	18319	95092	11840	87646	85330	58143	42023	28972	30657
39407	41126	44469	78889	54462	38609	58555	69793	27258	11296
29372	70781	19554	95559	63088	35845	60162	21228	48296	05006
07287	76846	92658	21985	00872	11513	24443	44320	37737	97360
07089	02948	03699	71255	13944	86597	89052	88899	03553	42145
35757	37447	29860	04546	28742	27773	10215	09774	43426	22961
58797	70878	78167	91942	15108	37441	99254	27121	92358	94254
32281	97860	23029	61409	81887	02050	63060	45246	46312	30378
93531	08514	30244	34641	29820	72126	62419	93233	26537	21179

* Reproduced with permission from The Rand Corp., *A Million Random Digits with 100,000 Normal Deviates.* Copyright, The Free Press, Glencoe, Ill., 1955, pp. 180–183.

TABLE IV (Continued). Table of Random Digits

03689	33090	43465	96789	56688	32389	88206	06534	10558	14478
43367	46409	44751	73410	35138	24910	70748	57336	56043	68550
45357	52080	62670	73877	20604	40408	98060	96733	65094	80335
62683	03171	77195	92515	78041	27590	42651	00254	73179	10159
04841	40918	69047	68986	08150	87984	08887	76083	37702	28523
85963	06992	65321	43521	46393	40491	06028	43865	58190	28142
03720	78942	61990	90812	98452	74098	69738	83272	39212	42817
10159	85560	35619	58248	65498	77977	02896	45198	10655	13973
80162	35686	57877	19552	63931	44171	40879	94532	17828	31848
74388	92906	65829	24572	79417	38460	96294	79201	47755	90980
12660	09571	29743	45447	64063	46295	44191	53957	62393	42229
81852	60620	87757	72165	23875	87844	84038	04994	93466	27418
03068	61317	65305	64944	27319	55263	84514	38374	11657	67723
29623	58530	17274	16908	39253	37595	57497	74780	88624	93333
30520	50588	51231	83816	01075	33098	81308	59036	49152	86262
93694	02984	91350	33929	41724	32403	42566	14232	55085	65628
86736	40641	37958	25415	19922	65966	98044	39583	26828	50919
28141	15630	37675	52545	24813	22075	05142	15374	84533	12933
79804	05165	21620	98400	55290	71877	60052	46320	79055	45913
63763	49985	88853	70681	52762	17670	62337	12199	44123	37993
49618	47068	63331	62675	51788	58283	04295	72904	05378	98085
26502	68980	26545	14204	34304	50284	47730	57299	73966	02566
13549	86048	27912	56733	14987	09850	78217	85168	09538	92347
89221	78076	40306	34045	52557	52383	67796	41382	50490	30117
97809	34056	76778	60417	05153	83827	67369	08602	56163	28793
65668	44694	34151	51741	11484	13226	49516	17391	39956	34839
53653	59804	59051	95074	38307	99546	32962	26962	86252	50704
34922	95041	17398	32789	26860	55536	82415	82911	42208	62725
74880	65198	61357	90209	71543	71114	94868	05645	44154	72254
66036	48794	30021	92601	21615	16952	18433	44903	51322	90379
39044	99503	11442	81344	57068	74662	90382	59433	48440	38146
87756	71151	68543	08358	10183	06432	97482	90301	76114	83778
47117	45575	29524	02522	08041	70698	80260	73588	86415	72523
71572	02109	96722	21684	64331	71644	18933	32801	11644	12364
35609	58072	63209	48429	53108	59173	55337	22445	85940	43707
81703	70069	74981	12197	48426	77365	26769	65078	27849	41311
88979	88161	56531	46443	47148	42773	18601	38532	22594	12395
90279	42308	00380	17181	38757	09071	89804	15232	99007	39495
49266	18921	06498	88005	72736	81848	92716	96279	94582	22792
50897	22569	48402	80376	65470	19157	49729	19615	79087	47039
20950	65643	52280	37103	66977	65141	18522	39333	59824	73084
32686	51645	11382	75341	03189	94128	06275	22345	86856	77394
72525	65092	65086	47094	14781	61486	61895	85698	53028	61682
70502	57550	29699	36797	35862	90894	93217	96158	94321	12012
63087	03802	03142	72582	44267	56028	01576	69840	67727	77419
16418	07903	74344	89861	62952	49362	86210	65676	96617	38081
67730	17532	39489	28035	13415	83494	26750	01440	01161	16346
27274	98848	59506	28124	33596	89623	21006	94898	03550	88629
44250	52829	22614	21323	28597	66402	15425	39845	01823	19639
57476	33687	81784	05811	66625	17690	46170	93914	82346	82851

TABLE IV (Continued). Table of Random Digits

09656	96657	64842	49222	49506	10145	48455	23505	90430	04180
24712	55799	60857	73479	33581	17360	30406	05842	72044	90764
07202	96341	23699	76171	79126	04512	15426	15980	88898	06358
84575	46820	54083	43918	46989	05379	70682	43081	66171	38942
38144	87037	46626	70529	27918	34191	98668	33482	43998	75733
48048	56349	01986	29814	69800	91609	65374	22928	09704	59343
41936	58566	31276	19952	01352	18834	99596	09302	20087	19063
73391	94006	03822	81845	76158	41352	40596	14325	27020	17546
57580	08954	73554	28698	29022	11568	35668	59906	39557	27217
92646	41113	91411	56215	69302	86419	61224	41936	56939	27816
07118	12707	35622	81485	73354	49800	60805	05648	28898	60933
57842	57831	24130	75408	83784	64307	91620	40810	06539	70387
65078	44981	81009	33697	98324	46928	34198	96032	98426	77488
04294	96120	67629	55265	26248	40602	25566	12520	89785	93932
48381	06807	43775	09708	73199	53406	02910	83292	59249	18597
00459	62045	19249	67095	22752	24636	16965	91836	00582	46721
38824	81681	33323	64086	55970	04849	24819	20749	51711	86173
91465	22232	02907	01050	07121	53536	71070	26916	47620	01619
50874	00807	77751	73952	03073	69063	16894	85570	81746	07568
26644	75871	15618	50310	72610	66205	82640	86205	73453	90232
74647	43756	41166	99976	17421	32448	89850	72057	49585	03135
88929	94478	11877	42740	07521	83086	13137	23515	19771	53849
41478	89775	60375	39730	42762	77883	18972	66837	54316	27994
99279	84845	21802	58502	65549	56355	21215	40751	28151	90988
97999	51695	94862	75507	29566	16672	71951	15069	10229	88950
10031	11928	84704	25444	35760	67118	52320	32635	12077	58310
59147	60196	09923	07309	29969	98532	64967	39756	00284	57492
91486	86685	17186	46640	93984	14182	08696	36159	97409	27130
27085	54597	97339	60919	84357	45315	42387	91043	38564	92503
50144	62974	38718	36759	77020	34348	55225	59783	41978	11609
06513	03197	77860	96289	01167	00520	44879	74560	93125	22650
27360	65908	66997	93904	30000	63094	96840	45926	50995	70954
02069	43135	77774	18334	91489	18933	12167	99099	61690	79700
32331	13458	66740	46873	03384	78807	23099	26258	03900	63311
94820	10308	97308	93927	85576	52209	10774	26012	52965	53336
13206	85146	62171	16627	80445	13768	19961	67852	12119	05382
73582	50471	64502	82034	78891	48501	74375	93870	64904	45325
88736	00087	82697	00602	83362	81536	97075	00237	56764	98875
31165	48243	42295	47680	53130	18748	74253	30705	79017	12329
48750	38352	38246	61165	65529	34619	50850	12049	42062	70280
56045	61964	77129	52519	13431	82935	27983	48463	22689	21620
40780	06235	63958	12790	38517	36319	66539	78278	67180	18498
67669	16111	45182	01628	24109	36756	26674	92319	44657	90665
89960	36272	16075	11989	49558	85586	32611	19691	91286	90352
79565	34513	66492	97391	79561	51275	22611	22780	85297	10285
66061	19829	83142	26585	42292	71700	08387	35325	63515	61581
09823	41434	14494	65752	93987	51716	87492	16260	25024	63202
72198	62911	43232	72708	39692	84770	33483	28671	37358	28994
86230	94033	66982	41148	00730	82222	48939	59481	79668	81598
88466	31228	37036	83284	51006	32468	94899	42609	80683	93013

TABLE IV (Continued).   Table of Random Digits

66558	78763	55932	15490	46790	47325	60903	15000	90970	06904
93810	69163	27172	10864	39108	79626	90431	44390	54290	70295
72045	47743	33163	88057	14136	55883	71449	68303	54093	95545
64251	86498	77947	21734	23571	86489	90017	24878	91985	03921
82220	31802	84619	51220	34654	60601	15088	26949	23013	72644
04991	91864	49269	66109	92609	37154	53225	73014	01890	04357
73895	65548	31996	73237	62411	22311	87875	79190	28237	73903
03515	01014	83955	11919	71533	71150	45699	95307	77713	66398
78808	89471	65152	62457	32410	14092	13813	08357	65485	83198
50648	45741	81584	54369	01575	92941	05484	41196	61946	89918
52074	39293	45087	07020	04753	69952	45199	83726	11602	57715
08209	01284	83775	89711	92322	31538	15808	94830	69581	94556
24292	33646	26925	04133	04895	07341	81441	53319	60118	98634
68189	39488	61468	23411	36471	65260	30134	55648	39176	61692
63096	33677	78900	30005	17324	83577	16699	62138	73469	89005
67106	05029	82711	17886	38351	42165	71101	37151	13547	38500
36272	89377	49623	71797	57532	90488	32967	60308	57256	66233
33143	08577	38507	85535	62784	29068	42392	41332	71636	49165
94138	78030	28934	91012	45780	66416	14003	05819	71031	00053
65199	99418	58039	96495	95954	48748	93022	46913	26250	35538
49897	14275	22123	84895	77567	17949	57969	31131	95882	08783
85679	52202	37950	09891	45369	48243	84985	08318	09853	86452
21441	75053	31373	89860	47671	33981	55424	33191	53223	54060
54269	06140	67385	01203	51078	48220	46715	09144	61587	63026
09323	22353	58095	97149	63325	18050	36840	26523	72376	89192
50214	26662	95722	78359	49612	75804	89378	96992	76621	91777
52022	22417	70460	91869	45732	54352	87239	41463	40310	45189
47176	39122	11478	75218	04888	49657	84540	49821	80806	83581
35402	23056	72903	95029	05373	35587	23297	11870	18495	79905
65519	29138	08384	41230	29209	87793	06285	90472	47054	57036
11259	05645	07492	16580	90016	22626	23187	25531	24281	05383
56007	97457	05913	74626	33923	25652	75099	73542	29669	82523
24558	05361	28136	58586	74390	95278	70229	15845	83717	91629
52889	89032	03429	81240	54824	16714	79590	91867	36732	16936
39534	82185	56489	40999	31361	98733	68769	77792	52694	14372
04948	01323	21617	23457	29217	65387	33130	30920	26298	84058
69496	38855	02249	50773	93315	41606	73918	32347	06673	95058
16068	36000	08084	66738	15982	82450	09060	49051	31759	54477
11907	18181	20687	05878	33617	16566	67893	50243	08352	64527
18382	61533	42865	90495	74809	70740	24939	43883	86674	40041
75960	66915	02595	66435	55610	42936	52336	15660	28110	10390
20156	11314	51105	46678	39660	54062	81972	55953	99513	41647
10528	02058	80359	99179	65642	93982	07133	38680	45791	79665
48514	83028	06720	33776	10023	14228	56367	04108	54855	77323
92644	48340	75864	50303	09037	02589	37463	81365	18567	65142
41477	25941	98283	49225	08721	84508	97549	46769	98389	19589
41630	05563	83127	71333	68606	49269	89244	53159	02762	18167
78489	08606	66190	02810	49460	63040	00221	27138	36645	02465
44971	55189	26570	98515	37222	54809	17570	64185	56333	72230
68023	51496	96693	76886	54420	59192	11645	54942	31693	28688

Index

Abruzzi, A., 133
Acceptance sampling, by attributes, 199–230
  AOQ curves, 214
  double sampling, 220
  OC curves, 200
  sequential sampling, 226
  single sampling, 205
  by variables, 230–235
  kinds of plans, 231
  economics of, 235
Ackoff, R. L., 249, 266, 416, 442
Activity chart, 115, 119, 120
AIIE, *see* American Institute of Industrial Engineers
Alberts, W., 505
Alcalay, J. A., 16
Alchian, A., 415
Allied Chemical Corporation, 419
Allocation problems, *see* Linear programming
AMA Management Game, 569
American Institute of Industrial Engineers, 540
American Society of Heating, Ventilating, and Air Conditioning Engineers, 97, 99
Analysis of variance, 167–169
Andlinger, G. R., 581
Annual cost, compared to *CERBS*, 414
Annuity, 379

Anthropometric data, 80–84
  chair and table heights, 81, 82
  strength and forces of body movements, 83
  work area limits, 81
AOQ, definition of, 205
AOQ curves, 214, 216
Armour, G. C., 66, 531, 533–535, 537–539
Armstrong Cork Company, 419
Arnoff, E. L., 249, 266, 442
Arrival rates, Poisson, *see* Poisson arrival rates
Arrow, K. J., 442
ASHRAE, 98
Asimow, M., 540, 545, 547, 567
Assembly charts, 33, 34
Attributes, sampling by, *see* Acceptance sampling
Average investment criterion, 383
  compared to *CERBS*, 414
  example of, 384, 385
Average outgoing quality (*AOQ*) curves, 214, 216
Average quality level, *see* AOQ

Baker, C. T., 567
Balance chart, 34, 55–59
Banbury, J., 540
Barlow, R., 285
Barnes, R. M., 66, 81, 112, 116, 126, 127, 133